The
Acyclic
Aliphatic Tertiary
Amines

THE ACYCLIC ALIPHATIC TERTIARY AMINES

LEONARD SPIALTER
Head, Organic Chemistry Section
Aerospace Research Laboratories
Wright-Patterson Air Force Base, Ohio

JOSEPH A. PAPPALARDO
Associate Professor of Chemistry
University of Dayton
Dayton, Ohio

THE MACMILLAN COMPANY, NEW YORK

COLLIER–MACMILLAN LIMITED, LONDON

First Printing

Library of Congress catalog card number: 65–10205

The Macmillan Company, New York
Collier–Macmillan Canada, Ltd., Toronto, Ontario

Printed in the United States of America

Dedication:

To our wives, Ruth C. Spialter and R. Agnes Pappalardo who, if they had complained, even slightly, could have prevented the writing of this book.

PREFACE

In the course of performing experimental research in the relationship between structure and base strength of certain aliphatic tertiary amines it became evident to the authors during the literature search, that no clear definitive review had ever been written on this class of compounds. With the intention of remedying this situation, the authors embarked on the preparation of a chapter on the subject for one of the "Reviews" journals. It soon became evident that the amount of available material had been seriously underestimated to the extent that even with extreme pruning it would be difficult to compress the interesting data into just one volume. Nevertheless, since only one volume was being contemplated the authors felt that their optimum contribution to other workers in the field would be to present a thorough coverage of certain aspects of acyclic aliphatic tertiary amine chemistry. These would include a complete listing of the pertinent compounds, their syntheses, physical properties, and derivatives. In addition, in order to facilitate further research, whether it be in syntheses of new compounds or in mechanistic studies, it was felt desirable to include also a substantial discussion on the scope and limitations of the useful preparative methods for these compounds.

Available data for most of the compounds in the present monograph are surprisingly meager. This is due to the "thinning out" of the literature over a large number of compounds. On the other hand there is fairly substantial background on the trialkyl amines where the alkyl groups are all alike and come from the shorter saturated aliphatic chains. In particular might be mentioned trimethylamine and triethylamine about each of which a large volume, alone, could be prepared. For example, the number of citations in Chemical Abstracts to trimethylamine and triethylamine between 1907 and 1959 total, with some duplications, 1100 and 840, respectively. However, in order to keep this monograph within reasonable limits, severe pruning had to be applied for such compounds. As a result, the total number of unduplicated references in this book is about 1600.

Another significant fact which has emerged is the rather rapid growth in the number of papers per year concerned with acyclic aliphatic tertiary amines. This growth has occurred in all aspects of the chemistry of these compounds, including new molecules, syntheses, physical, biological, and chemical properties, technology and commercial utilization. This is dramatically indicated, even for the narrow areas selected for this book, by the chart in Figure 1. On this is shown the number of references cited in this volume as a function of the decade in which such references were published. (Data for the incomplete 1960's are not cited.) The exponential character in the growth of the literature here used is clearly evident and is certainly not behind that of the general chemical literature.

It might be well to point out at this time that interest in tertiary amines is quite widespread and crosses many fields of endeavor. These compounds, alone, or in combination with other compounds, have been suggested as fungicides, bactericides, surfactants, ganglionic blocking agents, rust inhibitors, anti-oxidants, surface modifiers for textiles, metal complexing agents, viscosity stabilizers, hypergolic fuels, solvents, pH stabilizers, color stabilizers, etc. They also have found use as catalysts in a large variety of reactions such as condensation of carbonyl compounds, curing of epoxide resins, etc. In addition to the foregoing uses, the tertiary amines have been investigated to a significant extent from the theoretical point of view. For example, the correlation of structure of amines with base strength has been studied by many investigators.

The relative chemical inertness of tertiary amines compared to the rich storehouse of reactions for primary and secondary amines has tended to lessen interest in the tertiary amines. This, in turn, has even led some chemists to entertain the impression that not only are there actually fewer tertiary amines than primary and secondary, but that, theoretically, this must always be the case. While the former assumption is probably not true (we can only speculate because the literature of the other amines has not been scanned) the latter is certainly erroneous. Consideration of simple laws of probability indicates that if the total number of different synthetically-available alkyl substituents is n, then there could be theoretically synthesized (in the absence of mitigating circumstances, such as steric effects) n primary, n^2 secondary, and n^3 tertiary monoamines, all unique. If one includes polyamines, the population density is favored even more heavily in favor of the tertiary compounds. As a benchmark, the present monograph describes a total of 710 individual acyclic tertiary amines.

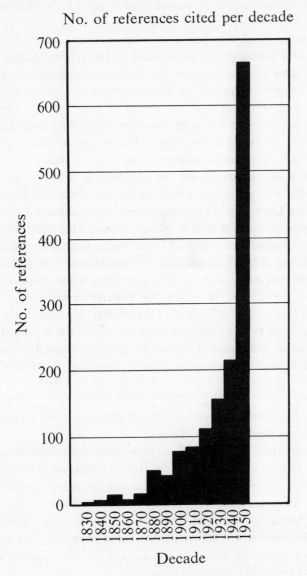

No. of references cited per decade

FIG. 1.

This book has been written, essentially, from perusal and study of the original literature, including patents. Although Chemical Abstracts and Beilstein's "Handbuch der organischen Chemie" provided excellent initial guidance, it was found eminently desirable for optimum completeness, cross-referencing, and accuracy to rely on the original work, itself. Although this increased the search time manyfold, there was developed the satisfaction of having a firm, reliable foundation to the work.

Incidentally, in an unexpected number of cases, errors, both typographical and experimental, were found in the original papers. Where pertinent, these are corrected in the present monograph. In addition, critical and explanatory notes are introduced into the text to clarify points of doubt, ambiguity, uncertain reliability of data, and the like. These have been omitted in a few cases, however, where data and analogy are insufficient to resolve an inconsistency. Where a given value is obviously questionable, it is frequently followed simply by the expression "(sic)".

Grateful acknowledgments are due to J. Ronald Riley, Jr. and Robert Warshawsky, who assisted so greatly in the early indexing efforts and to the following University of Dayton students who assisted in various tasks such as typing portions of the manuscript, and checking references: Teresa Faeta, Mary Louise Fecke, Robert Evers, Sheila Kerr, Orey Buzzelli, and Ronald Massey. Thanks are also due to Dorothy Shutz, Marcella Moore, Vonna Cole, and Ann Callin for typing portions of the manuscript.

Of prime importance, of course, has been the availability of library facilities in Dayton and other parts of the country. We want to express our special gratitude to the following libraries and to the indicated people who assisted us: University of Dayton Chemistry Library, Dayton, Ohio; Aerospace Research Laboratories Library (Anthony F. McGraw, Mrs. Patricia Wittgruber, and Carolyn Byers), and the Technical Library (George Burkhardt) at Wright-Patterson Air Force Base, Ohio; and the Monsanto Research Corporation Library (Mrs. Dorothy Crabtree and Mrs. Dorrance Dean), Dayton, Ohio.

Other important library facilities that were consulted include The Chemistry Library at the University of Notre Dame (special thanks to Mr. Frank Long); Chemistry Library of Rutgers University (special thanks are due to Professor Peter A. VanderMeulen, Chairman of the Department of Chemistry); the John Crerar Library in Chicago, Illinois; The Library of Congress in Washington, D.C.; the Chemists' Club and New York City Libraries in New York, N.Y.; and the Ohio State University Chemistry Library in Columbus, Ohio.

Most of all we tender our heartfelt gratitude to our employers, the Aerospace Research Laboratories and the University of Dayton, respectively, for providing encouragement and support, and for overlooking the numerous perturbations which our activities undoubtedly caused to our official duties, despite our best efforts to keep such disturbances to a minimum.

L.S./J.A.P.

CONTENTS

DATA ON INDIVIDUAL AMINES

The
Acyclic
Aliphatic Tertiary
Amines

INTRODUCTION
Scope

This book is restricted specifically to the class of acyclic aliphatic tertiary amines containing only carbon, nitrogen, and hydrogen. This includes both monoamines and polyamines with saturated and/or unsaturated hydrocarbon groups, but specifically excludes those compounds that contain alicyclic, heterocyclic, or aromatic substituents. Each nitrogen atom is bound to three different carbon atoms.

One part of this volume is devoted to a critical summary and evaluation of the general procedures, both synthetic and degradative, which have been applied to the preparation of these tertiary amines. Selected examples and tables are presented throughout this part to illustrate the general experimental conditions and utility of the more commonly used methods.

In the part that follows, there is a compilation of more than 700 acyclic aliphatic tertiary amines comprising, to the best of our knowledge, at least all such compounds reported in the original literature indexed through the middle of 1961 by *Chemical Abstracts*. For each of these compounds there are listed the available physical properties (boiling point, melting point, density, refractive index, base strength and the like), the reported methods of preparation (with yields), and the melting points of characteristic derivatives.

The references to more than 1600 papers in the original literature are formally listed in the bibliographic section. The abbreviations adopted for the journal titles are in accord, as much as possible, with the recommendations of the comprehensive *Chemical Abstracts Periodical Index for 1956* and subsequent supplements for the newer journals.

The index at the end of the book covers the subject matter of all sections except those devoted to the compound listings. The latter are self-indexing by virtue of the format adopted for them. An explanation of the system appears at the beginning of the pertinent section.

1

Historical Background

The early history pertinent to amines is a fascinating one replete with many interesting side lights and anecdotes.

The origin of the name "amine" is ascribed by the dictionary[WE3] to a nomenclature hybrid of "ammonia" (the nitrogen-hydrogen parent of all amines) and the chemical suffix "ine." In turn, "ammonia" is reportedly derived from "salt of Ammon"[KI7] or sal ammoniac (ammonium chloride), said to have been first obtained from camel dung near the temple of Jupiter Ammon, a famed oracle situated in the Libyan oasis of "Ammon" about the fourth century B.C. This term is a variant of "Amen," originally a local deity of Thebes who eventually became the chief ancient Egyptian god. Under the Greek hegemony over Egypt, there was a religious fusion and Ammon became an epithet for Zeus (or Jupiter).[WE3] A map of the empire of Alexander the Great shows clearly the well-known (in his day) village of "Ammonium"[*] in the Libyan desert.

Even until fairly recent times, the Egyptian process for the manufacture of ammonium chloride was detailed[BO12b] as involving the imperfect burning of dried camel dung (more like a crude pyrolysis) to give a dense smoke condensing to a soot containing the salt. Sublimation of this soot then yielded the raw commercial salt. Since in the wood-poor Libyan desert the use of such dung as fuel was common, von Lippman[LI10] has even suggested that the Ammonians (as Herodotus called the people[ME8]) may well have accidentally discovered sublimed ammonium chloride in the hot air heating ducts, chimneys, and vents associated with the public baths.

Further discussion and, unfortunately, some unnecessary confusion based on deduction from phonetically generated errors, such as conversion of the name sal ammoniac to "sal armoniacum," "sal armeniacum" (Armenian salt), "sal armeniacus," "hammoniacum" (related to the Greek word

---

* Ammonium was the westernmost village in Africa visited by Alexander the Great[PA1a] during his tour of conquest in 331 B.C.[CO11] Its modern name is Siwa or Siwah,[CO11,SE4,WE2] with a population of about four or five thousand.[SE4,WE2] The site, one of five great oases in the Libyan Desert,[CO11] is in the Western Desert province of Egypt just west of the Qattara Depression.[WI10]

2

hammos, sand), as well as the existence of "gum armoniacum" (or "ammoniacum"), can be found elsewhere.[LI10,ME8,SC17,TR5,UL1,WA14]

The chemical history of the amines as organic derivatives of ammonia had a rather stormy inauguration with the controversial background to aniline. The name "aniline" was coined by Fritzsche[FR11] in a compound priority claim in 1840 despite a blistering epithet-calling postscript by Liebig[LI5] which accused Fritzsche of knowingly ignoring the true earlier discovery of the compound by Unverdorben in 1826 (under the name "krystallin") and other subsequent reports by Dumas and by Erdmann. In essence, then, current use of the term "aniline" honors a "pirate," in the words of Liebig. We owe this perpetuated historic injustice to Berzelius who, when Hofmann suggested in 1843[HO1a] that the compound be called systematically "phenamid" (which today would have evolved to phenamine, or phenylamine), replied: "There is no basis to give a substance a name based on one property which most substances have."[GR1]

These events were occurring at the height of the controversy over molecular structure between the Berzelius dualist school and the substitution-type theorists led by Dumas and Liebig. The former believed that the nitrogen bases, as examplified then by aniline and alkaloids still of unknown structure, must contain the ammonia moiety, so that aniline was represented as $C_6H_4 \cdot NH_3$. The views of the latter are typified by the remarkably prophetic words of Liebig in 1842[LI6]: "Wenn wir im Stande wären den Sauerstoff in dem Aethyl- und Methyl-Oxyd, in den Oxyden von zwei basischen Radicalen, zu vertreten durch 1 Äquivalent Amid, so würden wir ohne den geringsten Zweifel Verbindungen haben, die sich ganz dem Ammoniak ähnlich verhalten würden. In einer Formel ausgedrückt, würde also eine Verbindung

$$C_4H_{10}, N_2H_4 = Ae, Ad$$

(In Liebig's nomenclature, C_4H_{10} or Ae is the modern ethyl
group, C_2H_5; N_2H_4 or Ad is the amino group.)

basische Eigenschaften besitzen."

It was *not until 1849, seven years later*, that the first alkyl amine was prepared and isolated by Wurtz.[WU2] Wurtz synthesized methylamine and ethylamine by the basic hydrolysis of the corresponding alkyl isocyanates, trialkyl cyanurates, and alkyl ureas. However, it remained for Hofmann, within the year, to describe the direct structure-proving substitution replacement of hydrogen on nitrogen by alkyl groups.

In a classic paper[HO3] Hofmann discussed the reaction of ammonia and aniline with methyl, ethyl, and isoamyl bromide to give not only singly alkylated but also higher alkylated amine products. This work was based on a delightful pattern of chemical serendipity.[FI8] A London pharmacist in 1849 had newly synthesized ethyl iodide for some anesthesia study and showed a large flask of this unusual sparkling dense liquid to Hofmann. The imagination of the latter was piqued and he requested a sample of the rare liquid, which he immediately tested with aniline. Overnight, large crystals formed, which were first thought to be the hydriodide of aniline. However, a more careful follow-up study was performed, and both the lack of ethylene evolution as well as analytical determinations sufficed to substantiate the validity of the interpreted course of this valuable chemical reaction as an alkylation-substitution.

By 1851, Hofmann[HO4] had discovered the further alkylation to quaternary ammonium salts, and hydroxide, as well as their pyrolysis, and suggested, although only provisionally (he had hoped), the cumbersome systematic "sesquipedalia verba" nomenclature still in use today. It was not, however, until 1868 in a lecture before the Chemical Society in London that the terms "primary," "secondary," and "tertiary" amines were first used by Hofmann.[FI8]

In summary, then, Hofmann in the brief span of years from 1849 to 1851 with one fell swoop presented the experimental basis for the type theory based on the ammonia molecule, and established many of the synthetic and property concepts we hold for amines to this day. It was truly a chemical milestone, worthy of a worker of Hofmann's caliber and one whose importance has not been dimmed by time.

Nomenclature

There are often several ways to name a simple trialkylamine. For example the following amine might be uniquely identified by any one of several names:

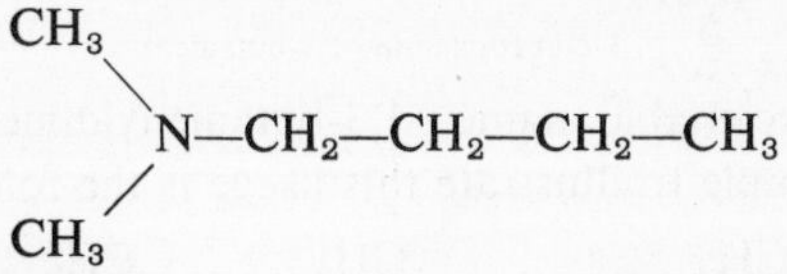

$$CH_3$$
$$N—CH_2—CH_2—CH_2—CH_3$$
$$CH_3$$

(a) Butyldimethylamine
(b) Dimethylbutylamine
(c) 1-Dimethylaminobutane
(d) Dimethyl-*n*-butylamine
(e) *n*-Butyldimethylamine
(f) *N,N*-Dimethyl-*n*-butylamine
(g) 2-Methyl-2-azahexane

According to the current interpretation of the I.U.C. (International Union of Chemistry) rules for nomenclature, butyldiethylamine, dimethylbutylamine, and 1-dimethylaminobutane are all acceptable. In the absence of other qualifying prefices, the alkyl group, such as propyl, butyl, octyl, etc., is assumed to have the normal, or straight-chain, configuration.

It is our desire to be reasonably consistent in naming the amines listed in the present monograph. When a choice of two acceptable names presented itself that name was selected which possessed the greater clarity. In some cases, however, alternative names were either equally simple or equally cumbersome. In such cases, the choice was made on the basis of consistency.

The selection of names usually was in accord with the following pattern:

1. R_3N.   For three identical alkyl groups on the amine nitrogen, the prefix tri- was used: e.g., $(n\text{-}C_6H_{13})_3N$, trihexylamine; $(CH_2\!\!=\!\!CH—CH\!\!=\!\!CH)_3N$, tri(1,3-butadienyl)amine. If the alkyl group is complex, the prefix "tris" before the parenthetic description serves to eliminate confusion.

2. **R_2NR'.** For amines with two identical and one differing alkyl groups two nomenclature systems were used:

(*a*) The unlike alkyl group was named first.

$$n\text{-}C_8H_{17}N(CH_3)_2$$
Octyldimethylamine

$$(n\text{-}C_8H_{17})_2NCH_3$$
Methyldioctylamine

This nomenclature was used whenever the alkyl groups involved lent themselves to simple naming.

(*b*) If the alkyl group is a bit more complex, the system was used which treated the unlike substituent as an alkane, alkene, or alkyne, and the dialkylamino portion as a substituent:

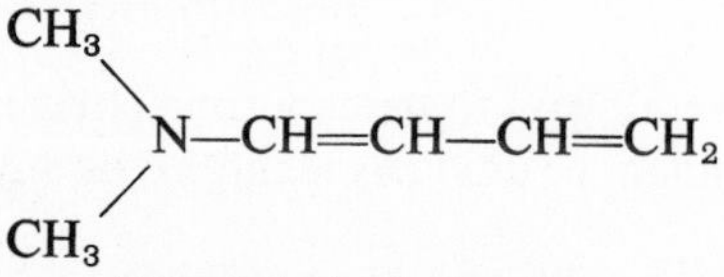

$$\begin{array}{c} CH_3 \\ \diagdown \\ \quad N-CH=CH-CH=CH_2 \\ \diagup \\ CH_3 \end{array}$$
1-Dimethylamino-1,3-butadiene

The other very acceptable name—1,3-butadienyldimethylamine—was not used. Another example to illustrate this usage is the following:

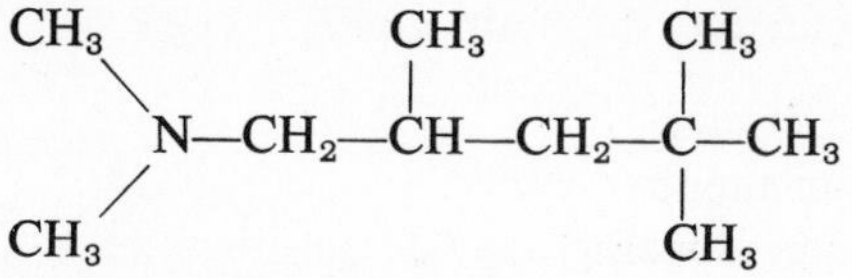

$$\begin{array}{c} CH_3 \qquad\quad CH_3 \quad\quad CH_3 \\ \diagdown \qquad\qquad | \qquad\quad | \\ N-CH_2-CH-CH_2-C-CH_3 \\ \diagup \qquad\qquad\qquad\qquad | \\ CH_3 \qquad\qquad\qquad\quad CH_3 \end{array}$$

1-Dimethylamino-2,4,4-trimethylpentane was preferred over 2,4,4-trimethylpentyldimethylamine.

3. **RR'R"N.** In the case of three unlike groups, each alkyl group was named in the order of increasing size and complexity. A few examples might best illustrate this point:

$$CH_3(C_2H_5)(n\text{-}C_4H_9)N$$
Methylethylbutylamine

$$CH_3(\text{i-}C_4H_9)(n\text{-}C_4H_9)N$$
Methylbutylisobutylamine

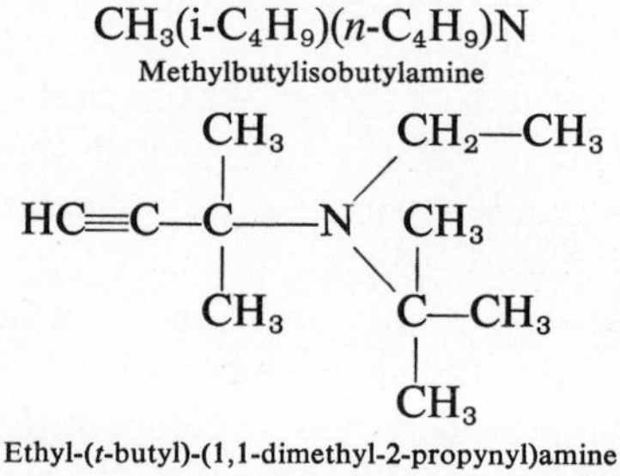

$$\begin{array}{c} CH_3 \qquad CH_2-CH_3 \\ | \qquad\quad \diagup \\ HC\equiv C-C-\!\!-N \quad CH_3 \\ | \qquad\quad \diagdown \quad | \\ CH_3 \qquad\quad C-CH_3 \\ \qquad\qquad\quad | \\ \qquad\qquad\quad CH_3 \end{array}$$
Ethyl-(*t*-butyl)-(1,1-dimethyl-2-propynyl)amine

The latter compound could just as well have been named 3-(ethyl-*t*-butylamino)-3-methyl-1-butyne; in fact, in a few cases, where greater clarity was thereby obtained, this latter type of nomenclature was used preferentially.

The common alkyl group names were in most cases used directly; for example, isobutyl instead of 2-methylpropyl and allyl instead of 2-propenyl.

In general, an effort was made to avoid the use of N and N,N', etc. nomenclature to indicate substitution on the nitrogen. This terminology is quite awkward and was accepted only in certain very complex polyamines for which other names were even more cumbersome.

POLYAMINES

There are usually several methods for naming diamines, as illustrated by the following example:

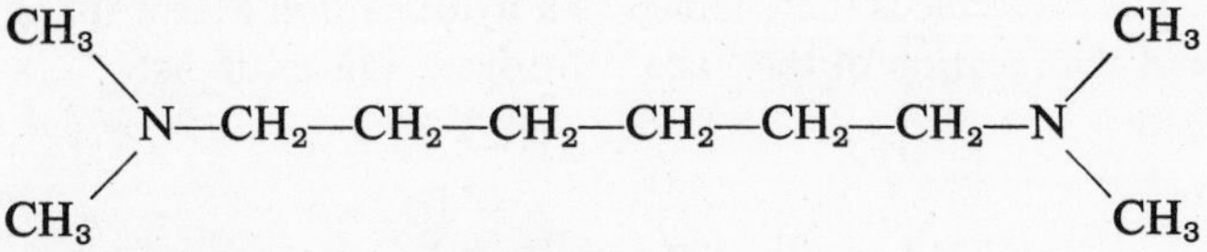

$$CH_3\diagdown \qquad\qquad\qquad\qquad\qquad\qquad\qquad\diagup CH_3$$
$$N-CH_2-CH_2-CH_2-CH_2-CH_2-CH_2-N$$
$$CH_3\diagup \qquad\qquad\qquad\qquad\qquad\qquad\qquad\diagdown CH_3$$

(a) 1,6-Bis(dimethylamino)hexane
(b) N,N,N',N'-Tetramethylhexamethylenediamine
(c) N,N,N',N'-Tetramethyl-1,6-hexanediamine
(d) 6-Dimethylaminohexyldimethylamine
(e) 2,9-Dimethyl-2,9-diazadecane

Our preference is for the first named, (a).

In the case of dissimilar alkyl groups, the compound still can be treated as a derivative of the parent hydrocarbon alkane, or alkene or alkyne:

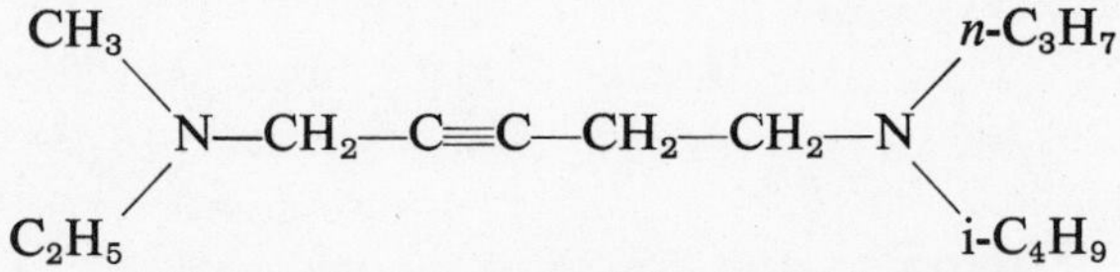

$$CH_3\diagdown \qquad\qquad\qquad\qquad\qquad\qquad n\text{-}C_3H_7$$
$$N-CH_2-C{\equiv}C-CH_2-CH_2-N$$
$$C_2H_5\diagup \qquad\qquad\qquad\qquad\qquad i\text{-}C_4H_9$$

1-(Methylethylamino)-5-(propylisobutylamino)-2-pentyne

An alternative name for the foregoing is N-methyl-N-ethyl-N'-propyl-N'-isobutyl-1,5-pentyn-2-diamine.

For tri-, tetra-, penta-, and higher polyamines, the name was selected that seemed to be simplest to read and understand. Usually, the core of the nomenclature was a symmetric central grouping to which the rest of the molecule consisted of readily combinable substituents.

The following examples are offered:

$$CH_2CH_2N(C_2H_5)_2$$
(a) $\qquad (C_2H_5)_2NCH_2CH_2N$
$$CH_2CH_2N(C_2H_5)_2$$

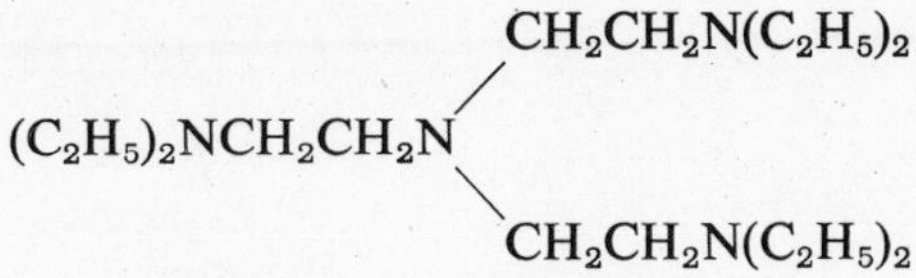

Tris(2-diethylaminoethyl)amine

(b)

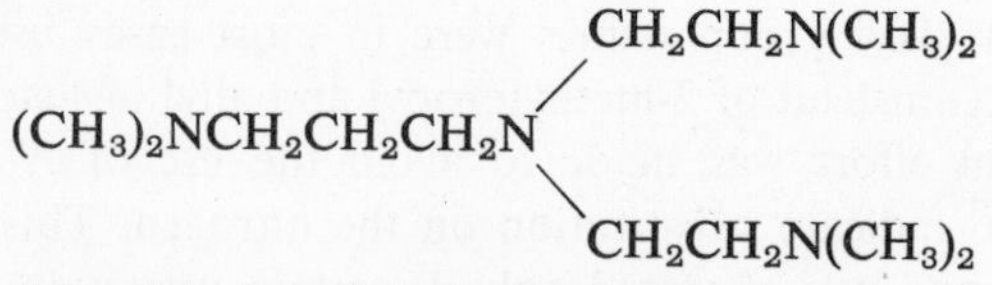

$$(CH_3)_2NCH_2CH_2CH_2N \begin{matrix} CH_2CH_2N(CH_3)_2 \\ \diagup \\ \diagdown \\ CH_2CH_2N(CH_3)_2 \end{matrix}$$

1-Dimethylamino-3-bis-(2-dimethylaminoethyl)aminopropane

(c)

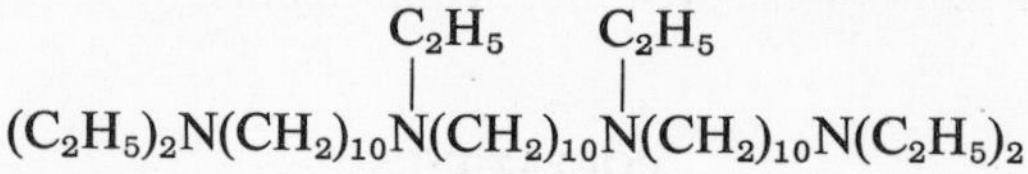

$$\begin{matrix} C_2H_5 & C_2H_5 \\ | & | \\ (C_2H_5)_2N(CH_2)_{10}N(CH_2)_{10}N(CH_2)_{10}N(C_2H_5)_2 \end{matrix}$$

N,N'-Diethyl-N,N'-bis-(10-diethylaminodecyl)decamethylenediamine

Mention might here be made of the "aza" nomenclature, in which each nitrogen atom is considered as having been substituted for a methine group, —CH—. The molecule is then named as a hydrocarbon except for additional prefixing of the location of the "aza" nitrogen. For example:

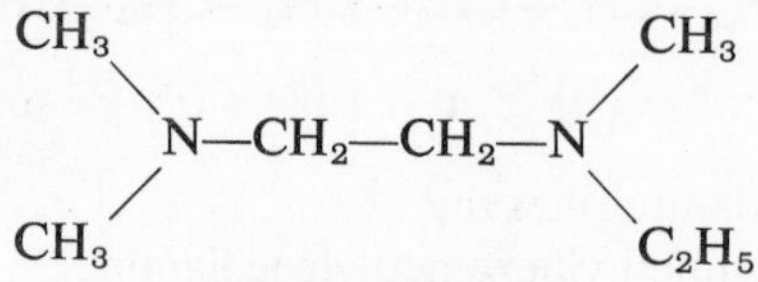

$$\begin{matrix} CH_3 & & CH_3 \\ \diagdown & & \diagup \\ & N—CH_2—CH_2—N & \\ \diagup & & \diagdown \\ CH_3 & & C_2H_5 \end{matrix}$$

2,5-Dimethyl-2,5-diazaheptane

This terminology is not used in the present volume because, while clear on paper, it is mentally confusing. It does not permit ready conversion in the mind to molecular structures familar to the chemist. Functional dialkylamino groups and other components are not carried along in the name, but appear only after the full molecule has been written down and examined.

General Properties

The acyclic aliphatic tertiary amines considered in this monograph possess a blending of properties derived from both the organic substituents and the nitrogen atom at the core. The former account for the ready combustibility of these compounds, good chemical inertness (if the substituent groups are saturated) or ready chemical attack (if such groups are unsaturated), their most common state as liquids, and their low solubility in water but good solubility in organic solvents. The tertiary nitrogen atom is responsible for most of their chemical properties, including basicity, ability to form quaternary ammonium derivatives and amine oxides, some polarizability and some polarization in the molecule. It also serves as a focus for chemical attack and degradation reactions.

These amines possess the alkaline properties of bases, with pK_a values in aqueous solution at 25° ranging from about 9.8, for trimethylamine, to 11.9, for methyl-(t-butyl)-(t-amyl)amine[A11] in the case of the saturated compounds. The linear correlation, based on the primacy of inductive effects, first reported by Hall[HA6] between pK_a and the sum of substituent σ^* values[TA1a]:

$$pK_a = -3.30\Sigma\sigma^* + 9.61$$

suggests, if the extrapolation is valid, that a pK_a as high as 12.6 may be obtainable from a tri-t-alkyl amine, although none such has yet been synthesized. Unsaturation in the alkyl substituents raises the σ^*, thus lowering pK_a. Although pK_a values of 8.31 for triallylamine, 8.2 for 3-ethylisopropylamino-3-ethyl-1-pentyne,[A11] and 7.05 for 3-dimethylamino-1-propyne[CA7] have been reported, the Hall equation predicts, if the linear relationship holds in this range, that pK_a's of 6.05 (from tri-1-propenylamine), and even much lower (from 1-alkynylamines) may be achievable. Conjugation within the substituents or with the unshared electron pair of the nitrogen may also be introduced, with resulting greater decrease in basicity.

Solubility limitations affect the use of water as a solvent. Aqueous alcohols or dimethylformamide have been used as media, but the pK_a values therein obtained are lower and not directly correlatable with those determined in water.

The solubility of the tertiary amines in water is dependent primarily on hydrogen bonding of the solvent to the amine nitrogen or the proton of its conjugate acid ammonium form.[TR6] The number of water molecules so bonded to a tertiary amine is open to conjecture,[HA6] but the nature of these bonds leads to a negative thermal coefficient of solubility in water—i.e., solubility decreases with increase in temperature.

However, the principal structural feature which differentiates the aliphatic tertiary amines from its primary and secondary analogs is the absence of nitrogen-to-hydrogen linkages. This absence has significant consequences with respect to both physical and chemical properties and behavior, since such a bond can serve as a focal point both for hydrogen bonding in the pure amine and as a center for chemical reaction.

The aliphatic tertiary amines display boiling and melting points roughly similar to those of their respective hydrocarbon analogs possessing a carbon-hydrogen group instead of the nitrogen atom. However, there are some interesting trends in the boiling points. The seven-carbon tertiary amines boil at the same temperature (within one or two degrees, usually) as do their hydrocarbon analogs. As one goes to amine molecules with fewer carbons, these boil increasingly higher (12–17°, for four-carbon amines), while those with more carbons (up to about eleven) boil increasingly lower than do the hydrocarbon analogs. In the smaller molecules the observed behavior may be attributed to intermolecular dipole-dipole attractive forces in the amines which become less effective as the molecular size increases. However the explanation for the lowered relative boiling points for larger molecules (up to 5–10° lower for nine-carbon compounds) is not obvious since these should become increasingly hydrocarbon-like. It may be that the flatter pyramidal geometry about the nitrogen compared to that about the C—H moiety may be responsible. This then becomes of negligible significance for the still larger molecules. The high molecular weight amines are usually viscous liquids of high boiling point and distillable without decomposition only at reduced pressure.

The melting points of the tertiary amines are generally well below 0° owing to the branching geometry introduced by the completely substituted trigonal nitrogen atom. In the few reported cases of solids among the smaller (fewer than nine-carbon) amines, the presence of a terminal acetylenic group seems to be the important feature. For example, 3-diethylamino-1-butyne melts at 10°, and 3-dimethylamino-3-methyl-1-butyne has a confirmed melting point at 102°! The thermodynamics of fusion for such molecules warrant further study.

The absence of hydrogen bound directly to the nitrogen atom prevents the tertiary amines from demonstrating the chemical behavior generally associated with the other amines: amide formation, reaction with nitrous acid, simple alkylation, N-halogenation, etc. On the other hand, they can form amine oxides, and not only the conventional acids salts but the completely dissociated quaternary ammonium salts wherein the cation consists of a nitrogen with four substituent organic groups at tetrahedral covalencies thereto.

The infrared absorption spectra of acyclic aliphatic tertiary amines lack a strong characteristic band such as that due to N—H stretching as is found in primary and secondary amines. However, the C—N stretching vibration, whose position does not differ much from that of C—C stretching, shows a somewhat enhanced absorption intensity because of the bond polarity. Nakanishi[NA2b] reports two moderate absorption bands of this vibrational type in the 1030–1230 cm^{-1} region for tertiary amines. When the amine is in the salt form, such as the hydrochloride, then, in addition to the trialkyl-ammonium N—H stretching at 2250–2700 cm^{-1}, there is a band at 1400–1440 cm^{-1} characteristic of C—H bending in a methylene group adjacent to the N$^+$ atom.[NA2b] Suffice it to say, however, that clear definitive classification of a molecule as an acyclic aliphatic tertiary amine on the basis of its infrared absorption spectrum alone is not considered reliable.

DISCUSSION OF PREPARATIVE METHODS—SCOPE AND LIMITATIONS

Prefatory Remarks

The present section reviews essentially all the methods that have been used in preparing aliphatic tertiary amines. Tables summarizing representative reaction conditions and yields along with selected detailed experimental examples are included for most of the more common procedures. The relatively large number of synthetic methods (various N-alkylations, etc.) precede the degradative ones. These are followed by two sections involving miscellaneous reactions. The reader's attention is directed to the Table of Contents for specific headings.

The Methods

1. N-ALKYLATION WITH ALKYL HALIDES AND OTHER ALKYL ESTERS OF STRONG ACIDS

$$\diagdown N-H + RX \rightarrow \diagdown N-R$$

Alkylation of Ammonia. The first synthesis of aliphatic tertiary amines, reported in 1850 by Hofmann,[HO2] involved the alkylation of ammonia, itself, by methyl bromide, ethyl bromide, and amyl bromide. In general, this reaction leads to a complex mixture which may include primary, secondary, and tertiary amines and their hydrohalides, as well as quaternary ammonium salts—all containing identical alkyl groups.[HO2,HO4,HO5] The general equation is as follows:

$$RX + NH_3 \rightarrow RNH_2 + R_2NH + R_3N + R_4NX$$

$$+ NH_4X + RNH_2{\cdot}HX + R_2NH{\cdot}HX + R_3N{\cdot}HX$$

where RX is the organic ester of a strong acid, HX, such as hydrochloric, hydrobromic, hydriodic, sulfuric, phosphoric, alkanesulfonic acid, and the like. The nonhalides, however, are not commonly used in the alkylation of ammonia.

During the period of more than a century since 1850, such direct alkylation of ammonia has been frequently employed in tertiary amine synthesis[BE9,BO13,BR11,CO14,FA7,FA8,FR10,GI5,MA14,PL3,SH5,ST4,TA6,WE9,WE17] yet one is truly amazed by the scarcity of reliable literature from which one can deduce the role of experimental variables, such as alkyl halide structure, temperature, medium, and time, on the course of the reaction. The alkylation all the way to the tertiary amine is complicated primarily by the apparent step-wise nature of the alkylation process and the complex interplay, in differing degrees, of electronic, steric, solvent, and other factors in the chemical reactivity of the intermediate primary and secondary amines. A discussion of some of the more pertinent experimental information acquired by various investigators over the years gives some insight into the complexity of this reaction.

14

Menschutkin, in addition to specialized studies on the rate of quaternization of tertiary amines as a function of alkyl halide[ME9] and nature of solvent,[ME10] also published an early classic paper on the kinetics of alkylation of various amine types by methyl, ethyl, propyl, and allyl bromides. In this latter investigation an alkyl bromide and amine mixture, of 1:2 molar ratio composition, dissolved in 15 times its volume of benzene was heated at 100° in a sealed glass tube. The course of the alkylation reaction was determined by titrating the ionic bromide. These data were substituted into the applicable integrated bimolecular rate equation:

$$k = \frac{1}{t} \log \frac{A - (X/2)}{A - X}$$

where k is the rate constant, t is the duration time, A is the amine concentration, and X is the concentration of bromide ion. The rate constants so obtained are listed in Table 1 with the full set of digits as given by Menschutkin. The data are primarily of qualitative interest since, at the time of publication, certain modern concepts and criteria in kinetics studies were unknown. Nevertheless they provide a useful and interesting correlation and point out the complexities in interpreting structural factors.

TABLE 1.[ME11]   RATE CONSTANTS FOR AMINE-ALKYL
BROMIDE REACTION IN BENZENE AT 100°

	$K \times 10^6$			
AMINE	WITH MeBr	WITH EtBr	WITH $CH_2{=}CH_2CHBr$	WITH PrBr
NH_3	5471	124	1380	44
$MeNH_2$	31910	490	8302	—
Me_2NH	59954	182	30833	—
Me_3N	31910	1053	34263	—
$EtNH_2$	19377	214	3807	65
Et_2NH	16886	182	2910	—
Et_3N	5380	30	757	—
$PrNH_2$	15215	184	3783	60
Pr_2NH	10264	101	2910	21
Pr_3N	5380	—	—	0.5

Although experimental details are very meager, Borrows et al.[BO13] appear to have used aqueous alcoholic ammonia solutions in autoclave reactions with various alkyl bromides and iodides at temperatures of about 140°. In the cases of hexyl bromide, octyl bromide, and dodecyl iodide, the reported yields of the respective tertiary (vs. secondary) amine are 28% (18%), 38%

(12.3%) and 52% (26.5%). Because the reactions were conducted with varying ratios of reactants reliable comparisons cannot be made. It is clear, however, that long-chain tertiary amines can be prepared by this method in respectable yields.

Patent claims drawn to the formation of primary, secondary, and tertiary amine mixtures under similar experimental conditions have also been reported.[FA7] However, the picture is confused by results cited in another patent[FA11] wherein apparently similar conditions gave essentially only secondary amine even when the alkyl halide-to-ammonia molar ratio was reduced to 1:100.

Nekrasova and Shuĭkin in 1952[NE2,NE3] published two studies of vapor phase alkylation of ammonia at 310° under catalysis by magnesium oxide. Although these workers planned to determine the effect of position isomerism, nature of halogen, and molecular chain length in their alkyl halide reactant, and did carry out the necessary reactions, their data not only are difficult to interpret but also show both ambiguities and inconsistencies. The main quotable data seem to be those given in Table 2. The uncertainties lie in the extent of reaction (since fixed reaction times were used), the percentage error

TABLE 2. SYNTHESIS OF ALIPHATIC AMINES BY
AMMONIA ALKYLATION AT 310° OVER MAGNESIUM
OXIDE[NE2]

ALKYL HALIDE	YIELD OF AMINE (%)		
	PRIMARY	SECONDARY	TERTIARY
Butyl chloride	39.2	18.1	2.7
Hexyl chloride	45.0	13.0	2.5
Heptyl chloride	50.5	9.0	1.5
Octyl chloride	58.0	4.2	0.8
Nonyl chloride	69.0	8.0	—
Decyl chloride	70.6	8.0	—

in the analytical methods used, and the uncertain significance of other auxiliary data. Nekrasova and Shuĭkin summarize their observations in a number of statements of which the following seem to have some experimental support:

(a) Magnesium oxide catalyzed vapor phase alkylation of ammonia at 310° by alkyl chlorides is feasible. The extent of such alkylation increases with alkyl chain length although the amount of tertiary amine formed diminishes.

(b) The amount of amino nitrogen in the alkylated products decreases as one goes from alkyl chloride to bromide to iodide.

(*c*) The amount of amino nitrogen in the alkylated products decreases as the chlorine atom in the alkyl chloride is shifted away from the 1-position.

In both statements *b* and *c* it is not clear how much of the reduced nitrogen content is due to lessened ammonia alkylation and how much to greater amine alkylation.

Shreve and Burtsfield[SH5] carried out their ammonia alkylation studies with alkyl halide and sodamide in liquid ammonia at $-50°$. This work, also, led to some discordant and unclear data as well as inexplicable results from adding varying small amounts of water during the post-reaction work-up period. The apparent effect of this water was to change in a nonsystematic manner the ratio of amines without affecting the total amine yield. The derived conclusions more or less supported by the experimental results for alkylation *under the cited conditions for fixed reaction times* appear to be the following:

(*a*) The yield of primary amines relative to higher alkylated products increases with chain length of the alkyl halide.

(*b*) Alkyl chlorides react more slowly than do the bromides but give a greater ratio of olefin to amines. These amines also showed higher secondary amine content.

(*c*) Significant amine formation (relative to olefin formation) occurs only with primary alkyl halides.

Alkylation, by alkyl halides, of liquid ammonia in sealed glass or metal bombs at room temperature was studied by von Braun.[BR11] The ratio of primary amine to higher alkylated products was much higher than when alcoholic or aqueous ammonia was used at similar temperatures and was found to increase rapidly with increasing molecular weight of the primary alkyl halide. For example, after 1 day at room temperature, liquid ammonia with amyl, octyl, and dodecyl bromides gave, respectively, 10, 45, and 90% of the primary, and 80, 43, and a small per cent of the pertinent secondary base. However, von Braun mixed his reactants by volume and in this case only 2 volumes of ammonia was used per volume of the alkyl halide. The molar excess of ammonia is significantly variable and small enough to have perturbed the significance of the reported yields. Another factor contributing to low yields (for fixed times of reaction with little or no stirring) is the existence of a heterogeneous reaction system, such as is the case with alkyl halides above C_{20} which become decreasingly soluble in liquid ammonia.[BR18]

Although von Braun[BR11] was unable to obtain any amines on substituting chlorides for bromides, Wibaut *et al.*[W11] succeeded in using dodecyl chloride as alkylating agent by operating at higher temperatures (75–80° for 72–90 hours). Yields of 28–33% primary, 36–27% secondary, and 0% tertiary amines were reported in experiments using dodecyl chloride and liquid ammonia in a 1:1 ratio by volume.

The obvious prediction that increasing the ratio of ammonia to alkyl halide would favor primary amine formation has been substantiated by

Werner.[WE13] He treated ammonia-saturated 90% ethanol with ethyl bromide and obtained the following yields of ethylamine for the stated ammonia-to-halide ratio: 1:1, 11.3%; 4:1, 24.4%; 6:1, 26.7%; 8:1, 28.1%; 16:1, 34.2%. It was also noted[WE13] that early precipitation of ammonium bromide from the reaction mixture such as occurred when the solvent ethanol was anhydrous led to higher yields of tertiary amine. This suggests to the authors that removal by salt precipitation of the liberated hydrogen halide from competition for the more basic amines favors further alkylation of the latter.

The effect of time of reaction and amine competition on the relative amounts of alkylation products has not been thoroughly studied. Werner[WE14] reported a set of experiments wherein 1.46 moles of butyl bromide was treated with 3 liters of ammonia-saturated 90% aqueous ethanol (containing 29 moles of ammonia). After 5 days, the respective molar quantities of butyl-amine, dibutylamine, and tributylamine isolated were 1.0, 0.22, and 0. When the reaction time was extended to 20 days and additional increments of butyl bromide were introduced every 3 days, these yields were 3.0, 1.4, and 0.25. It is evident that, despite the presence of a large ammonia excess, there is appreciable competition for the butyl bromide by the amines formed. However, many questions remain unanswered.

Tsuda and Matsumoto[TS5] reported briefly some studies on the reaction of a 1:2 molar ratio mixture of ethyl bromide and ammonia in 90% ethanol at 30°. Ethylamine was first detected 6 hours from the start of the reaction, triethylamine after 48 hours, and diethylamine after 84 hours. An equilibrium composition, reportedly reached after 200 hours, contained the primary, secondary, and tertiary ethylamines in the mole ratio of 3:1:3. The late appearance and low quantity of diethylamine observed was attributed to its high basicity and very rapid reaction rate with ethyl bromide.

Westphal and Jerchel[WE17] made a detailed study in which octyl, dodecyl, and hexadecyl chlorides were treated with liquid ammonia in ethanol at 70–170° for 19–24 hours. Despite a range in ammonia-to-alkyl halide ratio from 1.9:1 up to 8.0:1, the principal product was the secondary amine. A tertiary amine (in 22% yield) was obtained only in the case of octyl chloride, while one run with dodecyl chloride gave only the secondary amine, in 81% yield. Westphal and Jerchel state explicitly that increase in size of alkyl group in the halide results in a decrease in the tertiary amine content but an increase in the amount of primary amine yield. Unfortunately, no two of any of the experimental runs described were run under the same conditions of time, temperature, or ratio of reactants. It is difficult, therefore, to see how reliable conclusions may be drawn with respect to molecular structure effects.

In a comparative study of the alkylation of aqueous and of ethanolic ammonia by crotyl bromide under comparable but not equivalent conditions, Berthold[BE11] reported 14.1, 24.0, and 39.6% yields for primary, secondary, and tertiary amine products, respectively, in the former solvent, but 28.2, 13–16, and 16–19% in the latter solvent.

The alkylation of ammonia to give aliphatic tertiary amines is particularly feasible when the alkyl halides are of the more active less sterically hindered variety. Into this category fall the propargyl and allylic halides. Chauvelier and Gaudemar[CH1] describe the ready reaction of propargyl bromide with both liquid and aqueous ammonia to give mono-, di-, and tri-alkylation. Allyl chloride,[TA6] allyl bromide,[BU13] methallyl chloride,[BU13] 1-chloro-2,3-butadiene,[FA6] crotyl chloride,[BE11] and 1,4-dichloro-2-butyne[JO1] have been used as reagents under a variety of conditions including homogeneous and heterogeneous liquid systems.

In general, for saturated alkyl halides, the halide atom should be either bromine or iodine if the tertiary amine is desired. Hexyl chloride alkylates poorly[NE2] but hexyl,[BO13] heptyl,[CO14] and octyl bromides[BO13] react with aqueous ammonia to give acceptable yields of trialkylated products. For dodecyl and higher groups, the iodides appear to be the alkyl halides of choice.[BO13,WE9]

Fridau[FR10] found that cetyl iodide did not react with either liquid ammonia or solutions of ammonia in ether or ethanol at room temperature. However, when ammonia gas was bubbled through the cetyl iodide at 150°, a vigorous reaction occurred from which the only amine product isolable was tricetylamine. About seventy years later, Girard and Fourneau[G15] ran the same reaction, but at 200°, and obtained principally tetracetylammonium iodide and small amounts of both the secondary and the tertiary amine, which were not isolated. Subsequently, Staudinger and Rössler[ST4] claimed to have repeated Fridau's procedure but with tetradecyl, hexadecyl, and octadecyl bromides as the halides. However, no yields or experimental details are given. Wekua and Bergmann[WE9] used octadecyl iodide at 180° in their synthesis of the corresponding tertiary amine. The successful higher alkylations reported above for the cases of long-chain normal aliphatic groups contrast sharply with the more complex mixtures of amine products obtained with smaller alkyl halides.

Although the conditions that favor trialkylation of ammonia might be expected to lead to excessive quaternary ammonium salt formation, this has not been generally observed. It may be that such nonparallelism is attributable to differing solvent effects on the reaction of alkylation to amine compared to that leading to quaternary salt. This is admittedly contrary to the Hughes-Ingold classification of both these reactions into the same charge types from solvent-effects correlation,[IN3,RE4] but the quantitative differences in such effects may be a decisive factor.

In summary, the following conditions seem to be those favoring tertiary amine formation from the alkylation of ammonia:

(a) *Low concentration of ammonia.* This can be brought about by use of solvent such as water or alcohol. For large enough alkyl groups, the former may give a desirable two-phase liquid system by concentrating all of the reactants except ammonia in the organic phase. Alternatively, anhydrous ethanol as a solvent could keep all of the reaction homogeneous but favor removal of the annoying competing by-product hydrogen halide by its precipitation as the alcohol-insoluble ammonium halide salt. It is also possible to employ the alkyl halide itself, if it is high boiling, as the solvent at elevated temperatures and, by passing in a stream of ammonia gas, to maintain the ammonia concentration at a low but relatively constant value. In general, liquid ammonia is not a good medium for tertiary amine formation.

(b) *Reactive alkyl halide.* The iodides are preferable to the bromides, which in turn react better than the chlorides. It is also possible to have increased reactivity in the alkyl group if it has allylic or propargylic unsaturation.

(c) The liquid phase reactant system is preferred over the vapor phase. The higher boiling alkylated intermediates either condense out at low temperatures or pyrolyze at the higher ones. Moreover, high concentrations of these intermediates are not generally possible.

Some representative experimental results are given in Table 3. Two detailed preparative procedures also follow.

PREPARATION OF TRIALLYLAMINE.[BU13]　In a 3-liter 3-necked flask equipped with stirrer, condenser, thermometer, and dropping funnel 274 g. (4.5 moles) of 28% aqueous ammonia was diluted with 1050 g. of water. This solution was heated to 75°, and 363 g. (3 moles) of allyl bromide added through the dropping funnel at such a rate that gentle reflux was maintained. After addition was complete, stirring and heating at this temperature were continued for 3 hours. After cooling, the oily layer that separated was removed and dried over solid sodium hydroxide. The cold aqueous solution was saturated with sodium hydroxide and the resulting oily layer that separated was added to the main product. Drying over sodium hydroxide followed by efficient distillation gave triallylamine in 57.2% yield.

PREPARATION OF TRIETHYLAMINE.[GA5]　A mixture of 8000 ml. of alcohol and 3000 g. (27.6 moles) of ethyl bromide was saturated with ammonia (*Note:* weight of ammonia unspecified; from solubility data a good guess is about 800 g., 47 moles) several times during the day; the temperature of the mixture rose to about 30°, and after some time ammonium bromide began to crystallize out. After 24 hours the alcoholic ammonia solution was separated from the crystals of ammonium bromide, and the alcohol and unchanged ethyl bromide were distilled off. Water was added to the residue and the last traces of alcohol were removed by boiling. The hydrobromides of the mixed bases were then decomposed by a very concentrated solution of sodium hydroxide and the liberated amines distilled off. Fractionation of the amine mixture through a column effectively separated the amines to give 10.9% ethyl-, 17.9% diethyl-, and 19.1% triethyl-amine.

TABLE 3. DATA FOR REPRESENTATIVE PREPARATIONS OF TRIALKYLAMINES BY THE ALKYLATION OF AMMONIA

HALIDE/ NH$_3$	ALKYLATING AGENT	SOLVENT	REACTION TIME	REACTION TEMPERATURE	TERTIARY AMINE	YIELD (%)	REF.
1/10	CH$_2$=CHCH$_2$Cl	H$_2$O	2 min.	90° (autoclave)	(CH$_2$=CHCH$_2$)$_3$N	8	TA6
1/1.5	CH$_2$=CHCH$_2$Br	H$_2$O	3 hr.	75°	(CH$_2$=CHCH$_2$)$_3$N	57.2	BU13
1/1.5	CH$_2$=C(CH$_3$)CH$_2$Cl	H$_2$O	3 hr.	75°	[CH$_2$=C(CH$_3$)CH$_2$]$_3$N	13.7	BU13
1/23	CH$_2$=C=CHCH$_2$Cl	Liq. NH$_3$— H$_2$O	9 hr.	−40 to −50°	(CH$_2$=C=CHCH$_2$)$_3$N	23[a]	FA6
—	n-C$_6$H$_{13}$Br	C$_2$H$_5$OH— H$_2$O	[b]	[b]	(n-C$_6$H$_{13}$)$_3$N	28	BO13
1/1.8	n-C$_8$H$_{17}$Br	H$_2$O	[b]	[b]	(n-C$_8$H$_{17}$)$_3$N	36	BO13
1/4.3	n-C$_8$H$_{17}$Cl	C$_2$H$_5$OH	20 hr.	140° (sealed tube)	(n-C$_8$H$_{17}$)$_3$N	22	WE17

[a] Based on halide added. If yield is based only on halide consumed in the reaction, it becomes 55%. A higher yield is obtained when less liquid ammonia is used as solvent, but fewer preparative details are given.[FA6]

[b] These reactions were conducted "similarly" to others at 160° for 10 hours in an autoclave.[BO13]

Alkylation of Primary Amines.   The alkylation of primary amines with alkyl halides, sulfates, and sulfonates is simpler than the corresponding alkylation of ammonia. Since, in most cases, the reaction proceeds with relatively little, if any, quaternary salt formation, and since strong base is used to liberate the amines from their salts, the equation for the reaction can be simplified to the following expression:

$$RX + R'NH_2 \rightarrow RR'NH + RRR'N$$

Although this method can provide reasonable yields of tertiary amines in which two alkyl groups are the same, the method of choice for such compounds, when convenient, is alkylation of the appropriate secondary amine. In the case of alkyldimethylamines, N-methylation of primary amines by formaldehyde and formic acid (Eschweiler-Clarke modification of the Leuckart reaction, section 6) is the preferred method if the primary amine is readily available.

N-Methylation of primary amines with dimethyl sulfate[BO14,HE7,LI13] has not been used extensively but appears to be generally more satisfactory than the reaction with the halides. Methyl iodide,[BR9,HA11,ME14,VA2] and to a lesser extent dimethyl sulfate,[BR13] have been used in the presence of strong base to methylate exhaustively primary amines to the corresponding quaternary salts.[BR9,HA11,ME14,VA2] Even in the absence of strong base, considerable quaternary salt formation has been observed with methyl iodide. Bortnik et al.[BO14] treated t-butylamine (2 moles) in xylene with methyl iodide (1 mole) and obtained a 34% yield of t-butyltrimethylammonium iodide, 17.8% of t-butyldimethylamine, and 5.8% of t-butylmethylamine.

There are several factors that govern choice of alkylating agent. Because of their high reactivity, the iodides, especially the more readily available ones of lower molecular weight, can be used readily at lower temperatures and at atmospheric pressure even with other relatively volatile reactants. The bromides, on the other hand, are of lower reactivity and require higher temperatures to effect reaction in a comparable time. If the bromide and/or the primary amine are of relatively high volatility, this necessitates the use of an autoclave to arrive at the required reaction temperatures. Blicke and Zienty[BL3] used various bromides and found that the time necessary to alkylate primary amines that boil below 55° can be shortened from several days to several hours if the reactants are heated in an autoclave. Chlorides, being less reactive than the bromides, require higher temperatures for reactions in comparable time. The more active bromides and chlorides such as those of the allylic variety can be used at lower temperatures and at atmospheric pressure.

The alkyl sulfates and sulfonates are of relatively low volatility and are generally used in alkylations at atmospheric pressure. Although described much less frequently than the corresponding halides in alkylation reactions, they are quite satisfactory.

TABLE 4. DATA ON ALKYLATION OF PRIMARY AMINES $RNH_2 + R'X \rightarrow RR'NH + RR'R'N$

PRIMARY AMINE, RNH_2	ALKYLATING AGENT, R'X	MOLE RATIO $RNH_2/R'X$	SOLVENT	TIME (HRS.)	TEMP. (°C)	AMINE YIELD (%) RR'NH	RR'R'N	REF.
CH_3NH_2	$n\text{-}C_4H_9Cl$	1	C_2H_5OH	16	100–110° [a]	21	69	WE17
CH_3NH_2	$CH_2{=}C(CH_3)CH_2Cl$	2	$C_2H_5OH{-}H_2O$	[b]	[b]	15	78	WE15
CH_3NH_2	$n\text{-}C_{12}H_{25}Cl$	2	C_2H_5OH	12	160° [a]	59	37	WE17
CH_3NH_2	$n\text{-}C_{12}H_{25}Cl$	1	C_2H_5OH	12	160° [a]	—	51	WE17
$C_2H_5NH_2$	C_2H_5Br	1.3	None	3	100° [a]	—	70	RA1
$CH_2{=}CHCH_2NH_2$	$n\text{-}C_4H_9Br$	1.7	None	11[c]	[c]	57	23	BU8
$CH_2{=}CHCH(CH_3)NH_2$	C_2H_5I	0.5	None	[d]	[d]	—	66	YO5
CH_3NH_2	$n\text{-}C_9H_{19}I$	1.6	CH_3OH	6	100° [a]	17.6	75	KI3
$C(CH_2NH_2)_4$	$(CH_3)_2SO_4$	0.061	H_2O	[e]	[e]	—	52	LI13
$t\text{-}C_8H_{17}NH_2$[f]	$(CH_3)_2SO_4$	1	None	5	60–70°	40.4	21.6	BO14
$HC{\equiv}C{-}C(C_2H_5)(CH_3)NH_2$	$p\text{-}CH_3C_6H_4SO_2C_2H_5$	0.5	Benzene	[g]	[g]	—	37	HE11
$n\text{-}C_4H_9NH_2$	$p\text{-}CH_3C_6H_4SO_2{-}n\text{-}C_{16}H_{33}$	1	Toluene	6	reflux	51	33	SE3

[a] Sealed tube or pressure bottle.

[b] The pressure bottle containing reactants was shaken and warmed until reaction was complete. Time, temperature, and criteria for completeness of reaction were not specified.

[c] The butyl bromide was added with stirring over a period of 9.5 hours, during which time the mixture warmed spontaneously. The mixture was then heated for 1.5 hours on the steam bath.

[d] Kept below reflux temperature by intermittent cooling. Time unspecified.

[e] Dimethyl sulfate was added in small portions to an ice-chilled solution of tetramine in aqueous sodium hydroxide. This was followed by 2 hours of shaking, presumably at room temperature.

[f] $t\text{-}C_8H_{17}NH_2$ is $(CH_3)_3CCH_2C(CH_3)_2NH_2$.

[g] The ethyl-p-toluenesulfonate was added in two equal portions. After the first addition the solution was refluxed 2 hours, cooled, and the liberated p-toluenesulfonic acid extracted with sodium hydroxide solution. To the dried benzene layer was added the second portion of the sulfonate and the solution was refluxed 6 hours.

Table 4 lists representative reaction conditions encountered in primary amine alkylation. Detailed preparative procedures also follow.

PREPARATION OF 3-DIETHYLAMINO-1-BUTENE.[Y05] A solution of 30 g. (0.423 mole) of 3-amino-1-butene and 135 g. (0.846 mole) of ethyl iodide was placed in a flask equipped with reflux condenser. The temperature was kept below the reflux temperature by intermittent cooling with an ice bath. After the vigorous reaction had subsided, 27.4 g. (0.423 mole) of 87% potassium hydroxide was added to the solution. (Although unspecified in the publication, it is presumed that the potassium hydroxide was added in small portions.) The reaction was exothermic and maintained gentle reflux. After the reaction solution had been heated for 1 hour on a steam bath, an equal volume of water was added and the resulting solution evaporated to dryness. (Although not mentioned in the original procedure it is well to be sure that the solution is acidic before evaporation to minimize loss of amine.) The amine was isolated from the residual salt with potassium hydroxide. (Details not given, but reference is made to *Organic Synthesis*, Collective Volume, II, John Wiley and Sons, Inc., New York, 1943, p. 24, which states that the amine is liberated from its salt by means of aqueous potassium hydroxide and is distilled directly from the reaction flask, dried, and redistilled.) A middle fraction with constant boiling point and refractive index weighed 35 g. (66% yield).

PREPARATION OF BUTYLDIDODECYLAMINE (*n*-BUTYLDILAURYLAMINE).[SE3] A solution of butylamine (7.3 g., 0.1 mole) and lauryl *p*-toluenesulfonate (34.1 g., 0.105 mole) in 50 ml. of dry toluene was refluxed for about 6 hours. The mixture was treated with a concentrated solution of aqueous sodium hydroxide and distilled with steam to remove the toluene and any remaining butylamine. The residue in the distilling flask was extracted with ether, and the ether solution was dried over anhydrous potassium carbonate, filtered, and evaporated. The residue was distilled under reduced pressure. There was thus obtained 11.9 g. (47% yield) of *n*-butyllaurylamine boiling at 138–140° (6 mm.) and 6.9 g. (29% yield)* of *n*-butyldilaurylamine boiling at 224–226° (6 mm.).

PREPARATION OF METHYLDIBUTYLAMINE.[WE17] Thirty grams (0.324 mole) of butyl chloride, 10 g. (0.323 mole) of methylamine, and 6 ml. of ethanol were heated in a sealed tube for 16 hours at 100–110°. On cooling, methylamine hydrochloride precipitated. In order to prevent volatile amine from escaping, the mixture was acidified with an ether solution of hydrogen chloride. After the ether and alcohol were removed by distillation the residue

---

* To improve the yield of tertiary amine the authors here suggest that, after vigorous stirring with sodium hydroxide solution, the procedure of Hennion and Teach[HE11] be followed. In this, the toluene layer is separated, the aqueous layer is extracted with toluene, and the combined toluene layers are dried and filtered. This toluene solution then is again refluxed with an additional 0.1 mole of lauryl *p*-toluenesulfonate for an additional 6 hours.

was dissolved in water. The solution was made basic with strong sodium hydroxide solution and the amine separated as an oily layer on the surface. The mixture was extracted with ether and the ether layer was dried over sodium sulfate. After removal of most of the ether, distillation at 750 mm. gave a fore-run of 6 g. boiling at 85–110°, consisting mainly of methyl-butylamine, and 16 g. (69% yield) of pure methyldibutylamine boiling at 159–160°.

Alkylation of Secondary Amines. *N*-Alkylation of secondary amines by alkyl halides and, to a lesser extent, by sulfonates appears to be the most widely used general method for the preparation of trialkylamines. Since quaternary salt formation is usually quite low, the reaction can be represented by the following simple expression:

$$RR'NH + R''X \rightarrow RR''R'N \cdot HX$$

Two significant advantages that this method has over the alkylation of ammonia or of primary amines are the smaller number of by-products (hence higher yields of tertiary amines) and the capability of forming amines with differing alkyl groups.

High ratios of amine to alkylating agent, generally, give higher yields of tertiary amine. In studies using very large excesses of amine to alkylating agent (10:1 or larger), where the amine was used as both reactant and solvent, consistently good yields of tertiary amines were reported with alkyl bromides,[BR18] chlorides,[FA5] and sulfonates.[LA1,RE16]

Alkyl iodides, though used infrequently, are reactive enough to give alkylation under mild conditions. The alkyl bromides—the most widely used of the alkylating agents—are moderate in their reactivity and have been used both at atmospheric pressure and in sealed tube reactions. The chlorides, though the least reactive of the alkyl halides, have found frequent application in sealed tube reactions. An autoclave is not necessary if the chloride and secondary amine are of relatively high boiling point,[GR4] or if the chloride is of the allylic[YO5] or propargylic type.[BU8] The sulfonates, although used less frequently than the halides, have been employed both at atmospheric pressure and in sealed tubes.[EP2,MA22,MA30] Epsztein, Olomucki, and Marszak[EP2] obtained yields of 60–70% in the reaction of dimethylamine in dioxane with the three alkylating agents: 4-pentynyl iodide, 4-pentynyl bromide, and 4-pentynyl benzenesulfonate. The iodide and benzenesulfonate reacted at room temperature within 24 hours whereas the bromide required 2 hours in a sealed tube at 80°. Outside of this brief report no study has been made to compare directly the reactivity of halides *vs.* sulfonates. Sulfates, even the very common dimethyl sulfate, are used infrequently, although good results have been reported for such alkylating agents.[AI1] (The most frequently used method for methylation of dialkylamines is the Eschweiler-Clarke modification of the Leuckart reaction, *q.v.*)

Pruett et al.,[PR7] in a very unusual alkylation reaction, reported the preparation of tetrakis(dimethylamino)ethylene in 54% yield from dimethylamine (in large excess) and chlorotrifluoroethylene under pressure:

$$\begin{array}{c} F \\ \diagdown \\ \diagup \\ F \end{array} C = C \begin{array}{c} F \\ \diagup \\ \diagdown \\ Cl \end{array} + (CH_3)_2NH \rightarrow \begin{array}{c} (CH_3)_2N \\ \diagdown \\ \diagup \\ (CH_3)_2N \end{array} C = C \begin{array}{c} N(CH_3)_2 \\ \diagup \\ \diagdown \\ N(CH_3)_2 \end{array}$$

However, the proof of structure was based mainly on the proper elemental analysis of the bromine addition product of the olefinic tetramine.

Secondary allylic halides can react abnormally with dialkylamines to produce an isomer of the expected tertiary amine because of an allylic shift.[ME6,YO5] For example, Meisenheimer and Link[ME6] obtained 1-diethyl-amino-2-pentene on reaction of diethylamine with 3-chloro-1-pentene:

$$(C_2H_5)_2NH + CH_3CH_2\overset{\overset{\displaystyle Cl}{|}}{\underset{\underset{\displaystyle H}{|}}{C}}-CH=CH_2 \rightarrow (C_2H_5)_2NCH_2CH=CHCH_2CH_3$$

Tertiary propargyl halides (unlike ordinary tertiary alkyl halides, which dehydrohalogenate when reacted with amines or ammonia) have been found to alkylate secondary amines. Hennion and Hanzel[HE8] obtained a 28% yield of the expected tertiary amine by the reaction of 3-chloro-3-methylbutyne with dipropylamine at room temperature for 1 week:

$$(n\text{-}C_3H_7)_2NH + Cl\overset{\overset{\displaystyle CH_3}{|}}{\underset{\underset{\displaystyle CH_3}{|}}{C}}-C\equiv CH \rightarrow (n\text{-}C_3H_7)_2N\overset{\overset{\displaystyle CH_3}{|}}{\underset{\underset{\displaystyle CH_3}{|}}{C}}-C\equiv CH$$

(28% yield)

Table 5 presents data on selected examples of secondary amine alkylations. Some detailed experimental procedures also follow.

PREPARATION OF ALLYLDIETHYLAMINE.[CO25]   Allyl bromide (165 g., 1.37 moles) was added slowly with stirring to a solution of diethylamine (200 g., 2.74 moles) in 240 ml. of dry benzene in a 1-liter 3-necked flask fitted with a stirrer, dropping funnel, reflux condenser, and a thermometer dipping into the liquid. The flask was cooled intermittently to keep the reaction temperature from rising above 40–50°. After the addition was completed, the mixture was heated under reflux in a bath at 80° for 2 hours. After cooling, 150 ml. of concentrated hydrochloric acid and 100 ml. of water were added. The layers were separated, the benzene layer was extracted with two 50-ml. portions of 10% hydrochloric acid, and the combined acid extracts and aqueous phase were extracted with 50 ml. of benzene. The aqueous solution was made

TABLE 5. DATA ON ALKYLATION OF SECONDARY AMINES $RR'NH + R''X \rightarrow RR'R''N$

SECONDARY AMINE, RR'NH	ALKYLATING AGENT, R''X	MOLE RATIO RR'NH/R''X	SOLVENT AND OTHER REACTANTS	TIME (HR.)	TEMPERATURE	YIELD (%), TERTIARY AMINE	REF.
$(CH_3)_2NH$	$HC{\equiv}C(CH_2)_4Cl$	2.67	Benzene	13	80° [a]	60	CA7
$(CH_3)_2NH$	$(CH_3)_2NCH_2CH_2CH_2CH(CH_3)Cl$	2.7	H_2O—C_2H_5OH—Cu	5	150° [a]	ca. 100	MA23
$(CH_3)_2NH$	$n\text{-}C_{18}H_{37}Cl$	20	None	12	150° [a]	ca. 100	FA5
$(C_2H_5)_2NH$	$n\text{-}C_8H_{17}Cl$	1.6	C_2H_5OH	12	160° [a]	91	WE17
$(CH_3)(n\text{-}C_3H_7)NH$	$n\text{-}C_{10}H_{21}Cl$	2.4	Benzene	40	Room	72	CO23
$(n\text{-}C_3H_7)_2NH$	$ClCH_2CH{=}CHCH_2Cl$	6	None	[b]	[c]	91.3 [d]	MO12
$(CH_3)_2NH$	$Br(CH_2)_6Br$	6	H_2O—C_2H_5OH	16	70° [a]	65 [d]	CA19
$(C_2H_5)_2NH$	$i\text{—}C_3H_7Br$	1.3	Glycerol	72	Reflux	60	CA12
$(C_2H_5)_2NH$	$CH_3CH{=}CH(CH_2)_4Br$	2	Benzene	36	80° [a]	95	GL1
$(C_2H_5)_2NH$	$n\text{-}C_{10}H_{21}Br$	2.5	C_2H_5OH-toluene	[b]	Reflux	80	CO1
$(C_2H_5)_2NH$	$n\text{-}C_{11}H_{23}Br$	2.25	Xylene	6	170° [a]	80	PE1
$(C_2H_5)_2NH$	$n\text{-}C_{16}H_{33}Br$	126	None	24	50° [a]	100	BR18
$(CH_2{=}CHCH_2)_2NH$	$Br(CH_2)_7Br$	2	H_2O—$NaHCO_3$	9	Reflux	87.5 [d]	BU12
$(C_2H_5)_2NH$	$ICH_2C{\equiv}CCH_2I$	5.8	Ether	1	Reflux [e]	64 [d]	WI8
$(n\text{-}C_3H_7)(i\text{-}C_4H_9)NH$	C_2H_5I	1	Alc. KOH	6	Reflux	74	PO3
$(CH_3)_2NH$	$C_6H_5SO_2OCH_2CH_2C{\equiv}CH$	2.5	Ether	5	ca. 25° [e]	46	MA30
$(i\text{-}C_3H_7)_2NH$	$TsO{-}(CH_2)_3{-}OTs$ [f]	19	None	20	Reflux	87.5 [d]	RE16,LA1

[a] Sealed reaction vessel (tube, pressure bottle, or autoclave).

[b] "Overnight."

[c] After mixing of the reagents, the solution temperature reached 60°, at which time the mixture was cooled to 50° and allowed to stand overnight. It is not clear whether or not the temperature was maintained at 50° overnight.

[d] The N,N,N',N'-tetraalkyldiamine is the product.

[e] The mixture was cooled externally on mixing of reactants.

[f] Ts— is the p-toluenesulfonyl group, $p\text{-}CH_3C_6H_4SO_2{-}$.

alkaline by addition of a solution of 200 g. of sodium hydroxide in 500 ml. of water. The nonaqueous phase which appeared was separated and combined with two 50-ml. ether extracts of the water solution. The combined amine and ether extracts were dried over solid potassium hydroxide and fractionally distilled. Allyldiethylamine, boiling at 111°, was obtained in 79–84% yield.

PREPARATION OF ALKYLDIETHYLAMINES.[CO1] The following procedure exemplifies the general method used by Coan and Papa[CO1] for alkylating diethylamine with alkyl bromides.

A mixture of 0.75 mole of secondary amine, 0.3 mole of alkyl bromide, 100 ml. of anhydrous toluene, and 50 ml. of anhydrous ethanol was refluxed overnight. The mixture was cooled, poured into water, and extracted with 1:1 ether-benzene. The organic layer was extracted with dilute hydrochloric acid and the acid layer was made strongly basic with sodium hydroxide solution. The aqueous mixture was extracted with ether-benzene and the organic extracts were combined and dried over anhydrous potassium carbonate. Fractional distillation of this solution yielded the desired tertiary amine. With the pertinent reactants, there were obtained octyldiethylamine in 36% yield, decyldiethylamine in 80% yield, and dodecyldiethylamine in 76.5% yield.

PREPARATION OF METHYLPROPYLDECYLAMINE.[CO23] The decyl chloride (prepared from 0.5 mole of decyl alcohol) was dissolved in 250 ml. of benzene and cooled, and 86 g. (1.2 moles) of methylpropylamine was added. The solution was allowed to stand at room temperature for 40 hours, then dissolved in 500 ml. of ether, and the ether solution was extracted with two 250-ml. portions of 10% hydrochloric acid. The acid solution was cooled and made strongly alkaline with sodium hydroxide. The liberated amine was extracted with three 200-ml. portions of ether; the ether extracts were dried over potassium hydroxide pellets and concentrated. Distillation of the residue gave 76.4 g. (72% yield based on decyl alcohol) of methylpropyl-decylamine, b.p. 89–90° (1 mm.).

PREPARATION OF N,N,N′,N′-TETRALKYLDIAMINES.[LA1] The following procedure was used by Laakso and Reynolds[LA1,RE16] to prepare several tertiary diamines from glycol disulfonates and secondary amines.

Under anhydrous conditions a solution of 1,2-benzenesulfonoxy- or 1,2-toluenesulfonoxy-ethane and 20 equivalents of anhydrous secondary amine are refluxed with stirring for approximately 20 hours. The secondary amine is fractionally distilled, after which an excess of 40% sodium hydroxide solution is added. The oil layer is separated and the water layer extracted with ether. The oil and ether extracts are combined and dried over anhydrous potassium carbonate. After distillation of the ether, the residual oil is fractionated under reduced pressure.

In this way there was obtained 1,2-bis(diethylamino)ethane (55% yield), 1,3-bis(diisopropylamino)propane (85.7% yield), 1,4-bis(dibutylamino)butane (77.5% yield), and 1,3-bis(diisopropylamino)butane (65% yield).

PREPARATION OF DODECYLDIETHYLAMINE.[WE17] Thirty grams (0.146 mole) of dodecyl chloride, 20 g. of diethylamine (0.274 mole), and 20 ml. of ethanol were heated in a sealed tube at 140° for 18 hours. On cooling, diethylamine hydrochloride crystallized. After work-up in the usual way (details not specified, but other amine isolations are given), 30.5 g. (86% yield) of dodecyldiethylamine was obtained. (In a patent[FA5] it is claimed that, with a mole ratio of 20 to 1 of dimethylamine to stearyl chloride, an almost quantitative yield of stearyldimethylamine was obtained in 1 hour at 150° in an autoclave.)

2. N-ALKYLATION WITH ALCOHOLS, ETHERS, AND CARBOXYLIC ACID ESTERS

$$\text{>N-H} + RO \longrightarrow \text{>N-R} + \text{-OH}$$

N-Alkylation with Alcohols. In 1909, Sabatier and Maihle[SA3] passed ammonia and ethyl alcohol vapors over thorium oxide at 350–375° and obtained a mixture of mono-, di-, and triethyl-amines. This type of catalytic alkylation has developed into a very important industrial method for preparing simple amines.

Although amine mixtures generally comprise the main product several by-products are possible in such alkylations, as is illustrated by the following example with 1-propanol:

$$n\text{-C}_3\text{H}_7\text{OH} + \text{NH}_3 \rightarrow n\text{-C}_3\text{H}_7\text{NH}_2 + (n\text{-C}_3\text{H}_7)_2\text{NH} + (n\text{-C}_3\text{H}_7)_3\text{N}$$
$$+ \text{CH}_3\text{-CH=CH}_2 + n\text{-C}_3\text{H}_7\text{-O-}n\text{-C}_3\text{H}_7$$
$$+ \text{CH}_3\text{-CH}_2\text{-CHO} + \text{CH}_3\text{-CH}_2\text{-CN}$$
$$+ \text{H}_2\text{O} + \text{H}_2$$

N-Alkylation of ammonia has been studied with respect to many variables such as catalyst, temperature, pressure, ratio of reactants, flow rate, use of added hydrogen, and nature of the alcohol.[AR6,BA38,BE2,BR31,BR36,DA13,DE3,DO4, FA3,KO2,KO20,KO22,KR9,PO4,PO5,PO6,SM12,TA12,TA13,WH1,WH2,WI12] The complex interplay of these and other reaction parameters does not seem to have been fully appreciated. Even worse is the fact that not only is there too frequent lack of information on reproducibility or reliability limits of the data obtained but also insufficient describing and experimental planning have been done to allow objective cross-correlation of the results from different workers. The best that can be accomplished here is to summarize the data from the more representative and comprehensive papers of a rather extensive literature in an effort to give the interested investigator an insight into this field. Also included in the discussion are the alkylation of primary and secondary amines by alcohols, and the use of ether and carboxylic esters as alkylating agents.

The catalysts most frequently reported are of the dehydration type, such as the oxides of aluminum, thorium, silicon, tungsten, magnesium, and chromium. Of these, aluminum oxide seems to be the most popular. Metal salts like chlorides and sulfates of copper or iron also have been employed.[L17] To a lesser extent catalysts of the hydrogenation or dehydrogenation variety also have been used.[FA3,P04, P05,WA1,WH1] These include copper, nickel, cobalt, and platinum, which are frequently used in the presence of added hydrogen gas.[DA13,OL3,TA12]

In addition to the effects of reaction conditions in alkylation, catalyst efficiency is influenced by variables such as activation temperature, history, and aging, state of subdivision, and proportion of cocatalysts or promoters.[BE2,BR36,HE2,SA4] Because of these many yield-affecting interrelated factors it is not surprising that seemingly contradictory results on catalyst efficacy sometimes appear in the published literature.

Brown and Reid[BR36] studied the vapor phase alkylation of ammonia by alcohols at 300–500° and found that catalyst activity for production of amines decreased in the following order: specially prepared silica gel, silica gel impregnated with thoria, zirconium oxide, silica gel impregnated with nickel(II) oxide, alumina, commercial silica gel, and blue oxide of tungsten. From this grouping it can be seen that under the conditions studied one form of silica gel is the best while another is almost the poorest of the catalysts investigated.

Heinemann, Wert, and McCarter[HE2] studied the effects of catalyst activation temperature and the presence of cocatalyst (promoter). They used variously activated bauxites (impure aluminum oxides) and showed them to be superior to activated alumina. The iron oxide in the bauxite evidently promotes amine formation, and its maximum effectiveness was found to occur at a concentration of about 3%. A table from this paper is given here (Table 6) to illustrate typical reporting of data in catalysis studies.

Under different conditions, Bel'chev[BE2] also found that iron oxide, as cocatalyst, improved the efficiency of aluminum oxide in the production of butylamines even though his overall yields were lower than those of Heinemann et al.[HE2] In comparing the cocatalysts titanium dioxide and ferric oxide at various concentrations up to 15% he found that 85% Al_2O_3:15% Fe_2O_3 gave the optimum yield of amines (20–25%).

On the other hand Krishnamurthy and Rao[KR9] found that, in the high-pressure ammonolysis of various alcohols, from methyl through hexyl, iron oxide, as well as the oxides of thorium, zirconium, and molybdenum, acted as inhibitors. They also showed that alumina prepared from aluminum nitrate was more active than that prepared from aluminum chloride or aluminum sulfate, and that higher porosity catalysts were more effective than those of lower porosity.

Catalysts of the hydrogenation or dehydrogenation type also have been studied. For example,[WA1] a mixture of ammonia and 1-butanol (1:1 molar ratio), when passed over nickel on pumice at 250°, gave a 60% mixture of amines, in a ratio of 2:2:1 of mono-:di-:tri-butylamine. With copper instead of nickel, an 80% yield in a ratio of 3:4:2 was realized.

TABLE 6. AMINES FROM BUTYL ALCOHOL AND AMMONIA OVER ACTIVATED BAUXITE

Reaction temperature 320°; liquid space velocity of alcohol 0.3 vol./vol./hr.; molar ratio $NH_3:C_4H_9OH$, 1.6:1

CATALYST			BUTYL ALCOHOL RECOVERED (%)	PER CENT BUTYL ALCOHOL CONVERTED TO					
TYPE	Fe₂O₃ (%)	ACTIVATION TEMP.		OLEFIN	ETHER	TOTAL AMINE	PRIMARY AMINE	SECONDARY AMINE	TERTIARY AMINE
Bauxite	2.73	320°	48.5	19.1	0	33.4	24.0	9.4	0
Bauxite	2.73	370°	42.3	7.4	8.1	42.2	24.8	11.7	5.7
Bauxite	2.73	425°	19.2	13.2	9.1	58.5	20.6	28.8	9.1
Bauxite	2.73	480°	27.8	11.9	8.5	51.8	26.1	14.4	11.3
Bauxite	2.73	595°	29.0	15.3	13.4	42.3	26.1	5.4	10.8
Bauxite	2.73	705°	34.9	11.6	12.0	41.5	24.0	7.1	10.4
Alumina	0	425°	35.7	26.5	2.8	36.0	31.6	2.8	1.6
Bauxite	0.76	425°	27.8	11.9	8.5	51.8	26.1	14.4	11.3
Bauxite	2.73	425°	19.2	13.2	9.1	58.5	20.6	28.8	9.1
Bauxite	4.0	425°	27.6	12.3	9.5	50.6	19.3	25.1	6.2
Bauxite	5.65	425°	27.2	15.0	8.7	49.1	16.3	25.3	7.5

Reproduced with permission from *Industrial and Engineering Chemistry* **41**, 2930 (1949). See ref. HE2.

In a remarkably detailed table, Popov[PO5] reported his quantitative results on the alkylation of ammonia by all of the butyl alcohols using two catalyst systems: (1) activated charcoal and (2) platinum on silica gel. He lists the amount of nitriles, aldehydes, hydrogen, and olefins formed along with the percentages of mono-, di-, and tri-alkylamines (when *t*-butyl alcohol was used, the percentage of individual amines was not ascertained). Popov indicates much higher relative yields for trialkylamine formation in the amine mixture than have been reported by any other investigator using comparable ratios of ammonia to butyl alcohol. Moreover, he shows figures for the formation of substantial amounts of tri-*sec*-butylamine. For example, in one experiment[PO5] with *sec*-butyl alcohol and ammonia (molar ratio of 1 to 3.75) at 400° over activated charcoal as catalyst, a yield of 1.36% mono- and 40.19% tri-*sec*-butylamine was obtained (no value for di-*sec*-butylamine is given). This result is amazing in that no one has ever before unequivocally reported the preparation of tri-(*sec*-alkyl)amines by any method of direct alkylation of ammonia. Unfortunately, Popov's experimental details were very brief, and he did not characterize the amines obtained. His analytical data for amines come solely from questionable applications of the method of Weber and Wilson[WE1] (see below). In a later experiment using similar conditions, Popov and Shuĭkin[PO6] do not show any tri-*sec*-butylamine. However, they claimed triisopropylamine as the main product in the amine mixture in alkylation of ammonia with isopropyl alcohol. This amine was not characterized.

Krishnamurthy and Rao[KR9] also reported triisopropylamine (8% yield) in the alkylation of ammonia by isopropyl alcohol. Again no characterization of this amine was made.

The foregoing claims for tri-(*sec*-alkyl)amines should be considered extremely doubtful until adequate characterization has been made. If these claims are in error a possible explanation might be found in the common method of analysis of amine mixtures that makes use of several steps in which values are deduced by difference without isolation and characterization of the individual components. Initially, the ammonia is selectively precipitated from the basic nitrogen mixture with yellow mercuric oxide by the François method;[FR3] then the method of Weber and Wilson[WE1] is used. In this procedure the amines are distilled into excess acid and back-titrated with base to give total amine nitrogen. The primary amine is determined by the Van Slyke method. The dialkylamine forms the nitroso compound and remains behind when the solution is subsequently made strongly alkaline and distilled. The distillate, which contains trialkylamine, is collected in excess acid and back-titrated in the usual way. The secondary amine is estimated by difference.

In view of the large number of steps and the subtractions involved and since the method of analysis was developed for mixtures of amines containing primary alky groups only, it is felt that this analytical procedure should be checked against a careful absolute characterization for new amine mixtures.

Molybdenum oxide apparently can function as a dehydrogenation catalyst. Bishop and Denton[BI7] obtained mainly butyronitrile on treating butyl alcohol with ammonia at 435° over a catalyst composed of 10% molybdenum oxide and 90% activated alumina. The butyronitrile evidently arises from the dehydrogenation of the initially formed butylamine.

The use of added hydrogen represses such nitrile formation. Olin and McKenna[OL3] passed butanol, ammonia, and hydrogen over nickel at 181° and obtained an 86.3% conversion (92% yield) of mixed amines. Omission of hydrogen resulted in a 45% conversion of alcohol to nitrile. Taylor, Davies, and Reynolds obtained excellent conversions and yields of amines on treating various alcohols with ammonia and hydrogen at 190–200° under a total pressure of about 17 atmospheres. They used specially prepared nickel[TA12] and cobalt[DA13] catalysts. Yields of tertiary amines did not exceed 17%.

Although most of the studies of the alkylation of ammonia with alcohols have been conducted at atmospheric pressure in the temperature range of 300–450°, investigations have been made at other temperatures and at pressures above atmospheric. Differing results were reported by Krishnamurthy and Rao[KR9] and by Kozlov and Panova[KO20] in what might appear superficially to be similar experiments. In the alkylation of ammonia under pressures of about 9 atmospheres over alumina the former[KR9] obtained better yields of amines at 300° than at 325°, whereas the latter obtained better yields at 350–380° than at 250°. The differing results are not surprising, however, when examination of the experimental techniques discloses that there are significant difference in such experimental variables as mole ratios and method of metering reactants. Kozlov and Panova[KO20] also studied the effect of pressure as a variable and found that the yield of amines increased while the olefin formation decreased as the ammonia pressure was changed from 1 to 9 atmospheres.

High pressure and temperature seem to be preferred in some industrial applications. For example, the methylamines are prepared by passing methanol and ammonia at 450° and 13 atmospheres over alumina.[WI12]

As expected the higher the ratio of alcohol to ammonia the greater is the formation of trialkylamine, whereas primary amine formation is favored by a large excess of ammonia.[AR6,BR31,DA13,DO4,KR9,WH1] Most investigators have studied ratios of 1.5 to 2.5 moles of ammonia to 1 mole of alcohol. Such ratios lead generally to a preponderance of mono- and di-alkylamines. Whitaker[WH1] effectively obtained a very high ratio of alcohol to ammonia in a liquid phase reaction in which ammonia was bubbled through boiling, moderately high molecular weight, alcohols. The catalyst was Raney nickel and the water formed in the reaction was removed as formed. High yields of tertiary amines (triisodecylamine 67%, tris(isotridecyl)amine 58%) were

TABLE 7.[KO22] REACTION OF AMINES WITH AMMONIA OVER ALUMINA[a]

| AMINE USED | AMINE WEIGHT (g.) | YIELD CATALYZATE (g.) | PER CENT AMINES IN CATALYZATE | | | VOLUME BUTYLENE (LITERS) |
			PRIMARY	SECONDARY	TERTIARY	
n-BuNH$_2$	30	25	52.6	32.3	15.1	2
$(n$-Bu$)_2$NH	30	22	57.0	20.5	22.5	3
$(n$-Bu$)_3$N	13	9	52.8	22.2	25.0	1

[a] A known weight of amine in an atmosphere of ammonia at 9 atmospheres pressure was passed at a rate of 20 drops per minute over alumina at 370–375°.

attributed to the removal of water as formed. It was postulated that in the initial phases of the reaction Raney nickel dehydrogenated the alcohol to aldehyde, which in turn reacted with ammonia with the elimination of water.

Under conditions of vapor phase catalytic N-alkylation, extensive disproportionation (transalkylation) occurs, so that a mixture of the three amines can be obtained from any individual amine. (See also part l on "Disproportionation or Transalkylation of Amines" under section 18, "Miscellaneous Reactions.") Kozlov and Panova[KO22] obtained a mixture of the n-butylamines by reacting any one of them with ammonia over alumina, as shown in Table 7.

The preparation of mixed aliphatic trialkylamines by reaction of alcohols with amines has not been studied extensively. Smeykal[SM4] prepared dodecyldimethylamine in 90% yield by treating dimethylamine with dodecyl alcohol at a pressure of 190 atmospheres over alumina at 360°. He observed disproportionation in all reactions with primary amines; e.g., methylamine and dodecyl alcohol give methyldodecylamine and a small amount of dimethyldodecylamine. Yano et al.[YA2] treated diethylamine with cetyl alcohol in the presence of Raney nickel at an initial temperature of 200° and an initial pressure of hydrogen of 79 atmospheres and obtained a 44% yield of cetyldiethylamine. Other hydrogenation catalysts such as copper and cobalt also have been used effectively at elevated temperatures and with hydrogen at pressures of 40 to 220 atmospheres.[FA4]

Besides the aforementioned disproportionation reactions observed by Smeykal, others[SC12,SC14] have made similar observations with tertiary amines and alcohols. For example Schneider, Adkins, and McElvain[SC14] observed transalkylation on treating triethylamine with dodecyl alcohol under conditions of catalytic hydrogenation, and obtained mixed amines as follows:

$$(C_2H_5)_3N + n\text{-}C_{12}H_{25}OH \rightarrow (C_2H_5)_2N\text{—}n\text{-}C_{12}H_{25} + C_2H_5N(n\text{-}C_{12}H_{25})_2$$

$$\underset{(42\%)}{\qquad\qquad} \underset{(20\%)}{\qquad\qquad\qquad}$$

Instead of ammonia, certain of its derivatives such as urea and ammonium salts have been used in the alkylation reaction.[LI7] Primary amines can be replaced by such amine precursors as nitriles[SU1] if reaction is conducted under conditions of catalytic hydrogenation.

Sketches of equipment[BR31,DO4,KR9] used in catalytic vapor phase N-alkylation of ammonia by alcohols have been found in relatively few papers.

Although liquid phase N-alkylation by alcohols under mild conditions has received relatively little attention for the preparation of aliphatic trialkylamines, such a synthesis was reported recently by Leonard and Musker,[LE15] who obtained methylethylheptylamine by refluxing methylheptylamine with aqueous ethanol in the presence of Raney nickel:

$$\overset{\displaystyle H}{\underset{\displaystyle |}{CH_3\text{—}N\text{—}C_7H_{15}}} \xrightarrow[\text{reflux}]{C_2H_5OH,\ Ni} \overset{\displaystyle C_2H_5}{\underset{\displaystyle |}{CH_3\text{—}N\text{—}C_7H_{15}}}$$

It is interesting that they used this reaction to support their theory that, in the desulfurization of 2,4,6-tris-(6'-methylaminohexyl)trithane trihydrochloride by Raney nickel in the presence of ethanol, the formation of methylethylheptylamine arose from N-ethylation of the intermediate methylheptylamine by ethanol. Their overall reaction is shown as follows:

$$
\left[
\begin{array}{c}
CH_3NH(CH_2)_6 \overset{S}{\underset{S}{\bigcirc}} S \, (CH_2)_6NHCH_3 \\
(CH_2)_6NHCH_3
\end{array}
\right] \cdot 3HCl \xrightarrow[C_2H_5OH]{Ni} \quad CH_3{-}\overset{C_2H_5}{\underset{}{N}}{-}C_7H_{15}
$$

(49% yield)

Raney nickel catalyzed N-alkylation by alcohols under mild conditions had previously been reported with aromatic amines.[R11]

N-Alkylation with Ethers. Although ethers can be used instead of alcohols in catalytic N-alkyation reactions, the method has been studied relatively little because it presents no advantage over the use of alcohols. A review of this reaction has been made by Baum.[BA38]

Table 8 summarizes a reaction temperature study by Kozlov and Panova[KO19] in the catalytic alkylation of ammonia with dibutyl ether to give a mixture of the n-butylamines and butylene.

N-Alkylation with Esters of Carboxylic Acids. Under conditions similar to those used in catalytic N-alkylation with alcohols, carboxylic acid esters can be used as alkylating agents but offer no advantage over more conventional reactants.

Kozlov and Panova[KO21] obtained a mixture of the n-butylamines and acetonitrile in the amination of butyl acetate over aluminum oxide at 380°. Using milder conditions (200°), Class[CL5] obtained good yields of methyldiethylamine from diethylamine and methyl-p-toluate. McElvain and Tate[MC6] used an ortho ester, ethyl orthoacetate (at 200–220°) in the alkylation of dibutylamine to obtain ethyldibutylamine in 22% yield. The main product was N,N-dibutylacetamide.

3. N-ALKYLATION WITH ALKENES, ALKYNES, DIENES, DIYNES, AND ENEYNES

$$
\underset{/}{\overset{\backslash}{N}}{-}H + \underset{|}{\overset{|}{C}}{=}\underset{|}{\overset{|}{C}} \rightarrow \underset{/}{\overset{\backslash}{N}}{-}\underset{|}{\overset{|}{C}}{-}\underset{|}{\overset{|}{C}}{-}H
$$

The direct alkylation, under pressure, of ammonia, or primary or secondary amines, with unsaturated hydrocarbons to give tertiary amines has been mostly of industrial significance.

The simplest of the olefins, ethylene, has been used to introduce N-ethyl groups.[CL8,EN1,FR4,HO23,OF1,WH4] For example, the reaction of ethylene with

TABLE 8.[KO19] **PRODUCTS IN THE CATALYTIC AMINATION OF DIBUTYL ETHER**

Rate of ether passage 20 drops/min.; ammonia pressure 9 atm.; catalyst aluminum oxide.

AMOUNT OF DIBUTYL ETHER (g.)	TEMP.	YIELD OF AMINES (%) BASED ON		COMPOSITION OF AMINES			VOLUME OF BUTYLENE FORMED (LITERS)
		TOTAL ETHER USED	REACTED ETHER	PRIMARY	SECONDARY	TERTIARY	
23.0	300°	8.8	33.6	52.3	30.2	17.5	0.5
39.0	250°	27.6	67.7	58.2	31.4	10.4	2.0
36.0	370–375°	47.05	65.1	54.2	35.5	10.4	3.0
23.0	420°	7.9	12.1	55.6	35.3	9.1	10.0

ammonia provides a mixture of the three ethylamines as shown by the following equation:

$$CH_2{=}CH_2 + NH_3 \rightarrow C_2H_5NH_2 + (C_2H_5)_2NH + (C_2H_5)_3N$$

The only monoolefin that has been used for alkyl tertiary amine syntheses is ethylene. Other monoolefins produce only monoalkylamines and some dialkylamines, but no trialkylamines.[HO23,WH4] Steric hindrance probably accounts for the difficulty of trialkylation by such olefins. Even a compound of relatively low steric requirements such as diethylamine could not be alkylated with propylene to give a tertiary amine.[HO23]

The only diolefin reported as having been used in this reaction is 1,3-butadiene. With ammonia, 1,3-butadiene gives "tributenylamine."[HO23] In one patent a claim is made that the butadiene partly dimerizes; for example, methylamine and butadiene give a mixture of methyldibutenylamine and methylbutenyloctadienylamine.[DA6] However, the specific molecular structures are not unequivocally described.

Acetylenic compounds have been used in similar alkylation-by-addition reactions.[GA3,KR11,RE7] Over a uranium oxide catalyst at 350–400°, acetylene and ammonia yield triethylamine.[OF1] Reppe et al.[RE7] and Gardner et al.[GA3] showed that secondary amines react with acetylene under pressure in the presence of cuprous chloride to give 3-dialkylamino-1-butynes:

$$R_2NH + HC{\equiv}CH \xrightarrow{Cu_2Cl_2} R_2N-\overset{\displaystyle CH_3}{\underset{\displaystyle |}{C}}H-C{\equiv}CH$$

Kruse and Kleinschmidt[KR11] found that with 1-propyne a mixed zinc and cadmium acetate catalyst gave better yields than did cuprous chloride:

$$(C_2H_5)_2NH + CH_3C{\equiv}CH \xrightarrow{Zn,\ Cd\ acetates} (C_2H_5)_2N-\overset{\displaystyle CH_3}{\underset{\displaystyle \underset{\displaystyle CH_3}{|}}{\overset{\displaystyle |}{C}}}-C{\equiv}C-CH_3$$

$$(80\%)$$

According to Gardner et al.,[GA3] acetylene reacts with primary and secondary amines in the presence of a copper acetylide catalyst to give first a vinylamine, which then reacts with another molecule of acetylene to yield substituted 3-amino-1-butynes; for example:

$$(C_2H_5)_2NH \xrightarrow{HC{\equiv}CH} (C_2H_5)_2NCH{=}CH_2 \xrightarrow{HC{\equiv}CH} (C_2H_5)_2NCH(CH_3)C{\equiv}CH$$

Structure proof is presented to preclude the possibility that the reaction involves dimerization of acetylene to vinylacetylene with subsequent addition of the amine. This conclusion is also supported by the work of Englehardt,[EN2] who showed that the uncatalyzed addition of diethylamine to vinylacetylene (see detailed procedure at end of this chapter) yielded 1-diethylamino-2,3-butadiene. It has also been reported that lithiodibutylamine adds to 1-penten-3-yne to give 1-dibutylamino-2,3-pentadiene, though in poor yield.[PE10] These results support the conclusions of Gardner et al.[GA3] for the acetylene case cited above.

However, the allenic amine compounds may be isomerized further to internal or terminal acetylenic products by treatment with strong base[EN2] or alkali metals, [BA12] respectively. These ready unsaturated bond isomerizations as well as the differing modes of addition make the problem of exact structure identification of addition products to acetylenes a very important consideration not to be ignored. As a case in point one may cite the reported[FR4] reaction of diethylamine with 1,3-butadiyne (or diacetylene) to give "diethylaminovinylacetylene." It is stated that the use or nonuse of silver powder or silver acetylide catalyst affects only the yields but, apparently, not the nature of the product. Unfortunately, this reference has not clarified properly the structure of the amine obtained and it is not, therefore, unambiguous.

Recently, Petrov and Maretina[PE11,PE12] and Shostakovskiĭ et al.[SH4] (the latter reference states that yields of 60% are obtained but gives no experimental details or proof of structure) found that dialkylamines add to diacetylene in the cold and without a catalyst to give 1-dialkylamino-1-buten-3-ynes:

$$R_2NH + HC \equiv C-C \equiv CH \rightarrow R_2N-CH=C-C \equiv CH$$

The catalytic role of alkali metals, their hydrides, or their N-derivatives of secondary amines has been discussed in the literature. Howk et al.[HO23] give a brief outline of the literature, through 1953, on N-alkylation with unsaturated hydrocarbons and then[HO23,WH4] report that such reactions work best at a pressure of 800–1000 atmospheres and 175–200° with alkali metals or their hydrides as catalysts. In a patent issued in 1956, Classon et al.[CL8] claim that N-sodioamine derivatives, used as catalysts, allow reduction of the pressure to 55 atmospheres or less.

Representative examples of reaction conditions and yields are to be found in Table 9. Specific preparative procedures are also presented, in detail, at the end of this section.

Tertiary amines have also been found to undergo a remarkable reaction with acetylenes and monosubstituted acetylenes under pressure to yield the quaternary vinylammonium hydroxide, neurine[GA4]:

$$(CH_3)_3N + HC \equiv CH + H_2O \rightarrow [(CH_3)_3NCH=CH_2]^+OH^-$$

The reaction is quite temperature sensitive. Below 50° the main product is neurine, but with increasing temperature this compound decomposes, presumably by "transmethylation," to yield tetramethylammonium hydroxide, which is essentially the only product above 100°.

TABLE 9. REPRESENTATIVE EXAMPLES OF N-ALKYLATION BY UNSATURATED HYDROCARBONS

UNSATURATED HYDROCARBON	NITROGEN COMPOUND	MAXIMUM PRESSURE (ATM.)	MAXIMUM TEMPERATURE	CATALYST	PRODUCTS	YIELD (%)	REF.
$CH_2{=}CH_2$	$\dot{N}H_3$	980	252°	Li	$EtNH_2$ Et_2NH Et_3N	5.0 15.5 32.0	HO23
$CH_2{=}CH_2$	$C_6H_{13}NH_2$	41	159°	$NaNHC_6H_{13}$	$EtNHC_6H_{13}$ $Et_2NC_6H_{13}$	26.5 8.5 }	CL8
$CH_2{=}CH_2$	Bu_2NH	55	135°	Bu_2NNa	$EtNBu_2$	68	CL8
$CH_3C{\equiv}CH$	Me_2NH	37[a]	120°	Zn, Cd acetates	$Me_2N{-}C(CH_3)_2C{=}C{-}CH_3$	71	KR11
$CH_2{=}CHCH{=}CH_2$	$MeNH_2$	[a]	104°	$MeNHNa$	$MeN(C_4H_7)(C_8H_{13})$[b] $MeN(C_4H_7)_2$[b]	56 33.4 }	DA6
$HC{\equiv}\dot{C}CH{=}CH_2$	Me_2NH	[a]	100°	None	$Me_2NCH_2CH{=}C{=}CH_2$	56	EN1
$HC{\equiv}CC{\equiv}CH$	Et_2NH	[a]	45°	Ag°[c]	$Et_2NC_4H_3$[d]	29	FR4
$HC{\equiv}C{-}C{\equiv}CH$	Et_2NH	1	"Room"	None	$Et_2NCH{-}CH{-}C{\equiv}CH$	[e]	[e]

[a] Autogenous pressure.

[b] C_4H_7 is a butenyl group and C_8H_{13} is an octadienyl group (from dimerization of 1,3-butadiene) but which of the various isomers may have been obtained is not unequivocally stated.[DA6]

[c] Finely divided silver or silver acetylide give the same yield.

[d] The product is called diethylaminovinylacetylene[FR4] but which of the possible isomers that may have been obtained is not specified. Ref. SH4 reports that yields of 60% are obtained but gives no experimental details.

[e] Refs. PE11 and PE12 give experimental details but no yields.

PREPARATION OF 1-DIMETHYLAMINO-2,3-BUTADIENE (UNCATALYZED).[EN2] Aqueous 25% dimethylamine (540 g., 3 moles) was charged into a stainless-steel 1-liter reactor which had been flushed with nitrogen, evacuated, and cooled in a dry ice-acetone bath. The still partially evacuated reactor was connected to a cylindrical pressure vessel, with valves at both ends, containing vinylacetylene (156 g., 3 moles), which was then pressured into the reactor under nitrogen at 200 lb./sq. in. pressure. The reactor was then sealed and heated at 100° for 10 hours. After the reactor had been allowed to cool to room temperature, it was bled to the atmosphere and opened. The reaction mixture was saturated with potassium carbonate and then extracted with ether. The solution was first dried over potassium hydroxide and then over magnesium sulfate. After distillation of ether, the residual oil was distilled to give 164 g. (56% yield) of a clear, pale yellow liquid, b.p. 58–60° at 155 mm.

PREPARATION OF ETHYLDIBUTYLAMINE (CATALYZED).[CL8] N-Sodiodibutyl-amine catalyst was prepared from 11 parts of sodium, 10 parts of butadiene, and 307 parts of di-n-butylamine (preparative details for the catalyst are given in ref. CL8). The catalyst mixture was charged to the reactor along with an additional 153 parts of dibutylamine. The reaction was maintained at a temperature of 132–135° and an ethylene pressure of 20–25 atmospheres. The reaction time was 5 hours. A yield of 68% of ethyldibutylamine was obtained based on the dibutylamine used.

4. N-ALKYLATION WITH OLEFINS AND CARBON MONOXIDE

$$\diagdown \!\!\!\!\underset{\diagup}{N}\!\!-\!\!H \; + \; \underset{\diagup}{\diagdown}C\!\!=\!\!C\underset{\diagdown}{\diagup} \; + \; CO \; + \; H_2O \; \rightarrow \; \diagdown \!\!\!\!\underset{\diagup}{N}\!\!-\!\!\overset{|}{C}\!\!-\!\!\overset{|}{\underset{|}{C}}\!\!-\!\!\overset{|}{\underset{|}{C}}\!\!-\! \; + \; CO_2$$

Reppe et al.[RE6,RE10,RE12,RE14] found that ammonia, primary amines, or secondary amines can be alkylated under pressure by a mixture of a terminal olefin and carbon monoxide in the presence of iron pentacarbonyl and water. The nitrogen compound is used without prior neutralization,[RE6] or after neutralization with formic acid[RE12] or other acids.[RE10]

The reaction is illustrated by the following typical equations:

$$NH_3 + CH_2\!\!=\!\!CH_2 + 3\,CO + H_2O \rightarrow CH_3\!-\!CH_2\!-\!CH_2\!-\!NH_2 + 2\,CO_2$$

$$CH_3\!-\!CH_2\!-\!CH_2\!-\!NH_2 + CH_2\!\!=\!\!CH_2 + 3\,CO + H_2O \rightarrow$$
$$(CH_3\!-\!CH_2\!-\!CH_2)_2NH + 2\,CO_2$$

$$(CH_3\!-\!CH_2\!-\!CH_2)_2NH + CH_2\!\!=\!\!CH_2 + 3\,CO + H_2O \rightarrow$$
$$(CH_3\!-\!CH_2\!-\!CH_2)_3N + 2\,CO_2$$

With one exception (propylene[RE6]) this reaction (which has had industrial significance only) has been used with ethylene as the olefin. Alkylation of ammonia yields mono-, di-, and tri-propylamines.[RE6,RE10] The complexity of the amine mixture is increased by disproportionation. For example,[RE12] from 500 g. of diethylamine in a reaction with ethylene and carbon monoxide were obtained along with the expected product, propyldiethylamine (142 g.), diethylamine (20 g.), triethylamine (176 g.), ethyldipropylamine (70 g.), and diethylformamide (15 g.). This mixture of products indicates that disproportionation, such as the following known type,[KO22] probably occurs during the course of alkylation:

$$2 R_2NH \rightarrow RNH_2 + R_3N$$

The formation of triethylamine might also be explained on the basis of direct alkylation of diethylamine by ethylene. However, this seems unlikely because N-ethylation by ethylene under the subject conditions has not been observed for other compounds such as dimethylamine and propylamine.[RE6,RE12,RE14]

Only seven acyclic aliphatic tertiary amines are reported synthesized by this method. In Table 10 are presented selected data indicating representative yields.

TABLE 10.   PREPARATION OF AMINES BY N-ALKYLATION WITH ETHYLENE, CARBON MONOXIDE, AND WATER

N COMPOUND[a]	PRODUCTS[a]	REF.
NH_3 (15.6)	$PrNH_2$ (2), Pr_2NH (2), Pr_3N (1)	RE6
Me_2NH (23)	$PrNMe_2$ (20), Pr_2NMe (6)	RE14
Me_2NH^b (23)	$BuNMe_2^b$ (18)	RE6
$PrNH_2$ (230)	$PrNH_2$ (20), Pr_2NH (132), Pr_3N (96)	RE6
Et_2NH (500)	$PrNEt_2$ (142), Pr_2NEt (70), Et_3N (176)	RE12
Et_2NH (300)	$PrNEt_2$ (62), Et_3N (110)	RE10

[a] Numbers in parentheses indicate parts by weight.
[b] Propylene used instead of ethylene as the olefin reagent.

The following procedures taken from patents by Reppe *et al.* exemplify the details of the method:

(*a*) *Reaction of ammonia with carbon monoxide, ethylene, and water.*[RE6] One hundred parts of 15.6% aqueous ammonia and 20 parts of iron pentacarbonyl, pressurized with a 2:1 ethylene-carbon monoxide mixture at 180–200 atmospheres, were shaken in an autoclave at 120–135° for about 30 hours, after which time no further pressure drop was noticed. After cooling and venting of the system, distillation of liquid products gave 18 parts of iron pentacarbonyl (b.p. 75 to 80°) and a higher-boiling fraction which consisted of about 2 parts of propylamine, 2 parts of dipropylamine, and 1 part of tripropylamine.

(*b*) *Reaction of dimethylamine with ethylene and carbon monoxide.*[RE12] A solution of 190 g. of dimethylamine in 570 g. of water was neutralized with formic acid. This solution and 100 g. of iron carbonyl in a rocking autoclave was flushed three times with nitrogen at 5–10 atmospheres. The system then was pressurized to 100 atmospheres with a 1:2 mixture (by volume) of ethylene and carbon monoxide, followed by slow heating, with agitation, to 130°. The pressure was periodically restored to 200 atmospheres by re-pressurization with the ethylene-carbon monoxide gas mixture until no further pressure drop was noticed. After separation of the iron carbonyl, the free amines were liberated with sodium hydroxide and distilled. This amine mixiure was dried over potassium hydroxide and fractionated to yield 125 g. of propyldimethylamine and 43 g. of methyldipropylamine. (*Note:* From the article by Reppe *et al.*[RE14] the iron carbonyl used in the foregoing experiment is probably iron pentacarbonyl and the overall time of reaction is about 56 hours.)

5. N-ALKYLATION OF SECONDARY AMINES WITH OLEFINS AND FORMALDEHYDE

$$\begin{array}{c}\diagdown \\ \diagup\end{array}\!\!N\!\!-\!\!H + -CH\!-\!C\!=\!C- + CH_2O \rightarrow \begin{array}{c}\diagdown \\ \diagup\end{array}\!\!N\!\!-\!\!CH_2\!-\!C\!-\!C\!=\!C-$$

The reaction of secondary amines, olefins, and formaldehyde in an acid medium (acetic acid plus a mineral acid) to yield tertiary amines was reported by Schmidle *et al.*[SC7,SC8] and by Hennion, Price, and Wolff[HE10] according to the following general equation:

(1)
$$-CH\!-\!C\!=\!C- + CH_2O + HNR_2 \xrightarrow{H^+} -C\!=\!C\!-\!C\!-\!CH_2\!-\!NR_2 + H_2O$$

This synthesis can be considered as an aminomethylation of an allylic alkene accompanied by a double bond shift (in most cases). Superficially it might seem to resemble the Mannich aminomethylation of a terminal alkyne (see Section 15), but the experimental conditions and the course of the reactions differ.

The basic mechanism of the present reaction appears to involve,[HE10,SC8] first, addition of the secondary amine to formaldehyde to yield the methylol-amine. The latter loses the hydroxyl group under acidic conditions, giving rise to the dialkylaminocarbonium ion:

$$R_2NH + CH_2O \rightleftharpoons R_2NCH_2OH \overset{H^+}{\rightleftharpoons} R_2\overset{+}{N}CH_2 + H_2O$$

This cation adds to the olefin to produce a new carbonium ion postulated to pass through a cyclic transition state to a product having a shifted double bond:

The only examples of aminomethylation of a terminal olefin that have been recorded for the preparation of wholly aliphatic tertiary amines appear in a patent by Schmidle.[SC7] These amines were not characterized fully with respect to the location of the double bond. Two of these examples are represented by the following equations:

(2) $(CH_3)_3CCH_2—C=CH_2 + CH_2O + (CH_3)_2NH \rightarrow$
$\qquad\qquad\quad |$
$\qquad\qquad\ CH_3 \qquad\qquad\qquad\qquad (CH_3)_2NC_9H_{17} + H_2O$
$\qquad\qquad\qquad\qquad\qquad\qquad\qquad\quad$ (28% yield)

(3) $CH_3CH = CH_2 + CH_2O + (CH_3)_2NH \rightarrow (CH_3)_2NC_4H_7 + H_2O$
$\qquad\qquad\qquad\qquad\qquad\qquad\qquad\quad$ (23% yield)

From the course and mechanism of the reaction as reported in refs. SC8 and HE10, the foregoing products should have the structures:

For eq. (2), $(CH_3)_2N—CH_2—CH_2—C—CH_2—C(CH_3)_3$
$\qquad\qquad\qquad\qquad\qquad\quad ||$
$\qquad\qquad\qquad\qquad\qquad\ CH_2$

and/or $(CH_3)_2N—CH_2—CH_2—C=CH—C(CH_3)_3$
$\qquad\qquad\qquad\qquad\qquad\qquad |$
$\qquad\qquad\qquad\qquad\qquad\ CH_3$

For eq. (3), $(CH_3)_2N—CH_2—CH_2—CH=CH_2$.

The following detailed synthesis illustrates the preparative procedure for one of the reactions cited above.

PREPARATION OF NONENYLDIMETHYLAMINE.[SC7] To a mixture of 55 parts (expressed as parts by weight throughout) of tetramethylmethylenediamine (source of formaldehyde and dimethylamine) and 200 parts of glacial acetic acid were added 95 parts of sulfuric acid (although the concentration was not specified, it is quite probable that concentrated sulfuric acid was used) and 56 parts of diisobutylene. The resulting mixture was heated under reflux for 5 hours and allowed to cool, and after standing 16 hours was poured into 750 parts of water. After extraction with three 160-part portions of benzene, the resultant aqueous layer was separated and made alkaline with 25% sodium hydroxide. The liberated amine was extracted with two 160-part portions of benzene; these two portions were combined, and distilled to yield 31 parts of unsaturated amine, $C_9H_{17}N(CH_3)_2$, as a fraction distilling at 87–92° at 25 mm.

6. REDUCTIVE N-ALKYLATION WITH CARBONYL COMPOUNDS AND FORMIC ACID: THE LEUCKART REACTION

$$\text{\textbackslash} C=O + H—N \diagup\ + HCOOH \rightarrow\ —\overset{\overset{H}{|}}{C}—N\diagup$$

Ammonia or primary amines or secondary amines can be reductively alkylated with aldehydes or ketones to give tertiary amines. When the reducing agent is formic acid or one of its derivatives the reaction generally is referred to as the Leuckart reaction.

Leuckart discovered the reaction in 1885,[LE17] when he heated benzaldehyde with ammonium formate to get mono-, di-, and tri-benzylamines. The overall reaction might be represented as follows:

$$C_6H_5CHO + HCO_2NH_4 \rightarrow C_6H_5CH_2NH_2$$
$$+ (C_6H_5CH_2)_2NH + (C_6H_5CH_2)_3N + CO_2 + H_2O$$

The primary and secondary amines were obtained in part as the formyl derivatives. In general, the Leuckart reaction with ammonium formate and aldehydes or ketones has been used mainly for the preparation of primary amines. Although in the above equation ammonium formate was used as the source of ammonia and formic acid, one might just as readily use formamide as a source of these two reactants.

In the present monograph some of the variants on the Leuckart reaction are found to be much more important than the reaction as originally studied by Leuckart. The first of these modifications is referred to as the Eschweiler-Clarke modification, in which ammonia, primary amines, or secondary amines are methylated by formaldehyde and formic acid to give methylated tertiary amines.

Eschweiler[ES1,ES2] used formaldehyde alone to effect the methylation, whereas Sommelet and Ferrand[SO2] used formic acid alone. Clarke et al.[CL3] improved the method by using formic acid along with formaldehyde. An excellent review by Moore of the Leuckart reaction appears in *Organic Reactions*.[MO7]

The overall Eschweiler-Clarke reaction can be represented as follows:

(a) *N-Methylation of primary amines*

$$RNH_2 + CH_2O + HCO_2H \rightarrow RN(CH_3)_2 + CO_2 + H_2O$$

(b) *N-Methylation of secondary amines*

$$R_2NH + CH_2O + HCO_2H \rightarrow R_2NCH_3 + CO_2 + H_2O$$

This reaction is by far the most satisfactory and most frequently used for methylating primary or secondary amines. Table 11 presents typical data for this method.

Another modification of the Leuckart reaction, similar to the Eschweiler-Clarke reaction except wider in scope, is sometimes called the Wallach or the Leuckart-Wallach reaction. Wallach[WA15] used excess formic acid along with ammonium formate to obtain reaction at a lower temperature than did Leuckart. He also extended the method to the alkylation of amines.

In the present monograph there is only one entry for the Leuckart reaction: the preparation of 6-diethylamino-2-methyl-2-heptene from 6-methyl-5-hepten-2-one and diethylformamide by Doeuvre and Poizat.[DO3] For the

TABLE 11. REPRESENTATIVE DATA IN THE ESCHWEILER-CLARKE *N*-METHYLATION REACTION

AMINE METHYLATED	MOLE RATIO OF REACTANTS AMINE	HCOOH	HCHO	REACTION TIME (HR.)	REACTION TEMPERATURE	PRODUCT	YIELD (%)	REF.
i-$C_3H_7NH_2$	1	10	4.4	a	a	i-$C_3H_7N(CH_3)_2$	71	SP2
t-$C_4H_9NH_2$	1	4	2.5	2	90–100	t-$C_4H_9N(CH_3)_2$	95	ME2
$H_2NCH(CH_3)CH_2NH_2$	1	4.6	4.3	b	b	$(CH_3)_2NCH(CH_3)CH_2N(CH_3)_2$	76	MO16
n-$C_{12}H_{25}NH_2$	1	2.5	2.5	2	60–80	n-$C_{12}H_{25}N(CH_3)_2$	60	RE1
$(C_2H_5)_2NH$	1	5	2.2	a	a	$(C_2H_5)_2NCH_3$	79	SP2
(i-$C_3H_7)_2NH$	1	5	2.2	a	a	(i-$C_3H_7)_2NCH_3$	79	SP2
(n-C_4H_9)(i-C_4H_9)NH	1[c]	5[c]	3[c]	c	c	(n-C_4H_9)(i-C_4H_9)NCH_3[c]	97	CO23

[a] The mixture was heated at 60–90° while gas evolution occurred. This required 1 hour or less. The mixture was then refluxed 4 hours.

[b] Solution refluxed 48 hours after evolution of CO_2 ceased.

[c] The amine indicated and nine others were prepared by Cope et al.[CO23] in yields ranging from 56–97% by the method given in *Organic Syntheses*.[IC1] After CO_2 evolution ceased, the mixture was heated for 8 hours at 95–100°.

Leuckart-Wallach reaction there is the preparation of triamylamine from valeraldehyde, formic acid, and ammonium formate as reported by Wallach,[WA15] and of a series of six aliphatic tertiary amines from aliphatic secondary amines, aliphatic aldehydes, and formic acid by DeBenneville and Macartney.[DE1,DE2] The work of the latter authors shows that the Wallach variant on the Leuckart reaction is a good preparative method for tertiary amines.

Staple and Wagner,[ST3] who have reviewed and studied the Wallach reaction, conclude that the courses of the Leuckart and Wallach reactions are the same and might be represented by the following series of equations:

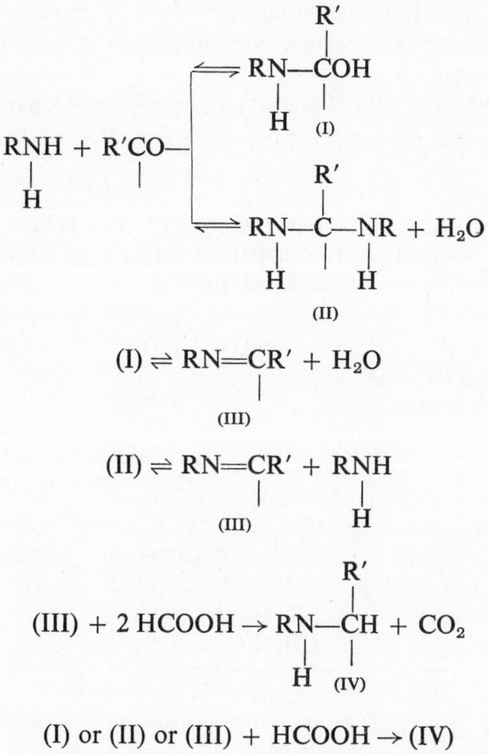

$$\begin{array}{c} \underset{\longleftarrow}{\longrightarrow} \ \underset{\underset{H}{|}}{RN}\underset{|}{\overset{R'}{\underset{|}{C}}}OH \\ (I) \end{array}$$

$$RNH + R'CO-$$

$$\underset{\rightleftharpoons}{} \ \underset{\underset{H}{|}}{RN}\underset{|}{\overset{R'}{\underset{|}{C}}}\underset{\underset{H}{|}}{NR} + H_2O$$

(II)

$$(I) \rightleftharpoons RN{=}CR' + H_2O$$

(III)

$$(II) \rightleftharpoons RN{=}CR' + RNH$$

(III)

$$(III) + 2\,HCOOH \rightarrow \underset{\underset{H}{|}}{RN}\underset{|}{\overset{R'}{\underset{|}{C}}}H + CO_2$$

(IV)

$$(I) \text{ or } (II) \text{ or } (III) + HCOOH \rightarrow (IV)$$

The resultant secondary amines can similarly form methylol compounds and/or diamines, but not Schiff bases, reducible to tertiary amines by formic acid.

In their work with aliphatic aldehydes and secondary amines, DeBenneville and Macartney[DE2] propose an additional possible intermediate, an enamine, $RC{=}CHNR_2$, for the Wallach reaction. In support of this hypothesis these authors showed that the reaction temperature and yield in the reduction of enamines to the saturated amines were close to those encountered in the direct Leuckart-Wallach reaction. The proposed course of the reaction is as follows:

$$RCHCHO + R_2'NH \rightarrow RCHCH\begin{array}{c}NR_2'\\ \diagup\\ \diagdown\\ NR_2'\end{array} \rightarrow RC{=}CHNR_2'$$
$$\quad\text{(I)}\qquad\quad\text{(II)}$$

$$RC{=}CHNR_2' \xrightarrow{\text{HCOOH}} RCHCH_2NR_2'$$
$$\quad\text{(III)}\qquad\qquad\qquad\text{(IV)}$$

The same product (IV) was obtained either by reaction of (I), (II), and formic acid, or by reaction of (III) and formic acid. Both methods of preparation of the saturated tertiary amines were carried out at about the same temperature and gave similar yields.

Table 12 shows the wholly aliphatic tertiary amines prepared by the direct Leuckart-Wallach reaction and by the reduction of the intermediate enamines with formic acid.

TABLE 12. PREPARATION OF ALKYL TERTIARY AMINES
BY THE DIRECT AND INDIRECT LEUCKART-WALLACH
REACTION[DE2]

REACTANTS		PRODUCTS	YIELD $(\%)^a$	YIELD $(\%)^b$ REDUC-TION OF ENAMINE
ALDEHYDE	AMINE (AS FORMATE)			
n-C_3H_7CHO	$(CH_3)_2NH$	$(CH_3)_2N{-}n$-C_4H_9	60	—
i-C_3H_7CHO	$(CH_3)_2NH$	$(CH_3)_2N{-}i$-C_4H_9	59	—
$C_7H_{15}CHO^c$	$(CH_3)_2NH$	$(CH_3)_2NCH_2C_7H_{15}{}^c$	60	—
$C_8H_{17}CHO^d$	$(CH_3)_2NH$	$(CH_3)_2NCH_2C_8H_{17}{}^d$	84	80
$C_8H_{17}CHO^d$	(i-$C_3H_7)_2NH$	(i-$C_3H_7)_2NCH_2C_8H_{17}{}^d$	47	62
$C_8H_{17}CHO^d$	$CH_3NHC_9H_{19}{}^e$	$CH_3N(C_9H_{19})_2{}^e$	54	57

^{a} Direct alkylation.   Intermediate enamine was not isolated.

^{b} Overall yield in indirect alkylation.   Intermediate enamine was isolated and then reduced with formic acid as a separate step.

^{c} C_7H_{15} is $-CH(C_2H_5)CH_2CH_2CH_2CH_3$.

^{d} C_8H_{17} is $-CH_2CH(CH_3)CH_2C(CH_3)_2CH_3$.

^{e} C_9H_{19} is $-CH_2CH_2CH(CH_3)CH_2C(CH_3)_2CH_3$.

Reducing agents other than formic acid have been used in reductive alkylation, e.g., zinc and sulfurous acid.[CH2]

PREPARATION OF TRIALKYLAMINES (LEUCKART-WALLACH PROCEDURE). DeBenneville and Macartney[DE2] described the following general procedure for the preparation of six acyclic aliphatic trialkylamines in 54–84% yield. (Other tertiary amines also were prepared.)

The amine formate was usually prepared by the addition of the appropriate amount of amine, as gas, or liquid, to formic acid (presumably with cooling) in 1:1 mole ratio. (A 1:2 mole ratio was used in some cases.) The temperature was then raised to about 60° and the aldehyde added dropwise over a 1-hour period. The mixture was then generally heated on the steam bath until carbon dioxide evolution ceased (about 1 hour). The contents of the flask were poured into hydrochloric acid. The mixture was extracted with ether to remove unused aldehyde. The aqueous portion was made basic with sodium hydroxide. The liberated amine was extracted with ether, and the ether extract was dried and distilled.

PREPARATION OF *t*-BUTYLDIMETHYLAMINE (Eschweiler-Clarke Procedure).[SP1] To 130 g. (2.5 moles) of 88% formic acid in a 1-liter 2-necked round-bottomed flask was added slowly with cooling and stirring 36.5 g. (0.50 mole) of *t*-butyl-amine. The temperature was kept below 27° during the mixing; 94 g. (1.1 moles) of 35% aqueous formaldehyde was added and the mixture heated at such a rate as to maintain a steady gas evolution. After about 1 hour of heating at 70–80° with stirring (magnetic stirrer), gas evolution slowed down considerably. The solution was then refluxed gently for 4 hours. After cooling, 43 ml. of concentrated hydrochloric acid was added with stirring. The resulting solution was concentrated to about 70–75 g., cooled, made strongly basic with 125 ml. of 25% sodium hydroxide, and distilled until the tempera-ture reached 99°. The amine was salted out with potassium hydroxide pellets, and the amine layer separated, and dried further with potassium hydroxide pellets. The *dry* amine was decanted into a distilling flask containing a few small chips of sodium. Distillation under nitrogen gave 38.2 g. (75.7% yield) of *t*-butyldimethylamine boiling at 88.9–89.6° (740 mm.)

7. REDUCTIVE *N*-ALKYLATION WITH CARBONYL COMPOUNDS AND HYDROGEN UNDER CONDITIONS OF CATALYTIC HYDROGENATION

$$\text{N–H} + \text{C=O} + H_2 \rightarrow \text{N–C–}$$

Tertiary amines can be obtained by alkylation of ammonia, primary amines, or secondary amines (or nitrogen compounds reducible *in situ* to such amines) with aldehydes or ketones in the presence of suitable reducing agents. The present section is limited to the direct use of hydrogen as reducing agent.

Except for purposely omitting the Leuckart reaction, which has been reviewed by others,[MO7] Emerson[EM10] has published a general review on reductive alkylation in which he presents the following reaction scheme:

$$RCHO + NH_3 \rightleftharpoons RCH(OH)NH_2 \rightleftharpoons RCH{=}NH + H_2O$$

$$RCH(OH)NH_2 + H_2 \rightleftharpoons RCH_2NH_2 + H_2O$$

$$RCH{=}NH + H_2 \rightarrow RCH_2NH_2$$

The primary amine thus obtained can be made to undergo a further similar series of reactions to give a secondary amine, and the secondary amine can be made to give tertiary amine.

Most of the tertiary amines synthesized by catalytic reductive alkylation have been prepared by alkylation of secondary amines. A significant portion of the published work on the scope and conditions of this reaction is due to Skita, Keil, and co-workers.[SK1,SK2, SK3, SK4, SK5] They found[SK5] that the applicability of aldehydes to reductive alkylation appears to be general, whereas alkylation by ketones is dependent on the structure and molecular size of the reagents. A high molecular weight secondary amine such as bis(3,7-dimethyloctyl)amine cannot be reductively alkylated by acetone. Secondary amines of medium molecular size and containing a methyl group on the nitrogen can be alkylated by methyl ketones, but the yield decreases as the size of the methyl ketone increases. (With aldehydes as the carbonyl component, molecular size of either reagent has no predictable effect on yield.) Of greater significance than the foregoing is the very sharp decrease in yield observed when either the ketone or the secondary amine possesses alpha-branched substituents on the functional group. For example, triisopropylamine cannot be prepared from diisopropylamine and acetone.[SK5]

Another limitation of the reaction arises from the possible reduction of other functional groups in the reagents other than those taking part in the alkylation.

Also, initial aldolization is sometimes observed under experimental conditions to diminish yields as well as to produce intermediates leading to higher molecular weight amines as by-products. For example, reductive alkylation of diisoamylamine with acetaldehyde and hydrogen gave a 34% yield of the expected ethyldiisoamylamine along with 15% of n-butyl-diisoamylamine.

Surprisingly, no tertiary diamines have been synthesized by catalytic reductive alkylation. Attempts to prepare 1,6-bis(dimethylamino)hexane from 1,6-diaminohexane and formaldehyde by this method were unsuccessful.[KL4,PA3] A mixture of partially N-methylated compounds was obtained with little or none of the tetramethylated material.

Amine precursors such as nitro or azo compounds have been used to prepare tertiary amines under conditions of reductive alkylation.[EM8,EM9,EM10,EM11] For example, methyldiethylamine was prepared in 92% yield from nitromethane, hydrogen, and acetaldehyde in acid medium using platinum as catalyst.[EM9] (Generally, tertiary amine formation is favored in acid media, while neutral or basic media favor secondary amines.)

Table 13 lists representative preparative data on tertiary amines. A detailed synthetic procedure for methylethylisoamylamine is also given.

PREPARATION OF METHYLETHYLISOAMYLAMINE. [SK4] Ten grams of ethyliso-amylamine (0.087 mole), 7 ml. of 40% aqueous formaldehyde (0.093 mole), and 50 ml. of colloidal platinum solution containing 0.5 g. of platinum and

TABLE 13. REPRESENTATIVE EXAMPLES OF CATALYTIC *N*-ALKYLATION OF AMINES WITH CARBONYL COMPOUNDS AND HYDROGEN

COMPOUNDS ALKYLATED	CARBONYL COMPOUND	REACTION CONDITIONS	PRODUCTS	YIELD (%)	REF.
Et$_2$NH	CH$_3$CHO	b	Et$_3$N	16	SK2
Et$_2$NH	CH$_3$CHO	c	Et$_3$N	90	CH9
[Me][2-Bu]NH	CH$_3$COCH$_3$	a	[Me][i-Pr][2-Bu]N	69	SK5
[Me][2-Bu]NH	2-Hexanone	a	[Me][2-Bu][2-Hexyl]N	8	SK5
[Me][2-Bu]NH	2-Heptanone	a	[Me][2-Bu][2-Heptyl]N	3	SK5
[Me][2-Bu]NH	2-Octanone	a	[Me][2-Bu][2-Octyl]N	0.5	SK5
i-Pr$_2$NH	CH$_3$CH$_2$CHO	a	[Pr][i-Pr][i-Pr]N	26	SK5
[Et][i-Am]NH	CH$_3$CH$_2$CHO	a	[Et][Pr][i-Am]N	57	SK4
Bu$_2$NH	CH$_3$CH$_2$CH$_2$CHO	c	Bu$_3$N	34	CH9
BuNH$_2$	CH$_3$CH$_2$CH$_2$CHO	d	Bu$_3$N	47	VA3
i-Am$_2$NH	CH$_3$COCH$_3$	a	[i-Pr][i-Am][i-Am]N	14	SK5
(C$_{10}$H$_{21}$)$_2$NH^e	Dihydrocitral	a	(C$_{10}$H$_{21}$)$_3$N^e	84	SK5
(C$_{10}$H$_{21}$)$_2$NH^e	Citral	a	(C$_{10}$H$_{21}$)$_3$N^e	64	SK5

^{a} Catalyst colloidal platinum; solvent water; pressure 3 atm.; room temperature.

^{b} Conducted at 1 atm.; otherwise same as a above.

^{c} Vapor phase reaction over nickel at 120°, no solvent.

^{d} Catalyst Raney nickel; solvent ethanol; pressure approximately 1000 lb.; room temperature.

^{e} C$_{10}$H$_{21}$ represents (CH$_3$)$_2$CHCH$_2$CH$_2$CH$_2$CH(CH$_3$)CH$_2$CH$_2$—.

1 g. of gum arabic were pressurized with 3 atmospheres of hydrogen. After 1 hour at room temperature, 2 liters (at STP) of hydrogen (0.09 mole) was absorbed. After addition of another 7 ml. of 40% aqueous formaldehyde (0.093 mole) and repressurization, an additional 1.2 liters (at STP) of hydrogen (0.054 mole) was absorbed. The pressure was then released. The platinum catalyst was flocculated by heating of the reaction mixture with 30 ml. of concentrated hydrochloric acid and was removed by filtration. The filtrate was concentrated under vacuum and made alkaline, and the liberated base was extracted with ether. Distillation gave methylethylisoamylamine, which boiled at 133–137°. (No yield is given for this specific synthesis but from analogous preparations of other amines in the same reference yields of about 50% would be expected here.)

8. ADDITION OF SECONDARY AMINES TO SATURATED ALDEHYDES

$$\begin{array}{c}\text{H}\qquad\qquad\qquad\qquad\qquad\text{H}\\ \diagdown\quad\ \ |\ \ |\qquad\qquad\diagdown\quad|\ \ \diagup\qquad\quad\diagdown\quad|\ \ |\\ \text{N--H} + \text{--C--C=O} \rightarrow\ \text{N--C--N}\ \ \rightarrow\ \text{N--C=C--}\\ \diagup\qquad|\qquad\qquad\diagup\quad\quad\diagdown\qquad\diagup\\ \qquad\qquad\qquad\qquad\qquad\text{--C--H}\\ \qquad\qquad\qquad\qquad\qquad\quad|\end{array}$$

Dialkylamines react with saturated aldehydes to give N-tetrasubstituted-gem-diamines which, if structurally possible, readily decompose to unsaturated monoamines.

In 1884 Laun[LA14] treated benzaldehyde with piperidine and obtained benzilidine-bis-piperidine. The first application of this reaction to the preparation of aliphatic 1,1-bis-dialkylamino compounds is due to Kolotow,[KO15] who in 1885 prepared $N,N,N'N'$-tetramethylmethylenediamine from diethylamine and formaldehyde (as polyoxymethylene) in a sealed tube at 100°:

$$2\,(C_2H_5)_2NH + CH_2O \rightarrow (C_2H_5)_2N\text{--}CH_2\text{--}N(C_2H_5)_2 + H_2O$$

Ehrenberg used this preparative procedure in 1887[EH1] and it is often called the Ehrenberg method. N-Tetrasubstituted methylenediamines are more frequently prepared by Henry's method,[HE15,HE16] which involves the use of aqueous formaldehyde and secondary amine at atmospheric pressure. Henry showed that the intermediate methylolamine also can be used to prepare the diamines:

$$R_2NH \xrightarrow{\text{CH}_2\text{O}} R_2NCH_2OH \xrightarrow{\text{R}_2'\text{NH}} R_2NCH_2NR_2' + H_2O$$

This modification makes possible the preparation of unsymmetrical N-tetrasubstituted methylenediamines.

The foregoing might be considered broadly as a variant on the Mannich reaction (see section 15), which consists of the interaction of a methylol compound (obtained by the reaction of ammonia, or a primary amine, or a secondary amine with formaldehyde) with an active hydrogen compound.

In the preparation of methylenediamines the secondary amine furnishes both the amine function and the active hydrogen.

The reaction is reversible and bis(dialkylamino)methanes can be hydrolyzed readily to the secondary amine and formaldehyde used in their preparation.[HU3]

Although wholly aliphatic acyclic compounds of the type $R_2NCH(R')NR_2$, in which the R's are alkyl groups, have not been isolated, they have appeared as enamine precursors.[DE2,MA21] In 1936 Mannich and Davidsen[MA21] showed that compounds of the type $(R_2N)_2CHCH_2R'$, derived from secondary amine and higher aldehydes, decompose on distillation to give enamines and secondary amine, as follows:

$$(R_2N)_2CHCH_2R' \rightarrow R_2NCH{=}CHR' + R_2NH$$

DeBenneville and Macartney[DE2] prepared a series of ten enamines by this method in overall yields of 23 to 95% in a study in which they postulated such compounds as additional intermediates in the Leuckart-Wallach reaction (see the earlier section 6).

The intermediate diamine is difficult to isolate. Mannich and Davidsen[MA21] were able to isolate diamine only in the lowest molecular weight molecule of the series they studied, namely, 1,1-bis-piperidinoethane, boiling at 58–60° at 3 mm. The synthesis follows the equation:

$$2\ C_5H_{10}NH + CH_3CHO \xrightarrow{K_2CO_3} (C_5H_{10}N)_2CHCH_3 + H_2O$$

In a recent patent[GE1] it is claimed that, if relatively large amounts of anhydrous potassium carbonate are used, the initially formed amino alcohol is dehydrated directly to the unsaturated amine instead of reacting with further secondary amine to give a diamine.

For example, dimethylamine and acetaldehyde give dimethylvinylamine, as follows, with the postulated aminoalcohol being shown in brackets:

$$(CH_3)_2NH + CH_3CHO \xrightarrow{K_2CO_3} [(CH_3)_2NCH(OH)CH_3] \longrightarrow$$
$$(CH_3)_2NCH{=}CH_2$$
$$\text{(42\% yield)}$$

No direct experimental evidence was advanced to exclude diamine as the intermediate. However, since yields of well over 50% were obtained in some examples in which a 1:1 molar ratio of aldehyde to secondary amine was used, it seems reasonable to assume that a diamine might not be exclusively the intermediate; hence the existence of the postulated amino alcohol as an intermediate is quite plausible.

PREPARATION OF 1-DIETHYLAMINO-1-HEPTENE.[MA21] To a well-stirred mixture of anhydrous diethylamine (12.5 g.), anhydrous ether (30 ml.), and 5 g. of potassium carbonate, heptanal (10 g.) was added drop-wise with cooling. (The temperature was not specified, but the synthesis was modeled after one in which the temperature was kept below 5° during addition of the aldehyde, and this was followed by 15 minutes of stirring, presumably without cooling.) The potassium carbonate was removed by filtration. After removal of the ether, the remaining 1,1-bis-diethylaminoheptane was decomposed by distillation at 110 mm. pressure. The diethylamine distilled first. This was followed by 1-diethylamino-1-heptene boiling at 134–140° at 110 mm. (Though the yield was unspecified, this reaction has been used by others[DE2] to obtain reasonable yields of enamines, e.g., 70% yield of enamine from 2-ethylhexaldehyde and a dialkylamine.)

PREPARATION OF BIS(DIALLYLAMINO)METHANE (HENRY'S METHOD).[BU10]   To 49 g. (0.5 mole) of diallylamine was added with stirring 20.5 g. (0.25 mole) of 37% aqueous formaldehyde. Cooling was required to keep the temperature below 50°. Then the mixture was heated on a steam bath for 2 hours and cooled, and the upper layer separated, dried, and distilled. There was obtained 51 g. (83% yield) of bis(diallylamino)methane.

9. ADDITION OF SECONDARY AMINES TO α,β-UNSATURATED ALDEHYDES

$$-\overset{|}{\underset{|}{C}}-\overset{|}{C}=\overset{H}{C}-\overset{|}{C}=O + \overset{\diagup}{\underset{\diagdown}{N}}-H \rightarrow -\overset{|}{\underset{|}{C}}-\overset{|}{\underset{\underset{\diagdown}{N}}{C}}-\overset{|}{\underset{|}{C}}-\overset{H}{\underset{|}{C}}-N\overset{\diagup}{\diagdown}$$

$$\text{and/or} -\overset{|}{C}=\overset{|}{C}-\overset{|}{C}=\overset{H}{\underset{|}{C}}-N\overset{\diagup}{\diagdown}$$

Secondary amines and α,β-unsaturated aldehydes condense in the presence of potassium carbonate to yield olefinic tertiary diamines and/or dienyl tertiary monoamines, as follows:

$$2\ \overset{R}{\underset{R}{\diagdown}}N-H + R'-CH_2-CH=CH-\overset{H}{\underset{|}{C}}=O$$

$$\overset{K_2CO_3}{\rightleftharpoons}\ R'-CH_2-\overset{H}{\underset{\underset{R\ \ \ R}{\diagup\ \diagdown}}{\underset{N}{C}}}-CH=CH-N\overset{\diagup R}{\diagdown R} + H_2O$$

$$\Updownarrow$$

$$R'CH=CH-CH=CH-N\overset{\diagup R}{\diagdown R} + \overset{R\ R}{\underset{R\ R}{\diagup\diagdown}}N-H$$

Mannich et al.,[MA22] who first used this reaction to prepare unsaturated diamines and monoamines, found that diamines could be obtained in good yield only within narrow temperature limits: below $-10°$ the reaction did not occur and above $20°$ the yields were reduced because of resin formation. Anhydrous potassium carbonate was found necessary to remove the water formed in the initial reaction. Dienylmonoamines were obtained when the diamines were heated under reduced pressure. Moreover, citral gave no diamine but, instead, the monoamine was isolated. This direct synthesis of the monoamine was attributed to instability of the intermediate diamine.

Mannich erroneously assigned the allene structure to the dienyl amine. That a conjugated diene represents the correct structure has been shown by ozonolysis,[LA9] ultraviolet absorption studies,[BO16,CA5] and the Diels-Alder reaction.[BO16,HU2,LA9]

Although monoamines have been obtained directly[BO16,CA5,MA22] by distillation of the condensation product of secondary amines with α,β-unsaturated aldehydes in the presence of potassium carbonate[BO16,MA22] certain modifications have been used. For example, the condensation in the presence of potassium carbonate has been followed by distillation in the presence of various quinones[HU2,LA11,LA12] or polycarboxylic acids.[LA10]

In the initial condensation reaction that produces the unsaturated 1,3-diamines Doss and Schnitzer[DO6] claim that higher yields are obtained if anhydrous magnesium sulfate is used instead of anhydrous potassium carbonate. They ascribe this to the shift of the equilibrium caused by more efficient water removal in the initial condensation step.

The condensation of secondary amines with α,β-unsaturated aldehydes has been conducted principally in nonaqueous systems. Mannich *et al.*,[MA22] however, used 45% aqueous dimethylamine in a reaction with acrolein to obtain 1,3-bis(dimethylamino)propene. These workers agitated a mixture of ether, acrolein, 45% aqueous dimethylamine, and anhydrous potassium carbonate at -5 to $0°$. This was followed by separation of the ether layer, and treating the ether layer with a relatively large amount of anhydrous potassium carbonate. (It seems likely to the authors that the condensation reaction actually occurred within the isolated ether layer, and that the initial step served only to extract the dimethylamine and acrolein from the water phase.)

As expected, the dienylmonoamines tend to polymerize on standing.[BO16] The unsaturated diamines darken gradually at room temperature and are decomposed by heating or by acids.[MA22]

Table 14 shows data on some representative preparations of unsaturated diamines. Some typical detailed preparative examples for both unsaturated diamines and dienylmonoamines follow.

PREPARATION OF 1,3-BIS(DIMETHYLAMINO)-1-BUTENE.[DO6] Anhydrous magnesium sulfate (120 g., 1 mole) was charged into a reactor. This was followed by a solution of dimethylamine (115.6 g., 2.56 moles) in methylcyclopentane (52 g.). The temperature was adjusted to $-10°$ and a solution of crotonaldehyde of high purity (60 g., 0.82 mole) in methylcyclohexane

TABLE 14. DATA ON PREPARATION OF UNSATURATED DIAMINES FROM SECONDARY AMINES AND α,β-UNSATURATED ALDEHYDES

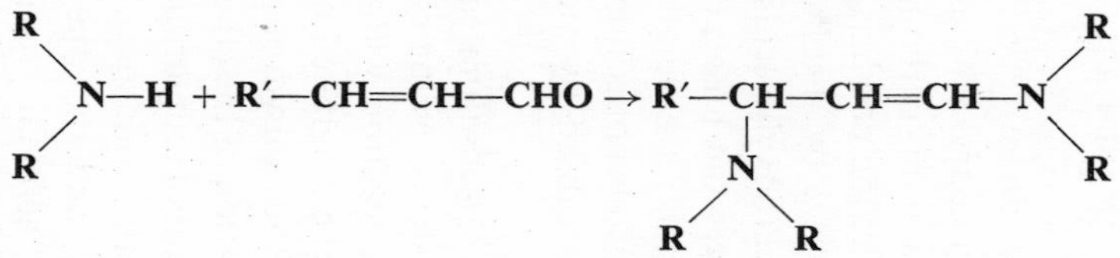

$$\begin{array}{c} R \\ | \\ N-H \end{array} + R'-CH=CH-CHO \rightarrow R'-CH-CH=CH-N \begin{array}{c} R \\ | \\ \\ R \end{array}$$

SECONDARY AMINE, R =	ALDEHYDE, R' =	DESICCANT	SOLVENT	TIME (HR.)	TEMPERA- TURE	YIELD (%)	REF.
—CH$_3$	—H	K$_2$CO$_3$	Ether—H$_2$O	1.75[a]	−5 to 0°	60	MA22
—CH$_3$	—H	K$_2$CO$_3$	C$_6$H$_{12}$[b]	[c]	−10°[c]	56	DO6
—CH$_3$	—H	MgSO$_4$	C$_6$H$_{12}$[b]	[d]	−10°[d]	65	DO6
—CH$_3$	—CH$_3$	K$_2$CO$_3$	C$_6$H$_{12}$[b]	[c]	−10°[c]	70	DO6
—CH$_3$	—CH$_3$	MgSO$_4$	C$_6$H$_{12}$[b]	[d]	−10°[d]	92	DO6
—CH$_2$—CH=CH$_2$	—H	K$_2$CO$_3$	Ether	12	5 to 10°	[e]	SM5

[a] After this time, the ether layer was separated and treated with additional potassium carbonate, then allowed to stand several hours in the refrigerator. The reaction probably occurred in the ether phase during storage.
[b] Methylcyclopentane.
[c] Stirred 24 hours at 20–30° after all reactants were mixed.
[d] Stirred 2 hours at 20–30° after all reactants were mixed.
[e] "Excellent."

(67 g.) was added slowly with constant stirring. After the addition was completed, the temperature was allowed to increase to 20–30° and the mixture was stirred at that temperature for 24 hours. After removal of magnesium sulfate by filtration, distillation gave 92% yield of 1,3-bis(dimethylamino)-1-butene.

Several examples of this type of reaction show that magnesium sulfate gives better yields than does potassium carbonate.[DO6]

PREPARATION OF 1-DIETHYLAMINO-1,3-BUTADIENE.[HU2]   A solution of crotonaldehyde (105 g., 124 ml.) (freshly distilled under an atmosphere of nitrogen) dissolved in 150 ml. of benzene was added over a period of 20 minutes to a mixture of diethylamine (225 g.) and anhydrous potassium carbonate (60 g.) while the temperature was maintained at −10 to −5°. With frequent swirling the mixture was kept at 0° for about 1 hour, when a little turbidity was noticed. The solution was allowed to warm to room temperature and to stand 4 hours. The liquid was decanted from the potassium carbonate and 0.9 g. of phenanthraquinone was added before vacuum distillation. After removal of the benzene the diethylamine suddenly began splitting off, as judged by the sharp increase in pressure. The fraction which boiled at 60–70° at 12 mm. was redistilled to give 114 g. (61% yield) of 1-diethylamino-1,3-butadiene, b_{10} 64–66°. (*Note:* Although the compound prepared is simply called 1-diethylaminobutadiene, it is undoubtedly 1-diethylamino-1,3-butadiene.)

10. REDUCTION OF N,N-DIALKYLAMIDES

$$\begin{matrix} & O & \\ & \parallel & \\ \diagdown N-C- & \xrightarrow{[H]} & \diagdown N-CH_2- \\ \diagup & & \diagup \end{matrix}$$

The reduction of N,N-dialkylamides in order to prepare tertiary amines has been carried out almost exclusively with lithium aluminum hydride as the reducing agent. The overall reaction can be represented as follows:

$$\begin{matrix} R & O & & R & \\ \diagdown & \parallel & & \diagdown & \\ & N-C-R'' & \xrightarrow{\text{LiAlH}_4} & & N-CH_2-R'' \\ \diagup & & & \diagup & \\ R' & & & R' & \end{matrix}$$

In attempting to effect the foregoing transformation by means of catalytic hydrogenation, Wojcik and Adkins[WO2] obtained a yield of only 4% of heptyldiethylamine on treating N,N-diethylheptamide with hydrogen at 200–300 atmospheres and 250° using a copper-chromium oxide catalyst. The other products isolated were ethylheptylamine in 64% yield and diheptylamine in 25% yield. However, they found that this reaction can be used satisfactorily for the conversion of unsubstituted amides to primary amines, and mono-N-substituted amides to secondary amines.

Swan[SW4] used electrolytic reduction to convert N,N-dimethylvaleramide to pentyldimethylamine in 80% yield (based on unrecovered amide).

Zakharkin and Khorlina[ZA3] effected reduction of N,N-dialkylamides in high yield (above 90%) by using diisobutyl aluminum hydride as reducing agent.

An interesting use of amide reduction by lithium aluminum hydride is that reported by Lunsford et al.,[LU24] who utilized this reaction in what might be considered a general method for the preparation of 1,4-bis-dialkylamino-butanes, as shown in the following scheme:

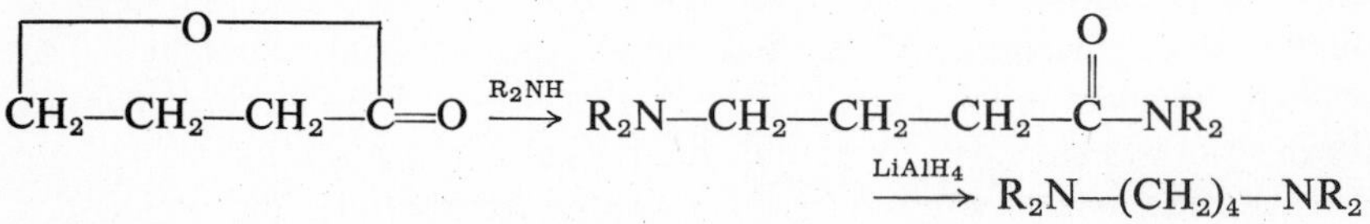

$$CH_2{-}CH_2{-}CH_2{-}C{=}O \xrightarrow{R_2NH} R_2N{-}CH_2{-}CH_2{-}CH_2{-}\overset{\displaystyle O}{\overset{\|}{C}}{-}NR_2$$

$$\xrightarrow{LiAlH_4} R_2N{-}(CH_2)_4{-}NR_2$$

Along with the above products as written there were also formed N,N-dialkyl-4-hydroxybutyramide and its reduction product, 4-dialkylamino-1-butanol. An overall yield of 30% of 1,4-bis(dimethylamino)butane was obtained from dimethylamine and butyrolactone.

When appropriate amides of carbonic acid are reduced with lithium aluminum hydride, N-methylation occurs. For example, methyldibutylamine was obtained from ethyl-N,N-dibutylcarbamate[DA7]:

$$Bu_2NCO_2Et \xrightarrow{LiAlH_4} Bu_2NCH_3$$

TABLE 15.   REDUCTION OF DIALKYLAMIDES WITH LITHIUM ALUMINUM HYDRIDE

AMIDE	PRODUCT	YIELD (%)	REF.
Et_2NCHO	Et_2NMe	64	BL1
Et_2NCOCH_3	Et_3N	50	UF1
$Me_2NCO{-}t$-Bu	$Me_2NCH_2{-}t$-Bu	25	BR41
Me_2NCOPr	Me_2NBu	50	BR41
Bu_2NCHO	Bu_2NMe	67	EM13
$Et_2NCOCONEt_2$	$Et_2NCH_2CH_2NEt_2$	87	AR4
$Bu_2NCOCONEt_2$	$Bu_2NCH_2CH_2NEt_2$	74	AR4
$Am_2NCOCONAm_2$	$Am_2NCH_2CH_2NAm_2$	80	AR4
$Et_2NCO(CH_2)_8C{\equiv}CH$	$Et_2N(CH_2)_9C{\equiv}CH$	70	CO1
$Me_2NCO(CH_2)_3NMe_2$	$Me_2N(CH_2)_4NMe_2$	30[a]	LU24
Bu_2NCO_2Et	Bu_2NMe	85	DA7

[a] Overall yield from butyrolactone used to prepare the amide.

Table 15 lists most of the amines described in the present monograph that have been prepared by amide reduction with lithium aluminum hydride. A typical preparative description for methyldibutylamine follows the table. It should be pointed out that a much more detailed procedure can be found in *Organic Syntheses*[CO19] for a cycloalkyl tertiary amine.

PREPARATION OF TERTIARY AMINES BY AMIDE REDUCTION.[CO1] The following procedure is typical of that used in preparing several trialkylamines from *N,N*-dialkylamides in 57–70% yield.

To a stirred suspension of 7.1 g. (0.144 mole + 30% excess) of lithium aluminum hydride in 500 ml. of anhydrous ether was added drop-wise 0.287 mole of the appropriate amide in 200 ml. of anhydrous ether. The mixture was stirred and refluxed for 2 hours, after which time the reaction vessel was cooled in an ice bath. The reaction mixture was decomposed by the cautious drop-wise addition in turn of 7 ml. of water, 7 ml. of 15% sodium hydroxide solution, and 21 ml. of water. Vigorous stirring was maintained during the addition and for 20 minutes afterward. The mixture was filtered and the precipitated salts washed with ether. The combined ether filtrates were extracted with 10% hydrochloric acid. The acid layer was rendered alkaline with sodium hydroxide and extracted with ether. The ether solution was dried over anhydrous potassium carbonate, concentrated *in vacuo* and distilled *in vacuo* to yield the desired amine.

11. BOUVEAULT REACTION OF *N,N*-DIALKYLAMIDES WITH EXCESS GRIGNARD REAGENT

$$\overset{\diagdown}{\underset{\diagup}{N}} - \overset{|}{C} = O + RMgX \rightarrow \overset{\diagdown}{\underset{\diagup}{N}} - \overset{|}{\underset{R}{C}} - R$$

The Bouveault method[BO15] for preparing aldehydes involves the interaction of 1 mole of Grignard reagent with 1 mole of a disubstituted formamide. A by-product of the reaction is a tertiary amine:

$$R_2N - \overset{O}{\overset{\|}{C}} - H + R'MgX \rightarrow R'CHO + R_2N - CH(R')_2$$

When a large excess of Grignard reagent is used (3 moles to 1 mole of amide), a practical amount of tertiary amine is formed.

Busch[BU9] was the first to apply the Bouveault reaction to *N,N*-disubstituted amides other than formamides and obtained a mixture of ketone and tertiary amine. The reaction of *N,N*-disubstituted amides with excess Grignard reagent is particularly useful for the introduction of certain complicated bulky secondary or tertiary alkyl groups on the nitrogen. The following cases are illustrative: Example (1) shows how, in 1951, Kuffner and Polke[KU1] successfully prepared tertiary amines with three secondary alkyl groups:

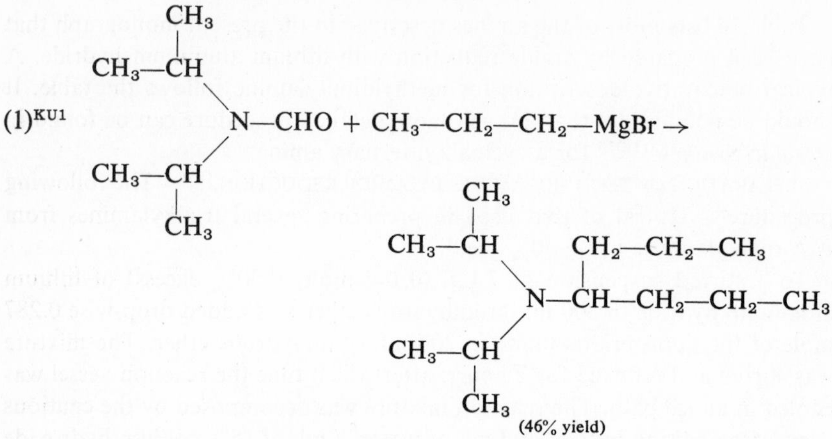

$(1)^{KU1}$

$$
\begin{array}{c}
CH_3 \\
| \\
CH_3-CH \\
\qquad\qquad N-CHO + CH_3-CH_2-CH_2-MgBr \rightarrow \\
CH_3-CH \\
| \\
CH_3
\end{array}
$$

$$
\begin{array}{c}
CH_3 \\
| \\
CH_3-CH \qquad CH_2-CH_2-CH_3 \\
\qquad\qquad N-CH-CH_2-CH_2-CH_3 \\
CH_3-CH \\
| \\
CH_3
\end{array}
$$

(46% yield)

Example (2) illustrates the introduction of an unusual tertiary alkyl group:

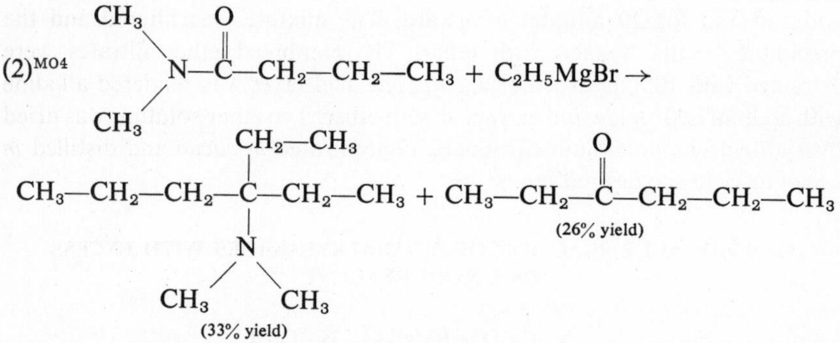

$(2)^{MO4}$

$$
\begin{array}{c}
CH_3 \qquad O \\
\diagdown \quad \| \\
N-C-CH_2-CH_2-CH_3 + C_2H_5MgBr \rightarrow \\
\diagup \\
CH_3
\end{array}
$$

$$
\begin{array}{c}
CH_2-CH_3 \qquad\qquad\qquad\qquad O \\
| \qquad\qquad\qquad\qquad\qquad \| \\
CH_3-CH_2-CH_2-C-CH_2-CH_3 + CH_3-CH_2-C-CH_2-CH_2-CH_3 \\
| \qquad\qquad\qquad\qquad\qquad \text{(26\% yield)} \\
N \\
\diagup \quad \diagdown \\
CH_3 \qquad CH_3
\end{array}
$$

(33% yield)

The use of a tertiary Grignard reagent should result in the introduction of a particularly bulky alkyl group on the nitrogen. However, when Bouveault[BO15] attempted such a reaction with t-amylmagnesium chloride and diethylformamide, 1-diethylamino-2,2-dimethylbutane along with 2-methyl-1-butene were obtained. Bouveault suggested that these products might result from the decomposition of the highly strained expected compound as follows:

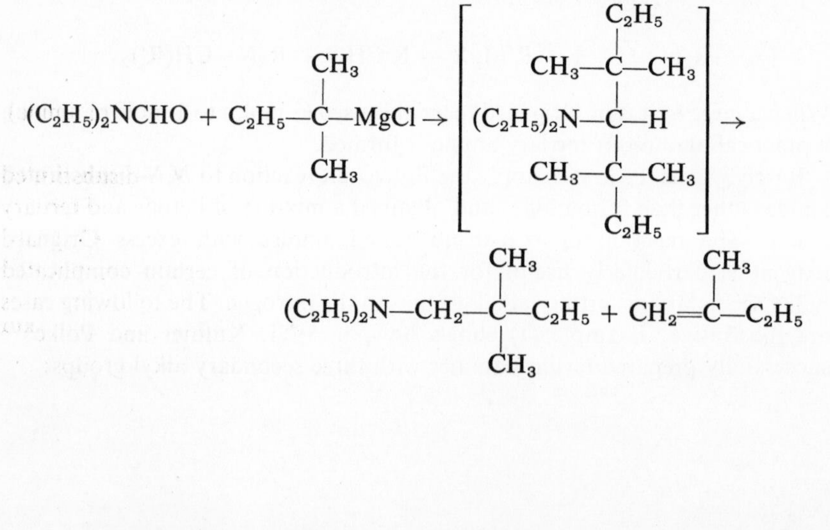

$$
(C_2H_5)_2NCHO + C_2H_5-\underset{\underset{CH_3}{|}}{\overset{\overset{CH_3}{|}}{C}}-MgCl \rightarrow
\left[
\begin{array}{c}
C_2H_5 \\
| \\
CH_3-C-CH_3 \\
| \\
(C_2H_5)_2N-C-H \\
| \\
CH_3-C-CH_3 \\
| \\
C_2H_5
\end{array}
\right]
\rightarrow
$$

$$
(C_2H_5)_2N-CH_2-\underset{\underset{CH_3}{|}}{\overset{\overset{CH_3}{|}}{C}}-C_2H_5 + CH_2=\overset{\overset{CH_3}{|}}{C}-C_2H_5
$$

Recently Ficini and Normant[F13] applied this reaction to a vinylog of a dialkylamide as follows:

$$CH_3CH{=}CHMgBr + (CH_3)_2NCH{=}CH-CHO \rightarrow$$

$$(CH_3)_2NCH{=}CH-CH(CH{=}CHCH_3)_2$$
(80% yield)

The reaction of excess Grignard reagent with disubstituted amides (other than formamides) has been studied extensively by Montagne.[M04] She found that, along with the expected tertiary amine and ketone—increasing temperature favored formation of the former at the expense of the latter—there is frequently obtained a significant amount of an alkane, RH, derived in some, unknown manner from the Grignard reagent, RMgX. For example, ethylmagnesium bromide (0.75 mole) and N,N-diethylpropionamide (0.21 mole) in benzene give 12% ketone, 33% amine, and about 20% ethane. Occasionally, she also observed an unexpected product when alkyl halide was used in excess of that needed to prepare the Grignard reagent. For example, in the presence of butyl iodide, N,N-diethylbutyramide reacts with methylmagnesium iodide to give 4-diethylamino-4-methylnonane along with the expected products:

$$(C_2H_5)_2N\overset{\displaystyle O}{\overset{\|}{-}}C-n\text{-}C_3H_7 + CH_3MgI + n\text{-}C_4H_9I \rightarrow$$

$$n\text{-}C_3H_7\overset{\displaystyle O}{\overset{\|}{-}}C-CH_3 + (C_2H_5)_2N\underset{\underset{\displaystyle CH_3}{|}}{\overset{\overset{\displaystyle CH_3}{|}}{C}}-n\text{-}C_3H_7 + (C_2H_5)_2N\underset{\underset{\displaystyle CH_3}{|}}{\overset{\overset{\displaystyle CH_2-n\text{-}C_4H_9}{|}}{C}}-n\text{-}C_3H_7$$

The analogous type of product was also obtained when methyl iodide or benzyl chloride was used as the added halide. Montagne proposed the following scheme for the formation of the anomalous product:

$$(C_2H_5)_2N\overset{\displaystyle O}{\overset{\|}{-}}C-C_3H_7 + CH_3MgI \rightarrow (C_2H_5)_2N\underset{\underset{\displaystyle C_3H_7}{|}}{\overset{\overset{\displaystyle CH_3}{|}}{C}}-OMgI$$

$$(C_2H_5)_2N\underset{\underset{\displaystyle C_3H_7}{|}}{\overset{\overset{\displaystyle CH_3}{|}}{C}}{\dashmapsto}OMgI + H{\dashmapsto}\underset{\underset{\displaystyle H}{|}}{\overset{\overset{\displaystyle H}{|}}{C}}{\dashmapsto}MgI + I{\dashmapsto}R \longrightarrow$$

$$(C_2H_5)_2N\underset{\underset{\displaystyle C_3H_7}{|}}{\overset{\overset{\displaystyle CH_3}{|}}{C}}-CH_2-R + MgIOH + MgI_2$$

The structure of the R-substituted amine, where R is methyl, was proved[MO4] by both degradative and synthetic procedures.

Recently one of the foregoing experiments was repeated by others[PA3a] in order to see if an isomer of the product reported by Montagne might not, indeed, be the true product of this anomalous reaction. Diethyl-n-butyramide was treated with methylmagnesium iodide and methyl iodide. The main product was found to be that reported by Montagne, 3-diethylamino-3-methylhexane. Proof of structure included use of nuclear magnetic resonance spectroscopy. An alternative mechanism was postulated in which the initially formed "normal" tertiary amine loses a hydrogen from the β-carbon to the methyl carbanion from the Grignard reagent. The resulting tertiary amine carbanion then displaces iodine from methyl iodide as follows:

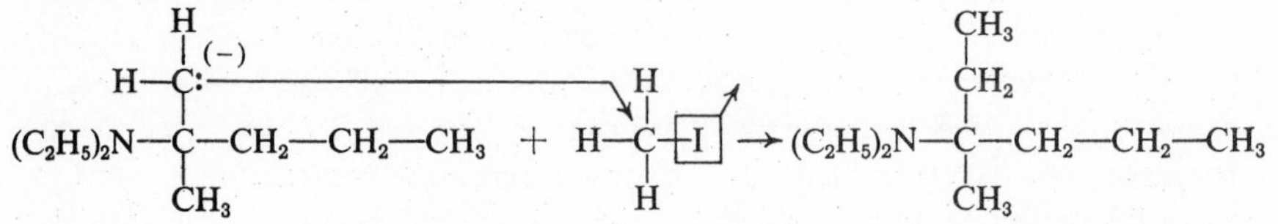

Table 16 shows the yields of selected tertiary amines prepared by the Bouveault method.

TABLE 16. TERTIARY AMINES FROM N-DISUBSTITUTED AMIDES AND GRIGNARD REAGENTS

AMIDE	GRIGNARD REAGENT	PRODUCT	YIELD (%)	REF.
Et$_2$NCHO	EtMgBr	Et$_2$NCHEt$_2$	51	MA43
Et$_2$NCHO	i-BuMgBr	Et$_2$NCH(i-Bu)$_2$	22[a]	MA43
i-Pr$_2$NCHO	MeMgBr	i-Pr$_3$N	0	KU1
i-Pr$_2$NCHO	EtMgBr	i-Pr$_2$NCHEt$_2$	"Small"	KU1
i-Pr$_2$NCHO	PrMgBr	i-Pr$_2$NCHPr$_2$	46	KU1
i-Pr$_2$NCHO	BuMgBr	i-Pr$_2$NCHBu$_2$	67	KU1
Et$_2$NĊPr (O‖)	EtMgBr	Et$_2$NCEt$_2$Pr	22[b]	MO4

[a] In addition to the amine, isovaleraldehyde was isolated in 29% yield.
[b] In addition to the amine, 3-hexanone was isolated in 45% yield.

PREPARATION OF 5-DIISOPROPYLAMINONONANE.[KU1]   To the butyl Grignard reagent from 54.8 g. (0.4 mole) of butyl bromide, 10 g. (0.42 g.-atom) of magnesium, and 80 ml. of absolute ether, a solution of 10.3 g. (0.08 mole) of diisopropylformamide in 40 ml. of ether was added drop-wise. After standing at 18° overnight the mixture, while cooled in an ice bath, was decomposed with 4N sulfuric acid. The solution was thoroughly extracted with ether. From the ether extract the hydrobromide salt of 5-diisopropylaminononane then precipitated.

An additional yield was obtained by steam distillation of the sulfuric acid solution until no more aldehyde was carried over and then, after alkalization of the solution, further steam distillation to carry over the amine.

Rapid titration with 1N hydrochloric acid to the first end point neutralized the diisopropylamine entrained. Then, extraction with ether, drying over lime, and distillation gave the desired tertiary amine, 5-diisopropylaminononane, in 67% yield.

12. CLEAVAGE OF ALKYL(DIALKYLAMINOMETHYL) ETHERS BY THE GRIGNARD REAGENT

$$\diagdown\!\!\text{NCH}_2\text{OR} + \text{R}'\text{MgX} \rightarrow \diagdown\!\!\text{NCH}_2\text{R}'$$

Robinson *et al.*[RO3] found that tertiary amines of the form $\text{RCH}_2\text{NR}'\text{R}''$ can be prepared in 55–70% yield by cleaving alkyl(dialkylaminomethyl) ethers with the Grignard reagent, as follows:

$$\begin{array}{c} \text{R}' \\ \diagdown \\ \text{N}-\text{CH}_2-\text{OR}''' + \text{RMgX} \rightarrow \\ \diagup \\ \text{R}'' \end{array} \quad \begin{array}{c} \text{R}' \\ \diagdown \\ \text{N}-\text{CH}_2-\text{R} + \text{MgX(OR}''') \\ \diagup \\ \text{R}'' \end{array}$$

In this equation none of the R groups represents hydrogen.

The intermediate amino ether is prepared from secondary amine, formaldehyde, and alcohol. Stewart and Hauser[ST12] were unable to substitute *n*-butyraldehyde for formaldehyde in the amino ether preparation, but did succeed with aromatic aldehydes, and thus prepared several mixed aliphatic-aromatic tertiary amines.

The reaction of alkyl(dialkylaminomethyl) ethers with Grignard reagents provides an indirect means of alkylating a dialkylamine with an alkyl group one carbon longer than that in the Grignard reagent. An interesting application of this method is due to Ficini and Normant,[FI2] who used various vinyl Grignard reagents to obtain excellent yields of tertiary amines containing 2-alkenyl groups. For example, 1-diethylamino-2-butene was prepared in 90% yield as follow:

$$\text{CH}_3-\text{CH}{=}\text{CH}-\text{MgBr} + (\text{C}_2\text{H}_5)_2\text{N}-\text{CH}_2-\text{O}-\text{C}_4\text{H}_9 \rightarrow$$
$$\text{CH}_3-\text{CH}{=}\text{CH}-\text{CH}_2-\text{N}(\text{C}_2\text{H}_5)_2$$

It is important to notice that this procedure provides a route to the preparation of allylic amines without the danger of molecular rearrangements which occur frequently when allyl halides are used directly in alkylations.[YO5]

Grignard reagents also react with N,N-bis(alkoxymethyl)-N-alkylamines of the type, $RN(CH_2OR')_2$, to give tertiary amines. For example, Robinson et al.[RO3] obtained methyldiethylamine from N,N-bis(butoxymethyl)-N-methylamine and methylmagnesium iodide.

Experimental details for the reaction of a Grignard reagent with an alkyl(dialkylaminomethyl) ether follow:

PREPARATION OF 4-DIETHYLAMINO-1-BUTENE.[*][RO3] A dilute ethereal solution of allylmagnesium chloride (probably, about 0.13 mole of Grignard reagent in about 100 ml. of ether) was added gradually to a solution of 19 g. (0.118 mole) of butyl(diethylaminomethyl) ether dissolved in anhydrous diethyl ether (probably, about 50 ml. of diethyl ether). The addition of each drop produced a vigorous reaction and a curdy precipitate. From this effect, it was possible to determine the point at which the whole of the amino ether had been decomposed. The mixture was allowed to stand a few hours and then water was added in sufficient amount to remove magnesium compounds from the ethereal solution. (Undoubtedly the water must have been added drop-wise with vigorous stirring.) The mixture was filtered and the sludge of magnesium hydroxide washed with fresh ether. The combined ether filtrate and wash solutions were extracted four times with dilute hydrochloric acid and this acid solution was concentrated to a small bulk. Cooling of the solution caused precipitation of the hydrochloride as a mass of deliquescent crystals. The amine was separated by the addition of concentrated potassium hydroxide, followed by careful distillation of the mixture. The distillate was taken up in ether, dried over solid potassium hydroxide, and distilled. The fraction boiling at 132° at 767 mm. is 4-diethylamino-1-butene. (Although the yield was not specified in this preparation, other similar preparations resulted in yields of 50–70%.)

13. CLEAVAGE OF METHYLENE-BIS-DIALKYLAMINO COMPOUNDS WITH GRIGNARD REAGENTS
$$R_2N—CH_2—NR_2 + R'—MgX \rightarrow R_2N—CH_2R'$$

Nomura, Yamamoto, and Oda[NO1] coupled bis(diethylamino)methane with aromatic Grignard reagents to prepare mixed aliphatic-aromatic tertiary amines as follows:

$$R_2NCH_2NR_2 + ArMgX \rightarrow R_2NCH_2Ar + MgX(NR_2)$$

---

* Although several preparations of tertiary amines are described by ref. RO3, the experimental details are incomplete in each case. Several comments are, therefore, included here, to indicate probable quantities derived from other analogous experiments in reference RO3.

A more detailed related preparative procedure can be found in a paper by Stewart and Hauser[ST12] for aromatic amines.

Undoubtedly, fully aliphatic amines can also be prepared in this way. This reaction is similar to the cleavage by Grignard reagents of alkyl(dialkylaminomethyl) ethers (see section 12 preceding) or of α-dialkylaminonitriles (see section 14 following). In comparing the cleavage of bis(diethylamino)methane with that of butyl(diethylaminomethyl) ether, Nomura et al.[NO1] obtained much better yields with the latter than with the former compound (21% vs. 100% using benzylmagnesium bromide).

14. CLEAVAGE OF α-DIALKYLAMINONITRILES BY THE GRIGNARD REAGENT

$$\overset{\diagdown}{\underset{\diagup}{N}} - \overset{|}{\underset{|}{C}} - CN + RMgX \rightarrow \overset{\diagdown}{\underset{\diagup}{N}} - \overset{|}{\underset{|}{C}} - R + \overset{\diagdown}{\underset{\diagup}{N}} - \overset{|}{\underset{|}{C}} - \overset{|}{\underset{|}{C}} - \overset{\diagup}{\underset{\diagdown}{N}}$$

Bruylants[BR49] found that α-dialkylaminonitriles react with Grignard reagents to give a mixture of mono- and di-amines along with an alkane:

$$R_2N - \overset{R'}{\underset{R''}{\overset{|}{\underset{|}{C}}}} - CN + R'''MgX \rightarrow$$

$$R_2N - \overset{R'}{\underset{R''}{\overset{|}{\underset{|}{C}}}} - R''' + R_2N - \overset{R'}{\underset{R''}{\overset{|}{\underset{|}{C}}}} - \overset{R'}{\underset{R''}{\overset{|}{\underset{|}{C}}}} - NR_2 + R'''R'' + MgXCN$$

where R and R''' are alkyl groups and R' and R'' are alkyl groups and/or hydrogen. The formation of the monoamine generally predominates.[BR49, BR50, GO2, VE2, WE16] Bruylants[BR49] prepared 3-diethylaminohexane in 83% by this reaction, as follows:

$$(C_2H_5)_2N - \overset{H}{\underset{CN}{\overset{|}{\underset{|}{C}}}} - CH_2 - CH_2 - CH_3 + C_2H_2MgBr \rightarrow$$

$$(C_2H_5)_2N - \overset{H}{\underset{C_2H_5}{\overset{|}{\underset{|}{C}}}} - CH_2 - CH_2 - CH_3$$

(83% yield)

In this reaction, when the piperidino group was substituted for the diethylamino group, yields of 90 to 100% were observed.

Westphal[WE16] used this reaction to prepare tridecyldiethylamine in 41% yield:

$$n\text{-}C_{12}H_{25}MgCl + (C_2H_5)_2N - CH_2 - CN \rightarrow n\text{-}C_{13}H_{27}N(C_2H_5)_2$$

(41% yield)

This provides a convenient method for placing on the amino nitrogen an alkyl group one carbon longer than that in the Grignard reagent.

At times Bruylants[BR50] and Velghe[VE2] observed the interesting side reaction leading to diamine. Surprisingly, only in the case of one nitrile, α-dimethylaminoisobutyronitrile, was the diamine found to be the main product.[VE2] The reactions involving a study with this nitrile are summarized as follows (per cent yield is shown in parentheses)[VE2]:

$$
(CH_3)_2N-\underset{\underset{CH_3}{|}}{\overset{\overset{CH_3}{|}}{C}}-CN + CH_3MgBr \rightarrow
$$

$$
(CH_3)_2N-\underset{\underset{CH_3}{|}}{\overset{\overset{CH_3}{|}}{C}}-\underset{\underset{CH_3}{|}}{\overset{\overset{CH_3}{|}}{C}}-N(CH_3)_2 \;+\; (CH_3)_2N-\underset{\underset{CH_3}{|}}{\overset{\overset{CH_3}{|}}{C}}-CH_3 \;+\; CH_3-CH_3
$$

(67%)   (—)   (ca 57%)

$$
(CH_3)_2N-\underset{\underset{CH_3}{|}}{\overset{\overset{CH_3}{|}}{C}}-CN + C_2H_5MgBr \rightarrow
$$

$$
(CH_3)_2N-\underset{\underset{CH_3}{|}}{\overset{\overset{CH_3}{|}}{C}}-\underset{\underset{CH_3}{|}}{\overset{\overset{CH_3}{|}}{C}}-N(CH_3)_2 \;+\; (CH_3)_2N-\underset{\underset{CH_3}{|}}{\overset{\overset{CH_3}{|}}{C}}-C_2H_5 \;+\; n\text{-}C_4H_{10}
$$

(69%)   (ca 15%)   (—)

$$
(CH_3)_2N-\underset{\underset{CH_3}{|}}{\overset{\overset{CH_3}{|}}{C}}-CN + n\text{-}C_3H_7MgBr \rightarrow
$$

$$
(CH_3)_2N-\underset{\underset{CH_3}{|}}{\overset{\overset{CH_3}{|}}{C}}-\underset{\underset{CH_3}{|}}{\overset{\overset{CH_3}{|}}{C}}-N(CH_3)_2 \;+\; (CH_3)_2N-\underset{\underset{CH_3}{|}}{\overset{\overset{CH_3}{|}}{C}}-n\text{-}C_3H_7 \;+\; n\text{-}C_6H_{14}
$$

("slight amount")   (ca 20%)   (—)

The reaction yielding monoamine is normally expected if one considers the nitrile group as behaving like a pseudo-halide. The abnormal diamine formation is reminiscent of free radical reactions involving Grignard reagents[KH2] wherein the most reactive radicals formed (here the alkyl from the reagent) dimerize and the more stable radicals derived from the amino-nitrile subsequently are left to combine with each other. The appearance of the hydrocarbon component is generally associated with the diamine forma-tion. When the benzyl Grignard reagent is used, the relatively stable benzyl radicals do not drive the dimerization reaction, and only the monoamine is reported. Unfortunately, however, mono- *vs.* di-amine yields do not follow a completely consistent pattern. This difficulty in arriving at a more specific correlation is compounded by the vagueness in the experimental descriptions. An additional contributing factor may have been the presence or absence of catalytic metal ions which are found to be important in free radical reactions of Grignard reagents.[KH2]

The following example is illustrative of the application of the reaction.

PREPARATION OF TRIDECYLDIETHYLAMINE.[WE16] The reaction between dodecyl chloride (51 g., 0.25 mole) dissolved in 150 ml. of ether and magnesium turnings (6.1 g., 0.25 mole) was initiated by preliminary heating. After the reaction had subsided the mixture was gently refluxed for 3 hours. At this point a substantial amount of the magnesium remained unreacted. The solution was cooled in an ice bath and diethylaminoacetonitrile (28 g., 0.25 mole) dissolved in 100 ml. of ether was slowly added drop-wise. After this addition the solution was still clear with no apparent change. It was allowed to stand overnight at room temperature and then decomposed with an excess of ice-cold 2N hydrochloric acid. (*Note:* Caution should be taken because hydrogen cyanide evolution occurs.) The solution was then made alkaline with sodium hydroxide. The ether layer was separated, dried over potassium carbonate, and concentrated by evaporation. Distillation yielded 44 g. of a yellow oil which boiled at 140–205° at 12 mm. Treatment of this oil with ethereal hydrogen chloride resulted in evolution of heat and the precipitation of the hydrochloride of tridecyldiethylamine. After filtration and drying 30 g., 41% yield, of the crude hydrochloride was obtained. Two recrystallizations from dioxane-ethyl acetate mixture gave shiny plates melting at 77–79° (corrected). The free base liberated by treatment of the aqueous solution of the hydrochloride with alkali gave an oil, tridecyldiethylamine, boiling at 169° at 12 mm.

15. SYNTHESES OF ACETYLENIC TERTIARY AMINES

(1)
$$\diagdown\!\!\diagup N-H + \diagdown\!\!\diagup C=O + H-C\equiv C- \rightarrow \diagdown\!\!\diagup N-\overset{|}{C}-C\equiv C-$$

(2)
$$\diagdown\!\!\diagup N-\left[\overset{|}{\underset{|}{C}}\right]_n C\equiv CNa + RX \rightarrow \diagdown\!\!\diagup N-\left[\overset{|}{\underset{|}{C}}\right]_n C\equiv C-R$$

A significant fraction of the amines reported in the present monograph contain at least one carbon-to-carbon triple bond. Two methods of synthesis utilized to an equivalent extent account for a little more than one-half of such compounds. These two methods are based on the Mannich reaction and on variants of the Picon synthesis. (Two fine reviews on acetylenic tertiary amines have appeared in recent years: one by Fisher in 1958 with 108 references,[FI9] and the other by Olomucki in 1960 with 245 references.[OL6])

Since alkynes can be reduced selectively to the corresponding *cis* or *trans* olefins, many acetylenic amines have been prepared as precursors of alkenyl-amines.

The Mannich Reaction

$$\backslash \!\!\!\diagdown N—H + H_2C{=}O + H—C{\equiv}C— \rightarrow \diagdown N—CH_2—C{\equiv}C—$$

The Mannich reaction consists of the interaction of ammonia or a primary or secondary amine (usually as the hydrochloride) with formaldehyde and an active hydrogen compound to give a variety of aminomethyl compounds. Terminal acetylenes can serve as the active hydrogen component.

The reaction may proceed through formation of the intermediate methylol (i.e., hydroxymethylamino) compound resulting from initial combination of the secondary amine with formaldehyde. A good general review of the Mannich reaction has been written by Blicke.[BL2] However, it pays minimal attention to the reaction involving alkynes.

Mannich and Chang[MA20] first used this method to prepare 3-diethylamino-1-phenylpropyne according to the following equation:

$$C_6H_5—C{\equiv}CH + CH_2O + (C_2H_5)_2NH \rightarrow$$
$$C_6H_5—C{\equiv}C—CH_2N(C_2H_5)_2 + H_2O$$

Since then, the Mannich reaction has been used, frequently with catalysis by copper salts, to prepare a variety of 1-dialkylamino-2-alkynes, and 1,4-bis-(dialkylamino)-2-butynes according to the following general equation:

(1)

$$R—C{\equiv}C—H + CH_2O + \underset{R_2}{\overset{R_1}{\diagdown N—H}} \rightarrow R—C{\equiv}C—CH_2—\underset{R_2}{\overset{R_1}{N}} + H_2O$$

When acetylene itself is used as the alkyne, two products are possible because of the two active hydrogens in the molecule:

(2) $$H—C{\equiv}C—H + CH_2O + \underset{R_2}{\overset{R_1}{\diagdown N—H}} \rightarrow$$

$$H—C{\equiv}C—CH_2—\underset{R_2}{\overset{R_1}{N}} + \underset{R_2}{\overset{R_1}{N}}—CH_2—C{\equiv}C—CH_2—\underset{R_2}{\overset{R_1}{N}} + H_2O$$

One of the two products can be made to predominate by controll relative amounts of reactants.

Reppe *et al.*[RE7,RE11] extended the Mannich reaction to include aldehydes and also ketones as the carbonyl reagents. For example, 3-dime amino-2-propyl-1-propyne was obtained in the copper salt catalyzed reaction of acetylene, dimethylamine, and *n*-butyraldehyde under pressure.

Coffman[CO2] and Carothers[CA11] used vinylacetylene as the alkyne component to prepare 1-dialkylamino-4-penten-2-ynes. In 1958, 25 years later, Nazarov and Mistryukov[NA3] showed that carefully purified paraformaldehyde and diethylamine were practically inert to vinylacetylene hydrocarbons, and that the success of the reaction by other investigators was due to fortuitous catalysis by iron impurities.

In Table 17 are listed experimental data for a few representative preparations of acetylenic tertiary amines obtained from the Mannich reaction. Detailed synthetic procedures for certain compounds are also given.

PREPARATION OF 1-DIMETHYLAMINO-2-HEPTYNE.[CA7] Dimethylamine (45 g., 1.0 mole) was added during 15 minutes to a cold suspension of 30 g. of paraformaldehyde in 100 ml. of anhydrous dioxane. The clear solution was transferred to an autoclave, 1-hexyne (82 g., 1.0 mole) was added, and the mixture was heated at 100° for 12 hours (maximum pressure 35 lb. sq. in.). The solvent was removed at atmospheric pressure, and the residue was fractionated under reduced pressure. There was obtained 112 g. (81%) of 1-dimethylamino-2-heptyne, b.p. 110° at 90 mm.

PREPARATION OF 1-DIETHYLAMINO-4-METHYL-4-PENTEN-2-YNE.[NA3] To paraformaldehyde (75 g., 2.5 moles) in a flask bearing a reflux condenser, diethylamine (234 ml., 2.28 moles) was added rapidly. After the vigorous exothermic reaction had subsided, the methylolamine was cooled and transferred to a 1-liter stainless-steel reactor fitted with a stirrer. Isopropenyl-acetylene (212 ml., 2.27 moles) and 300 ml. of dioxane, in which a few crystals of iron(III) chloride had been dissolved, were then added and the reactor was pressurized with nitrogen to 30–40 atmospheres. The system was heated at 95–100° for 15 hours. The cooled reaction mass was neutralized with dilute sulfuric acid (60 ml. of concentrated sulfuric in 200 ml. of water) and the dioxane and much of the water were removed under reduced pressure. The desired base was liberated by a concentrated solution of sodium hydroxide or ammonia, washed with 150 ml. of water, dried over potassium carbonate, and vacuum distilled. 1-Diethylamino-4-methyl-4-penten-2-yne (284 g., 83% yield) was obtained.

The Picon Synthesis.

$$\diagdown \!\!\!\!\diagup N \!-\!\! \left[\begin{array}{c} | \\ C \\ | \end{array} \right]_n \!\!\! C \!\equiv\! CNa + RX \rightarrow \diagdown \!\!\!\!\diagup N \!-\!\! \left[\begin{array}{c} | \\ C \\ | \end{array} \right]_n \!\!\! C \!\equiv\! C \!-\! R$$

Lebeau and Picon[LE2] found that disodium acetylide in liquid ammonia

TABLE 17. REPRESENTATIVE PREPARATIONS OF ACETYLENIC TERTIARY AMINES BY THE MANNICH REACTION

SECONDARY AMINE	ALKYNE	CARBONYL COMPOUND	CATALYST	SOLVENT	TEMPERATURE	PRESSURE (ATM.)	TIME (HR.)	PRODUCT	YIELD (%)	REF.
Me_2NH	$HC{\equiv}CH$	CH_2O	$Cu(OAc)_2$	H_2O	35°	10	10–20	$Me_2NCH_2C{\equiv}CH$ and	70	RE7
								$Me_2NCH_2C{\equiv}CCH_2NMe_2$	10	RE7
$Me_2NCH_2NMe_2$[a]	$HC{\equiv}CH$	CH_2O	Cu_2Cl_2	H_2O	50°	1.3	4	$Me_2NCH_2C{\equiv}CH$ and	9	FE2
								$Me_2NCH_2C{\equiv}CCH_2NMe_2$	73	FE2
Me_2NH	$BuC{\equiv}CH$	CH_2O	—	Dioxane	100°	2	12	$Me_2NCH_2C{\equiv}CBu$	81	CA7
Et_2NH	$HC{\equiv}CCH{=}CH_2$	CH_2O	[c]	Dioxane	100°	[b]	15	$Et_2NCH_2C{\equiv}CCH{=}CH_2$	91	CO2
Me_2NH	$HC{\equiv}CH$	Me_2CO	Cu_2Cl_2	EtOH	80°	—	—	$Me_2NC(CH_3)_2C{\equiv}CH$	"Good"	RE11

[a] $Me_2NCH_2NMe_2$ hydrolyzes to give Me_2NH and CH_2O.

[b] Autogenous pressure in autoclave.

[c] Ref. NA3 claims that the success of this reaction was due to the catalytic effect of iron impurities.

reacts with alkyl halides to give alkylacetylenes as follows:

$$NaC \equiv CNa + RX \rightarrow R-C \equiv CNa + NaX$$

$$R-C \equiv CNa + H_2O \rightarrow R-C \equiv CH + H_2O$$

The reaction can be repeated to introduce another alkyl group[N13]:

$$R-C \equiv CNa + R'X \rightarrow R-C \equiv C-R' + NaX$$

Because of the many contributions by Picon to the development of this reaction[N13] the authors of the present monograph would like to refer to this process as the Picon synthesis.

The preparation of acetylenic tertiary amines by this method is represented as follows:

$$R_2N-(CH_2)_x-C \equiv CNa + R'X \rightarrow R_2N-(CH_2)_x-C \equiv C-R' + NaX$$

Parcell and Pollard[PA5,PA6] were the first to prepare acyclic aliphatic acetylenic tertiary amines by this method.

It is generally assumed that a synthetic procedure for a tertiary amine involves reaction at the nitrogen atom, such as N-alkylation. The method under discussion, however, is one of the few exceptions to this interpretation, and is being included because of its importance in the preparation of substituted acetylenic tertiary amines.

The reaction is conducted most frequently in liquid ammonia but also can be performed in organic solvents such as toluene. Sodamide, which may be prepared *in situ*, converts the terminal acetylene to the sodio derivative.

The amino function may be present in the alkyne or the alkyl halide, or in both.[B11,B13,CA7] For example, Campbell et al.[CA7] prepared several acetylenic tertiary amines using dialkylamino halides, as illustrated by the following equation:

$$(CH_3)_2NCH_2CH_2Br + NaC \equiv C-C_4H_9 \xrightarrow{\text{liq. NH}_3}$$
$$(CH_3)_2NCH_2CH_2C \equiv C-C_4H_9$$

Biel and DiPierro[B13] used both an acetylenic amine and an amino halide to prepare a series of acetylenic diamines in 50–90% yield as follows:

$$R_2NCH_2C \equiv C-Na + R'_2N(CH_2)_xCl \xrightarrow{\text{toluene}} R_2NCH_2C \equiv C(CH_2)_xNR'_2$$

Table 18 shows representative preparative examples of the Picon synthesis.

To illustrate the use of sodium acetylides and alkyl halides for the preparation of acetylenic tertiary amines, the following three examples are presented in detail. The solvent systems are liquid ammonia (Method A), liquid ammonia and toluene (Method B), and toluene (Method C).

METHOD A. PREPARATION OF 1-DIETHYLAMINO-2-BUTYNE.[PA5] In a 3-liter, 3-necked, round-bottomed flask equipped with a mercury-sealed stirrer, dropping funnel, and a reflux condenser cooled with dry ice and acetone

TABLE 18. REPRESENTATIVE ACETYLENIC TERTIARY AMINES PREPARED BY THE PICON REACTION IN LIQUID AMMONIA

REACTANTS		PRODUCT	YIELD (%)	REF.
ALKYNE	ALKYL HALIDE			
i-Pr$_2$NCH$_2$C≡CH	MeI	i-Pr$_2$NCH$_2$C≡CCH$_3$	43	PA6
Pr$_2$NCH$_2$C≡CH	MeI	Pr$_2$NCH$_2$C≡CCH$_3$	81	PA6
Bu$_2$NCH$_2$C≡CH	EtBr	Bu$_2$NCH$_2$C≡CC$_2$H$_5$	76	PA6
Me$_2$N(CH$_2$)$_3$C≡CH	MeI	Me$_2$N(CH$_2$)$_3$C≡CCH$_3$	60	EP2,MA31,OL6
Me$_2$N(CH$_2$)$_4$C≡CH	n-C$_6$H$_{13}$I	Me$_2$N(CH$_2$)$_4$C≡C-n-C$_6$H$_{13}$	—	OL6
Et$_2$NCH$_2$C≡CH	PrBr	Et$_2$NCH$_2$C≡C—Pr	78	PA5
HC≡CH[a]	Et$_2$NCH$_2$CH$_2$Cl	Et$_2$NCH$_2$CH$_2$C≡CCH$_2$CH$_2$NEt$_2$	88	B13
Et$_2$NCH$_2$C≡CH[b]	Et$_2$NCH$_2$CH$_2$Cl	Et$_2$NCH$_2$C≡CCH$_2$CH$_2$NEt$_2$	73	B13

[a] Both toluene and liquid ammonia were used as the solvents.
[b] Toluene, instead of liquid ammonia, was used as the solvent.

mixture, a solution of sodamide (30.5 g., 0.78 mole) in 2 liters of liquid ammonia was prepared by the method of Nieuwland et al.[VA7] (*Note:* The preparation of sodamide is quite common; for example, see the procedure given by Hancock and Cope in *Organic Syntheses.*[HA10]) 1-Diethylamino-2-propyne (66.5 g., 0.6 mole) was added drop-wise with stirring into the flask over a period of 0.5 hour. Stirring was continued for an additional hour. The dropping funnel was rinsed with ether and replaced on the flask. Methyl iodide (110 g., 0.78 mole) was then added dropwise over a period of 2 hours. Refluxing of the ammonia was continued for 3 hours. The reflux condenser was replaced by a tube leading into the hood to permit evaporation of the ammonia. In 3 to 4 hours the total volume had decreased to about 500 ml., and the reaction was stopped by the cautious addition of 500 ml. of ether and 500 ml. of water. When the ice had melted from the flask, stirring was discontinued, and the contents of the flask were filtered. The ether layer was removed from the filtrate and dried over solid sodium hydroxide. After evaporation of the ether the residue was fractionally distilled. There was obtained 46 g. (73.5% yield based on 1-diethylamino-2-propyne) of 1-diethylamino-2-butyne boiling at 152–152.6° (corrected).

METHOD B. PREPARATION OF 1,6-BIS(DIETHYLAMINO)-3-HEXYNE.[BI3] To sodium amide (39 g., 1.0 mole) in 2 liters of liquid ammonia was added acetylene until the color of the reaction mixture had changed (*sic*). Stirring was continued for another half-hour and diethylaminoethyl chloride (136.5 g., 1.0 mole) in 150 ml. of toluene was added. The mixture was allowed to reflux with stirring for 1 hour, and the ammonia then permitted to evaporate. When all the ammonia had evaporated, the mixture was stirred while heated at reflux for 20 hours. To the cooled reaction mixture 250 ml. of water was then added to dissolve the solids. The toluene layer was washed with three 150-ml. portions of dilute aqueous hydrochloric acid. The aqueous acid solution was then washed with ether and the ether washings were discarded. The aqueous phase was saturated with solid potassium hydroxide and extracted with ether. The combined ether extracts were dried over potassium carbonate and the product (100 g., 88% yield) was collected by fractional distillation. It boiled at 80–85° at 0.5 mm.

METHOD C. PREPARATION OF 1,5-BIS(DIETHYLAMINO)-2-PENTYNE.[BI3] To sodium amide (31 g., 0.80 mole) in 100 ml. of toluene was added 3-diethyl-amino-1-propyne (100 g., 0.90 mole). The reaction mixture was brought gradually to the reflux temperature and refluxing continued until the copious evolution of ammonia had ceased. To the hot mixture was added 3-diethyl-aminoethyl chloride (135 g., 1.0 mole); stirring and refluxing were continued for 16 hours. The reaction mixture was cooled to room temperature and the salts were dissolved by the addition of 250 ml. of water. The toluene layer was separated and extracted repeatedly with dilute aqueous hydrochloric acid. The acid extracts were washed with ether and then treated with solid potassium hydroxide until two well-defined layers appeared. The alkaline mixture was extracted with ether, the ether extracts were dried with potassium carbonate, and the product collected by fractional distillation, b.p. 85–90° at 1.5 mm., amounted to 122 g. (73% yield).

16. THERMAL DECOMPOSITION OF QUATERNARY AMMONIUM COMPOUNDS. HOFMANN DEGRADATION

$$\left[-\underset{|}{\overset{|}{C}}-\underset{\underset{R''}{|}}{\overset{\overset{R}{|}}{C}}-\underset{|}{\overset{|}{N}}-R' \right]^{+} OH^{-} \rightarrow RR'R''N + -\overset{|}{C}\!\!=\!\!\overset{|}{C}- + H_2O$$

In 1851 Hofmann[HO4] found that thermal decomposition of quaternary ammonium hydroxides resulted in the formation of tertiary amines and olefins. This highly important reaction has found extensive use and is variously called the Hofmann elimination reaction, the Hofmann exhaustive methylation reaction, and the Hofmann degradation reaction. The name "Hofmann exhaustive methylation reaction" is most commonly used in proof-of-structure studies of the type first proposed by Hofmann. The reaction can be illustrated by the following general equation:

$$\left[R-\underset{\underset{R''}{|}}{\overset{\overset{R'}{|}}{N}}-\underset{|}{\overset{|}{C}}-\underset{|}{\overset{|}{C}}- \right]^{+} OH^{-} \xrightarrow{heat} RR'R''N + -\overset{|}{C}\!\!=\!\!\overset{|}{C}- + H_2O$$

Many of the tertiary amines reported in the literature have been made by this method in the process of trying to determine the structure of compounds with basic nitrogen, especially natural products.[SM1] To a lesser but still significant extent this method has been used both to study the mechanism of elimination reactions[CO24,DO1a,HA11,IN2,IN8,SH3,ST10,WE18,WI25,WI28] and to prepare specific olefins.

Ingold and coworkers[HA11,IN2] investigated the theoretical aspects of this reaction and helped strengthen the Hofmann rule which, in its present form, states that the thermal decomposition of a quaternary ammonium hydroxide containing only primary alkyl groups produces mainly the least substituted ethylene. For example, pyrolysis of dimethylethylpropylammonium hydroxide[HA11] produces ethylene as the main olefin, although small amounts of propylene also form:

$$\left[CH_3CH_2CH_2-\underset{\underset{CH_3}{|}}{\overset{\overset{CH_3}{|}}{N}}-CH_2CH_3 \right]^{+} OH^{-} \xrightarrow{heat} \left. \begin{array}{l} (CH_3)_2NCH_2CH_2CH_3 \\ CH_2\!\!=\!\!CH_2 \end{array} \right\} mainly$$

$$\left. \begin{array}{l} (CH_3)_2NCH_2CH_3 \\ CH_3CH\!\!=\!\!CH_2 \end{array} \right\} \begin{array}{l} small \\ amount \end{array}$$

$$\left. \begin{array}{l} CH_3OH \\ CH_3(C_2H_5)(n\text{-}C_3H_7)N \end{array} \right\} \begin{array}{l} slight \\ amount \end{array}$$

If no olefin can be formed (owing to absence of β-hydrogen) an alcohol is obtained instead.

The mechanism proposed by Ingold and co-workers[HA11,IN2,IN8] for the formation of olefin involves second-order kinetics in a β-elimination:

$$HO^- + -\overset{\underset{|}{H}}{C}\overset{\overset{+}{NR_3}}{\underset{|}{C}}- \rightarrow \underset{/}{\overset{\backslash}{C}}=\underset{\backslash}{\overset{/}{C}} + H_2O + R_3N:$$

A base such as hydroxyl ion attacks the β-hydrogen and removes it. The indicated shift of electrons then produces the olefin, tertiary amine, and water. The increase in electron density at the β-carbon that results from attachment of electron-releasing groups makes it more difficult for the base to abstract the proton. Hence, Hanhart and Ingold[HA11,IN2] place primary alkyl groups in the following order with respect to ease of olefin formation:

ethyl > n-propyl > n-amyl ~ n-octyl > isoamyl > isobutyl

This order had also been found earlier by von Braun.[BR9]

Relatively recently there has been an increase in the number of studies on the Hofmann degradation mechanism in isotopically labeled quaternary ammonium hydroxides[FR7,SH3,WE18] and related isotope exchange reactions.[DO1a,SH3] This has been occasioned by the suggestion in the work of Wittig et al.[WI25,WI27,WI28,WI29] of the existence of an intramolecular ylid intermediate, formed by elimination of an α-hydrogen ion, which then is cleaved (through a cyclic transition state with β-elimination of another alkyl group) to the observed products:

$$\left[RCH_2CH_2-\overset{\overset{CH_3}{|}}{\underset{\underset{CH_3}{|}}{N^{\oplus}}}-CH_3 \right] OH^- \rightarrow R-\overset{\overset{H}{|}}{\underset{\underset{H}{|}}{C}}-CH_2-\overset{\overset{CH_3}{|}}{\underset{\underset{CH_2}{|}}{N^{\oplus}}}-CH_3 + H_2O$$

$$\longrightarrow RCH{=}CH_2 + N(CH_3)_3$$

This so-called α',β-elimination has been proved by Weygand et al.[WE18] and by Shiner and Smith[SH3] to be a minor mechanistic route compared to the more prevalent simple β-elimination, except in the case of halomethyl-substituted quaternary ammonium compounds treated with strongly basic organolithium compounds,[WE18] and possibly in the Hofmann degradation of quaternary compounds with two bulky alkyl groups on the β-carbon.[CO24]

The reader's attention is directed to a recent excellent review by Cope,[CO16a] of the Hofmann reaction. Entitled, "Olefins from Amines: The Hofmann Elimination Reaction and Amine Oxide Pyrolysis," it gives a thorough discussion of the theoretical aspects of this reaction.

Von Braun[BR9,BR10,BR14,BR27] studied the Hofmann degradation as a preparative tool for tertiary amines and prepared several such compounds in good yields.

The Hofmann degradation is so sensitive to reaction conditions that several investigators have reported widely differing results. For example, in what was thought to be identical conditions, von Braun[BR9] and Ingold and Vass[IN8] reported different yields of alkyldimethylamines from alkyltrimethylammonium hydroxides, as shown in Table 19. Later von Braun, Teuffert, and Weisbach[BR27] suggested that the lower yields of alkyldimethylamines by Ingold and Vass[IN8] might be due to their exclusion of atmospheric carbon dioxide in the degradation step. Von Braun et al.[BR27] showed that, in the absence of carbon dioxide, decyltrimethylammonium hydroxide gives 62% olefin and 30% decyldimethylamine, while in the presence of atmospheric carbon dioxide the yields are 25 and 72%, respectively.

TABLE 19. ALKYLDIMETHYLAMINE FROM THE THERMAL DECOMPOSITION OF $[(CH_3)_3NR]^+OH^-$

R =	YIELD OF $(CH_3)_2NR$ (%)	
	REF.[BR9]	REF.[IN8]
n-C_4H_9	50	21
n-C_5H_{11}	60	23
n-C_6H_{13}	73	24
n-C_7H_{15}	75	26
n-C_8H_{17}	75	25

Later Stevens and Richmond[ST10] reported that the yield of tertiary amines and olefin was influenced by the temperature of decomposition. Pinacolyltrimethylammonium hydroxide in a nitrogen atmosphere was found to yield 52 and 0% of pinacolyldimethylamine at 100–160° and at 30°, respectively, according to the following scheme:

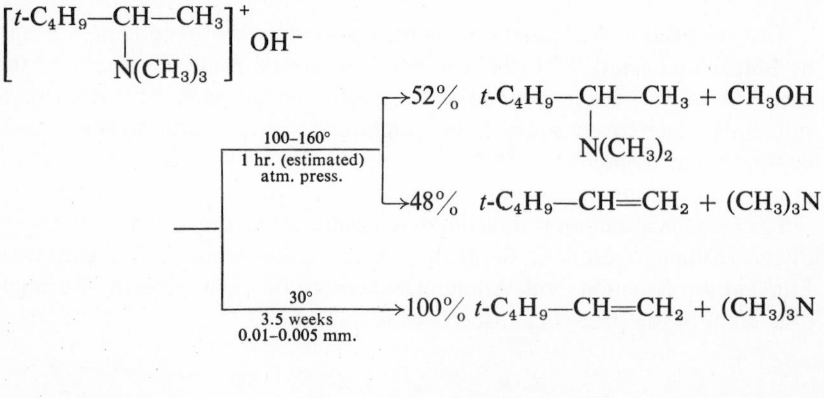

$$\left[\begin{array}{c} t\text{-}C_4H_9\text{—CH—CH}_3 \\ | \\ N(CH_3)_3 \end{array}\right]^+ OH^-$$

100–160°
1 hr. (estimated)
atm. press.

→52% t-C_4H_9—CH—CH$_3$ + CH$_3$OH
        |
        N(CH$_3$)$_2$

→48% t-C_4H_9—CH=CH$_2$ + (CH$_3$)$_3$N

30°
3.5 weeks
0.01–0.005 mm.

→100% t-C_4H_9—CH=CH$_2$ + (CH$_3$)$_3$N

Von Braun and Buchman[BR14] showed that the course of elimination can be altered by conducting the decomposition of various *N*-substituted piperidinium hydroxides in the presence of potassium hydroxide (ionic hydroxyl) as compared to the reaction in the presence of glycerol (covalent hydroxyl). More elimination *via* ring opening is observed in the former case.

In most instances of the Hofmann reaction the quaternary hydroxide is formed by precipitation of silver halide from the interaction of the corresponding quaternary ammonium halide (usually the iodide) with moist silver oxide. Von Braun and Anton[BR13] found that a method reported in 1851 by Hofmann[HO4] for preparing the hydroxides by precipitation of barium sulfate on mixing quaternary ammonium sulfates and barium hydroxide was frequently convenient and more economical. The Hofmann degradation also has been found to work in certain cases by simply heating quaternary halides with aqueous sodium hydroxide.[BA10,BA11,BA13,KN6]

Strong bases other than hydroxyl ion can be used also. Kharasch and Fuchs[KH3] heated 1,1-diethyl-2-methylpyrrolidinium chloride with sodium phenylacetylide and with sodamide in xylene for 12 hours at 150–155° and obtained 1-diethylamino-4-pentene in 68 and 57% yield, respectively. In certain special cases, organolithium compounds have also been used as bases.[HA3,WE18,WI29]

The reaction of active metals such as potassium or sodium in liquid ammonia with quaternary ammonium halides results in reductive cleavage to give an alkane and tertiary amine.[GR14,HA29,JO4] This is a variant on the Emde reaction (see section 17 following). Along with the expected alkane there also is observed alkene, which results from a Hofmann-type elimination brought about by amide ion formed *in situ*.

The synthesis of a tertiary amine by the Hofmann elimination reaction will be illustrated with the preparation of pinacolyldimethylamine from pinacolylamine.

DECOMPOSITION OF PINACOLYLTRIMETHYLAMMONIUM HYDROXIDE.[ST10] Pinacolylamine was converted to pinacolyltrimethylammonium iodide by two treatments with excess methyl iodide in the presence of sodium hydroxide. The quaternary iodide, 84 g., was treated with excess silver oxide in water solution to give the quaternary hydroxide. After filtration of the silver iodide, the hydroxide solution was distilled under a current of nitrogen at ordinary pressure. After considerable water had been removed, the base began to decompose, and the temperature rose gradually to 160°. The tertiary amines were collected in 6N hydrochloric acid cooled to −10°, and the olefin in a trap at −78°. The acid solution on distillation yielded appreciable amounts of methyl alcohol, identified as the 3,5-dinitrobenzoate. The remaining salts were treated with strong caustic, and the free bases fractionally distilled. The trimethylamine, 7 g., was thus removed and identified as the picrate. The less volatile amine, 17 g., was dried over sodium hydroxide, and identified as pinacolyldimethylamine (52% yield) through the picrate. Also obtained was 8 g. of the hydrocarbon, 3,3-dimethyl-1-butene.

THERMAL DECOMPOSITION OF QUATERNARY AMMONIUM SALTS. Thermal decomposition of quaternary ammonium salts also leads to the formation of tertiary amines, as follows:

$$R_4NX \rightarrow R_3N + RX$$

Collie and Schryver[CO3] pyrolyzed ethyltrimethylammonium chloride and obtained ethyldimethylamine and methyl chloride in agreement with Lossen's[LO2] observation; in addition they also obtained a small amount of trimethylamine and ethyl chloride:

$$(CH_3)_3(C_2H_5)NCl \xrightarrow{\text{heat}} (CH_3)_2NC_2H_5 + CH_3Cl + (CH_3)_3N + C_2H_5Cl$$
(small amount)

In the decomposition of simple mixed aliphatic quaternary salts the alkyl group that forms the most volatile halide seems to be expelled most readily. Hünig and Baron[HU1] found that decomposition of alkyltrimethylammonium iodides by heating in 10–15 molar excess of ethanolamine at 150° provides a good means for preparing alkyldimethylamines in excellent yields in many cases. The reaction proceeds according to the following equations:

$$[(CH_3)_3\overset{+}{N}R]I^- + HOCH_2CH_2NH_2 \nearrow (CH_3)_2NR + HOCH_2CH_2NH(CH_3) + HI$$
$$\searrow (CH_3)_3N + HOCH_2CH_2NHR + HI$$

One exception was noticed. When R— is 2-butenyl, a gas, butadiene, is eliminated. They reported also that the chloride, bromide, and iodide worked equally well in the one case in which comparison was made. This decomposition is essentially quantitative and the relative yields of amines are listed in Table 20.

TABLE 20. RELATIVE YIELDS OF AMINES IN THE CLEAVAGE OF $[(CH_3)_3N—R]^+I^-$ IN ETHANOLAMINE AT 154°[HU1]

R =	$(CH_3)_3N$ (%)	$(CH_3)_2N—R$ (%)
—$CH_2CH_2CH{=}CH_2$	99	1
—$CH_2CH{=}CHCH_3$	68	32
—$CH_2CH{=}CH_2$	66	34
—$CH(CH_3)_2$	12	88
—CH_2CH_3	5	95
—$CH_2CH_2CH_3$	5	95
—$CH_2CH_2CH_2CH_3$	2	98
—$CH_2CH(CH_3)_2$	1	99

Hünig and Baron found that, with dimethyldiethylammonium iodide in ethanolamine, there were obtained a 9.5% yield of ethyldimethylamine and a 90% yield of methyldiethylamine. These proportions are counter to those expected from pyrolysis of the dry salt.

In 1913 Clarke[CL2] reported that thermal decomposition of quaternary ammonium sulfides gave very good yields of tertiary amines:

$$[RN(CH_3)_3]_2^+ S^= \rightarrow RN(CH_3)_2 + (CH_3)_2S$$

This method was used to prepare a series of N,N,N',N'-tetramethyldi-amines,[CL2] but has been used relatively little since then.

17. REDUCTIVE FISSION OF QUATERNARY AMMONIUM COMPOUNDS. EMDE DEGRADATION

$$\begin{bmatrix} R' \\ | \\ R''\!-\!N\!-\!R \\ | \\ R'' \end{bmatrix}^+ X^- \xrightarrow{(H)} RH + R'R''R''N + HX$$

A reaction that resembles the Hofmann degradation (see section 16 preceding) was discovered by Emde,[EM1,EM3,EM5,] who found that quaternary ammonium halides can be reductively cleaved by sodium amalgam in water to yield a tertiary amine and a hydrocarbon (saturated at the point of cleavage). For example, (3-phenyl-2-propenyl)trimethylammonium chloride yielded trimethylamine and 1-phenyl-1-propene.[EM3] The corresponding triethyl-ammonium halide yielded the same hydrocarbon along with triethylamine as follows:

$$[C_6H_5CH\!=\!CH\!-\!CH_2N(C_2H_5)_3]^+Cl^- \xrightarrow[H_2O]{Na-Hg}$$
$$(C_2H_5)_3N + C_6H_5CH\!=\!CH\!-\!CH_3 + HCl$$

The method has been restricted chiefly to degradative structural studies of nitrogen bases such as alkaloids, but is overshadowed by the similar but much more frequently used Hofmann degradation ($q.v.$). A variant on the Emde reductive cleavage using lithium aluminum hydride has been suggested as a suitable preparative procedure[CO24] as discussed later in this section.

Although the process as described by Emde was not found applicable to quaternary ammonium salts containing four saturated alkyl groups, such compounds have been reductively cleaved by variants on the original reaction. For example, sodium or potassium in liquid ammonia converts tetraethyl-ammonium halides into triethylamine, ethane, and ethylene.[GR14,HA29,JO4] The ethylene arises from the Hofmann-type elimination brought about by some amide ion formed in the reaction of sodium with ammonia:

$$(C_2H_5)_4NX \xrightarrow[\text{liq. NH}_3]{Na} (C_2H_5)_3N + C_2H_6 + C_2H_4 + NaX$$

Grovenstein *et al.*,[GR14] in studying the mechanism of the reaction, treated various tetraalkylammonium halides with sodium in liquid ammonia and observed the following order of decreasing ease of alkyl cleavage:

$$t\text{-Bu} \gg \text{Me} > sec\text{-Bu} > \text{i-Pr} > n\text{-Pr} > (n\text{-Bu} \approx \text{Et})$$

Thus, whereas *t*-butyltrimethylammonium iodide gave mainly trimethylamine as the amine product, it was found that butyltrimethylammonium iodide gave butyldimethylamine almost exclusively. In both cases relatively small amounts of olefin were formed by the competing Hofmann-type elimination. However, tetraethyl-, tetrapropyl-, and tetrabutyl-ammonium bromides gave significant quantities (up to about 50%) of olefin.

Reactions of sodium in dioxane[GR13] with tetraalkylammonium salts also give rise to reductive cleavage along with elimination. The Hofmann-type elimination is postulated as arising from a small amount of sodium alkoxide formed in the reaction of sodium with dioxane.

Kenner and Murray[KE3] found that a methyl group from methiodides can be reductively cleaved by lithium aluminum hydride to yield tertiary amines. Cope *et al.*[CO20,CO24] suggested this method as a general useful alternative to the Eschweiler-Clarke method (see section 6) for preparing *N,N*-dimethyl tertiary amines from primary amines. The degradation can be illustrated by the following sequence:

$$RNH_2 \xrightarrow{CH_3I} RN(CH_3)_3I \xrightarrow{LiAlH_4} RN(CH_3)_2 + CH_4 + RH + (CH_3)_3N$$

The relative ease of cleavage of methyl groups makes it possible to obtain high yields (up to 96%) of alkyldimethylamines.

Electrolytic reductive cleavage also has been observed with quaternary ammonium compounds. Thus, Emmert[EM12] prepared several trialkylamines in yields up to 70% by the electrochemical reduction of an aqueous solution of aryltrialkylammonium iodide at a lead cathode. His preparation of methylethylpropylamine can be represented as follows:

$$\begin{bmatrix} n\text{-}C_3H_7 \\ | \\ CH_3\text{—}N\text{—}C_2H_5 \\ | \\ C_6H_5 \end{bmatrix}^+ I^- \xrightarrow[\text{(H)}]{\text{electrolysis}} \underset{\text{(47.5\% yield)}}{\overset{n\text{-}C_3H_7}{\underset{|}{CH_3\text{—}N\text{—}C_2H_5}}} + C_6H_6 + HI$$

As in the Emde degradation, aqueous solutions of tetraalkylammonium salts containing only saturated alkyl groups do not undergo reductive fission.

PREPARATION OF *N,N*-DIMETHYL-2-*t*-BUTYL-3,3-DIMETHYLBUTYLAMINE (LITHIUM ALUMINUM HYDRIDE CLEAVAGE).[CO24] In a 1-liter, 3-necked flask fitted with a reflux condenser and a magnetic stirrer, under an atmosphere of nitrogen, a suspension of 25.1 g of (2-*t*-butyl-3,3-dimethylbutyl)trimethylammonium iodide in 450 ml. of tetrahydrofuran was stirred under reflux with 17.4 g. of lithium aluminum hydride for 96 hours. After cooling in an ice bath, 35.6 ml. of 15% sodium hydroxide solution was slowly added drop-wise with stirring. Following this, 71.5 ml. of 30% potassium hydroxide solution was added and the mixture was steam distilled until the distillate samples were neutral (total distillate volume of about 2.75 liters). The distillate was acidified with 20 ml. of concentrated hydrochloric acid and concentrated to dryness under reduced pressure. The residue was dissolved in 75 ml. of water, made basic by the cautious addition of 80 ml. of a cold 50% sodium hydroxide solution, and the product was extracted with four 50-ml. portions of ether and one 50-ml. portion of pentane. The combined extracts were dried over potassium hydroxide pellets. The solvent was removed and the residue distilled through a semimicro column, giving 12.5 g. (88%) of N,N-dimethyl-2-t-butyl-3,3-dimethylbutylamine, b.p. 98–99° (27 mm.).

18. MISCELLANEOUS PREPARATIONS INVOLVING CARBON-NITROGEN BOND FORMATION

a. *Reaction of Metallodialkylamides with Alkyl Bromides*

For the preparation of aliphatic tertiary amines the alkylation of metal derivatives of secondary amines by alkyl halides offers no obvious advantage over the direct alkylation of dialkylamines by the Hofmann method (see section 16). Horning and Bergstrom [HO22] prepared butyldiethylamine from lithium diethylamide and butyl bromide:

$$(C_2H_5)_2NLi + n\text{-}C_4H_9Br \rightarrow n\text{-}C_4H_9N(C_2H_5)_2$$
$$\text{(53%)[HO22]}$$

Surprisingly, in contrast to this case, they found that ethyl iodide gives ethylene and tar, while methyl iodide gives only tar in reactions with lithium dialkylamides.

Puterbaugh and Hauser[PU2] found lithium dialkylamides in ether as solvent gave higher yields of tertiary amine than did the corresponding sodio derivatives in benzene. Yields of tertiary amine were improved substantially when an excess of the lithium dialkylamide was used. For example, in the reaction of lithium diethylamide with octyl bromide in ether a 47% yield of octyl-diethylamine was obtained at a 1:1 molar ratio of reactants, and an 89% yield at 2:1 molar ratio.

b. *Reaction of 1,1-Diethoxyethene with Dialkylamines*

McElvain and Tate[MC6] found that ketene diethylacetal reacts with diethyl-amine or with dibutylamine to produce 1,1-bis(dialkylamino)ethylenes, as in the following example:

$$(C_2H_5)_2NH + CH_2{=}C(OC_2H_5)_2 \rightarrow [(C_2H_5)_2N]_2C{=}CH_2$$
$$\text{(41%)}$$

This reaction is restricted to the preparation of aliphatic tertiary diamines of the 1,1-bis-dialkylamino-1-alkene type.

c. *Reaction of Ethoxyacetylene with Dialkylamines*

In attempting to conduct a Mannich reaction under anhydrous conditions by the interaction of diethylamine, formaldehyde, and ethoxyacetylene, Arens et al.[AR2,AR3] observed instead that the acetylene compound reacted directly with the diethylamine as follows:

$$(C_2H_5)_2NH + C_2H_5OC{\equiv}CH \rightarrow H_2C{=}C{\overset{N(C_2H_5)_2}{\underset{N(C_2H_5)_2}{}}}$$

Thus ethoxyacetylene gives the same product when treated with diethylamine as does the previously discussed ketene diethylacetal.

d. *Reaction of Grignard Reagents with Tetraalkyl Methylene Immonium Salts*

Reiber and Stewart[RE3] obtained *t*-butyldiethylamine from the reaction of isopropylidenediethylimmonium iodide with methylmagnesium iodide as follows:

$$[(CH_3)_2C{=}N(C_2H_5)_2]^+I^- + CH_3MgI \rightarrow (CH_3)_3CN(C_2H_5)_2$$
$$\text{(11\%)}$$

The reaction is of limited interest but does provide a means of placing a tertiary alkyl substituent on a nitrogen atom.

e. *Catalytic Hydrogenation of Compounds with Carbon-Nitrogen Unsaturation*

Under conditions of catalytic hydrogenation certain compounds (amine precursors) that contain a carbon-to-nitrogen double or triple bond yield a mixture of primary, secondary, and tertiary amines. Among these the most frequently used have been the alkyl cyanides.[SA1,SA5,SK3] The overall reaction can be represented as follows:

$$RCN + H_2 \rightarrow RCH_2NH_2 + (RCH_2)_2NH + (RCH_2)_3N$$

The yields of tertiary amines are usually low, although occasionally yields as high as 85% have been reported,[SK3] as in the preparation of triethylamine from the platinum-catalyzed hydrogenation of acetonitrile. The reaction has found most frequent use in primary amine preparation, especially in the presence of added ammonia, which suppresses secondary and tertiary amine formation.[SC22]

Similarly, catalytic hydrogenation of oximes,[GU4,SK1] and azines[MA13] have been found to give amine mixtures.

The formation of secondary and tertiary amines in these reactions may involve addition of the initially formed primary amine or, even, the later secondary amine, to an intermediately formed imine. These reactions are similar to some of those postulated in section 7, "Reductive *N*-Alkylation with Carbonyl Compounds and Hydrogen." Alternatively, the products may arise from disproportionation or transalkylation reactions.

A reaction that involves a different type of carbon-nitrogen unsaturation—namely, one in which an alkyl group is attached to an unsaturated nitrogen—has been reported to give very small quantities of a tertiary amine. By hydrogenating ethylisocyanate in the presence of nickel, Sabatier and Mailhe[SA2] obtained mainly methylethylamine along with small quantities of ammonia and of mono-, di-, and tri-ethylamines.

Utilization of other amine precursors in tertiary amine syntheses have been discussed under "Reductive *N*-Alkylation with Carbonyl Compounds and Hydrogen" (section 7) and "*N*-Alkylation with Alcohols, Ethers, and Carboxylic Acid Esters" (section 2).

f. Catalytic Hydrogenation of Alkyl Nitrites

In the amine mixture, predominantly secondary amine, obtained from the catalytic hydrogenation of alkyl nitrites,[GA7,SA1] very small yields of the tertiary product are found. The overall reaction might be schematically represented as follows:

$$RONO + H_2 \rightarrow RNH_2 + R_2NH + R_3N$$

It appears that initial reduction of the nitrite ester produces ammonia, which in turn is alkylated to the amines either by more alkyl nitrite and/or by the alcohol formed in the hydrogenation.

g. Reactions Involving Alkylchloramines

In an attempt to prepare tetramethylhydrazine, Klages *et al.*[KL2] treated dimethylchloramine with the magnesium salt of dimethylamine. Instead of obtaining the desired hydrazine, these workers isolated methylamine, dimethylamine, and *N,N,N',N'*-tetramethylmethylenediamine. These results were explained on the assumption that the chloramine lost the elements of hydrogen chloride, under the strongly basic reaction conditions, to give methylenemethylimine, a formaldehyde-derived Schiff base. This latter compound could add and condense dimethylamine in the same way as does formaldehyde, itself.[DZ1,HE15,IS1] The reaction scheme is descriptively as follows:

$$(CH_3)_2NCl + [(CH_3)_2N]_2Mg \rightarrow CH_3N{=}CH_2 + (CH_3)_2NH + MgCl_2$$

$$CH_3N{=}CH_2 + (CH_3)_2NH \rightarrow CH_3NH_2 + (CH_3)_2N{-}CH_2{-}N(CH_3)_2$$

Surprisingly, when Klages *et al.*[KL2] heated dimethylchloramine with copper-bronze in an alternative effort to prepare the desired tetramethyl-hydrazine by a coupling reaction, they again obtained only methylamine, dimethylamine, and tetramethylmethylenediamine. This was attributed to the formation, again, of the same reactive intermediate as above, the methyl-enemethylimine, arising from the disproportionation of dimethylamino free radicals generated from the chloramine as follows:

$$(CH_3)_2NCl + Cu \rightarrow (CH_3)_2N\cdot + CuCl$$

$$2(CH_3)_2N\cdot \rightarrow (CH_3)_2NH + CH_3N{=}CH_2$$

The remaining addition and condensation proceeded as before.

Although Klages et al.[KL2] do not give complete proof for their identification of tetramethylmethylenediamine, and they have no direct experimental support for the proposed intermediate, their arguments are reasonable, based on analogies in the literature. The synthesis of their desired product, tetramethyl-hydrazine, was eventually accomplished by Class, Aston, and Oakwood,[CL6] twelve years later, in 1953.

Other studies with chloramines have been concerned with attempts to alkylate the chlorine positions by the use of organometallic compounds. Coleman[CO4] found that the reaction of Grignard reagents with either alkyl-dichloramines or dialkylchloramines produced aliphatic tertiary amines in low yields (less than 10%). The reactions are exemplified as follows:

$$C_2H_5NCl_2 + n\text{-}C_4H_9MgCl \rightarrow C_2H_5N(n\text{-}C_4H_9)_2$$
$$\underset{(9\%)^{CO4}}{}$$

$$(n\text{-}C_4H_9)_2NCl + n\text{-}C_4H_9MgCl \rightarrow (n\text{-}C_4H_9)_3N$$
$$\underset{(4\%)^{CO4}}{}$$

By treating diisopropylchloramine with isopropylpotassium, Kuffner and Seifried,[KU2] in 1952, claimed to have performed the first substantiated syn-thesis of triisopropylamine, according to the equation:

$$(i\text{-}C_3H_7)_2NCl + (CH_3)_2CHK \rightarrow (i\text{-}C_3H_7)_3N$$
$$\underset{(3\%)^{KU2}}{}$$

Tetraisopropylhydrazine was also isolated therefrom in 4.5% yield.

The low yields in these chloramine reactions preclude their finding accept-ance as general practical synthetic routes for tertiary amines. They may, however, achieve limited application in the preparation of tertiary and secondary amines with high steric requirements, as judged by their use for obtaining triisopropylamine[KU2] and di-t-butylamine.[KL2] In certain cases of sterically hindered trialkylamines, however, the reaction of N,N-dialkylamides with Grignard reagents (see section 11), or the alkylation of di-t-alkylamines (prepared by the method of Hennion and Hanzel,[HE8]) are efficient and pre-ferred synthetic routes.

The role of the preliminary elimination reaction postulated by Klages et al.[KL2] (see above) in bringing about low yields and products of unexpected structure has not been properly appreciated. (It remains possible that Kuffner and Seifried's reputed triisopropylamine[KU2] may have another structure, such as 2-isopropylamino-2,3-dimethylbutane, arising from addition of isopropylpotassium to the intermediate, acetoneisopropylimine.)

h. Methylation with Diazomethane

Müller et al.[MU2a] methylated primary and secondary amines with diazomethane in the presence of boron trifluoride-etherate. It is postulated that a BF_3-amine complex precedes the methylation step.

i. Alkaline Hydrolysis of Alkylureas and Alkylisocyanates

Berthold[BE11] obtained mixtures of primary, secondary, and tertiary crotylamines (in yields of 53, 26, and 13%, respectively) upon alkaline hydrolysis of the crotylurea prepared by the reaction of crotyl bromide with urea. He postulated that higher alkylated products, such as 1,1-dicrotylurea and the quaternary salt, $[(C_4H_7)_3NCONH_2]^+Br^-$, were precursors for the secondary and tertiary amine, respectively. The authors of the present monograph maintain reservations with respect to this conclusion since the aforementioned higher alkylated ureas would have to constitute a major impurity (at least 39%); yet formation of such products from direct alkylation of urea has not been reported elsewhere in the literature. Nevertheless, the reaction may be represented as follows:

$$CH_3CH{=}CHCH_2Br + H_2NCONH_2 \longrightarrow \overset{NaOH}{\underset{H_2O}{\longrightarrow}}$$

$$CH_3CH{=}CHCH_2NH_2 + (CH_3CH{=}CHCH_2)_2NH$$
$$\text{(53\%)} \qquad\qquad \text{(26\%)}$$
$$+ (CH_3CH{=}CHCH_2)_3N$$
$$\text{(13\%)}$$

In certain rare instances, the analogous situation has been reported to occur in cases involving alkylation of potassium cyanate by alkyl halides[LI1] or by alkylsulfuric acid salts.[SI2,WU1] Again, here, subsequent alkaline hydrolysis yielded a mixture of the three alkylamines as represented by the following general scheme:

$$RX + KOCN \longrightarrow \overset{OH^-}{\longrightarrow} RNH_2 + R_2NH + R_3N$$

Since the alkylation of cyanates gives only alkylisocyanates,[TA15] which obviously cannot exist in higher alkylated forms, the course of the above reaction to give the indicated mixture of amines remains obscure. It must be emphasized that in the hydrolysis of alkylisocyanates usually only the primary amine has been isolated, and the cited cases in which secondary and tertiary amines have been reported are very few in number.

j. Reaction of α-Haloaldehydes with Dialkylamines

α-Haloaldehydes containing an α-hydrogen react with dialkylamines to produce 1,2-bis(dialkylamino)-1-alkenes.[DO5,MA4] For example, Doss and Bost[DO5] obtained 1,2-bis(dimethylamino)ethene from dimethylamine and chloroacetaldehyde:

$$(CH_3)_2NH + ClCH_2CHO \rightarrow (CH_3)_2NCH{=}CHN(CH_3)_2$$

This reaction resembles that of addition of secondary amines to α,β-unsaturated aldehydes (see section 9) which also produces unsaturated diamines, but of the 1,3-variety:

$$R_2NC{=}C{-}C{-}NR_2$$

k. Pyrolysis of Alkylated Phosphoramidates and Phosphonamidates

Cadogan[CA1] heated ethyl-N,N,P-triethylphosphonamidate at the boiling point for about 18 hours and observed the formation of triethylamine in 67% yield. Baumgarten and Setterquist[BA39] used a mono-N-alkyl compound as a method for preparing olefins by pyrolysis. They obtained tertiary amine along with the olefin. For example dimethyl-N-hexylphosphoramidate gave 1-hexene and hexyldimethylamine according to the following equation:

$$\underset{\text{(46\%)}}{(CH_3O)_2\overset{\overset{O}{\uparrow}}{P}NH{-}n\text{-}C_6H_{13} \rightarrow n\text{-}C_4H_9CH{=}CH_2} + \underset{\text{(40\%)}}{n\text{-}C_6H_{13}N(CH_3)_2}$$

The reaction apparently involves N-alkylation by the ester. The preparation of tertiary amines by N-alkylation with carboxylic acid esters has been discussed under "N-Alkylation with Alcohols, Ethers, and Carboxylic Acid Esters" (section 2).

l. Disproportionation or Transalkylation of Amines

Disproportion reactions of the type:

$$R_nNH_{3-n} \rightarrow NH_3 + RNH_2 + R_2NH + R_3N$$

(where $n = 1$ or 2), have been commonly found. The work of Kozlov and Panova[KO22] with butylamines in the presence of ammonia has been discussed, along with other related citations, in the section entitled "N-Alkylation with Alcohols, Ethers, and Carboxylic Acid Esters" (section 2).

Pure disproportionation in the absence of any added reactants has been described by Smeykal.[SM3] He found that heating a dialkylamine, at superatmospheric pressures as high as 200 atmospheres at temperatures of about 370° in the presence of a dehydration catalyst, such as aluminum oxide, silica gel, clay, or oxides of thorium or tungsten, gave extensive molecular reshuffling, with tertiary amine predominant among the products. When the starting material was dimethylamine, from the product mixture were isolated: trimethylamine (60–65%), dimethylamine (18–30%), methylamine (about 8%), and ammonia (4–10%), depending on the experimental conditions.

m. *Transamination**

$$-\underset{|}{\overset{|}{C}}-N\overset{R}{\underset{R'}{\diagup}} + H-N\overset{R''}{\underset{R'''}{\diagup}} \rightleftharpoons -\underset{|}{\overset{|}{C}}-N\overset{R''}{\underset{R'''}{\diagup}} + H-N\overset{R}{\underset{R'}{\diagup}}$$

Finch et al.[F17] found that ammonia, primary amines, or secondary amines exchange with the amino group of variously N-substituted 1,3-propenedi-amines. Although no purely acylic aliphatic tertiary diamines were prepared by this reaction, such compounds undoubtedly can be prepared as judged by the preparation of closely related compounds. For example, Finch et al. exchanged the isopropylamino group by the piperidino group as follows:

$$\langle\text{NH} + \overset{i\text{-}C_3H_7}{\underset{H}{N}}-CH_2-CH=CH-\overset{i\text{-}C_3H_7}{\underset{H}{N}} \longrightarrow$$

$$\langle N-CH_2-CH=CH-N\rangle + i\text{-}C_3H_7NH_2$$

Since this reaction exists as series of equilibria, one or both isopropylamino groups can be replaced by distilling off the isopropylamine, the most volatile component of the mixture, as it forms. The exchange can also be forced by the use of a large excess of the monoamine. These equilibria might be represented as follows:

$$\overset{R}{\underset{R'}{\diagdown}}N-(C_3H_4)-N\overset{R}{\underset{R'}{\diagup}} + \overset{R''}{\underset{R'''}{\diagdown}}N-H \rightleftharpoons \overset{R}{\underset{R'}{\diagdown}}N-(C_3H_4)-N\overset{R''}{\underset{R'''}{\diagup}} + \overset{R}{\underset{R'}{\diagdown}}N-H$$

$$\overset{R}{\underset{R'}{\diagdown}}N-(C_3H_4)-N\overset{R''}{\underset{R'''}{\diagup}} + \overset{R''}{\underset{R'''}{\diagdown}}N-H \rightleftharpoons \overset{R''}{\underset{R'''}{\diagdown}}N-(C_3H_4)-N\overset{R''}{\underset{R'''}{\diagup}} + \overset{R}{\underset{R'}{\diagdown}}N-H$$

Since the position of the double bond was not established in the mixed diamine, the $-CH_2CH=CH-$ group is represented by $-(C_3H_4)-$.

Fegley, Bortnick et al.[FE4,FE6] used this type of exchange, but with acid catalysis, in the reaction of several secondary amines with 1,4-bis(dimethyl-amino)-1,3-butadiene. They used the descriptive term "transamination" for

---

* This term was used by Fegley, Bortnick et al.[FE4,FE6] to describe the exchange of one amino group by another. This is a broader application than the usual definition, which is of biological origin[BE8,FI6]: "using nitrogen of one amino acid for synthesizing another amino acid *in vivo*,"[BE8] or "the reversible transference of amino groups by enzymes. . . into ammodicarboxylic acids and ketoacids."[GR5]

this process. Evidently, with 1,4-bis(dimethylamino)-1,3-butadiene, only secondary amines can be used. The nitrogen of a primary amine exchanges with both dimethylamino groups to give N-substituted pyrroles.[FE3]

Transamination reactions seem to require specific unsaturated structures for their success. Only the aforementioned two types (both unsaturated diamines) have been reported. Fegley, Bortnick *et al.* [FE4] have advanced a mechanism for this reaction which suggests that exchange may occur in other molecular structures, e.g., unsaturated monoamines.

Experimental details for a transamination follow:

PREPARATION OF *trans,trans*-1,4-BIS(DIBUTYLAMINO)-1,3-BUTADIENE.[FE4] A mixture of 35 g. (0.25 mole) of 1,4-bis(dimethylamino)-1,3-butadiene (apparently the *cis,trans*-isomer was used), 75 g. (0.58 mole) of dibutylamine, 10 drops of acetic acid, and 5 drops of concentrated hydrochloric acid was stirred at $54 \pm 5°$ at 65 ± 5 mm. pressure for 7.5 hours. Treatment with 1 g. of potassium carbonate and distillation under reduced pressure gave 37.5 g. (49% yield) of *trans,trans*-1,4-bis(dibutylamino)-1,3-butadiene boiling at 145–157° at 0.03 to 0.04 mm.

19. MISCELLANEOUS PREPARATIONS FROM OTHER TERTIARY AMINES

$$\diagdown N{-}R \rightarrow \diagdown N{-}R'$$

Generally, methods of preparation of tertiary amines involve the formation of new carbon-to-nitrogen bonds. There are some notable exceptions to this in such reactions as dialkylamide reduction, reaction of Grignard reagents with various N,N-dialkylamides, and the Hofmann degradation. In many other cases one tertiary amine has been converted to another by some simple reaction on the organic substituents already on the nitrogen. A brief discussion of some of these transformations is presented here to show types of structure that lend themselves to modification.

a. *Reduction, Hydrogenation, Hydrogenolysis*

Alkynylamines can be converted to *cis*-alkenylamines by catalytic hydrogenation or to the *trans*-isomers by reduction with sodium in liquid ammonia.[BI4,CA7,OL5,OL6]

$$(CH_3)_2NCH_2C{\equiv}CCH_3 \xrightarrow[Pd]{H} (CH_3)_2NCH_2CH{=}CHCH_3$$
$$(cis, 74\%)^{OL6}$$

$$(CH_3)_2NCH_2C{\equiv}CCH_3 \xrightarrow[\text{liq. } NH_3]{Na} (trans, 60\%)^{OL6}$$

By catalytic hydrogenation an alkynylamine also can be converted to the corresponding alkylamine without isolation of the intermediate alkenylamine.[AI1,BI4,KR11,RO14,TE3]

$$(C_2H_5)_2NCH_2C{\equiv}CCH_2CH_2N(C_2H_5)_2 \xrightarrow[Ni]{H} (C_2H_5)_2N(CH_2)_5N(C_2H_5)_2$$
$$(63\% \text{ yield})^{BI4}$$

The yield of alkylamines by catalytic hydrogenation of alkynyl- or alkenyl-amines is, surprisingly enough, lowered significantly in many cases by hydrogenolysis. For example, Young et al.[YO5] observed the formation of a considerable amount of volatile amines, boiling below 80°, in the platinum-catalyzed hydrogenation of diethylamino-1-butene:

$$(C_2H_5)_2NCH_2CH_2CH{=}CH_2 \xrightarrow[Pt]{H} (C_2H_5)_2N{-}n{-}C_4H_9$$
$$(47\%)^{YO5}$$

Ainsworth and Easton[AI1] obtained a yield of only 10% in the conversion of the acetylenic amine, methylisopropyl-(1,1-dimethyl-2-propynyl)amine to the corresponding saturated amine. They used Raney nickel as the catalyst and ethanol as the solvent.

Kruse and Kleinschmidt[KR11] observed that much better yields of saturated tertiary amines were obtained in the platinum-catalyzed hydrogenation of 4-dialkylamino-4-methyl-2-pentynes conducted in glacial acetic acid rather than in ethanol. They postulated that diethylamine formed in hydrogenolysis inhibits reduction of the intermediate alkenylamine, and that the role of acetic acid is to neutralize the diethylamine. (See also Hennion and Hanzel,[HE8] footnote 7.)

While the reduction of acetylenic amines is frequently used as a preparative procedure for the corresponding cis- or trans-olefinic compounds, the ethyl-enic amines are rarely used for synthetic purposes. Conversion of alkenyl- to alkyl-amines is generally conducted for purposes of identification.

Gol'dfarb and Ibragimova[GO1] treated some thiophene derivatives of tertiary amines with hydrogen in the presence of Raney nickel to obtain trialkylamines in yields of 46 to 66%:

$$(C_2H_5)_2NCH_2{-}\!\!\!\overset{\displaystyle\fbox{}}{\underset{S}{}}\!\!\!{-}CH_3 \xrightarrow{\ H\ }_{Ni} (C_2H_5)_2N{-}n{-}C_6H_{13}$$
$$(46\%)^{GO1}$$

In this case hydrogenolysis (desulfurization) and hydrogenation both occurred.

McElvain and Tate[MC6] hydrogenated 1,1-bis(diethylamino)ethylene in the presence of Raney nickel and observed extensive hydrogenolysis. No satur-ated diamine was obtained. The reaction might be represented as follows:

$$[(C_2H_5)_2N]_2C{=}CH_2 \xrightarrow[Ni]{H} (C_2H_5)_2NH + (C_2H_5)_3N$$
$$\text{(main product)}$$

Another type of reduction that has been encountered is that of an alcohol function by red phosphorus and hydriodic acid:

$$\overset{\displaystyle C_2H_5}{\underset{\displaystyle OH}{(CH_3)_2NCH_2{-}\overset{|}{\underset{|}{C}}{-}CH_2N(CH_3)_2}} \xrightarrow[\text{red P}]{HI} \overset{\displaystyle C_2H_5}{\underset{\displaystyle H}{(CH_3)_2NCH_2{-}\overset{|}{\underset{|}{C}}{-}CH_2N(CH_3)_2}}$$
$$\text{(almost quantitative yield)}^{MA26}$$

b.   *Isomerization*[BA14,EN1,FE2,FE5,MC8,RE7]

Alkynylamines have been isomerized to alkadienylamines and *vice versa*. Also, alkynylamines have been converted to isomers which differ only in the position of the triple bond. Sodium is the usual catalyst, but lithium, potassium, sodium alkyls, sodium alkoxides, chromium oxide, etc. also can be used. The following equations illustrate some of these transformations:

(1) $Me_2NCH_2C\equiv CCH_3 \xrightarrow{Na} Me_2NCH_2CH_2C\equiv CH$
$$\text{(50\%)BA14}$$

(2) $Me_2NCH_2CH_2-C\equiv CH \xrightarrow[\text{EtOH}]{\text{KOH}} Me_2NCH_2C\equiv C-CH_3$
$$\text{(84\%)BA14}$$

(3) $Me_2NCH_2CH=C=CH_2 \xrightarrow{\text{NaOMe}} Me_2NCH_2C\equiv CCH_3$
$$\text{(75\%)EN1}$$

(4) $Me_2NCH_2C\equiv CCH_2NMe_2 \xrightarrow{Na} Me_2NCH=CH-CH=CHNMe_2$
$$\textit{(cis, trans 85\%)}\text{FE2}$$

In reaction (4), isomerization over a chromium oxide catalyst gives what is probably the *trans,trans*-isomer instead of the *cis,trans* one obtained with sodium.[FE2,MC8]

c.   *Grignard and Other Coupling Reactions*[KH3,KH5]

The reaction of Grignard reagents with various *N,N*-dialkyl compounds such as *N,N*-dialkylamides, *N,N*-dialkylaminonitriles, etc. are discussed separately as methods of preparation of tertiary amines.

Grignard reagents and, possibly, other reactive organometallic compounds, can also be made to couple with halo-substituted tertiary amines to give larger amines, as shown by the following examples:

$(C_2H_5)_2NCH_2CH_2Cl + CH_2=CHCH_2MgCl \rightarrow$

$$(C_2H_5)_2NCH_2CH_2CH_2CH=CH_2$$
$$\text{(69\%)KH5}$$

$(ClCH_2CH_2)_3N + CH_2=CHCH_2MgCl \rightarrow$

$$(CH_2=CHCH_2CH_2CH_2)_3N$$
$$\text{(90\%)KH3}$$

Coupling of sodium acetylides with dialkylaminoalkyl halides is discussed under "Syntheses of Acetylenic Tertiary Amines" (section 15).

d.   *Elimination by Dehydrohalogenation, Dehydration, etc.*

Dehydrohalogenation[BU17,CA7,KO8,KO10,PA5] and, to a much smaller extent, dehydration,[CA6,TE3] have been used to prepare olefinic or acetylenic tertiary amines. As expected, the formation of mixtures of isomeric compounds, when it occurs, is a limitation to the utility of this technique. The following are examples of these reactions:

$$(C_2H_5)_2NCH_2C(Br)\!\!=\!\!CH_2 \xrightarrow[\text{liq. NH}_3]{\text{NaNH}_3} (C_2H_5)_2NCH_2C\!\!\equiv\!\!CH$$
$$(82.5\%)\text{PA5}$$

$$\overset{\displaystyle CH_3}{\underset{\displaystyle OH}{(C_2H_5)_2NCH_2CH_2\!\!-\!\!\overset{|}{\underset{|}{C}}\!\!-\!\!C\!\!\equiv\!\!C\!\!-\!\!CH\!\!=\!\!CH_2}} \xrightarrow{\text{H}_2\text{SO}_4}$$

$$\overset{\displaystyle CH_3}{(C_2H_5)_2NCH_2CH\!\!=\!\!\overset{|}{C}\!\!-\!\!C\!\!\equiv\!\!C\!\!-\!\!CH\!\!=\!\!CH_2}$$
$$(75\%)\text{TE3}$$

Pyrolysis of the Grignard complex of an amino alcohol was used by Campbell and Campbell[CA6] to give an olefinic tertiary amine:

$$\overset{\displaystyle OMgCl}{\underset{\displaystyle CH_3}{(CH_3)_2NCH_2\!\!-\!\!\overset{|}{\underset{|}{C}}\!\!-\!\!CH_3}} \rightarrow (CH_3)_2NCH\!\!=\!\!C(CH_3)_2$$
$$\text{(14\% yield as the hydrochloride)}$$

e. Coupling of Terminal Acetylenic Amines by Air Oxidation

Terminal acetylenic amines can be made to couple readily by air oxidation in the presence of copper salts to produce conjugated diynes.[KA7,KA8,RO14] The reaction is illustrated by the following examples:

$$(CH_3)_2NCH_2C\!\!\equiv\!\!CH \xrightarrow[\text{air}]{\text{Cu}_2\text{Cl}_2 \quad \text{CuCl}_2} (CH_3)_2NCH_2C\!\!\equiv\!\!C\!\!-\!\!C\!\!\equiv\!\!CCH_2N(CH_3)_2$$
$$(85\%)\text{KA8}$$

$$(C_2H_5)_2NCH_2CH\!\!=\!\!CHC\!\!\equiv\!\!CH \xrightarrow[\text{air}]{\text{CuCN}}$$

$$(C_2H_5)_2NCH_2CH\!\!=\!\!CHC\!\!\equiv\!\!C\!\!-\!\!C\!\!\equiv\!\!CCH\!\!=\!\!CHCH_2N(C_2H_5)_2$$
$$(66\%)\text{RO14}$$

f. Tertiary Diamines via Free Radical Coupling of Trialkylamines

$$R_2N\!\!-\!\!\overset{|}{\underset{|}{C}}\!\!-\!\!H \rightarrow R_2N\!\!-\!\!\overset{|}{\underset{|}{C}}\!\!-\!\!\overset{|}{\underset{|}{C}}\!\!-\!\!NR_2$$

Trialkylamines can be made to couple with the aid of such free radical initiators as γ-rays, ultraviolet light, and dialkyl peroxides. Coupling occurs at the α-carbons.

(1) γ-Rays

Swan, Timmons and Wright[SW3] obtained 2,3-bis(diethylamino)butane in 1% yield on irradiation of triethylamine with γ-rays for 300 hours (total dose 2.08×10^{23} e.v.). This small amount of diamine was made up of about equal amounts of meso and racemic isomers. They postulated that γ-radiolysis of triethylamine leads to free radicals which dimerize as shown in the following scheme:

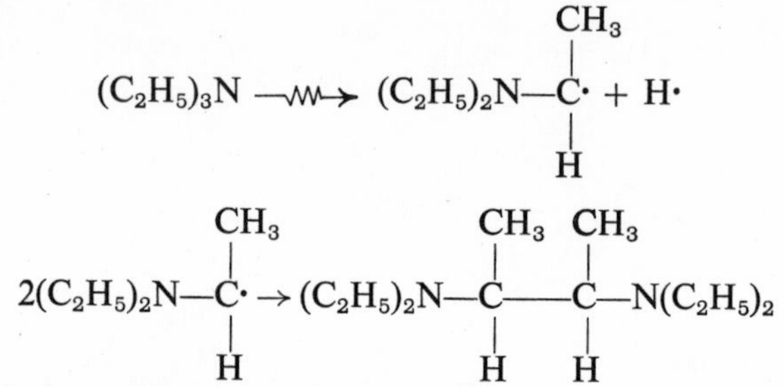

$$(C_2H_5)_3N \xrightarrow{\quad\quad} (C_2H_5)_2N\overset{\overset{\displaystyle CH_3}{|}}{\underset{\underset{\displaystyle H}{|}}{C}}\cdot + H\cdot$$

$$2(C_2H_5)_2N\overset{\overset{\displaystyle CH_3}{|}}{\underset{\underset{\displaystyle H}{|}}{C}}\cdot \rightarrow (C_2H_5)_2N\overset{\overset{\displaystyle CH_3}{|}}{\underset{\underset{\displaystyle H}{|}}{C}}\!-\!\!\overset{\overset{\displaystyle CH_3}{|}}{\underset{\underset{\displaystyle H}{|}}{C}}\!-\!N(C_2H_5)_2$$

Later, Smith and Swan[SM11] showed that with methyldiethylamine three diamines were obtained, as might be expected from the two different types of free radicals obtainable by removal of α-hydrogens:

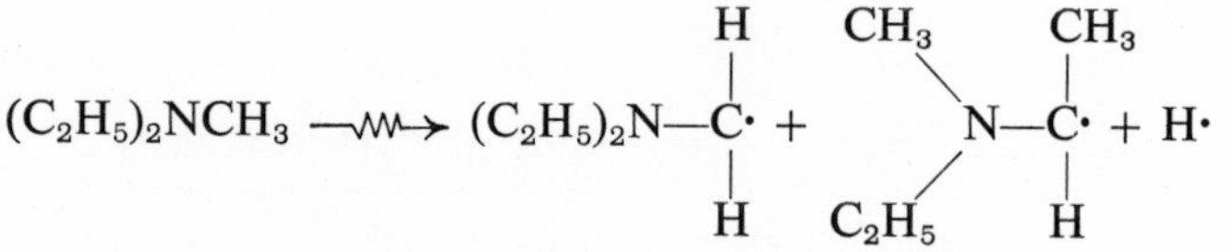

$$(C_2H_5)_2NCH_3 \xrightarrow{\quad\quad} (C_2H_5)_2N\!-\!\underset{(I)}{C}\cdot + \quad N\!-\!\underset{(II)}{C}\cdot + H\cdot$$

$$(I) \rightarrow (C_2H_5)_2NCH_2CH_2N(C_2H_5)_2$$

$$(II) \rightarrow \quad N\!-\!C\!-\!C\!-\!N$$

$$(I) + (II) \rightarrow (C_2H_5)_2N\!-\!CH_2\!-\!CH\!-\!N$$

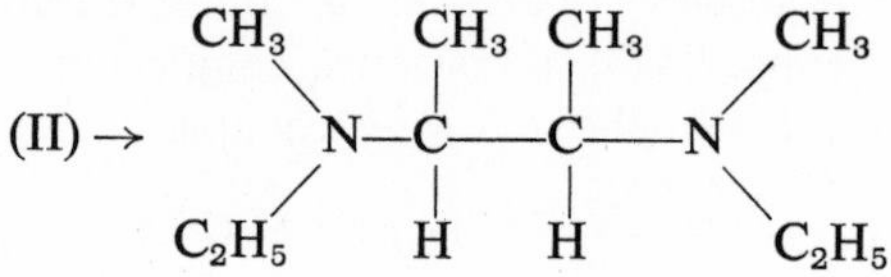

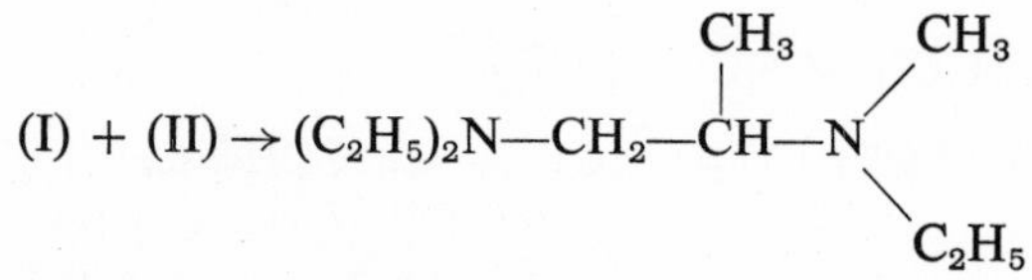

Swan and co-workers,[SM11,SW3] have shown also that in certain cases products are obtained in which some carbon-nitrogen scission of the original trialkylamine has occurred.

(2) Ultraviolet Light

Pfordte and Leuscher[PF1] irradiated triethylamine for 24 hours with unfiltered ultraviolet light from a high-pressure mercury arc and obtained a 3% yield of a mixture of *meso* and racemic 2,3-bis(diethylamino)butanes. These were the same products as were obtained by Swan *et al.*[SW3] (see above) using γ-rays instead of ultraviolet light.

(3) Alkyl Peroxides

Raley and Seubold[RA2] obtained 4,5-bis(dibutylamino)octane in 25% yield on heating tributylamine with di-*t*-butyl peroxide in the absence of solvent (the controllable reaction with alkyl peroxides came as a surprise to these workers since they knew that others[BA32] had observed explosively violent reactions upon mixing acyl peroxides with amines):

$$2(n\text{-}C_4H_9)_3N + t\text{-}C_4H_9\text{—}O\text{—}O\text{—}t\text{-}C_4H_9 \rightarrow$$

$$(n\text{-}C_4H_9)_2N\text{—}\underset{\underset{n\text{-}C_3H_7}{|}}{\overset{\overset{H}{|}}{C}}\text{———}\underset{\underset{n\text{-}C_3H_7}{|}}{\overset{\overset{H}{|}}{C}}\text{—}N(n\text{-}C_4H_9)_2 + 2\,t\text{-}C_4H_9OH$$

Although the nitrogen analysis and molecular weight determination agreed with the indicated diamine fairly well, the possibility of isomeric alternative structures was not excluded. However, indirect evidence from other reactions make the indicated diamine assignment reasonable.

g.   C-Alkylation of Olefinic Amines with Trialkylaluminum

Zakharkin and Savina[ZA4] ethylated the alkenyl group of terminal alkenyl-dialkylamines by means of triethylaluminum. A branched alkyl group is obtained from the alkenyl group in this Markownikoff-type addition. For example, from 5-diethylamino-1-pentene is obtained 1-diethylamino-4-methylhexane in 43% overall yield according the following equations:

$$(C_2H_5)_2NCH_2CH_2CH_2CH{=}CH_2 + (C_2H_5)_3Al \rightarrow$$

$$(C_2H_5)_2NCH_2CH_2CH_2\text{—}\underset{\underset{C_2H_5}{|}}{\overset{\overset{H}{|}}{C}}\text{—}CH_2Al(C_2H_5)_2$$

(I)

$$(I) + H_2O \rightarrow (C_2H_5)_2NCH_2CH_2CH_2CH(CH_3)CH_2CH_3$$

(43% overall yield)[ZA4]

DATA ON INDIVIDUAL AMINES

Monoamines, page 100
Polyamines, page 349

Prefatory Remarks

In the following sections are to be found, to the best of our efforts, a comprehensive listing of all acyclic aliphatic tertiary amines reported in the open literature up through those covered by *Chemical Abstracts* in June, 1961. They are divided into the categories, monoamines and polyamines, depending on whether the molecule contains one, or more than one, nitrogen atom, respectively. With each compound are to be found tabulations of the reported characteristic physical properties, methods of preparation (with yields, where available), and the melting points of all significant derivatives. All data are referenced to the original citations published in the literature.

THE AMINES

Each compound is identified by its graphic "stick formula," which shows only the carbon and nitrogen atoms in its molecular skeleton. This convention was adopted for its clarity and lessened potential for typographic error. Further, there is included a suitable systematic name consonant with the principles enunciated in the "Nomenclature" section of the "Introduction," although, on occasion, consistency has been sacrificed in favor of simplicity of compound comprehension. In order to facilitate even more the scanning of the list, additional identification aids also introduced are the molecular formula, as well as an abbreviated tabulation of the alkyl substituents on each nitrogen (except for the triamines and higher polyamines).

The following abbreviations were used: Me (methyl), Et (ethyl), Vin (vinyl), n-Pr (propyl), i-Pr (isopropyl), All (allyl), n-Bu (n-butyl), sec-Bu (sec-butyl), i-Bu (isobutyl), t-Bu (tert-butyl), n-Pent (n-pentyl), i-Pent (isopentyl), t-Pent (tert-pentyl), pri. act. Pent (primary active pentyl), n-Hex (n-hexyl), i-Hex (isohexyl), n-Hept (n-heptyl), i-Hept (isoheptyl), n-Oct (n-octyl), and i-Oct (isooctyl). More complicated alkyl substituents are indicated by the total number of carbons and hydrogens. In addition, for the diamines the hydrocarbon group between the nitrogens is also listed, enclosed by the symbols, (and).

A self-indexing character was obtained for this listing by assigning priority values to the various recognition and identification aids. The simple rules for the ordering of the compounds are as follows, in order of decreasing precedence or priority:

Rule 1. Number of nitrogen atoms: Monamines precede diamines, which precede higher polyamines.

Rule 2. Number of carbon atoms: The smaller the number of carbon atoms, the earlier is the compound entered.

Rule 3. Number of hydrogen atoms: The smaller the number of hydrogen atoms, the earlier is the compound entered. This assigns higher priority to unsaturation.

Rule 4. Number and size of alkyl substituents: For isomeric molecules, the maximum number of smaller alkyl substituents is favored (e.g., dimethylamino-precedes methylethylamino-, which precedes diethylamino-, etc.) This rule is particularly useful for arranging the polyamines.

Rule 5. Alkynyl-, alkadienyl-, and dialkenyl- substituents: "Concentrated" unsaturation precedes "dispersed" unsaturation (e.g., all alkynes come before allenes before 1,3-dienes before 1,4-dienes. . . . before two separate alkenyl substituents on a nitrogen).

Rule 6. Proximity of unsaturation to nitrogen atom: Precedence is given to closer proximity of the unsaturated bond in the smaller substituent to nitrogen (e.g., vinyl- before 1-propenyl- before 2-propenyl-) and to triple bond before double bond in eneynes (H_2C=CH—C≡C— before HC≡C—CH=CH—).

Rule 7. Straight chains compared to branched chains: Normal or "straight-chain" alkyl- substituents precede their branched isomers.

Rule 8. Branched-chain substituents: Precedence is given to fewer and, *then,* smaller branches (e.g., 3-propyloctyl comes before 2-methyl-3-ethyl-octyl- before 2,4,5-trimethyloctyl-).

Rule 9. Position of branch in chain: For isomers with the same type and number of branches in the alkyl-substituent, precedence is given to closer proximity of the branch point to the nitrogen atom.

Rule 10. Miscellaneous: Compounds not clearly finding an unambiguous orderly place after application of the above rules are then positioned by giving precedence to apparently simpler molecular structures. Only a very few compounds fall into this category.

THE PHYSICAL PROPERTIES

Since essentially all of the acyclic aliphatic amines are liquids at room temperature, the most frequently cited physical properties are boiling point, density, and refractive index. All such quantities reported in the literature up through the earlier mentioned cut-off date are here listed under the pertinent compound, with the attempt being made to point out the more reliable values. However, for trimethylamine and triethylamine, the sheer volume of such data, particularly of the boiling point, required actual discarding of a majority of the values in the literature in favor of only the most valuable and reliable ones.

The data listed also include values for many of the other more frequently used or consulted physical properties, such as base strength—characterized by pK_a, the negative common logarithm of the dissociation equilibrium constant for the Brønsted conjugate acid of the amine—electrical parameters (dipole moment, dielectric constant, Kerr constant, polarizability), and fluid characteristics (viscosity, surface tension, etc.). For properties of limited interest or more difficult to describe by simple numerical quantities—spectral absorptions, phase diagrams for binary and higher systems with water and other components, nuclear magnetic resonance, chromatographic behavior, and the like, citations are given to original literature references for consultation by the reader.

An examination of the data listed shows that the number of physical properties given under most of the amines is rather small (boiling point, refractive index, and/or density). This is representative of the rather limited depth of study in the general field of these amines, in which the main attention has been placed on a relative few compounds because of historical accident, ready synthesis, or commercial availability, for the most part.

A great amount of information has accumulated about trimethylamine for various reasons—its unique natural occurrence among the tertiary amines, its premier antiquity, its being first member of the series, its small size and simple geometry (attractive for structure studies), its higher reactivity, its gaseous state under normal conditions, its ready availability, etc. As a consequence of this importance, trimethylamine has been accorded a separate critical treatment in this volume in a narrative type of format more amenable to the nature of the presentation.

THE PREPARATIONS

For each amine listed are given all preparative procedures found in the literature. On occasion, the tertiary amine may have been only a by-product.

Nevertheless, the data are included not only for the sake of completeness but also because the results might have mechanistic significance. In addition, a simple or obvious change in conditions or relative concentrations of reactants might make the tertiary amine the predominant product. For a few compounds, the procedure cited, poor as it is, may be the only synthetic method ever reported. Finally, in a limited number of cases, when a derivative but no parent compound has been described, the preparation of the derivative is indicated. This serves as a guideline to available reactants and facilitates identification and characterization of the parent compound when it is synthesized.

Because of space limitations, the reported methods of preparation for each amine are indicated briefly by a statement of the main reactants used, yields (if available), and other salient features at the discretion of the authors. For detailed procedures, and for reviews of the pertinent reactions, the reader's attention is directed to the preceding section, "Discussion of Preparative Methods—Scope and Limitations."

THE DERIVATIVES

The list of described derivatives appended to each amine has at least four functions. The first is to provide representative compounds for characterizing and proving the identity of a product prepared by a researcher. The second is to provide, especially in the case of trimethylamine and other such common amines, an indication of the coordinate chemistry and the identity and isolability of unusual compounds derived therefrom. Specifically might be mentioned the complexes with boron and aluminum hydrides, halides, and alkyls which provided a substantial bulk of the trimethylamine studies between 1955 and 1962. A third purpose is to describe derivatives that may have acquired specialized commercial and/or scientific importance. In this class are many of the long-chain alkyltrimethylammonium-, tetraalkylammonium-, and aralkyl- or aryltrialkylammonium salts. Finally, some compounds are included solely for their unusual structural or esthetic attributes.

Some desirable derivatives, although reportedly synthesized, were not listed because no melting point or decomposition* values were available in the literature. This was a particularly frequent occurrence in the older references, and, occasionally, even in recent ones, where the compounds were being used for analytical, structural, or other physical studies and were not satisfactorily characterized.

Discussion of the nomenclature adapted for the listing of the derivatives

---

* Decomposition of amine derivatives (salts) at or near the melting point is quite common. Sometimes it is not clear if the decomposition reported is accompanied by melting. For the sake of consistency when a value is reported either as a melting point with decomposition or only as a decomposition point it is here listed as a melting point followed by the abbreviation (dec.).

is appropriate. The common hydrohalide acid salts are described as the hydriodide, hydrobromide, etc., under the pertinent amine. For more complex acids, only the anion is cited: chloroaurate ($AuCl_4^-$), chloroplatinate ($PtCl_6^=$), picrate, nitrate, etc. For example, the picric acid complex with triethylamine is referenced as the picrate and not as the hydropicrate, or triethylammonium picrate. The latter name is not commonly used, while the former has never, to our knowledge, been affixed to the amine.

The chloroplatinates are salts of the diprotic chloroplatinic acid, H_2PtCl_6. Hence, the trialkylaminechloroplatinate has the formula, $(R_3NH)_2^+PtCl_6^=$. When more complex or exotic derivatives are given, it has been found desirable, in order to prevent confusion, to list the molecular formula.

Coordinate compounds are described either by name (e.g., oxide), or by formula (e.g., $Me_3N{\cdot}BF_3$).

The quaternary ammonium salt derivatives are identified under the parent amine as the appropriate alkylo- or arylo- halide, sulfonate, etc. Common alkylo- groups include the abbreviated terms, metho-, etho-, propo-, and buto-, except for the iodide salts, for which the final letter (o) is dropped, as in ethiodide and butiodide. For the higher alkyl groups in which the shortened forms could cause confusion with complex anions such as pentiodide (I_5^-), heptiodide (I_7^-), etc., the alkylo- names become pentylo-, hexylo, heptylo-, and so on, as exemplified by the pentyloiodide of triheptylamine.

One difficulty encountered with the quaternary salts is that several different combinations of tertiary amine and alkylating agent may lead to the identical product. For example, methylethylpropylbutylammonium iodide is derivable from ethylpropylbutylamine, methylpropylbutylamine, methylethylpropyl-amine, or methylethylbutylamine and the appropriate alkyl iodide. To minimize the number of listings, the parent amine is taken to be, irrespective of the compound used in the synthesis, the tertiary amine with the largest and most complicated substituents. In the example cited, the parent compound would be ethylpropylbutylamine. In a few cases, particularly for the small molecules, listing may also appear under other alternatives. For example, dimethyldiethylammonium iodide is found as the methiodide of methyl-diethylamine and also as the ethiodide of ethyldimethylamine. For important quaternary ammonium salts containing a phenyl, a benzyl, or another aralkyl or alkaryl group, the parent amine is always the acyclic aliphatic tertiary amine.

A few miscellaneous derivatives that do not conform to the above rules are identified in a manner that is self-explanatory.

Monoamines

C_3H_9N

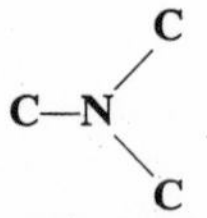

C—N with C above and C below (structure)

Me
Me
Me

TRIMETHYLAMINE

Trimethylamine, the first and simplest member of the class of aliphatic acyclic tertiary amines, has been so widely studied with respect to its synthesis and physical and chemical properties that the voluminous literature on these items alone could provide enough material for a substantial monograph on this compound itself. However, in view of the goal of broad coverage of the subject amines for the present publication and the limitations of space, neither can the complete data on trimethylamine be presented nor can they be entirely omitted. It has therefore been decided to devote one full section to this compound but to select only the significant and reliable information on trimethylamine compatible with the presentations for the other amines described.

Phys. Props.:

Many physical properties of trimethylamine have been studied, ranging all the way from the simple ones, such as melting and boiling points, up through the derived thermodynamic quantities, phase diagrams, absorption spectra, etc. For this section the data have been selected—whether they are direct measurements or mathematical interpretations therefrom—that appear to present best the physical nature of trimethylamine. Typical omitted information includes solution properties,[BE10,DE3a,HO14a,IS5,MO1,PI2, SM8,TE4] partition and distribution coefficients,[CO5,CO6,FE7,GO3,HA18,HA19,HE20, MO8,MO10,PE1a,SA9,SM7,SM8,TA2,TS10] certain electrolytic properties,[HA9,MC4] polarographic and electrochemical studies,[CH8,HO20a] various magnetic resonances,[EB1,GR15,OG2,OK1,MU4a,SC9,SP4] azeotrope data,[AL1,HO13,IS3] magnetic rotatory power,[GA1a,GA2] theoretical structural deductions and speculations,[AL1,BU1,DE9,FR7a,GI0,MA39,PH2,SA9b,SH2,SI1,TR5a,WE15a] heterogeneous adsorption,[BA30a,BO4,HA3a,YO3a] activation quenching,[DA7a] X-ray diffraction,[GO5] and various chemical properties and kinetic-thermodynamic parameters for reactions or complexes with alkene oxides,[HA12,HA13,HA14] oxygen,[CUO] boron compounds,[BA37,BR42,BR46,DA2,GA5a,HO19,MC2] esters,[BE7] silver ion,[FY1] silicon compounds,[WI7] alkyl halides,[PE9a,PE9b] and aluminum halides.[CA10] (A few recent citations are given for the above topics to serve as starting points for those interested in further pursuit of the literature.)

BOILING POINT AND VAPOR PRESSURE. The most reliable boiling value appears to be 2.87° (or 276.03 ± 0.05°K) at 760 mm. as determined by Aston et al.[AS3] Other reported values include 3.2–3.8° at 764.6 mm.,[HO8] and 2.8°,[WI3] 2.9°,[FE7a,SI4] 3.2°,[TH3] and 3.9°[LE6] at 760 mm. An oft-used criterion for purity and identity has been the vapor pressure at 0°: 680 mm.,[BU5,SI4] 681.2 mm.[HO14b] (Other values are 675.5[FI8] and 658 mm.[LE6])

For the vapor pressure-temperature relationship of the form:

$$\log p_{mm.} = -(A/T) + B \log T - 10^{-3} CT + D$$

where common logarithms are used and temperature is in °K, the following coefficients have been reported for the temperature regimes cited:

Temperature range

(°C)	A	B	C	D	Ref.
−93 to 0°	1357.8	1.75	3.9161	4.6091	W13
−90 to 12°	1490.62	1.75	6.1046	5.6927	S14
−83 to 3°	2141.7743	11.400327	6.349001	36.715267	AS3
−70 to 0°	1342	0	0	7.7580	HO14a
−20 to 45°	1410.5	0	2.1158	8.57435	FE7a
−6.2 to 11.0°	1265	0	0	7.45	TH3
0 to 40°	2018.37	6.0303	0	24.91300	SW7
60 to 130°	1202.2908	0	0	7.250828	DA17
130 to 160°	738.6065	0	2.9426	4.914884	DA17

Again, the most careful work below a pressure of 1 atm. seems to have been that of Aston et al.[AS3]

Critical temperatures of 160.15 ± 0.10°,[DA17] 160.9°,[BE7a] and 160.5°[VI4] and critical pressures of 40.24 ± 0.05 atm.[DA17] and 41 atm.[VI4] have been reported, with the former of each pair of values being much more recent and reliable, although the discrepancies are not very great.

The molal heat of vaporization at the normal boiling point is given as 5.4824 ± .007 kcal. per mole by Aston[AS3] and probably less trustworthily, elsewhere, as 5.81,[WI3] 5.706,[FE7a] and 5.65[SI4] kcal. per mole. At 250°K and 250 mm. pressure, it is 5.8226 kcal. per mole.[AS3]

The gas law equation of state for the vapor phase from 65 to 185° has been determined[ST6] as well as the second virial coefficient.[AS3] Vapor densities at 0° are 0.5336 g./l. (0.2 atm.), 1.0790 g./l. (0.4 atm.), 1.6363 g./l. (0.6 atm.), and 2.2054 g./l. (0.8 atm.)[AR11]; at 25°, from 1.980 g./l. (0.79968 atm.) to 2.356 g./l. (0.94670 atm.).[AS3]

MELTING POINT. Equilibrium melting points reported include Aston's $-117.02 \pm 0.05°$ (or $156.08 \pm 0.05°K$)[AS3] and the well-agreeing earlier values of $-117.3°$[W13] and $-117.2°$.[S15] The last figure was a correction by the same authors of an earlier value of $-123.80°$[S14] that resulted from confusion of a solid-solid transition to a clear glass above this temperature. Another melting point report gives -123.8 to $-124.0°$.[T16] Whether the same misinterpretation—to the phenomenon or an impurity—is responsible for the discrepancy is not known, although the latter has been considered more likely.[AS3]

A value of 1564.0 ± 1.0 cal. per mole has been reported for the heat of fusion.[AS3]

LIQUID PHASE PROPERTIES. In a sealed system under autogenous pressure, viscosities of 1.94 at 15°, 1.77 at 25°, and 1.61 centipoises at 35° have been found.[SW6] Under the same conditions, density values reported[SW6] were as follows:

t (°C)	d_4^t	Approximate vapor pressure
0°	0.65673	1 atm.
15°	0.63913	2 atm.
25°	0.62710	3 atm.
35°	0.61472	4 atm.

Felsing and Phillips[FE7a] claim a density-temperature equation accurate to 1 part in 5000 over the range -20 to $45°C$ ($253 - 318°K$):

$$d_4^{T°K} = 0.87406 - 4.433 \times 10^{-4}T - 1.29236 \times 10^{-6}T^2$$

Densities reported by Grosse et al.[GR11a] for -40 to $20°C$ yield the equation:

$$d_4^{t°C} = 0.6576 - 0.0011t$$

Other values[LE6]: $d_4^{-10.4}$ 0.6667, d_4^0 0.6557, $d_4^{14.4}$ 0.6395, d_4^{25} 0.6267.

Surface tensions at -73, -52, -32, -19, and $-4°$ have been reported to be 24.8, 22.2, 20.2, 18.7, and 17.4 dyne cm.$^{-1}$ respectively.[JA3] For liquid in equilibrium with vapor above the boiling point, values given[SW6a] at 15, 25, and 35°C are 14.53, 13.47, and 12.24 dyne cm.$^{-1}$, respectively.

Refractive indices for -60 to $0°C$, obtained by Grosse et al.,[GR11a] are summarized by the expression:

$$n_D^{t°C} = 1.3630 - 0.0006t$$

THERMODYNAMIC PROPERTIES. The standard heat of formation at constant pressure has been evaluated as 15.87 kcal. per mole for the gas phase[TH4] and as 12.60 kcal. per mole for the liquid.[LE12] Values of heats of combustion at constant pressure of gaseous trimethylamine include 582.63[TH4] and 593.7 kcal. per mole.[MU3] For the liquid phase these have been given as 579.8 and 580.8 kcal. per mole at constant volume and at constant pressure, respectively.[LE12]

The molal heat capacity data of Aston[AS3] led to the following equations for the temperature regions and phases described:

20 to 60°K (solid) $C_p = -4.200 + 0.3663T - 0.00234T^2$
60 to 150°K (solid) $C_p = 0.1137T + 2.96$
160 to 280°K (liquid) $C_p = 33.12 - 7.45 \times 10^{-2} T + 2.5 \times 10^{-4} T^2$

where C_p is in cal./deg./mole and T is in °K. For the region 0 to 1200°C (273 to 1473°K) an equation, presumably for the vapor phase, has been calculated[KO1] from some earlier spectroscopic data[AS4] to give the following:

$$C_p = -2.098 + 9.6187 \times 10^{-2} T - 5.5488 \times 10^{-5} T^2 + 1.2432 \times 10^{-9} T^3$$

or:

$$C_p = 20.290 + 6.8656 \times 10^{-2} t - 4.5300 \times 10^{-5} t^2 + 1.2432 \times 10^{-9} t$$

where t in the second equation is in °C. The ratio C_p/C_v has been reported to be 1.184 at 20°.[FE8]

SPECTRAL ABSORPTION, IONIZATION POTENTIAL, AND POLARIZABILITY. The absorption spectra of trimethylamine have been published for the far-ultraviolet (from 1600 to 2600 Å),[TA8] the near-ultraviolet,[B15,HA25,HE22,ST14b,TH2] the infrared,[BA25,BA36a,BE6,GI6,HA2a,LO1c,PI4,RO2a,ST1,ST14b] the Raman,[AS3,BE6, DA1,KO5a,KO5b,KO6,LO1c,RO15] and the microwave regions.[BA35,BA36,IL1,LI0] The mass spectrum has also been described.[CO9,DO3a]

Ionization potentials have been determined both by photoionization[FR6a, OM1,WA18,WA19] and by electron impact[BR2,CO9a,CO9b,OM1,SU2a] studies. The former gives values of 7.82[FR6a,WA19] and 7.86[WA18] electron volts (e.v.), while the latter yields significantly higher values near 9.02 e.v.[OM1] The reason for the discrepancy has not yet been completely and satisfactorily resolved.[CO10]

Bond dissociation energy: D_{Me_2N-Me} 75–77 kcal. per mole.[GO9]

Many values for the dipole moment of trimethylamine have been reported.[AL3,AR10,BI6a,GH1,GR12,GR14a,LE6,SA9a,ST6,YO1] The most reliable seem to be 0.72 D[LE6] and 0.612 D[LI0,SA9a] for the liquid and gaseous states, respectively, and 0.86 D for the extrapolation from a benzene solution of the amine.[AR10,LE6]

Dielectric constants reported for the liquid phase are 2.44 at 25°,[LE6] 2.496 at 16°,[LE6] and 2.57 at 0°.[LE6] A discordant older value of 2.95 at 4°[SC6] is probably not reliable. Dielectric constant for the vapor state is 1.001456 at 65°, 1.001429 at 105°, 1.001394 at 145°, and 1.001364 at 185°.[SA9a]

Molar Kerr constant is reported as 8.94×10^{-13}.[AR10]

Molar distortion polarization values include 20.2,[GR14a] 20.01,[LE6] and 20.0 cc.[HE20] (other values[SA9a,HA2]).

Molar total polarization has been reported as 28.6 (gas) 30.6 (liquid), and 35.4 (benzene solution) cc.[LE6] For the gas, $P = 21.5 + 2230/(T°K)$.[SA9a]

MOLECULAR STRUCTURE. The trimethylamine molecule is a trigonal pyramid with C_{3v} skeletal symmetry.[CH3,SI1] The structural parameters, as determined by microwave spectroscopy (m.s.) and by electron diffraction (e.d.) are as follows:

Parameter	Values by m.s.[LIO]	by e.d.[BR35]
C—N—C angle	$108.7 \pm 1.0°$	$108 \pm 4°$
C—N distance	1.472 ± 0.008 Å	1.47 ± 0.002 Å
H—C—H angle	$108.5 \pm 1.5°$	109.5° (assumed)
C—H distance	1.090 Å	1.06 Å (assumed

The microwave method is generally believed to give more reliable values.

AQUEOUS SOLUTION.   One liter of a saturated aqueous solution of trimethyl-amine at 19° contains 409.6 g. of the amine and has a density of d_4^{16} 0.858.[BE10] The partial vapor pressures of the amine in 0.248 − 1.961 molar aqueous solution have been determined and lead to 2.090 kcal./mole for the free energy of solution.[FE7a]

BASE STRENGTH.   The negative logarithm of the conjugate acid, the pK_a, of trimethylamine is 9.80 at 25°.[BR29,EU2,HA9a,MO9] Other reported values at the same temperature are 9.87,[UD1] 9.81,[AK2] 9.79,[GU5] 9.72;[HA6] 9.93 at 20°;[HA15] and 8.63 at 25° (the last in acetone).[UD1] Determinations have also been made in other solvents.[GU5,HA5]

The influence of pressure on pK_a in aqueous solutions at 25° has been examined.[HA9a] There is a progressive increase in pK_a: 10.26 at 1000 atm., 10.64 at 2000 atm. and 10.96 at 3000 atm.

Natural Occurrence

In decaying fish the olfactorily identifiable and chemically isolable trimethylamine results from the reduction of normally present trimethylamine oxide, a compound found in quantity in most kinds of fresh crustacea and seafish (in much smaller amounts in fresh water fish[AN3,JO3,ME4,OB4]) where it constitutes a part of the nitrogenous extractives of the muscle and the entrails, including the intestine and its contents. The reduction process is apparently the result not of chemical autolysis[AN2] but of bacterial action.[PR6] However, the enzymes of bacteria rather than their growth processes have been concluded to be more important from the results of irradiation studies.[NI1] The existence of both decomposition mechanisms in shrimp has been discussed.[FI4]

The close connection between fish deterioration and the reduction of trimethylamine oxide has suggested measurement of trimethylamine content as a chemical means of indicating spoilage,[BE1,BE1b,JO3,ME4,NA1,NA5,SH1a,TA9a] although this is not universally supported.[WI5] So much literature from all over the world has been published on studies of this compound in sea organisms, including cuttelfish[OB3] and whales,[RO5] that space limitations permit citing only a few references.[AN2,AN3,BE1a,CA15,CA16,CA17,DY1,DY2,DY3,] [DY5,DY6,DY7,HO15,NI1,NO2,PA9,PR6,SH1,TA9,TA9b,TA10,TA11,WI21,WO6,YU1] A particularly good review on trimethylamine oxide in marine products, covering occurrence, properties, and historical, synthetic, analytical, and commercial aspects of this compound, has been given by Ronold and Jakobsen.[ROll]

Preparation

The literature on the preparation of trimethylamine is so voluminous that one can hope to cover the subject within the confines of this monograph only in a cursory fashion. However, the attempt will be made to present as representative a picture as possible of the methods and chemical systems that have been used.

Trimethylamine has been obtained basically by one of two methods: synthesis from simpler molecules, such as the alkylation of ammonia, or degradation of more complex molecules, such as the pyrolysis of quaternary ammonium compounds or reduction of the amine oxide. In the latter category one might also include the various enzymatic and chemical breakdowns of nitrogen-containing natural products.

SYNTHESIS. (a) *Alkylation with Formaldehyde.* In the most straightforward laboratory reaction trimethylamine results from the alkylation of ammonia or one of its salts with an excess of formaldehyde or one of its polymeric precursors, such as paraformaldehyde or trioxymethylene. Detailed procedures giving 85–90% yields are available in *Organic Syntheses.*[AD1] Similar reactions have been used by others.[KO3,PL5,SC13]

The excess of formaldehyde functions apparently as a reducing agent acting on the intermediate methylols formed. It has been replaced by formic acid,[SO3] giving yields of about 90%, and also by hydrogen at 50–300 atm. pressure over nickel, copper, and cobalt catalysts.[ST14]

The ammonia has also been replaced by its partially alkylated derivatives such as the methylamines[BR34] (with electrochemical reduction[KN7]) and hexamethylenetetramine[ES2] (with formic acid as reductant[SO2]). Hexamethylenetetramine, alone[KN7] or with added formaldehyde,[BO7,KN7] has been successfully reduced electrochemically in acid solution to trimethylamine. (See additional references under part (c) below, "Reduction of Hexamethylenetetramine.") Even hydrazine has been used to supply the nitrogen in the presence of formic acid and paraformaldehyde, although a mixture of methylamines was obtained in only 17% yield overall.[KL2]

(b) *Alkylation with Methanol or Methyl Esters.* Commercially, the most important process for the preparation of trimethylamine is the alkylation of ammonia by methanol in a flow system at temperatures of 300–500° over a heterogeneous catalyst, usually of the alumina-silicate type.[AN4,BR36,CH7,PA13, UC3,UC4,UC5,WA15a] Most of the references to this method are patents, but excellent review articles have been published describing the influence of experimental variables such as temperature and pressure.[EG1,GR10a,HA1a,RIla] Yields as high as 57% have been reported[GR10a] but conversion is generally not complete and the other methylamines are also obtained. The separation of such methylamine mixtures is the subject of very many patents and publications.[CE1a,DE11,DE12,GR7,IS1,KR2,MI3,M01a,SE1,WA15a]

Other heterogeneous catalysts described have been zinc chloride[TU2] and various salts of iron and copper,[LI7] but yields have been generally poor.

Instead of ammonia, nitrogen-supplying components have included ammonium salts (resulting also in some tetramethylammonium compounds as products in a closed reaction system),[WE8,LI7] urea,[LI7] magnesium nitride,[SZ2] and various methylamines.[SW2]

Alkylation of ammonia with methyl chloride in a closed pressurized system was tried early[DU8,HO5,VI3] but proved to be inconvenient, giving a complex mixture of methylamines in low yield. Much cleaner is the alkylation of dimethylamine by diazomethane in the presence of boron trifluoride-ethyl ether complex at low temperatures.[MU2a]

Unsymmetric dimethylhydrazine has been converted to trimethylamine by trimethyl phosphate and by trimethyl phosphite.[KL1] The product could also be obtained in low yield by reacting the magnesium salt of 1,1-dimethyl-2-ethylhydrazine with methyl bromide.[KL1]

Disproportionation, both inter- and intra-molecular, provide particularly interesting synthetic routes. The former is exemplified by dimethylamine which, at a pressure of 200 atm. over an alumina catalyst at 380°, gives a mixture of ammonia and methylamines, containing as much as 64% trimethylamine.[FA9,SM3]

Similarly, trimethylamine is obtained in about 50% yield when benzyldimethylamine or related analogs, such as furfuryl-, 2-thienyl, or p-nitrobenzyl-dimethylamine, are heated in the presence of catalytic amounts of the respective quaternary salt, such as the methiodide.[SN3] Particularly novel formally intramolecular reactions are the boiling of the methylbetaine of dimethylsulfamic acid:

$$(CH_3)_3\overset{\oplus}{N}\overset{\ominus}{S}O_3$$

in alcoholic solution to yield the ethylsulfuric acid salt of trimethylamine,[TR1] and the pyrolysis of the ammonium salt of methylsulfuric acid:

$$(NH_4)^+(OSO_2OCH_3)^-$$

at 260° to a mixture of methylamines.[DE9a]

(c) Reduction of Hexamethylenetetramine. Hexamethylenetetramine, the compact polycyclic condensation product of formaldehyde and ammonia, has been reduced to trimethylamine by a variety of techniques. Electrochemical reduction in acid solution in the absence[KN7] or presence[BO7] of formaldehyde has been described. Heating with formic acid also has given a 50–60% yield[SO2] of the desired product. The acid-metal system, copper and hydrochloric acid, operated successfully,[HU4] as did also hydrogenation of the hexamethylenetetramine over various nickel, cobalt, and copper catalysts at 100–200° with 50 to 300 atm. of hydrogen pressure.[ST14]

(d) *Reduction of Trimethylamine Oxide.* Trimethylamine oxide, which is the principal precursor in fish of trimethylamine (see earlier section on "Natural Occurrence") and which can also be prepared from this amine by various oxidants,[RO11] is reducible back to trimethylamine. Reagents used for this reduction have included zinc in either acid or alkaline solution,[DU5] cysteine in the presence of iron salts,[VA1] bacterial enzymes,[CA16,MO3,RO5] including triamine oxidase[NE1a] and those from *Achromobacter* and *Pseudomonas putrefaciens*,[CA18] tin(II) chloride,[CO16] zinc,[DU5] Devarda's alloy,[DY5,LI9] and titanium(III) chloride.[HJ1,JA5,RO11] In the references cited the last three reagents have also been used for the amine oxide analysis by either direct titration[RO11] or indirectly by colorimetric determination of the liberated trimethylamine.[DY5]

(e) *Reduction of Miscellaneous Carbon-Nitrogen Compounds.* In a series of patents, the hydrogenation of hydrogen cyanide to trimethylamine over nickel, copper, and zinc cyanide[DR2] or silicate[KI5a] catalysts has been claimed. Another report describes formation of the amine from the hydrogenation of strychnine.[CL7] Hydrogenolysis of furfuryltrimethylammonium tosylate over Adams platinum or Raney nickel catalyst was successful.[PO7]

(f) *Oxidation Reactions.* Oxidation of choline or neurine with alkaline aqueous potassium permanganate in the presence of sodium tetrathionate, $Na_2S_4O_6$, gives trimethylamine quantitatively.[CO29] With either betaine or choline phosphate this oxidizing system gives somewhat less than quantitative yields, and potassium manganate, K_2MnO_4, appears to be a superior reagent.[KA3] Alkaline solutions of potassium peroxydisulfate, $K_2S_2O_8$, are less specific than alkaline permanganate and liberate trimethylamine quantitatively not only from choline and neurine, but also from the sulfuric, phosphoric, and acetic acid esters of choline.[CO30] Some attack also occurs on betaine, tetramethylammonium salts, and trimethylamine oxide.[CO30]

Derivs.:

SIMPLE SALTS OF PROTONIC ACIDS:

·Hydrochloride: m. 281–283°,[SE2] 280–282°,[HI2] 280° (dec.),[TI9] (other values: m. 277–278°,[WA2] 273–275° (dec.),[DE8] 271–272°,[BA3,WI22] 257–259°[SW1])

·HCl[(C₆H₅)₃COH]₂: m. 190–195° (dec.)[HU2a]

·HCl·Br₂: m. 37°[ME13a]

·HCl·2Br₂: m. 11.5°[ME13a]

·HCl·4Br₂: m. 11.5°[ME13a]

·Hydrobromide: m. 243–245°,[KA17] 244°,[WA2] 243°[LU23]

·HBr·Br₂: m. 34°[ME13a]

·HBr·2Br₂: m. 6°[ME13a]

·HBr·3Br₂: m. 1.5°[ME13a]

·HBr₂ [structure is $(Me_3NH)_2^+ Br_3^- Br^-$][RO9a]: m. 118°,[RO9a] 105° (dec.)[SA6a]

·HBr₃: m. 65–66° (dec.)[RO9a,SA6a]

·Hydriodide: m. 263° (darkens at 251–255°),[WA2] 260° (prior darkening),[DE8] 255–260° (darkens at 230–255°),[TA14a] 243–245°[KA17]

  ·HNO_3: m. 153°[CO13a,FR1]

  ·$HBCl_4$: m. 160–163°[KY2]

  ·$HB(C_6H_5)_4$: m. 170–172°[CR1]

·Picrate: m. 221.5–224°,[SN3.] 221–223°,[WI30] 220–223°,[WI30] 220°,[HE5] 218–219°,[LU14] 218°,[HE5] 216°,[BA3,BA8,DE8,HO20,TS6,TS8] 215–126°,[LU23] 211°[TO2*]

·Styphnate: m. dec. gradually above 200°[JE2]

·Chloroaurate: m. 248°,[WI22] 238°[SA13]

·Picrolonate: m. 250–252°[OB3]

·2,4-Dinitro-1-naphthol-2-sulfonate (flavianate): m. (dec.) 220–223°[HO20]

·Phenyldithiocarbamate: m. 145–150°[SZ1]

·4-Chlorophenyldithiocarbamate: m. 173–175°[SZ1]

Me_3N salt of:

  ·Dibenzenesulfonimide: m. 163–164°[RU3]

  ·Bis-(4-chlorobenzensulfon)imide: m. 171–172°[RU4]

  ·2-Nitro-1,3-indanedione oxime: m. >265°[VI6]

  Group I—Lithium

    $Me_3N \cdot LiCl$: m. dec. −15°[SI3]

    $(Me_3N)_2 \cdot LiCl$: m. dec. −41°[SI3]

    $Me_3N \cdot LiBr$: m. dec. 23°[SI3]

    $(Me_3N)_2 \cdot LiBr$: m. dec. −15°[SI3]

    $Me_3N \cdot LiI$: m. dec. 30°[SI3]

    $Me_3N \cdot 2\ LiI$: m. dec. −16°[SI3]

    $Me_3N \cdot LiAlH_4$: m. dec. 100°[WI2]

  Group II—Beryllium

    $Me_3N \cdot BeMe_2$: m. 36°[CO1c]

    $Me_3N \cdot Be(t\text{-Bu})_2$: m. 42–47°[CO1a]

  Group III—Boron

    $Me_3N \cdot BH_3$: m. 94–94.5°,[BU7] 94°,[HE23a] 93–94°,[BA21a] 93.5°,[NO3] 93°,[PA6a,SC1] 92–93°,[BA40] 92–92.5°,[BU16] 92°[TA14]; b_{760} 171°[BU7]

    $Me_3N \cdot B_3H_7$: m. 119–120°[GR7]

    $Me_3N \cdot BF_3$: m. 146–146.5°,[PH2] 139–147° (sealed tube),[BU5a] 138° (sealed tube),[BR30a,HU3b] 133–135°,[BR47] 133–134°[DO3b]

    $Me_3N \cdot BCl_3$: m. 245° (dec.),[PH2] 243–244°,[PH2] 237–240° (dec.)[KA14]

    $(Me_3N \cdot B_2Cl_4)_4$: m. 228°[UR1]

    $Me_3N \cdot BBr_3$: m. 230–232°[BA40]

    $Me_3N \cdot BI_3$: m. 248–250°[MU1b]

    $Me_3N \cdot BMe_3$: m. 128° (softens at 120°),[BR45] 120°[SC3a]

    $Me_3N \cdot B(C_6H_5)_3$: m. 135–137° (dec.)[KR5a]

    $Me_3N \cdot BH_2Me$: m. 0.8°[SC3a]

---

* The amine contains radioactive C^{14} due to synthesis by autodecomposition of choline methyl-C^{14} chloride.[TO2]

$Me_3N \cdot BH_2(Bu)$: b_3 72°[HA28]

$Me_3N \cdot BH_2(sec\text{-}Bu)$: $b_{2.5}$ 60°[HA28]

$Me_3N \cdot BH_2(t\text{-}Bu)$: $b_{3.5}$ 60°[HA28]

$Me_3N \cdot BH_2(cyclohex)$: m. 40–41°[HA28]

$Me_3N \cdot BH_2(CH_2C_6H_5)$: m. 58–60°[CA8]

$Me_3N \cdot BH_2SMe$: m. 13–15°[BU7a]

$Me_3N \cdot BHCl_4$: m. 160–163°[KY2]

$Me_3N \cdot BHMe_2$: m. −18.0°[SC3a]

$Me_3N \cdot BH(C_6H_5)_2$: m. 68–69°[HA28a]

$Me_3N \cdot BH(C_6H_5)_4$: m. 170–172°[CR1]

$Me_3N \cdot BF_2Me$: m. 35°[BU5a]

$Me_3N \cdot BF_2Et$: m. 25.3°,[ST14a] 23.9–25.3°[BA32a]

$Me_3N \cdot BCl_2(NMe_2)$: m. 76–77° (dec.)[BR37]

$Me_3N \cdot BCl_2(NEt_2)$: m. 20° (dec.)[OS1a]

$Me_3N \cdot BFMe_2$: m. 33°[WI1b]

Group III—Aluminum

$Me_3N \cdot AlH_3$: m. 76°,[RU2] 60–65°[ST5a]

$Me_3N \cdot AlD_3$: m. 77–78°[RU2]

$Me_3N \cdot Al(BH_4)_3$: m. 79°[ST5a]

$Me_3N \cdot AlH_2Cl$: m. 51–53°[RU1,WI4]

$Me_3N \cdot AlH_2Br$: m. 33–34°,[RU1] 33–33.5°[WI4]

$Me_3N \cdot AlH_2I$: m. 11°[WI4]

$(Me_3N)_2 \cdot AlH_2Cl$: m. 72–75° (dec.)[WI4]

$(Me_3N)_2 \cdot AlH_2Br$: m. 68–70° (dec.)[WI4]

$(Me_3N)_2 \cdot AlH_2I$: m. 27–28° (dec.)[WI4]

$Me_3N \cdot AlHCl_2$: m. 100–103°,[RU1] 99–103°[WI4]

$Me_3N \cdot AlHBr_2$: m. 105–108°,[WI4] 104–106°[RU1]

$Me_3N \cdot AlHI_2$: m. 131°[WI4]

$(Me_3N)_2 \cdot AlHCl_2$: m. 88–91° (dec.)[WI4]

$(Me_3N)_2 \cdot AlHBr_2$: m. 82–83° (dec.)[WI4]

$(Me_3N)_2 \cdot AlHI_2$: m. 110° (dec.)[WI4]

$Me_3N \cdot AlCl_3$: m. 156–157°,[RU1] 156.4°[EL3]

$Me_3N \cdot AlBr_3$: m. 156.9°[EL3]

$Me_3N \cdot AlI_3$: m. 156.4°[EL3]

$Me_3N \cdot AlMe_2Cl$: m. 124°[DA12a]

$Me_3N \cdot AlMe_2(SMe)$: m. 37°[DA12a]

$Me_3N \cdot AlMe_3$: m. 105°,[DA12a] 92°[ST5a]

$Me_3N \cdot Al(CH{=}CH_2)_3$: $b_{10^{-2}}$ 40°[RU1]

$Me_3N \cdot Al(C{\equiv}C{-}C_3H_7)$: m. 38–39°[RU1]

$Me_3N \cdot AlBu_3$: $b_{10^{-4}}$ 73–75°[RU1]

$Me_3N \cdot Al(C_6H_5)_3$: m. 227–229°[RU1]

Group III—Gallium

$Me_3N \cdot GaMe_3$: m. 96.2°[WI2a]

$Me_3N \cdot GaMe_2(OC_6H_5)$: 39–40°[CO1b]

$Me_3N \cdot GaMe_2(SMe)$: m. $26.0–26.2°$ [CO1b]
$Me_3N \cdot GaMe_2(SC_6H_5)$: m. $51°$ [CO1b]
$Me_3N \cdot GaMe_2(SeMe)$: m. $29.8–30.0°$ [CO1b]

Group III—Indium
$Me_3N \cdot InMe_3$: m. $66.2–66.4°$ [CO1d]

Group III—Thallium
$Me_3N \cdot TlMe_3$: m. just below $0°$ [CO1d]

Group III—Rare Earths
$(Me_3N \cdot HCl)_4 \cdot LaCl_3$: m. $287°$ [BO12a]
$(Me_3N \cdot HCl)_4 \cdot CeCl_3$: m. $289°$ [BO12a]
$(Me_3N \cdot HCl)_4 \cdot Pr^*Cl_3$: m. $295°$ [BO12a]
$(Me_3N \cdot HCl)_4 \cdot NdCl_3$: m. $296°$ [BO12a]

Group IV—Silicon
$(Me_3N)_2 \cdot SiCl_4$: m. $102.0°$ [RP1a]
$Me_3N \cdot SiF_3Me$: m. $-51.5°$ [FE8a]
$Me_3N \cdot SiF_4$: m. $81.5°$ [WI7]
$(Me_3N)_2 \cdot SiF_4$: m. $89°$ [WI7]

Group IV—Germanium
$Me_3N \cdot GeF_4$: m. $129–131°$ (dec.)[FE8a]
$(Me_3N)_2 \cdot GeF_4$: m. dec. $120°$ [FE8a]
$Me_3N \cdot GeCl_4$: m. $75–76°$ [FE8a]

Group IV—Tin
$(Me_3N)_2 \cdot SnCl_4$: m. $174–175°$ (dec),[FE8a] $171°$ (dec.)[LA13a]
$(Me_3N)_2 \cdot SnBr_4$: m. $196–198°$ [BO8]
$Me_3N \cdot (SnClEt_3)_2$: m. $8.3°$ [NA1a]

Group IV—Titanium
$(Me_3N)_4 \cdot TiBr_4$: m. $288°$ [PR1d]

Group V—Antimony
$Me_3N \cdot SbCl_3$: m. dec. $200–210°$ [HO14b]
$Me_3N \cdot SbCl_5$: m. $134–135°$ [BO8]

Group VI—Oxygen
$Me_3N \cdot O$: m. $220°$,[HA2] $212°$,[LI7a] $209°$ (dec.)[HU2c]
$Me_3N \cdot O \cdot 2H_2O$: m. $96°$ [PH2,HU2c,DU5]
$Me_3N \cdot O \cdot HCl$: m. $210°$ [RU5]

Group VI—Sulfur
$Me_3N \cdot SO_2$: m. $77°$ [MO1]; $b_{2.8}$ $19.7°$ [BU5]
$Me_3N \cdot SO_3$: m. $240°$ [BU5,MO1,TR1]

Group VII—Halogens
$Me_3N \cdot Cl_2$: m. explodes on heating[BO9a]
$Me_3N \cdot Br_2$: m. $84°$ [BO9a]
$Me_3N \cdot Br_3$ (structure reported by ref. SA6a was shown to be $Me_3N \cdot HBr_3$[RO9a] *q.v.*)
$Me_3N \cdot I_2$: m. $66°$,[BO9a] dec. $66°$ [KU5,ST20]

---

* Pr represents praseodymium.

Group VIII
Me$_3$N·*trans*-ethylene·PtCl$_2$: m. dec. 105–111°[CH1a]

Quaternary Ammonium Compounds—Simple Alkyl

Methochloride: m. 420 ± 10° (sealed tube),[RA5] > 310°,[HO20] dec. 230°[LA15,WA2]
Methobromide: m. dec. 230°[WA2]
Methiodide: m. >355°,[SN3] dec. >230°[KA13,WA2]
Methotriiodide: m. 116°,[GE5] 110°[MU5]
Methopentiodide: m. 130°,[GE5] 126°[MU5]
Methoheptiodide: m. 108°[GE5]
Methononiodide: m. 110°[GE5]
Me$_4$N$^+$(ICl$_2$)$^-$: m. 216–220° (dec.)[DO1]
Me$_4$N$^+$(IBr$_2$)$^-$: m. 190°[DO1]
Me$_4$N$^+$(B$_3$H$_8$)$^-$: m. >275°[GR7]
Me$_4$N$^+$(B$_{10}$H$_{13}$)$^-$: m. >250°[HA28c]
Methotetraphenyl borate: m. >360°[CR1]
Methochloroplatinate: m. *ca.* 278° (dec.)[RI5]
Methododecyl sulfate: m. 256°[BO11]
Methotetrachloroborate: m. 264° (dec.)[KY2]
Methopicrate: m. 314–316°,[WI30] 312–313°[LO2]
Methohydroxide: m. 130° (dec.)[WA14a]
Methohydroxide·3H$_2$O: m. 60°[WA14a]
Methohydroxide·5H$_2$O: m. 62–67°,[EA1] 62–63°[WA14a]
Methotribenzyl pyrophosphate: m. 74–75°[KE3a]
Methoflavianate (metho-2,4-dinitro-1-naphthol-7-sulfonate): m. 263–265° (dec.)[HO20]
Ethobromide: m. 338°,[MC5] 322–325 (dec.)[GR13]
Ethiodide: m. 300–301° (dec.),[SP2] >280°[KA3]
Ethotriiodide: m. 64°[MU5]
Ethopentiodide: m. 68°,[MU5,ST19] 26°[GE5] (ref. GE5 acknowledges discordance with earlier ref. MU5 but makes no further comment)
Ethoheptiodide: m. 32°[GE5]
Ethononiodide: m. 67°,[ST19] 38°[GE5]
Ethochloroplatinate: m. *ca.* 266° (dec.)[RI5]
Ethoperchlorate: m. *ca.* 300° (dec.)[HO11]
Ethothiocyanate: m. 131–132°[MC3]
Etho-*p*-toluenesulfonate: m. 185–188° (sealed tube)[SP2]
Ethopicrate: m. 299–300°[LO2]
Isopropobromide: m. 317° (dec.)[GR13]
Isopropiodide: m. 316–316.8° (dec.)[GR13]
Propiodide: m. 192–192.5°[SM9]
Allylopicrate: m. 216–218°[GR13]
Butochloride: m. 223.7–224.0°[GR13]
Butiodide: m. 231–232°[SM9]

t-Butiodide: m. 260–260.5° (dec.)[GR13]
Isopentyloiodide: m. 203–204°[SM9]
Neopentyloiodide: m. 240° (dec.)[IN6]
4,4-Dimethylpentyloiodide: m. 285° (subl.)[SM9]

QUATERNARY AMMONIUM COMPOUNDS—COMPLEX SUBSTITUTED ALKYLS, BETAINES, ZWITTERIONS, ETC.:

Chloromethobromide: m. 164°[WI8a] (this compound was erroneously described
   by ref. FO2a to be dichloromethochloride from reaction of chloroform
   with trimethylamine; it was later shown to arise from an impurity,
   bromochloromethane[FO2b,WI8a]
Trichloromethiodide: m. 100° (dec.)[PV1]
Iodomethiodide: m. 227–230° (dec.)[WI30]
Iodomethopicrate: m. 194–195° (dec.)[WI30]
2-Hydroxyethiodide: m. 266°[CO1b]
2-Ethoxyethiodide: m. 97–98°[AK1]
Me_3N^+—$CH_2CH_2OB^-F_3$: m. 296–298°[ME1a]
Me_3N^+—$C^-(CN)_2$: m. 153° (no dec.!)[AR9]
2-Chloroethochloride: m. 240–242° (dec.),[LU4] 240°[BA3]

QUATERNARY AMMONIUM COMPOUNDS—HYDROXYLAMINE DERIVS.:

Methoxyloiodide: m. 161°[PA1]
Ethoxyloiodide: m. 122°[PA1]
Propoxyloiodide: m. 125–138°[PA1]
Butoxyloiodide: m. 120–122°[PA1]
Pentyloxyloiodide: m. 113°[PA1]
Hexyloxyloiodide: m. 120°[PA1]
Decyloxyloiodide: m. 129°[PA1]

QUATERNARY AMMONIUM COMPOUNDS—ARALKYL:

Benzyloiodide: m. 180°[NA1a]
Benzylododecyl sulfate: m. 38°[BO11]
Benzhydrylobromide: m. 145° (dec.)[HU2b]
Benzhydrylotribromide: m. 138°[HU2b]
Benzhydryloiodide: m. 170–175° (dec.)[HU2b]
Benzhydrylopicrate: m. 152° (dec.)[HU2b]
1-Naphthylmethyloiodide: m. 215–216°[NA1a]
α,α-Diphenylethyloiodide: m. 205° (dec.)[HU2b]
α,α,β-Triphenylethyloiodide: m. 238°[HU2b]
α,α,β-Triphenylethylopicrate: m. 214°[HU2b]
9-Fluorenobromide: m. 189–190° (dec.)[IN5]
9-Fluorenopicrate: m. 175°[IN5]
Phenacylobromide: m. 206°[BO9a]

QUATERNARY AMMONIUM COMPOUNDS—ARYL:

Phenyloiodide: m. 216°[NA1a]
2-Quinolyloiodide: m. 168°[RE2a]

MISCELLANEOUS:

Trimethyl- and tetramethyl-ammonium salts of various cyanocarbon acids and derivatives[MI1a]

C_4H_7N

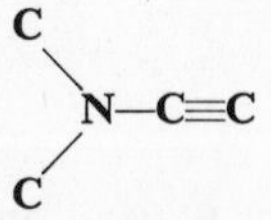

$$\begin{array}{c} C \\ \diagdown \\ N-C{\equiv}C \\ \diagup \\ C \end{array}$$

Me
Me
C_2H

ETHYNYLDIMETHYLAMINE

Derivs.:

Methochloroaurate: m. 245°[BO3]
Methochloroplatinate: m. 218°[BO3]
These derivatives were made from the corresponding quaternary ammonium hydroxide, which was prepared from 2-bromovinyltrimethyl-ammonium bromide and alcoholic potassium hydroxide.[BO3]

C_4H_9N

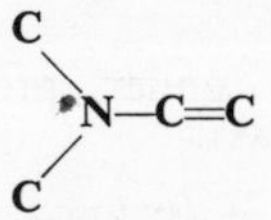

$$\begin{array}{c} C \\ \diagdown \\ *N-C{=}C \\ \diagup \\ C \end{array}$$

Me
Me
Vin

VINYLDIMETHYLAMINE*

Phys. Props.:

b. 37–38°[ME16]; b_{720} 38–40°[GE1]

Prepn.:

1. Thermal decomposition of vinyltrimethylammonium chloride (5% yield)[GA4]; of choline or neurine (10% yield).[ME16]
2. Dimethylamine + acetaldehyde in the presence of potassium carbonate (*ca.* 42% yield).[GE1]

Derivs.:

Methiodide: m. 196°[BO3]
Methobromide: m. 194°,[RE5] 193°[BO3]
Methochloride: m. 193–194°[BA4]
Methochloroaurate: m. 238–239°[SC11]
Methochloroplatinate: m. 213–214°,[BO3,SC11] 213°[LU1]
Methopicrolonate hydrate: m. 178° (dec. *ca.* 230°)[KO1a]
Methoperchlorate: explodes at 298°[DA10]

---

* Polymerizes readily to a white powder[GA4,ME16]; reacts violently with acidic reagents.[BA27,GA4]

$C_4H_{11}N$

Me
Me
Et

ETHYLDIMETHYLAMINE

Phys. Props.:

b. 37–39°,[SC3] 37.5°,[HU1,KO8] 36–38°,[HA11] 36–37°[WA2]; b_{760} 37°[GA9]; b_{752} 37.2°[HA15]
  b_{740} 35.8–35.9°[SP2]
m. −140°[SP2]
d_4^{25} 0.6694,[SP2] 0.6692[HA15]; d_4^{23} 0.698[WO7]; d_4^{20} 0.6751,[SP2] 0.6748[HA15]
n_D^{25} 1.3702,[SP2] 1.3700,[HA15] 1.3697[WO7]; n_D^{20} 1.3720,[SP2] 1.3728[HA15]; n_C^{25} 1.3676[HA15];
  n_C^{20} 1.3704[HA15]; n_F^{25} 1.3755[HA15]; n_F^{20} 1.3782[HA15]
pK_a 10.06 at 25°[SP1]; 10.16 at 20°[HA15]
(Other values: b. 39–41°,[CO8] 35–37°,[WI30] 28–30°[HE17]; d_4^{23} 0.698[WO7])

Prepn.:

1. Ethylamine + formaldehyde under pressure (39% yield),[HA11] (60% yield),[SC3] (unspecified yield).[HA15]
2. Ethylamine + formaldehyde + formic acid (74% yield),[GA9] (38% yield).[SP2]
3. Dimethylamine + ethyl iodide.[HE17]
4. Catalytic hydrogenation of vinyldimethylamine.[GE1]
5. Thermal decomposition of the following compounds:
   a. 1,4-Bis(dimethylethylammonium)-2-butyne dibromide in the presence of aqueous sodium hydroxide (88% yield).[BA11]
   b. Dimethylethyl-2-butynylammonium bromide in the presence of aqueous sodium hydroxide[BA11]; (74% yield).[BA13]
   c. 2-Phenylethyldimethylethylammonium hydroxide ("excellent yield").[HA11]
   d. Dimethylethyl (2-diethylaminoethyl)ammonium hydroxide (20% yield).[HA11]
   e. Dimethylethyl (2-hydroxyethyl)ammonium hydroxide (26% yield).[HA11]
   f. Dimethylethyl-(2-chloroethyl)ammonium hydroxide.[HA11]
   g. Ethyltrimethylammonium iodide in ethanolamine (*ca.* 95% yield).[HU1]
   h. Dimethyldiethylammonium iodide in ethanolamine (6.5% yield); main product is methyldiethylamine.[HU1]
   i. Dimethyldiethylammonium hydroxide.[WA2]
   j. Dimethylethylpropylammonium hydroxide (minor yield).[HA11]
   k. Ethyltrimethylammonium hydroxide, or chloride.[CO8]
   l. Codeine methiodide in alcoholic potassium hydroxide.[SK7]

m. 1,4-Bis(dimethylethylammonium)-2-chloro-2-butene dibromide in the presence of sodium hydroxide (79% yield).[BA11]

n. "Methylthebainone-methine" in sodium ethoxide solution.[KN5]

6. Cleavage by sodium of the following quaternary compounds in the solvents indicated: ethyltrimethylammonium iodide in liquid ammonia[GR14]; ethyltrimethylammonium bromide in dioxane[GR13]; tetramethylammonium bromide in dioxane (yields 48.1% of trimethylamine and 0.6% ethyldimethylamine).[GR13]

7. Electrolysis of dimethylethylphenylammonium iodide (69% yield).[EM12]

Derivs.:

Hydrochloride: m. 221–222°[WA2]

Hydrobromide: m. 196–197° (with sintering)[WA2]

Hydriodide: m. 108–109°[WA2]

Picrate: m. 208–210°,[WI30] 206–208°,[WA2] 203–204°,[BA13] 202–204°,[DU3] 202–203°,[HA11] 200–201°,[GE1] 195°,[SC3] 193–194°,[KO8] 192–194°[HU1]

Perchlorate: m. 123–126° (dec.)[SC3]

Chloroaurate: m. *ca.* 220,[KN5] 218°,[DU3] 208–209°,[KO8] 206° (dec.)[SC3]

Chloroplatinate: m. 240° (dec.),[KN5] *ca.* 227° (dec.),[SC3] 215° (dec.),[KO8] 193°[SK7]*

Methobromide: m. 338°,[MC5] 322–325.6°[GR13]

Methiodide: m. 300–301° (dec.),[SP2] above 280°,[KA13]

Methopicrate: m. 299–300°[LO2]

Methochloroplatinate: dec. *ca.* 266°[RI5]

Methotriiodide: m. 64°[MU5]

Methopentiodide: m. 68°,[MU5,ST19] 26°[GE5]†

Methoheptiodide: m. 32°[GE5]

Methononiodide: m. 67°,[ST19] 38°[GE5]†

Methotosylate: m. 185–188° (sealed tube)[SP2]

Methoperchlorate: m. *ca.* 300° (dec.)[HO11]

Methothiocyanate: m. 131–132°[MC3]

Bis-benzenesulfonylochloroplatinate: m. 211° (dec.)[SC3]

Benzenesulfonylopicrate: m. 120–124°[SC3]

Benzenesulfonylochloroaurate: m. *ca.* 167°[SC3]

Benzenesulfonyloperchlorate: m. 123–126° (dec.)[SC3]

Phenopicrate: m. 127–128°[MU1a]

Benzhydrylopicrate: m. 141°[HU2b]

1-Naphthylmethyloiodide: m. 171–173°[NA1a]

Complex quaternary ammonioalkylammonioalkanoate halides[HA8a]

---

* Ref. KN5 claims that ref. SK7 did not obtain either the amine or its chloroplatinate.

† Ref. GE5 acknowledges the discordant value of earlier ref. MU5 but comments no further.

C_5H_9N

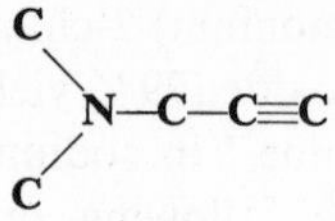

$$\begin{array}{c} C \\ \diagdown \\ N-C-C\equiv C \\ \diagup \\ C \end{array}$$

Me
Me
C_3H_3

1-DIMETHYLAMINO-2-PROPYNE

Phys. Props.:

b. 82°,[CA7,FE2] 81–82°,[MA32] 79–81°,[GU2,RE7] 79–80°,[RE11] 78–80°[SC20]
m. *ca.* −44°[DO2]
d_4^{20} 0.7792[CA7]
n_D^{20} 1.4180[CA7]; n_D^{18} 1.4210[MA32]; n_D^{15} 1.4224,[MA32] 1.4217[GU2]
Heat of combustion: 4330 cal./lb.[DO2]
Nuclear magnetic resonance[HA26]
pK_a 7.05 (temperature unspecified)[CA7]

Prepn.:

1. Dimethylamine + acetylene + formaldehyde in the presence of copper (II) acetate (70% yield),[RE7,RE11] (45% yield).[GU2]
2. 2-Bromo-1-dimethylamino-2-propene + sodamide (25% yield),[CA7] (60% yield)[MA32]; + potassium hydroxide (30% yield).[MA32]
3. Propargyl bromide + dimethylamine (45% yield)[GU2,MA32]; (unspecified yield in the range 50 to 95%)[BI1,BI3]; same reaction with propargyl bromide or chloride (exact halide not specified).[DO2]
4. Bis(dimethylamino)methane + formaldehyde + acetylene in the presence of copper(I) chloride (9% yield). Main product is 1,4-bis(dimethylamino)-2-butyne in 73% yield.[FE2]

Derivs.:

Oxalate: m. 122–123° [CA7,SC20]
Methiodide: m. 180°,[GU2,MA32,SC20]
Methochloride: m. 171–172°[MA32,GU2]
Methobromide: m. 178–179°[MA32,PA7]*

---

* Although ref. PA7 assigns the 2-cyclopropenyl structure to the C_3H_3 substituent based on a bromine absorption study on this methobromide, the authors believe this group to be 2-propynyl for several reasons, among which are the following: analysis of the bromine absorption data does not support the cyclopropenyl structure in view of later knowledge on absorption characteristics of unsaturated compounds[HE14]; moreover, the melting point of the methobromide agrees with that obtained later by others for 2-propynyldimethylamine.[MA32]

$C_5H_{11}N$ Me
Me
C_3H_5

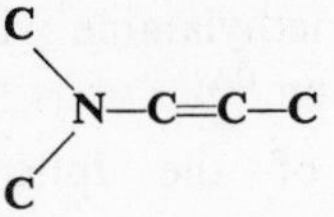

1-DIMETHYLAMINO-1-PROPENE

Derivs.:

Methopicrate: m. 170–172°[RO19] (this salt, prepared from 2-chloropropyl-trimethylammonium chloride and alcoholic potassium hydroxide,[RO19] differs from the allyl isomer, as shown by ozonolysis studies[RO19])
Methochloroaurate: m. 199–202°[SC11]*
Methochloroplatinate: m. 249° (dec.)[SC11]*

$C_5H_{11}N$ N–C–C=C Me
Me
All

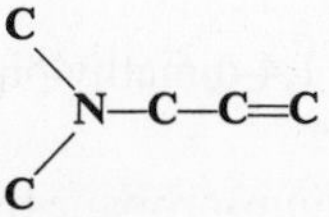

ALLYLDIMETHYLAMINE

Phys. Props.:

b. 64°,[CO25] 61–64°[WE15]; b_{752} 64°[BA20]; b_{745} 62° [CA7]; b_{744} 63–64°[BA20]; b_{743} 64° (cor.)[KN6]; b_{726} 61°[CR2]; b_{680} 58–60°[BA15]
d_4^{25} 0.7094[CO25]; d_4^{20} 0.7172[CA7]
n_D^{25} 1.3981,[CO25] 1.3977[BA20]; n_D^{20} 1.3998,[WE15] 1.3995[CA7]
pK_a 8.72 (temperature unspecified)[CA7]
Infrared absorption: strong bands at 880, 980, 1280, and 2000 cm.$^{-1}$; medium bands at 810, 947, 1080, 1145, 1213, 1270, and 2090 cm.$^{-1}$[BA20]

Prepn.:

1. Dimethylamine + the following halides:
   a. Allyl chloride (39–43% yield),[CO25] (30% yield).[WE15]
   b. Allyl bromide[PA8] (33% yield),[BA20] (10% yield),[ME5] (95% yield).[CR2]
   c. Allyl iodide.[KN6]

---

* In these cases the parent quaternary halide was obtained by reaction of propylene bromide and trimethylamine with loss of hydrogen bromide at some point. Schmidt and Kleine[SC11] postulate the elimination as occurring first to give 1- and 2-bromopropenes. Since only 1-bromopropene is isolable as reaction by-product, they then argue that the 2-isomer, in "nascent state," reacted with the trimethylamine to produce 2-dimethylaminopropene. However, since current theories favor first a displacement by trimethylamine of the primary bromide in the propylene bromide, and then dehydrobromination, formation of the allyl isomer would be expected. That this is not observed is surprising.

2. Reduction of propargyldimethylamine with sodium in liquid ammonia, or by catalytic hydrogenation.[CA7]

3. Thermal decomposition of the following quaternary ammonium compounds:

   a. Allyltrimethylammonium acetate[LU21]; chloride (trace yield)[CO8]; hydroxide (trace yield).[CO8]

   b. Allyl(3-butenyl)dimethylammonium hydroxide.[LU21]

   c. Dimethylallylbutynylammonium bromide in 20% sodium hydroxide (76% yield).[BA13]

   d. Allyltrimethylammonium iodide in ethanolamine (*ca.* 34% yield).[HU1]

   e. Allyltrimethylammonium chloride in the presence of sodium in dioxane.[GR13]

   f. Dimethylallylbenzylammonium chloride in the presence of methylphenylamine gives a mixture of products including a 3% yield of allyldimethylamine.[IN1]

   g. Bis-methochloride of 1,4-dimethylpiperazine in the presence of potassium hydroxide.[KN6]

   h. 1,3-Bis(trimethylammonium)propane hydroxide (18% yield)[BR10] (*Note:* ref. LU23 was unable to obtain any allyldimethylamine in an attempt to duplicate this reaction).

   i. Allyldimethyl-(3-chloro-2-butenyl)ammonium bromide in the presence of sodium hydroxide.[BA15]

4. Thermal decomposition of β-dimethylaminoisopropyl benzoate (61% yield).[BA20]

Derivs.:

Picrate: m. 122–124°,[LU21]* 112°,[BA13,BA15] 108°,[IN1] 100°,[BR10] 95–96°,[BA20] 95°,[KN6] 94–96°[CR2]

Amine oxide picrate: m. 136°[ME5]

Methiodide: m. 104°,[HU1,PA7] 102–104°[KA13]

Methopicrate: m. 220.3–220.5° (dec.),[HO24] 216–218°,[GR13,LU23] 215–216°,[LU21] 214–216°,[RO18] 213–216°[HU1]

Methochloroaurate: m. 211°,[EM2] 210°[WE7]

Methochloroplatinate: m. 228–229° (dec.),[EM2] 215–216° (dec.),[LU1] 215° (dec.)[PA7,WE7]

Methoperchlorate: m. 90°[HO10]

·AlH$_3$ (alane): m. 12°[RU2]

Complex quaternary ammonioalkylammonioalkanoate halides[HA8a]

---

* Ref. LU21 reports this melting point and acknowledges that it is much different from those reported by others.

$C_5H_{11}N$

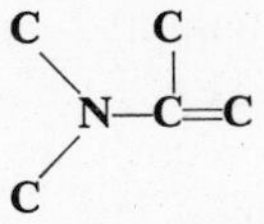

Me
Me
C_3H_5

2-DIMETHYLAMINO-1-PROPENE

Phys. Props.:

b_{756} 41°[BA20]

n_D^{25} 1.3988[BA20]

Infrared absorption: strong bands at 816, 890, 945, 985, 1082, 1160, 1210, 1302, and 2000 cm.$^{-1}$; medium bands at 910, 1035, 1053, 1260, 1427, and 2090 cm.$^{-1}$[BA20]

Prepn.:

Pyrolysis of 2-dimethylaminopropyl benzoate (64% yield).[BA20]

$C_5H_{13}N$

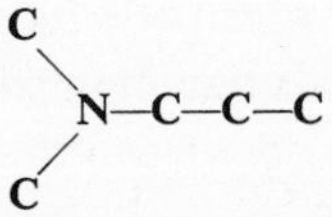

Me
Me
n-Pr

PROPYLDIMETHYLAMINE

Phys. Props.:

b. 65–67°,[PA15,RE6,RE14] 65–66°,[HA11] 64–66°[RE12]; b_{743} 64.5°[HA15] (other values: b_{760} 73°[GA9]; b_{745} 60°[CA7])

d_4^{25} 0.6966[HA15]; d_4^{20} 0.7006,[CA7] 0.7012[HA15]

n_D^{25} 1.3843[HA15]; n_D^{20} 1.3860,[CA7] 1.3866[HA15]; n_C^{25} 1.3820[HA15]; n_C^{20} 1.3843[HA15]; n_F^{25} 1.3899[HA15]; n_F^{20} 1.3924[HA15]

pK_a 10.16 at 20°,[HA15] 9.25[CA7] *

Prepn.:

1. Dimethylamine + ethylene + carbon monoxide under pressure in the presence of iron carbonyl (24% yield),[RE6] (34% yield),[RE12] (46% yield).[RE14]
2. Propylamine + formaldehyde under pressure[HA15]; propylamine + formaldehyde + formic acid (73% yield).[GA9]
3. Thermal decomposition of the following compounds:
   a. Propyltrimethylammonium hydroxide[CO8,IN8] (19% yield).[HA11]
   b. Propyltrimethylammonium chloride.[CO8,HA11]
   c. Propyltrimethylammonium iodide in ethanolamine (*ca.* 95% yield)[HU1]; in the presence of sodium in dioxane.[GR13]

---

* The higher value of 10.16 is more consistent with values for related compounds. See ref. HA6.

    d. 1,4-Bis(dimethylpropylammonium)-2-chloro-2-butene dibromide in aqueous sodium hydroxide (82.6% yield).[BA11]

    e. 1,4-Bis(dimethylpropylammonium)-2-butyne dibromide in aqueous sodium hydroxide (89.8% yield).[BA11]

4. Degradation of propyltrimethylammonium iodide in liquid ammonia.[GR14]

5. Obtained as a degradation product in the study of the structure of desoxypithecolobine.[W16]

6. Catalytic hydrogenation of 1-dimethylamino-2-propyne (poor yield).[CA7]

7. 1-Dimethylamino-2-chloropropane + sodium (39% yield).[PA15]

Derivs.:

Picrate: m. 110°,[PA15] 108–109°[BA13,HA11]
Methobromide: m. 242.5–243.0° (dec.)[HO24]
Methiodide: m. 190°,[LA7] 192–192.5°,[SM9] 188–189°,[KA13] 189°[EM2]
Methoperchlorate: 118°[HO10]
Methochloroaurate: m. 221°,[EM2] 215°[WE7]
Methopicrate: m. 207°,[RI6] 200–202°,[HO24] 195–196°[HA11]
Methochloroplatinate: m. 280° (dec.),[EM2] 260° (dec.)[RI5]
Complex quaternary ammonioalkylammonioalkanoate halides[HA8a]

$C_5H_{13}N$

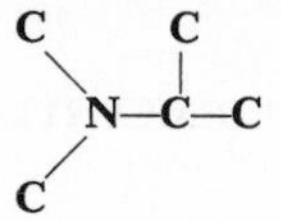

$$
\begin{array}{ccc}
C & & C \\
 & \diagdown & | \\
 & N & -C-C \\
 & \diagup & \\
C & & \\
\end{array}
$$

Me
Me
i-Pr

ISOPROPYLDIMETHYLAMINE

Phys. Props.:

b. 67–67.5°[SK3]; b_{752} 65.5°[HA15]; b_{745} 65.5–65.7°[SP2]; b_{740} 63.8–64.2°[GR13]; b_{733} 63°[WO7]

d_4^{25} 0.7106[HA15,SP2]; d_4^{20} 0.7151,[SP2] 0.7152[HA15]

n_D^{26} 1.3887[WO7]; n_D^{25} 1.3883,[HA15] 1.3874[SP2]; n_D^{20} 1.3905,[SP2] 1.3907[HA15]; n_C^{25} 1.3860[HA15]; n_C^{20} 1.3884[HA15]; n_F^{25} 1.3939[HA15]; n_F^{20} 1.3963[HA15]

pK_a 10.38 at 25°,[SP1] 10.47 at 20°[HA15]

(Other values: d_4^{25} 0.695[WO7])

Prepn.

1. Reaction of isopropylamine with formaldehyde and formic acid (41% yield),[GR13] (71% yield)[SP2]; with formaldehyde under pressure.[HA15]

2. Degradation of isopropyltrimethylammonium iodide in ethanolamine (*ca.* 88% yield).[HU1]

3. Thermal decomposition of propyltrimethylammonium chloride or hydroxide (trace yield implied).[CO8]

4. Acetone + dimethylamine + hydrogen (at 3 atm. pressure) in the presence of platinum (15% yield).[SK3]

5. 2-Dimethylamino-2-methylpropionitrile + lithium aluminum hydride (trace yield).[WE10]
6. Cleavage of isopropyltrimethylammonium iodide by sodium in dioxane,[GR13] in liquid ammonia[GR14]; of the bromide in liquid ammonia.[GR14]

Derivs.:

Hydrochloride: m. 205–206°[SK3]
Methobromide: m. 317° (dec.)[GR13]
Methiodide: m. 316–316.8° (dec.),[GR13]* 294–295° (dec.),[SP2] 286°[KA13]
Methotosylate: m. 187–190° (sealed tube)[SP2]
Methochoroplatinate: m. 237°[RI5]
Methopicrate: m. 305°[RI6]
Complex quaternary ammonioalkylammonioalkanoate halides[HA8a]

$C_5H_{13}N$

Me
Et
Et

METHYLDIETHYLAMINE

Phys. Props.:

b. 66–67° (cor.),[CO8] 66°,[RO3] 65–66°,[HU1] 65°[BR13]; b_{768} 65.7°[HA15]; b_{760} 65.95° ± °0.05[CO27]; b_{740} 65.5–65.7°[SP2]; b_{728} 63°[WO7]
$\log_{10} p_{mm.} = 6.91578 - 1184.8/(t°C + 227.67)$[CO27]
d_4^{25} 0.7016,[SP2] 0.7017[HA15]; d_4^{20} 0.7061,[SP2] 0.7065[HA15]
n_D^{25} 1.3879,[WO7] 1.3865,[SP2] 1.3869[HA15]; n_D^{20} 1.3891,[SP2] 1.3894[HA15]; n_C^{25}1.3845[HA15]; n_C^{20} 1.3870[HA15]; n_F^{25} 1.3926[HA15]; n_F^{20} 1.3951[HA15]
m. (supercools to glass at −196°)[SP2]
pK_a: 10.43 at 25°,[BR29] 10.38 at 25°,[RE6] 10.46 at 20°[HA15]
Lower critical consolute temperature in water: 49.42°[CO27]
(Other values: b. 66–69°,[TE1] 63–65°,[EM12,PA12] 61–62°[CL5]; d_4^{23} 0.703[WO7]; n_D^{25} 1.3879[WO7])

Prepn.:

1. Diethylamine + formaldehyde + formic acid (79% yield),[SP2] (60% yield).[CO27]
2. Diethylamine + formaldehyde under pressure.[HA15]
3. *N,N*-Diethylformamide + lithium aluminum hydride (64% yield).[BL1]
4. Nitromethane + acetaldehyde + hydrogen (92% yield).[EM8,EM9,EM11]

---

* Ref. GR13 notes the lower value of ref. KA13, but makes no further comment.

5. Diethylamine + potassium methyl sulfate[PA12]; + methyl-*p*-toluate (73% yield; other product is *N,N*-diethyl-*p*-toluamide).[CL5]
6. Methylamine + potassium ethyl sulfate.[PA12]
7. Thermal decomposition of the following compounds:
    a. Dimethyldiethylammonium chloride.[LO2,ME17]
    b. Methyltriethylammonium hydroxide[CO8,LO2,WA2] (*ca.* 50% yield).[BR13]
    c. Methyldiethyl(ethoxymethyl)ammonium hydroxide (90% yield).[ST13]
    d. Methyldiethyl(*n*-butoxymethyl)ammonium hydroxide (>64% yield).[RO3]
    e. Dimethylsulfate salt of β-diethylaminopropionitrile.[TE1]
    f. Dimethyldiethylammonium iodide in ethanolamine (79% yield).[HU1]
8. Electrolysis of methyldiethylphenylammonium iodide (68% yield).[EM12]
9. Methylmagnesium iodide + methyldi(*n*-butoxymethyl)amine.[RO3]
10. Oxidation of 1,3-bis(methyldiethylammonium)propene dichloride with potassium permanganate.[IN7]
11. Degradation of the following methyltriethylammonium salts by sodium in the specified solvent: chloride, bromide, or iodide in liquid ammonia[GR14]; chloride or iodide in dioxane.[GR13]
12. Degradation of methyltriethylammonium halide by potassium in liquid ammonia.[HA29]

Derivs.:

Hydrochloride: m. 178.5°[WA2]
Hydrobromide: m. 169°[WA2]
Hydriodide: m. 115–118°[WA2]
Picrate: m. 185–186°,[BL1] 185°,[IN7] 183–185°,[EM8,EM9,EM11] 184°,[TE1] *ca.* 182°,[RI6] 180°[HU1]
Chloroplatinate: m. 231°[RO3,ST13]
·AlH₃ (alane): m. liquid[RU2]
·BH₃: m. −40° to −38°[BR39]
Methiodide: m. 298–299° (dec.),[SP2] 293°[HU1]
Methopicrate: m. 285–287°,[LO2] 284–286°[HU1]
Methotosylate: m. 132–135°[SP2]
Methochloroplatinate: m. 259° (dec.)[RI5]
Ethochloride: m. 284° (dec.)[GR13]
Ethobromide: m. 307.4° (dec.)[GR13]
Ethiodide: m. 308.4–309.5° (dec.),[GR13] 293°,[CA1] 290°[HU1]
Ethotriiodide: m. 62°[GE5]
Ethopentiodide: m. 16°[GE5]
Ethoheptiodide: m. 42°[GE5]
Ethopicrate: m. 276.5–277.4°,[CL7a] 268–268.5°,[MU1a] 267–268°[LO2]
Benzyloiodide: m. 152–154°[NA1a]
Complex quaternary ammonioalkylammonioalkanoate halides[HA8a]

C_6H_9N
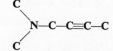
Me
Me
C_4H_3

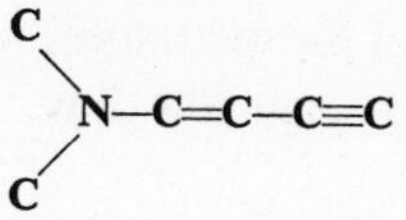

1-DIMETHYLAMINO-1-BUTEN-3-YNE

Phys. Props.:

b_5 32–34°[PE11]

d_4^{20} 0.8590[PE11]

n_D^{20} 1.5152[PE11]

Infrared absorption: 942, 1610–1620, 2072, and 3288 cm.$^{-1}$ (conjugated vinylacetylene frequencies).[PE11]

Prepn.:

Uncatalyzed reaction of diethylamine with diactylene.[PE11,PE12]

$C_6H_{11}N$
Me
Me
C_4H_5

1-DIMETHYLAMINO-2-BUTYNE

Phys. Props.:

b. 117°,[EN2] 116–117°,[LU22] 115.5–116°,[EN2] 114–115°[EN2,GU2,MA32]; b_{680} 112–115°[BA14,MO18]

d_4^{20} 0.7960[BA14]

n_D^{25} 1.4333–1.4342,[EN1] 1.4330–1.4337[EN2]; n_D^{20} 1.4383[BA14]; n_D^{14} 1.4392[GU2,MA32]

Prepn.:

1. Sodio derivative of 1-dimethylamino-2-propyne + methyl iodide[EN2] (41% yield).[MA32]
2. Sodium methylate catalyzed isomerization of 1-dimethylamino-2,3-butadiene (75% yield).[EN1,EN2]
3. Dehydrohalogenation of 1-dimethylamino-3-chloro-2-butene with a solution prepared from sodium in ethylene glycol (51% yield).[LU22]
4. Vinylacetylene + dimethylamine (10–25% yield).[EN1,EN2]
5. Dimethylbis(3-chloro-2-butenyl)ammonium chloride + sodium hydroxide (85% yield).[BA16]
6. Component of a mixture of amines in the thermal decomposition of 1,1-dimethyl-3-pyrrolinium hydroxide.[LU22]
7. Isomerization of 4-dimethylamino-1-butyne in alcoholic potassium hydroxide (84% yield).[BA14]

8. Cleavage by aqueous base of the quaternary ammonium salt derived from 1-dimethylamino-5-methoxy-2-pentyne and 1,3-dichloro-2-butene (33% yield).[BA2]

9. Cleavage by aqueous base of the quaternary ammonium salt derived from 1-dimethylamino-3-chloro-5-methoxy-2-pentene and 1,3-dichloro-2-butene (62.8% yield).[BA2]

Derivs.:

Picrate: m. 122–123°,[LU22] 120°,[BA2,IN1] 118–119°[BA14]
Methiodide: m. 165–166°,[EN1] 164–165°,[EN2] 163°[GU2,MA32,MA33]
Methobromide: m. 60°[BA13]
Ethobromide: m. 102–103°[BA13]
Propobromide: m. 134–135°[BA13]

$C_6H_{11}N$

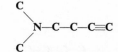

Me
Me
C_4H_5

4-DIMETHYLAMINO-1-BUTYNE

Phys. Props.:

b. 105–108[CA7]; b_{680} 102–105°[BA12,BA14]; b_{200} 61–63°[MA30]
d_4^{20} 0.7896,[CA7] 0.78067[BA12,BA14]
n_D^{20} 1.4290,[CA7] 1.4275[BA12,BA14]; n_D^{17} 1.4282[MA30]
pK_a 8.33 (temperature unspecified)[CA7]
(Other values: b. 97–98°[MA30])

Prepn.:

1. 3-Butynyl bromide + dimethylamine (50% yield).[CA7]
2. Dimethylamine + 3-butynylbenzenesulfonate (46% yield).[MA30]
3. Sodium-catalyzed isomerization of 2-butynyldimethylamine (50% yield),[BA14] (53% yield).[BA12]
4. Sodium acetylide + 2-bromoethyldimethylamine (28% yield).[CA7]

Derivs.:

Hydrochloride: m. 147–148°[CA7]
Picrate: m. 116–117°[BA14]
Methiodide: m. 224°,[BA12] 224–226°[BA14,JA1]
Quaternary salt formation with the benzenesulfonic acid ester of 3-butyne-1-ol gives dimethyldi-(3-butyne-1-yl)ammonium benzenesulfonate, m. 118°[OL6]

$C_6H_{11}N$

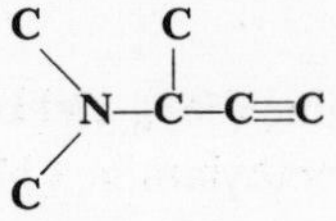

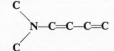

Me
Me
C_4H_5

3-DIMETHYLAMINO-1-BUTYNE

Phys. Props.:

b. 96°,[RO12,WE12] 95–96°[GA3,RE7,RE13]; b_{755} 95–96°[CO26]
Nuclear magnetic resonance[HA26]

Prepn.:

1. Dimethylamine + acetaldehyde + acetylene + formic acid in the presence of copper(I) chloride ("good yield").[RE7]
2. Dimethylamine + acetylene in the presence of copper(I) chloride (65% yield),[GA3] (63% yield).[RE7,RE13]

Derivs.:

Methiodide: m. 214–216° (dec.)[GA3]

$C_6H_{11}N$

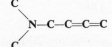

Me
Me
C_4H_5

1-DIMETHYLAMINO-1,3-BUTADIENE

Phys. Props.:

b_9 36.5°[AR8]
n_D^{20} 1.5350[AR8]

Prepn.:

Dimethylamine + crotonaldehyde + potassium carbonate followed by distillation at reduced pressure in the presence of phenanthraquinone (55% yield).[AR8]

$C_6H_{11}N$

Me
Me
C_4H_5

4-DIMETHYLAMINO-1,2-BUTADIENE

Phys. Props.:

b_{760} 106–107°[EN2]; b_{155} 58–60°[EN2]; b_{150} 57.5–59.5°,[EN1] 57.5–58.5°[EN2]
n_D^{25} 1.4468,[EN1] 1.4477,[EN2] 1.4479[EN2]
Infrared absorption: 5.10, 6.0, 10.1, 11.0, 11.8 μ[EN2]; bands ascribed to allene structures, 5.09, 5.86, 11.85[WO8]
Raman band (slight) at 2103 cm.$^{-1}$[EN2]

Prepn.:

1. Vinylacetylene + dimethylamine (56% yield).[EN1,EN2]
2. 1-Chloro-2,3-butadiene + dimethylamine (34% yield).[EN2]

Derivs.:

Methiodide: m. 193–194°[EN1,EN2]
Picrate: m. 123.5–124.5°,[EN2] 122–123°[EN2]

$C_6H_{13}N$

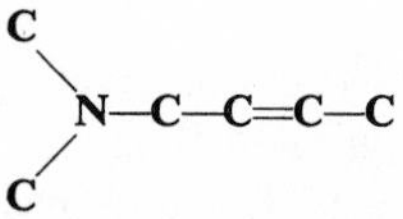

$$\begin{array}{c} C \\ \diagdown \\ N-C-C=C-C \\ \diagup \\ C \end{array}$$

Me
Me
C_4H_7

1-DIMETHYLAMINO-2-BUTENE

Phys. Props.:

cis isomer
    b. 90–91°[OL6]
    d_{20}^{20} 0.7563[OL6]
    n_D^{20} 1.4210[OL6]
trans isomer
    *b. 97–99°,[YO6] 88–89°[OL6]
    d_{20}^{20} 0.7444[OL6]
    n_D^{25} 1.4138, 1.4129[YO6]; n_D^{20} 1.4220[YO6]
Infrared absorption: characteristic band of *trans* isomer at 10.28 μ[YO6]

Prepn.:

cis isomer
    1. Catalytic hydrogenation of 1-dimethylamino-2-butyne with hydrogen
       in the presence of palladium (76% yield).[OL6]
    2. In the isomerization of 1-dimethylamino-2-butyne to 1-dimethyl-
       amino-1-butyne in the presence of sodium, some 1-dimethylamino-2-
       butene (*cis*?) is formed.[BA4]
trans isomer
    1. Dimethylamine + *trans*-1-chloro-2-butene (95% yield).[YO6]
    2. Reduction of 1-dimethylamino-2-butyne with sodium in liquid
       ammonia (62% yield).[OL6]

---

* Refs. YO6 and OL6 do not agree on boiling point for the *trans* isomer, but both claim
to have this isomer based on infrared absorption data. Comparison with the physical
properties of the isoelectronic hydrocarbon analogs, *cis*- and *trans*-5-methyl-2-hexenes,[DR1]
favors the data of ref. OL6. For characteristic absorption maxima (infrared and Raman)
of the *cis* and *trans* isomers of this type of compound, see listing for 1-dimethylamino-2-
heptene.

3. Dimethylamine + 3-chloro-1-butene *via* allylic shift (at least 25% yield).[YO6]
4. Reduction of 1-dimethylamino-2-butyne with sodium in liquid ammonia (62% yield).[OL6]

Unspecified isomer

1. Heating 2-butenyltrimethylammonium iodide in ethanolamine (*ca.* 32% yield).[HU1]
2. 3-Chlorobutyldimethylamine + alcoholic sodium hydroxide.[BA5]

Derivs.:

cis-Methiodide: m. 169° [OL6]
cis-Methochloride: m. 184.5–185.0° (dec.)[YO4]
trans-Methiodide: m. 164° [OL6]
trans-Methochloride: m. 187.8–188.0° (dec.)[YO4]
trans-Picrate: m. 79–79.5° [OL6]
Methiodide: m. 151° [BA5] *

$C_6H_{13}N$ 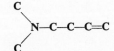   Me
                                                                         Me
                                                                         C_4H_7

4-DIMETHYLAMINO-1-BUTENE

Phys. Props.:

b. 94–96°,[BA42,WI25] 92° [HO22a]
n_D^{20} 1.4130[WI25]
Infrared absorption[WI25]
(Other values: b. 90–93°,[WI25] 89–92°,[LU13] 82–85° [BR20])

Prepn.:

1. Thermal decomposition of 1,1-dimethylpyrrolidinium hydroxide[LU13] (63% yield).[WI25]
2. Degradation of 1,1-dimethylpyrrolidinium bromide with potassium amide in liquid ammonia (56.5% yield)[WI25]; with butyl lithium in ether (10% yield).[WI25]
3. Thermal decomposition of 1,4-bis(trimethylammonium)butane dihydroxide.[BR20]
4. Heating 3-butenyltrimethylammonium salt in ethanolamine (*ca.* 1% yield).[HU1]
5. Dimethylaminomethyl(*n*-butyl ether) + allylmagnesium bromide.[HO22a]

---

* This methiodide is presumably derived from a *cis-trans* isomer mixture.

6. Dehydration of 1-dimethylamino-3-butanol with sulfuric acid[BA42] (structure proof depends on subsequent Hofmann degradation to 1,3-butadiene).

7. On treating α-allylbenzylamine with formic acid and formaldehyde the subject product is obtained instead of the expected N,N-dimethyl-α-allylbenzylamine.[HO22a]

Derivs.:

Picrate: m. 111–112°,[WI25] 110.2–111°[HO22a]
Methiodide: m. 240–241°[HO22a]
Methopicrate: m. 109–110°[LU21]

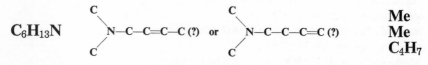

$C_6H_{13}N$ **Me**
Me
C_4H_7

DIMETHYLBUTENYLAMINE*

Phys. Props.:

b. 76–78°[SC7]
n_D^{25} 1.3994[SC7]

Prepn.:

1,2-Bis(dimethylamino)ethane + propene + sulfuric acid. Heptenyldimethyl-amine was also formed, apparently from propylene dimer.[SC7]

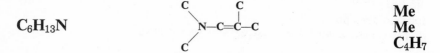

$C_6H_{13}N$ **Me**
Me
C_4H_7

1-DIMETHYLAMINO-2-METHYL-1-PROPENE

Prepn.:

1. Dehydrogenation of isobutyldimethylamine with chloranil is postulated as giving the subject enamine but the product was not directly isolated.[BU2]

2. Pyrolysis of the Grignard complex of 2-methyl-2-hydroxy-1-dimethyl-aminopropane (14% yield as the hydrochloride).[CA6]

3. Dimethylacetaldehyde + dimethylamine in the presence of anhydrous potassium carbonate (73% yield).[GE1]

---

* The authors of the present monograph believe the structure of this compound to be $(CH_3)_2NCH_2CH=CHCH_2$ and/or $(CH_3)_2NCH_2CH_2CH=CH_2$. See "Discussion of Preparative Methods," Section 5. However, the physical properties are lower than expected and suggest impure product.

Derivs.:

Hydrochloride: m. 142–150°[CA6]
Methochloroplatinate: m. 206–207°[SC11]*
Methochloroaurate: m. 190–191[SC11]*

C$_6$H$_{13}$N

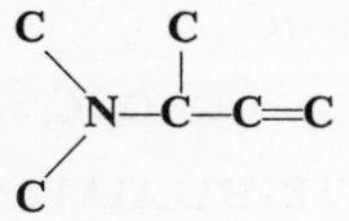

Me
Me
C$_4$H$_7$

3-DIMETHYLAMINO-1-BUTENE

Phys. Props.:
b. 90–93°,[BA41] 91°[YO4]
n$_D^{25}$ 1.4102[YO4]

Prepn.:
1. 3-Amino-1-butene + formaldehyde + formic acid (90% yield).[YO4]
2. Thermal decomposition of 1,1,2-trimethyltrimethyleniminium hydroxide.[BA41]

Derivs.:
Methochloride: m. 203° (dec.)[YO4]

C$_6$H$_{13}$N

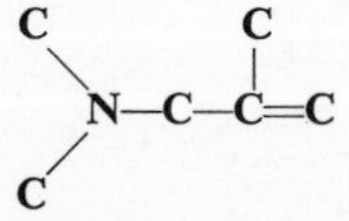

Me
Me
C$_4$H$_7$

3-DIMETHYLAMINO-2-METHYL-1-PROPENE

Phys. Props.:
b. 82–83.5°[CO21]; b$_{750}$ 82.4–82.6°[WE15]
n$_D^{25}$ 1.4055[CO21]; n$_D^{20}$ 1.4092[WE15]

Prepn.:
1. 2-Methylallyl chloride + dimethylamine (82% yield),[CO21] (41% yield).[WE15]
2. Thermal decomposition of $(CH_3)_2NCH_2C(CH_3)_2OMgCl$.[CA6]†
3. Dehydration of 1-dimethylamino-2-methyl-2-propanol with sulfuric acid.[CA6]†

---

* Ref. SC11 does not prove conclusively the location of the double bond in the quaternary ammonium salts. There is some possibility that the parent amine is 1-dimethylamino-2-methyl-2-propene (*q.v.*) but lack of similar derivatives prevents satisfactory comparison.

† Ref. CA6 does not make a formal assignment for the structure of the amine prepared but the experimental data support the structure indicated above.

Derivs.:

Hydrochloride: m. 142–144° CA6*
Chloroaurate: m. 116–118° CA6*

C$_6$H$_{13}$N

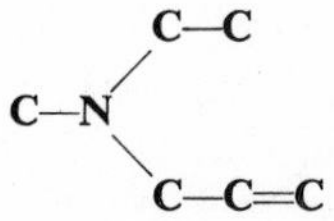

Me
Et
All

METHYLETHYLALLYLAMINE

Phys. Props.:

b$_{762}$ 88–89°ME7

Prepn.:

Methylethylamine + allyl bromide (20% yield).ME7

Derivs.:

Picrate: m. 90°ME7
dl-Amine oxide picrate: m. 134–135°ME7
d-(or *l*-)Amine oxide picrate: m. 133–134°ME7
l-Amine oxide *d*-bromocamphorsulfonate monohydrate: m. 66–68°ME7
d-Amine oxide *d*-bromocamphorsulfonate dihydrate: m. 57–58°ME7

C$_6$H$_{13}$N

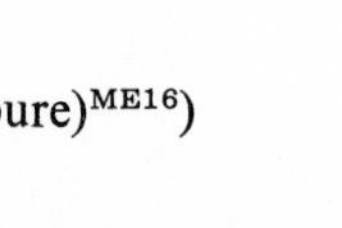

Et
Et
Vin

VINYLDIETHYLAMINE

Phys. Props.:

b$_{95}$ 45–45.5°GE1
(Other value: b. 65–71° (impure)ME16)

Prepn.:

1. Diethylamine + acetaldehyde in the presence of potassium carbonate *ca.* 46% yield).GE1
2. Thermal decomposition of (CH$_3$)$_3$N(OH)CH$_2$CH$_2$N(C$_2$H$_5$)$_2$ (3% yield)ME16
3. *N,N*-Diethyl-(2-hydroxyethyl)amine + hydriodic acid + red phosphorus in a sealed tube.LA3

---

* Ref. CA6 does not make a formal assignment for the structure of the amine prepared but the experimental data support the structure indicated above.

4. Postulated as being formed in the dehydrogenation of triethylamine[BU2] and diethylamine[HE6] by various quinones. Benzoyl peroxide also has been used in the presence of a quinone.[HE6] In each case diethylaminovinyl-quinones have been isolated.

Derivs.:

Chloroaurate: m. 138–140°[LA3]
Ethochloroplatinate: m. 208° (dec.)[LU1]

$C_6H_{15}N$

$$\begin{array}{c} C \\ \diagdown \\ N-C-C-C-C \\ \diagup \\ C \end{array}$$

Me
Me
n-Bu

BUTYLDIMETHYLAMINE

Phys. Props.:

b. 96°,[BR9] 95°,[CL2] 94°[CL3]; b_{761} 95°[CL2]; b_{760} 94–96°,[DE2] 93–94°[GA9]; b_{750} 93.3°[HA13]; b_{749} 94.7–95.2°[BR41]; b_{726} 90°[WO7]

d_4^{25} 0.7164[HA13]; d_4^{20} 0.7206[HA13]

n_D^{25} 1.3953[HA13]; n_D^{20} 1.3970,[BR41] 1.3954,[EN2] 1.3951,[WO7] 1.3976[HA13]; n_C^{25} 1.3929[HA13]; n_C^{20} 1.3953[HA13]; n_F^{25} 1.4010[HA13]; n_F^{20} 1.4034[HA13]

pK_a 10.31 (from rate of reaction with epoxides),[HA14] 10.19 at 20°,[HA13] 10.06 at 25°[HA13]

(Other values: b. 93–96°,[HA11] 90–95°,[RE14] 90°[EN2]; b_{760} 90–95°[RE6]; d_4^{28} 0.721[WO7])

Prepn.:

1. Reaction of butylamine with formic acid and formaldehyde (80% yield),[CL3] (75% yield),[GA9] with formaldehyde under pressure.[HA13]
2. *n*-Butyraldehyde + formic acid + dimethylamine (60% yield).[DE2]
3. Butyl iodide + dimethylamine.[CL2]
4. Butyl chloride + dimethylamine.[FA5]
5. Pyrolysis of butyltrimethylammonium hydroxide,[IN8] (51% yield),[BR9] (25% estimated yield).[HA11]
6. By-product in the hydrolysis of the butiodide of 1,3,5-trimethylhexa-hydro-*s*-triazine with hydrochloric acid.[BL5]
7. Dimethylamine + propylene + iron carbonyl + carbon monoxide under pressure (35% yield).[RE6,RE14]
8. *N,N*-Dimethylbutyramide + lithium aluminum hydride (50% yield).[BR41]
9. Catalytic hydrogenation of dimethyl-2-(or -3-)butenylamine,[MA23] or dimethyl-2,3-butadienylamine,[EN2] or 1-dimethylamino-2-butyne.[MA32]
10. Crotonaldehyde + dimethylformamide (poor yield).[MO17]
11. Decomposition of dimethylbutyl-(2-butynyl)ammonium bromide in 20% NaOH (81% yield).[BA13]

12. Decomposition of 1,4-bis(dimethylbutylammonium)-2-butyne dibromide in 20% NaOH (93% yield).[BA11]
13. Decomposition of butyltrimethylammonium iodide in ethanolamine at 150° (*ca.* 98% yield).[HU1]
14. Degradation by sodium of the following quaternary ammonium salts in the solvents indicated: trimethylbutylammonium bromide, chloride, or iodide in liquid ammonia[GR14]; butyltrimethylammonium chloride or iodide in dioxane[GR13]; dimethyldibutylammonium chloride in *t*-butyl alcohol-dioxane (60% yield)[GR13]; dimethyldibutylammonium iodide in liquid ammonia.[GR14]

Derivs.:
Picrate: m. 99.5–100.5°[BL5]; 98°[BR9]; 97–98°[EN2]; 96°[CL2]; 95–96°[BA13,DE2]
Chloroplatinate: m. 110°[BR9]
Amine oxide picrate: m. 72°[HO21]
Hydrochloride: m. 183–185°[BL5]
·B(CH$_3$)$_3$: m. 16.4–19.0°[BR43]
Methochloride: m. 223.7–224.0°[GR13]
Methobromide: m. 212°,[MC5] 182°[BR24]
Methiodide: m. (dec.)[BR9]; 229–230°,[MA32] 226°[KA13]
Methopicrate: m. 96°[RI6]
Methoperchlorate: m. *ca.* 186°[HO10]
Methochloroplatinate: m. *ca.* 259° (dec.)[RI5]
Complex quaternary ammonioalkylammonioalkanoate halides[HA8a]

$C_6H_{15}N$

Me
Me
sec-Bu

2-DIMETHYLAMINOBUTANE

b. 93–93.5°[CO23]; b$_{755}$ 92.6°[HA15]; b$_{739}$ 92.8–93.0°[GR13]
d$_4^{25}$ 0.7340,[CO23] 0.7339[HA15]; d$_4^{20}$ 1.4027[HA15]
n$_D^{25}$ 1.4000,[CO23] 1.4003[HA15]; n$_D^{20}$ 1.4027[HA15]; n$_C^{25}$ 1.3980[HA15]; n$_C^{20}$ 1.4004[HA15]; n$_F^{25}$ 1.4058[HA15]; n$_F^{20}$ 1.4083[HA15]
pK$_a$ 10.57 at 20°[HA15]

Prepn.:
1. *sec*-Butylamine + formic acid + formaldehyde (64% yield).[GR13]
2. Hydrogenation of a mixture of methyl ethyl ketone and dimethylamine over platinum oxide (25% yield).[CO23]
3. Dimethylamine + acetylene under pressure in the presence of copper(I) chloride in tetralin solvent, followed by catalytic hydrogenation.[RE13]
4. Thermal decomposition of *sec*-butyltrimethylammonium hydroxide (very low yield).[HA11]

5. *sec*-Butylamine hydrochloride + formaldehyde under pressure.[HA15]

6. Decomposition of *sec*-butyltrimethylammonium iodide by sodium in dioxane,[GR13] in liquid ammonia.[GR14]

Derivs.:

Picrate: m. 197–198 (dec.)[CO23]

Amine oxide picrate: m. 166.8–167.5[CO23]

Methiodide: m. 258–259° [CO23]

$C_6H_{15}N$

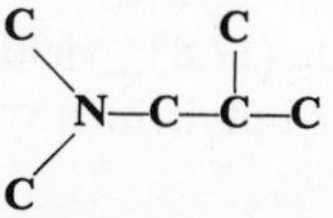

Me
Me
i-Bu

ISOBUTYLDIMETHYLAMINE

Phys. Props.:

b. 80–81°[HA11]; b_{753} 81°[HA15]

d_4^{25} 0.7045[HA15]; d_4^{20} 0.7097[HA15]

n_D^{25} 1.3884[HA15]; n_D^{20} 1.3907[HA15]; n_C^{25} 1.3980[HA15]; n_C^{20} 1.4004[HA15]; n_F^{25} 1.3949[HA15]; n_F^{20} 1.3975[HA15]

pK_a 10.08 at 20°[HA15]

Prepn.:

1. Isobutyraldehyde + the formic acid + dimethylamine (59% yield).[DE2]

2. Heating isobutyltrimethylammonium iodide in the presence of ethanolamine (*ca.* 99% yield).[HU1]

3. Heating isobutyltrimethylammonium hydroxide[CO8] (37% estimated yield).[HA11]

4. Isobutylamine + formaldehyde under pressure.[HA15]

Derivs.:

Picrate: m. 125–126°,[DE2] 124°[HA11]

Methiodide: m. 182–185°[KA13]

Methobromide: m. 187–188°[BR22]

Methochloroplatinate: m. 220°[RI5]

Methopicrate: m. 177–178°,[RI6] 173–174°[HA11]

$C_6H_{15}N$

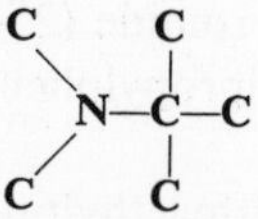

Me
Me
t-Bu

t-BUTYLDIMETHYLAMINE

Phys. Props.:

b. 90–91°, [CA4] 89–90°, [BO14] 89°[ME2]; b_{753} 89.1°[HA15]; b_{740} 89.6–89.9°[SP2]

d_{25}^{25} 0.7372[BO14]; d_4^{25} 0.7377, [SP2] 0.7390[HA15]; d_4^{20} 0.7419, [SP2] 0.7436[HA15]

n_D^{25} 1.4024,[HA15] 1.4021,[SP2] 1.4020,[WO7] 1.4020[BO14]; n_D^{20} 1.4041,[SP2] 1.4047[HA15]; n_C^{25} 1.4001[HA15]; n_C^{20} 1.4024[HA15]; n_F^{25} 1.4078[HA15]; n_F^{20} 1.4101[HA15]

pK_a 10.62 at 25°,[SP1] 10.69 at 20°[HA15]

(Other values: b. 88.3–89.2°[GR13]; b_{735} 90°[WO7]; d_4^{25} 0.735[ME2]; n_D^{25} 1.4015[ME2]; n_D^{23} 1.4035[CA4])

Prepn.:

1. *t*-Butylamine + formaldehyde + formic acid (76% yield),[SP2] (95% yield),[ME2] (85% yield),[GR13] (50% yield).[CA4]
2. *t*-Butylamine + methyl iodide (17.8% yield).[BO14]
3. Thermal decomposition of *t*-butyltrimethylammonium hydroxide (trace yield implied).[HA11]
4. *t*-Butylamine hydrochloride + formaldehyde under pressure.[HA15]
5. Degradation of *t*-butyltrimethylammonium iodide by sodium in dioxane,[GR13] in cumene,[GR13] or in liquid ammonia.[GR14]

Derivs.:

Picrate: m. 289° (dec.)[CA4]

Methiodide: m. 260–260.5°,[GR13] 258° (dec.),[BO14] 240–241° (dec.),[SP2] 225–226°[ME2]*

Methotosylate: m. 184–187° (sealed tube)[SP2]

$C_6H_{15}N$ Me
Et
n-Pr

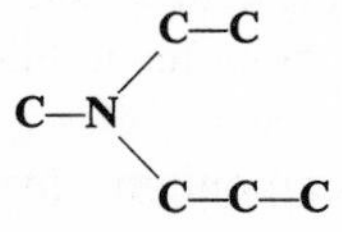

METHYLETHYLPROPYLAMINE

Phys. Props.:

b. 91–92°[CO23,ME3]

d_4^{25} 0.7180[CO23]

n_D^{25} 1.3952[CO23]

Prepn.:

1. Ethylpropylamine + formaldehyde + formic acid (56% yield).[CO23]
2. Methylethylamine + propyl bromide (25–30% yield).[ME3]
3. Electrolysis of methylethylpropylphenylammonium iodide (47.5% yield).[EM12]
4. Thermal degradation of dimethylethylpropylammonium hydroxide (very low yield).[HA11]
5. Exhaustive methylation of codeine.[GE2]

---

* Ref. ME2 claims that the melting point cited agrees with the value reported by ref. BO14. This claim seems to be in error.

Derivs.:

Hydrochloride: m. 177–179°[ME3]
Picrate: m. 94–95°,[ME3] 94.5–95.2[CO23]
Chloroplatinate: m. 176–177°[ME3]
Oxide: m *ca.* 62°[ME3]
Amine oxide picrate: m. 106–107°,[ME3] 104.5–105.3°[CO23]
Amine oxide chloroplatinate: m. 204–216°[ME3]
Methochloroplatinate: m. 256° (dec.)[RI5]
Methopicrate: m. 183.4–184.4°,[CO23] 185–187°[HA11]

$C_6H_{15}N$

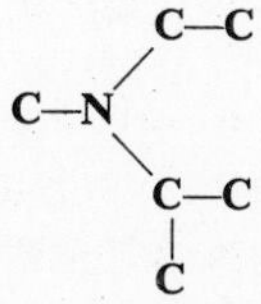

Me
Et
i-Pr

METHYLETHYLISOPROPYLAMINE

Phys. Props.:

b. 91–92°,[CO23] 90°[RO4]
d_4^{25} 0.7214[CO23]
n_D^{25} 1.3981,[CO23] 1.3998[RO4]

Prepn.:

Ethylisopropylamine + formaldehyde + formic acid[RO4] (72% yield).[CO23]

Derivs.:

Picrate: m. 208–208.7°[CO23]
Amine oxide picrate: m. 190.5–192° (dec.)[CO23]
Methiodide: m. 268–269° (dec.)[CO23]
Ethobromide: m. 277° (cor.)[RO4]

$C_6H_{15}N$

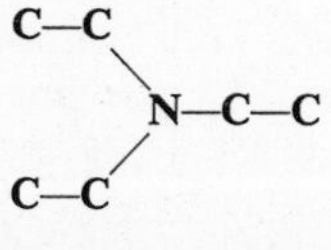

Et
Et
Et

TRIETHYLAMINE*

Phys. Props.:

b_{760} 89.55–89.59°,[CO27a,CO27b] 89.40°,[KO5,TI4a] 89.2°[HO14b]; b_{748} 88.9°[CO28]; b_{580} 80.0°[PE2a]; b_{400} 70.0°[PE2a]; $b_{190.7}$ 48.7°[PE2a]; $b_{125.5}$ 39.0°[PE2a]; $b_{43.5}$ 16.7°[PE2a]; $b_{40.0}$ 15.7°[PE2a]; $b_{30.0}$ 9.8°[PE2a]; $b_{18.3}$ 0°[HO14b]

---

* As in the case of trimethylamine, the overabundance of literature on this compound has necessitated limitation of the data presented.

$\log_{10} p_{\text{mm.}} = 7.00853 - 1307.8/(t°C + 227.3)^{\text{CO27a}*}$

(Other values: b. $91°,^{\text{BU3}}$ $89–90°,^{\text{BO13}}$ $89–89.5°,^{\text{SC14}}$ $89°,^{\text{WO7}}$ $88–89°^{\text{HE21}}$; $b_{767.8}$ $89–90°^{\text{HO8}}$; b_{762} $88.9°^{\text{BA25a}}$; b_{759} $89.5°^{\text{VO1}}$; $b_{758.3}$ $88.8–89.0°^{\text{SC2}}$; $b_{735.5}$ $89–89.5°^{\text{BR48}}$; see also refs. JO10, PO0 and TH3)

m. $-114.75°,^{\text{TI2}}$ $-114.7°,^{\text{ST18,TI4}}$ $-114.5°^{\text{BE7a}}$

d_4^{262} 0.251^{HE21}; d_4^{260} 0.335^{HE21}; d_4^{240} 0.437^{HE21}; d_4^{220} 0.488^{HE21}; d_4^{200} 0.523^{HE21}; d^{180} 0.552^{HE21}; d_4^{160} 0.5864^{CO28}; d_4^{140} 0.6097^{CO28}; d_4^{120} 0.6310^{CO28}; d_4^{100} 0.6513^{CO28}; d_4^{89} 0.6621^{SC2}; d_4^{80} 0.6710^{CO28}; d_4^{70} 0.6815^{KU6}; d_4^{62} 0.6899^{VO1}; $d_4^{60.5}$ 0.6912^{VO1}; d_4^{60} $0.6910,^{\text{KU6}}$ 0.6903^{CO28}; d_4^{50} $0.7012,^{\text{HO4}}$ 0.7005^{KU6}; $d_4^{42.2}$ 0.7083^{VO1}; $d_4^{41.7}$ 0.7087^{VO1}; d_4^{40} $0.7099,^{\text{KU6}}$ 0.7091^{CO28}; d_4^{35} 0.71345^{SW6}; d_4^{30} 0.7194^{KU6}; d_4^{25} $0.7255,^{\text{JA4}}$ $0.7241,^{\text{KU6}}$ $0.72273,^{\text{SW6}}$ $0.72271,^{\text{CO27b}}$ 0.7225^{BA25a}; $d_4^{22.3}$ 0.7255^{VO1}; $d_4^{21.2}$ 0.7280^{GL2}; d_4^{20} $0.7288,^{\text{KU6}}$ $0.7277^{\text{BR48,CO28}}$; d_4^{15} 0.73197^{SW6}; d_4^{4} 0.7426^{PE3}; d_4^{0} 0.74561^{SW6}; d_4^{-20} 0.7650^{CO28}; d_4^{-40} 0.7829^{CO28}; d_4^{-60} 0.8005^{CO28}

(Other values: d_{25}^{25} 0.7257^{PE3}; d_4^{25} 0.725^{PE3}; d_{20}^{20} 0.7294^{PE3}; d_4^{20} 0.73^{WO7}; d_{15}^{15} 0.7331^{PE3}; d_4^{15} 0.735^{SC2}; densities at elevated temperatures and superatmospheric pressures$^{\text{HE21,WA17a}}$

n_D^{26} 1.3980^{WO7}; n_D^{25} $1.3989,^{\text{MO14a}}$ $1.3987,^{\text{SC14}}$ 1.3978^{CO27b}; n_D^{20} $1.40101,^{\text{VO1}}$ n_C^{20} 1.39859^{VO1}; n_F^{20} 1.40670^{VO1}; n_G^{20} 1.41099^{VO1} (see also ref. TI5)

pK_a 10.21 at $45°^{\text{FY1}}$; 10.45 at $35°^{\text{FY1}}$; 10.77 at $25°^{\text{MO9}}$; 10.74 at $25°^{\text{BR29,HA6}}$; 10.82 at $20°^{\text{HA15}}$; 10.83 at $18°^{\text{FY1}}$; 10.81 at $18°^{\text{BR33}}$ (other values$^{\text{AB1}}$ $^{\text{BR33,FY1,HA13,HA16,OS1,SC15,TS4}}$); 9.25 in 70% ethanol$^{\text{BO13}}$; 11.01 in nitromethane$^{\text{ST18a}}$; in various nonaqueous solvents$^{\text{DA14a,HA5}}$; in deuterium oxide$^{\text{SC21}}$

Critical temperature: $259°,^{\text{VI4}}$ $258.9°^{\text{BE7a}}$

Critical pressure: 30 atm.$^{\text{BE7a,VI4}}$

Molar Kerr constant: $3.81 \times 10^{-12\,\text{AR10}}$

Magneto-optic rotation: $[\rho]_M = 608^{\text{GA1a}}$

Dipole moment at 25°, (Debyes): gas, 0.660^{BA25a}; liquid, 0.758^{BA25a}; benzene solution, $0.913,^{\text{BA25a}}$ 0.90^{FO1} (other values: benzene solution, $0.789,^{\text{HI1}}$ $0.80,^{\text{BO14c}}$ $0.82,^{\text{GH2}}$ 0.87^{AR10}; hexane solution, $0.80,^{\text{BO14c}}$ 0.749^{HI1})

---

* Despite otherwise excellent careful work by Copp and Everett,$^{\text{CO27a}}$ their frequently referenced vapor pressure-temperature Antoine-type equation for triethylamine:

$$\log_{10} p_{\text{mm.}} = 7.00853 - 1307.8/(t°C + 272.3)$$

was found not to agree by a very substantial error with the boiling point values of other workers. Unfortunately, Copp and Everett did not give their experimental data. However, by the use of values reported by others, coupled with trial and error and, eventually, a little intuition, the present authors were able to deduce that two digits in the constant additive term of the denominator had been accidentally transposed. The correct number in the equation is 227.3.

Incidentally, it should also be pointed out that Copp and Everett$^{\text{CO27a}}$ noted discrepancies between dynamic and static vapor pressure determinations; for example, at 760 mm., the latter gave a temperature of 88.6°, lower by 1° than that obtained by the dynamic method. This they attributed to the accumulation of pyrolytic products within the isoteniscope.

Dielectric constant (liquid): 3.15 at 25°,[WA3a] 2.408 at 25°,[BA25a] 2.425 at 20°[TI6a]

Dielectric relaxation time: 9.2 × 10⁻¹² sec. at 9516 mc./sec., 20°[VY1] (other values[LA58a])

Molar distortion polarization: 33.8,[BO14c] 33.04[BA25a]

Molar total polarization: gas, 41.93 at 25°,[BA25a] 40.24 at 100°[BA25a]; benzene solution, 50.1,[BA25a] 47.0[BO14c]

Ionization potential: 7.50 e.v. (photo)[WA19]

Magnetic susceptibility[FR2]

Surface tension: 21.12, 20.05, 18.98 dyne cm.⁻¹ at 15°, 25°, and 35°, respectively.[SW6a] Parachor.[SW6a] (see also refs. TI5 and VO1)

Molecular structure, by electron diffraction: C—C distance 1.54 ± 0.02A C—N distance 1.47 ± 0.02A, C—C—N angle 113 ± 3°, C—N—C angle 113 ± 3°.[SH3a]

Azeotropes: with ethanol,[CO27a] propanol,[CO27b] acetic acid[HO13]

Lower critical consolute temperature in water: 18.40° (*ca.* 30 wt. % amine),[RO2] 18.33° (31.0 wt. % amine),[KO5] 18.30° (30 wt. % amine),[KR8] 18.25° (34 wt. % amine)[TI5] (other values[CO6,KR7,LO16,MO6,MO14,RO16 SE5,TS1])

Lower critical consolute temperature in deuterium oxide: 14.45° (35.1 wt. % amine)[TI7]

Physical chemical studies of binary system with:
(a) water[CO27a,CO31,GU7,HA1,HA18,KA18,KO3a,KO4,KO5,KO11,KO18a,KR8,KR8a,LA13, LI14,MA41,ME1,MO6,PI2,RO2,RO16,SE5,SE5a,SE6,SK8a,SK8b,ST15,TI1,TI7, ZH2,ZO1]

(b) alcohols[CO5,CO27a,CO27b,FI7a,HE18,JO10,ZE1]

(c) chloroform[SM7,TA7]

(d) aromatic hydrocarbons[JO10,KO4a,KO13,MO9,NE1,SM7]

(e) phenol[JU1,MA28]

(f) organic acids[HO12,JO10]

(g) esters[KI6]

(h) ethyl ether[JO10]

(i) miscellaneous[JO10,MO1]

Physical chemical studies of ternary system with water and:
(a) organic halides[SA9]

(b) alcohols[HE18,HE19]

(c) ethyl ether[CO6,KR10a,SA9]

(d) aromatic hydrocarbons[KO13,KO14,HA18,MO10]

(e) phenols[ST15a,ST16,MA28a]

(f) miscellaneous[FE7,ME1,TI1,WI11]

Paper chromatography[KA1,VE1a]

Vapor phase chromatography[BA23a,CH4,FR1a,JA6]

Analysis of amine mixtures[BA18,BA23a,CH4,DA15,DU1,FR1a,KR5b,KR6,KR10,LO4,SA11, ST18,TS2,TS4,TS9]

Ultraviolet absorption: near-[LE14a]; far- (max at 2120 A.)[TA8]
Raman spectrum[DA1]
Infrared absorption: 1–2.6 μ,[MC7a] 2.5–4.5 μ[BR32a]
Nuclear magnetic resonance[HO1,MA42a,SP4]
Viscosity (cp.): 0.225 at 70°,[KU6] 0.246 at 60°,[KU6] 0.270 at 50°,[KU6] 0.296 at 40°,[KU6] 0.327 at 30°,[KU6] 0.344 at 25°,[KU6] 0.362 at 20°[KU6]; changes with pressure up to 2000 kg./cm.[2 KU6] (see also refs. FR10a and TI5)
Heat of combustion (kcal./mole) at constant volume: 1038.3,[MU4] 1038.8,[LE11] 1034.9[LE12]
Heat of combustion (kcal./mole) at constant pressure: gas, 1036.8,[KH1a] 1040.7[LE11]; liquid, 1047.1,[LA14a,MU4] 1052.38[TH4]
Heat of solution in water: 42 joule/mole solute at infinite dilution[WA17c]
Flash point: −6.4° (20°F)[PE2a]

Prepn.:

1. A mixture of mono-, di-, and tri-ethylamines is obtained in the following alkylation reactions on ammonia (per cent yield refers to triethylamine):
   a. With ethanol under various conditions of temperature, pressure, and catalyst.[BR36,DA13,KO2,KR9,IS4,NI4,PO6,SM12,TA12,TA13,WH3]
   b. With ethanol and hydrogen in two steps over copper and nickel catalysts (11.6% yield).[LE10,NI4]
   c. With ethyl chloride[DU8,HO2,VI3] over magnesium oxide or calcium hydroxide ("good yield" under some conditions).[OX1]
   d. With ethyl bromide.[HO2,RA1,TS5]
   e. With ethyl iodide.[HO2,WA21]
   f. With ethyl sulfate.[HE4,HE4a]
   g. With ethyl nitrate.[LE1]
   h. With ethylene over alkali metal[HO23,WH4] and/or alkali metal hydride as catalyst (up to 32% yield).[KU6]
   i. With acetaldehyde and hydrogen over nickel-alumina[VA3] or nickel-chromia catalyst (*ca.* 20% yield)[TR4]; over platinum catalyst.[OL1,SK1]
   j. With acetylene over uranium oxide (U_3O_8) catalyst.[OF1]
2. Higher yields are obtained by the alkylation of mono- and/or di-ethylamine with the following:
   a. With ethyl bromide (*ca.* 60% yield).[RA1]
   b. With ethyl nitrate.[G11]
   c. With ethylene over alkali metal catalyst (20.8% yield)[HO23]; in presence of formic acid (29% yield).[RE12]
   d. With acetaldehyde and a reducing agent such as hydrogen over platinum,[SK2] zinc and acid ("good yield"),[CH2] (85% yield),[SK3] ammonia over chromia,[CH10] excess aldehyde and/or hydrogen over nickel (90% yield).[CH9,OL1]
3. Reduction of the following compounds:
   a. Acetaldoxime by hydrogen over palladium.[GU4]

b. Acetonitrile by hydrogen over platinum (85% yield),[SK3] over nickel.[SA5]

c. Ethyl nitrite by hydrogen over nickel or copper catalyst.[GA7]

d. Acetaldazine by hydrogen over nickel catalyst.[MA13]

e. Vinyldiethylamine by hydrogen over platinum catalyst.[GE1]

f. *N,N*-Diethylacetamide by lithium aluminum hydride (50% yield)[UF1]; by diisobutylaluminum hydride (low yield).[ZA3]

4. Aluminum nitride + ethanol at elevated temperature.[FI1]

5. Disproportionation of ethylamine over copper or cobalt catalyst,[FA6,NI2] over alumina.[FA9]

6. Reductive alkylation of acetonitrile by acetaldehyde with hydrogen over nickel catalyst (62% yield).[PR1]

7. Nickel-catalyzed hydrogenolysis of 1,1-bis(diethylamino)ethylene.[MC6]

8. Chloromethyldiethylamine + methylmagnesium iodide.[PR3]

9. 1-Diethylamino-2-chloroethane + sodium (30% yield).[PA15]

10. *N,N*-Diethylpropionamide + ethylmagnesium bromide.[MD4]

11. Pyrolysis of diethyl *N,N*-diethylphosphoramidate (14% yield)[CA1]; of ethyl *N,N*-triethylphosphonamidate (67% yield)[CA1]; of other diethylaminophosphorus compounds.[CA2]

12. In 71% yield in the desulfurization by Raney nickel of 1,4,7-trithia-2,5,8-endazacyclononane[TH1]:

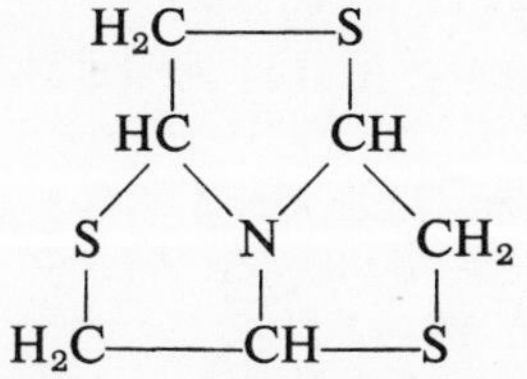

$$H_2C\!-\!\!-\!\!-\!S$$
$$HC\qquad CH$$
$$S\quad N\quad CH_2$$
$$H_2C\!-\!\!-\!CH\!-\!\!-\!S$$

13. Pyrolysis of *N,N*-diethyl-3-chloro-2-butenylamine hydrochloride (17% yield).[BA8]

14. Cleavage of tetraethylammonium and alkyl-(or aryl)-triethylammonium halides:

a. By alkali metals.[HA29,JO4,SC5,SC19a]

b. By alkali metal amides.[HA29,JO4]

c. By alkali metallo-organics such as butyllithium.[HA3]

d. By electrolysis in liquid ammonia.[SC19b]

15. Pyrolysis of tetraethylammonium hydroxide.[WA2]

Derivs.:

SIMPLE SALTS OF PROTONIC ACIDS

·Hydrochloride: m. 260° (dec.),[EA1] 255–256°,[HE2a] 254–255°,[BU2a] 253–254°[WA2]

·Hydrobromide: m. 248–250°,[HA8a] 248°,[BO10,WA2] 247°,[TS4] 246°[TS9]

·Hydriodide: m. 181°,[WA2] 175–176°[NO1a]

·Sulfate: m. 74–75°[MO1]

·Nitrite: m. 97–98°[WO4a]

·Chloroplatinate: m. 219°[EM2]
·Tetrafluoborate: m. 106.5–108.0°[MU1]
·Tetrachloroborate: m. 71–75°[KY2]
·Tetrachlorostibnite: m. 92–94°[KL2a]
·Tetraphenyl borate: m. 172–174°[CR1]
·Picrate: m. 176°,[PA15] 175°,[IN4,IN5] 174.5°,[WA12] 173–174°,[TH1,TR2] 173°,[JE2,RI6,TS4,TS9] 172–173°[GE1]
·Reineckate [Cr(NH$_3$)$_2$(SCN)$_4^-$]: m. 205–208° (dec.),[AY1] 200–207° (dec.)[KU5]
·Styphnate: m. 170°[JE2]
·Trifluoromethanesulfonate: m. 41°[GR4a]
·3,5-Dinitrobenzoate: m. 153°[VE3]
·p-Acetamidobenzoate: m. 137–138°[LA12a]
·8-Nitrotheophylline-7-acetate: m. 245°[SE6a]
·2-Acetamido-3-methylthiolcrotonate: m. 90.5°[FO1a]
·N-Trityl-L-glutamate: m. ca. 100°[AM1a]
·N-(p-Propylphenyl)dithiocarbamate: m. 92–93°[FA1a]
·N-(p-Butylphenyl)dithiocarbamate: m. 91–92°[FA1a]
·N-(2-Pyridyl)dithiocarbamate: m. 88–89° (dec.),[FA1a] 84–85°,[KN6a] 68–74°[EC1]
·N-(3-Pyridyl)dithiocarbamate: m. 87° (dec.),[KN6a] 85–86°[FA1a]
·N-(4-Pyridyl)dithiocarbamate: m. 141°[KN6a]
·N-(6-Methyl-2-pyridyl)dithiocarbamate: m. 76°[KN6a]
·N-(3-Quinolyl)dithiocarbamate: m. 89°[KN6a]
·N-(2-Thiazolyl)dithiocarbamate: m. 142°,[KN6a] 141–142°,[FA1a] 130°(dec.)[HA24a]
·2-Methyldithiocarbanilate: m. 72–76°[FI7c]
·3-Methyldithiocarbanilate: m. 73.5–77.5°[FI7c]
·2,6-Dimethyldithiocarbanilate: m. 82–86°[FI7c]
·3-Nitrodithiocarbanilate: m. 89–92°[FI7c]
·3-Acetyldithiocarbanilate: m. 77–80°[FI7c]
·2-Methoxydithiocarbanilate: m. 62–71°[FI7c]
·4-Dimethylaminodithiocarbanilate: m. 79–84°[FI7c]
·5-Chloro-2-methoxydithiocarbanilate: m. 76–81°[FI7c]
·Various other substituted dithiocarbanilates[FI7c]
Et$_3$N salts of:
    Bis-(2-cyano-5-nitrophenol): m. 89.3–90.8°[CL7a]
    Dibenzenesulfonimide: m. 109–110°[RU3]
    Bis-(4-chlorobenzenesulfon)imide: m. 83–84°[RU4]
    p-(2,2,4-Trimethyl-4-chromanyl)phenol: m. 158–159°[BA20a]
    Tetradecafluoroheptane-4,4-diol: m. 87.5–88.5°[HA26a]
    Hexachloropropane-2,2-diol: m. 48–49°[HA26a]
    2-Phenyl-1,3-indanedione: m. 111°[VA2a]
    2-Nitro-1,3-indanedione oxime: m. 80–83°[VI6]
    3,3′-Methylene-bis-(4-hydroxycoumarin) ("Dicoumarol"): m. 199–201°[EC1]
    Rhodanine[LO1] and various substituted rhodanines[DE6a,DE6b,LO1a]
    (Bis-Et$_3$N salt), 2,6-bis(dithiocarboxyamino)pyridine: m. 112°[KN6a]

Group III—Boron

$Et_3N \cdot BH_3$: m. $-2°,^{NO3}$ $-4°^{BR39,KO18,ZH1}$; b_{12} 100–101°,^{KO18} 97.0°,^{AS1} 96–97°^{FA2a}; b_1 28°^{BR39}

$(Et_3N)_2 \cdot B_{10}H_{12}$: m. 233–235° (dec.)^{HA28b}

$Et_3N \cdot B_{10}H_{14}$: m. 98° (dec.)^{HA28c}

$Et_3N \cdot BF_3$: m. 29.5°^{KR3a}; b_3 80°^{KR3a}

$Et_3N \cdot BMe_3$: m. -15 to $-13°$ (dec.)^{BR47}

$Et_3N \cdot B(C_6H_5)_3$: m. 177–178°^{BO8a}

$Et_3N \cdot BH_2Cl$: m. 39°^{RA6}; b_1 120°^{RA6}

$Et_3N \cdot BHF_4$: m. 106.5–108.0°^{MU1}

$Et_3N \cdot BHCl_2$: m. 5°^{RA6}; b_1 132°^{RA6}

$Et_3N \cdot BH(C_6H_5)_2$: m. 64–65°^{HA28a}

$Et_3N \cdot BH(C_6H_5)_4$: m. 172–174°^{CR1}

$Et_3N \cdot BCl_2(C_6H_5)$: m. 80–84°^{MI1b}

$Et_3N \cdot BCl(C_6H_5)_2$: m. 125–133°^{MI1c}

Group III—Aluminum

$Et_3N \cdot AlH_3$: m. 18–19°^{RU2}

$Et_3N \cdot AlCl_3$: m. 121.6–122.1°^{EL3}

$Et_3N \cdot Al(i\text{-}Bu)_3$: b_1 90°^{ZA3}

Group III—Rare Earths

$Et_3N \cdot ScCl_3$: m. dec. $> 70°^{KI8}$

Group IV—Tin

$(Et_3N)_2 \cdot SnBr_4$: m. 195–205° (dec.)^{BO8}

$(Et_3N)_4 \cdot SnBr_4$: m. 90–92°^{BO8}

$(Et_3N)_6 \cdot Sn(NO_3)_4$: m. 125–126°^{BO8}

Group IV—Gallium

$Et_3N \cdot GaMe_3$: m. 96.0°^{WI2a}

Group IV—Titanium

$(Et_3N)_4 \cdot TiBr_4$: m. 309–310°^{PR1e}

Group V—Antimony

$Et_3N \cdot SbCl_5$: m. 126–127°^{BO8}

$Et_3N \cdot SbHCl_4$: m. 92–94°^{KL2a}

Group V—Wolfram

$Et_3N \cdot W(CO)_5$: m. 5–10°^{ST18b}

Group VI—Oxygen

$Et_3N \cdot O$: m. 80°^{HU2c}

$Et_3N \cdot O \cdot 3 H_2O$: m. $-16.15°$ (estimated)^{KO4}

$Et_3N \cdot O \cdot HCl$: m. 152–153°,^{HO23} 152°^{RU5}

$Et_3N \cdot O \cdot picrate$: m. 165°^{CO17,HU2c}

Group VI—Sulfur

$Et_3N \cdot SO_3$: m. 91.5°^{MO1}

Group VIII

$(Et_3N)_3 \cdot FeI_2$: m. 215° (dec.)[PR1b]

$Et_3N \cdot NiI_2$: m. 174°[PR1c]

$(Et_3N)_4 \cdot NiI_2$: m. 179°[KO18a]

QUATERNARY AMMONIUM COMPOUNDS—ALKYL

Methochloride: m. 284° (dec.)[GR13]

Methobromide: m. 307.4° (dec.)[GR13]

Methiodide: m. 308.4–309.5° (dec.),[GR13] 293°[CA1]

Methochloroplatinate: m. dec. 250°,[RI5] 290°[HU1]

Methotriiodide: m. 62°[EK1]

Methopentiodide: m. 16°[GE5]

Methoheptiodide: m. 42°[GE5]

Methoperchlorate: m. > 280°[HO10]

Methopicrate: m. 276.5–277.4°,[CL7a] 268–268.5°,[MU1a] 267–268°[LO2]

Ethiodide: m. 302°[SM9]

Ethotriiodide: m. 142°,[DA3,MU5] 135°[GE5]

Ethochloroplatinate: m. dec. *ca.* 250°[RI5]

Ethotetrafluoborate: m. 235°[TH3a]

Ethotetrachloroborate: m. 222–224°[KY2]

Ethostyphnate: m. explodes at 210°[JE2]

Ethoperchlorate: m. > 280°[HO10]

Ethopicrate: m. 254°[JE2]

QUATERNARY AMMONIUM COMPOUNDS—COMPLEX SUBSTITUTED ALKYLS

Trichloromethiodide: m. 45°[PU1]

Benzyloiodide: m. 168–170°[NA1a]

4-Chlorobenzyloiodide: m. 188–190°[NA1a]

4-Bromobenzyloiodide: m. 175–176°[NA1a]

1-Naphthylmethochloride: m. 180°[NA1a]

9-Fluorenopicrate: m. 166°[IN5]

2-Phenylethiodide: m. 165–166°[NA1a]

Phenylopicrate: m. 122°[MU1a]

MISCELLANEOUS:

Triethyl- and tetraethyl-ammonium salts of various cyanocarbon acid anions and derivatives[MI1a]

Complex triethylammonioalkylammonioalkanoate halides[HA8a]

C_7H_9N  Me C_3H_3 C_3H_3

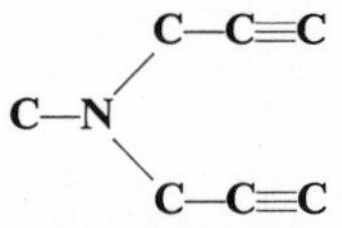

METHYLDIPROPARGYLAMINE

Phys. Props.:

Heat of combustion: 4440 cal./lb.[DO2]

Prepn.:

Methylamine + propargyl bromide, or chloride.[DO2]

Derivs.:

Methiodide: m. 134–135° [GU2,MA32]

$C_7H_{11}N$ **Me**
                                                    Me
                                                    C_5H_5

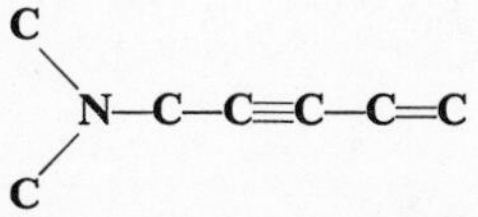

5-DIMETHYLAMINO-1-PENTENE-3-YNE

Phys. Props.:

b_{752} 133–135° [CO2,CA11]; b_{116} 82° [CA11]
d_4^{20} 0.8208 [CO2,CA11]
n_D^{20} 1.4700 [CO2,CA11]

Prepn.:

Dimethylamine + formaldehyde + vinylacetylene under pressure (74% yield).[CO2,CA11]

Derivs.:

Acid oxalate: m. 140–142° [CA11]

$C_7H_{13}N$ 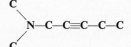   **Me**
                                                    Me
                                                    C_5H_7

1-DIMETHYLAMINO-2-PENTYNE

Phys. Props.:

b. 133–134° [GU2,MA32]
n_D^{12} 1.4400 [MA32,GU2]

Prepn.:

Sodio derivative of 3-dimethylamino-1-propyne + ethyl iodide (60% yield).[GU2,MA32]

Derivs.:

Methiodide: m. 177° [GU2,MA32,MA33]

$C_7H_{13}N$

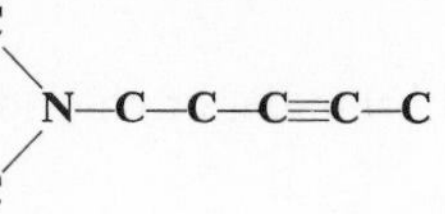

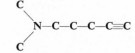

Me
Me
C_5H_7

5-DIMETHYLAMINO-2-PENTYNE

Phys. Props.

b. 140–144°[LU17]; b_{680} 135–139°[BA14]; b_{53} 69–70°[MA30]
n_D^{20} 1.4450[BA14]; n_D^{15} 1.4450[MA30]

Prepn.:

1. Methyl iodide + sodio derivative of 4-dimethylamino-1-butyne in liquid ammonia (56% yield).[MA30]
2. Thermal degradation of 1,1-dimethyl-2-methylenepyrrolidinium hydroxide (20% overall yield).[LU17]

Derivs.:

Methiodide: m. 285–286°,[JA1,MA30] 282°[LU17]

$C_7H_{13}N$

Me
Me
C_5H_7

5-DIMETHYLAMINO-1-PENTYNE

Phys. Props.:

b. 129°[CA7]; b_{680} 120–123°[BA14]; b_{115} 72–72.5°[EP2,MA31,OL6]
d_4^{20} 0.7985,[CA7] 0.7856[BA14]
n_D^{20} 1.4319,[CA7] 1.4299[BA14]; n_D^{15} 1.4340[EP2,MA31,OL6]
pK_a 8.88 (temperature unspecified)[CA7]

Prepn.:

1. Dimethylamine + 1-chloro-4-pentyne (40% yield).[CA7]
2. In 60–70% yield in the following reactions of dimethylamine: (a) with 1-iodo-4-pentyne[EP2,MA31,OL6]; (b) with 1-bromo-4-pentyne[EP2,OL6]; and (c) with the benzenesulfonic ester of 4-pentyn-1-ol.[EP2,OL6]
3. Dehydrobromination of 1-dimethylamino-4,5-dibromopentane with sodamide in liquid ammonia (25% yield).[EP2,MA31,OL6]
4. Isomerization of 5-dimethylamino-2-pentyne in the presence of sodium (51.7% yield).[BA14]

Derivs.:

Hydrochloride: m. 135°,[OL6] 133–134°[CA7]
Picrate: m. 100–101°[BA14]
Methiodide: m. 224–225°[EP2,OL6]

$C_7H_{13}N$

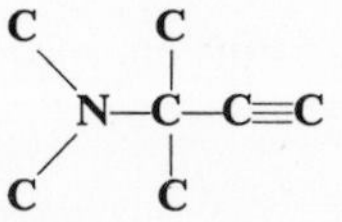

C \ C
   \ |
    N—C—C≡C
   / |
  C   C

Me
Me
C_5H_7

3-DIMETHYLAMINO-3-METHYL-1-BUTYNE

Phys. Props.:

m. 100.5–102° (sealed tube),[HE7] 99–102,[HE9] 97–98° (sub.),[RE7,RE11] 95–97°[CO26]

Prepn.:

1. 2-Amino-2-methyl-3-butyne + dimethyl sulfate (27% yield).[HE7]
2. 3-Chloro-3-methyl-1-butyne + dimethylamine (70% yield).[HE9]
3. In "good yield" by the reaction of 2-dimethylamino-2-hydroxypropane (prepared *in situ* from dimethylamine and acetone with sodium ethoxide catalysis) and acetylene in the presence of copper(I) chloride.[RE7,RE11]
4. Methylation of 3-*t*-butylamino-3-methyl-1-butyne with formic acid and formaldehyde can be made to yield either the expected amine or 3-dimethyl-amino-3-methyl-1-butyne. High formic acid concentration favors the latter *via* loss of isobutylene. Methylation with methyl iodide proceeds similarly to give expected and anomalous products (the latter as the methiodide).[AI1]

Derivs.:

Hydrochloride: m. 241–242.5°,[HE9] 234–236.5° (sealed tube, dec.)[HE7]
Methiodide: m. 210°[AI1]

$C_7H_{13}N$

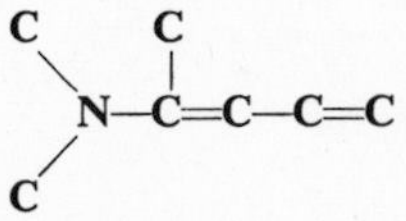

C \ C
   \ |
    N—C=C—C=C
   /
  C

Me
Me
C_5H_7

4-DIMETHYLAMINO-1,3-PENTADIENE*

Phys. Props.:

b. 137–140°,[LA4]† 136–138°[BR25]; b_{100} 73–75°[SL1]
d_4^{20} 0.8024[SL1]; d_4^{19} 0.7979[BR25]

---

* The structure of this compound has been in question. The present assignment is based on Raman data of Ref. SL1. See controversy in refs. BR25, LA4, LU17 and SL1.

† Ref. LA4 had assumed this compound to be 2-dimethylamino-1,4-pentadiene, while ref. BR25 later claimed it to be 5-dimethylamino-1,2-pentadiene.

n_D^{20} 1.4618[SL1]; n_D^{19} 1.4635[BR25]

Raman spectrum[SL1]

Prepn.:

1. Thermal degradation of 1,1-dimethyl-2-methylenepyrrolidinium hydroxide (71% yield).[BR25]*
2. Silver oxide + the iodine addition product of 5-dimethylamino-1-pentene.[LA4]

Derivs.:

Methiodide: m. 257° [BR25]

$C_7H_{13}N$

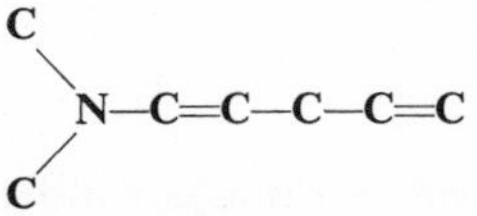

$$\begin{array}{c} C \\ \diagdown \\ N-C=C-C-C=C \\ \diagup \\ C \end{array}$$

Me
Me
C_5H_7

1-DIMETHYLAMINO-1,4-PENTADIENE

There has been a prolonged controversy over a product reported as having this structure.[LA4] It is now claimed[SL1] to be principally 4-dimethylamino-1,3-pentadiene (*q.v.*).

$C_7H_{13}N$

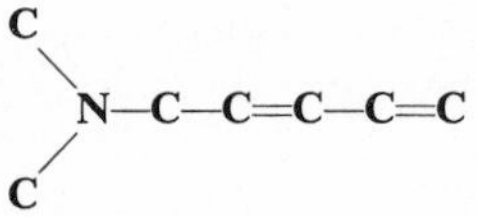

$$\begin{array}{c} C \\ \diagdown \\ N-C-C=C-C=C \\ \diagup \\ C \end{array}$$

Me
Me
C_5H_7

5-DIMETHYLAMINO-1,3-PENTADIENE

Phys. Props.:

b. 129.0–129.3°,[LU4a] 129°[LU13]

d_4^{20} 0.7837[LU13]

n_D^{20} 1.4650[LU13]

Prepn.:

Thermal decomposition of 1,1-dimethyl-1,2,5,6-tetrahydropyridinium hydroxide,[LU4a] or formate.[LU14]

Derivs.:

Acid maleate: m. 73°[LU13]

Methiodide: m. 169°[LU14]

---

* In a reaction similar to the one reported here (see ref. LU17) an acetylene rather than an allene was found to be the product.

$C_7H_{13}N$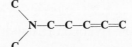

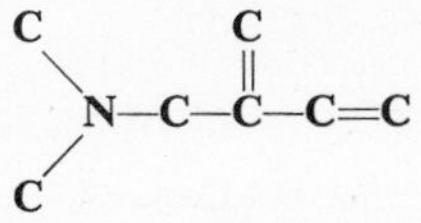

Me
Me
C_5H_7

2-(DIMETHYLAMINOMETHYL)-1,3-BUTADIENE

Phys. Props.:

b_{760} *ca.* $101°$[MA26]

Prepn.:

In low yield by the Hofmann degradation of $MeCH(NMe_3I)CH(CH_2NMe_3I)$-
$CH_2NMe_2·HI$. An amine is obtained which is considered to be the
subject compound. The "dimer" of this amine, however, is the main
product.[MA26]

Derivs.:

Hydrobromide: m. $231°$[MA26]

$C_7H_{13}N$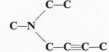

Me
Me
C_5H_7

5-DIMETHYLAMINO-1,2-PENTADIENE

There is a controversy over a product reported as having this structure.[BR25]
It is now claimed[SL1] to be principally 4-dimethylamino-1,3-pentadiene (*q.v.*).

$C_7H_{13}N$

Me
Et
C_4H_5

METHYLETHYL-2-BUTYNYLAMINE

Phys. Props.

b_{680} $133–135°$[BA14,BA15]
d_4^{20} 0.8165[BA14,BA15]
n_D^{20} 1.4397[BA14,BA15]

Prepn.:

Reaction of bis-(3-chloro-2-butenyl)ethylmethylammonium hydroxide with
sodium hydroxide (77.4% yield).[BA15]

Derivs.:

Methobromide: $102–103°$[BA13]

C₇H₁₃N

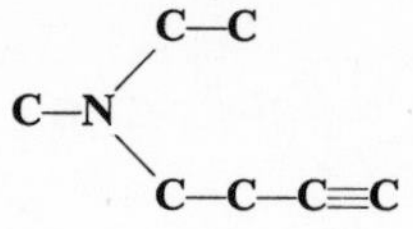

Me
Et
C₄H₅

METHYLETHYL-3-BUTYNYLAMINE

Phys. Props.:
b₆₈₀ 123–126°[BA14]
d₄²⁰ 0.79327[BA14]
n_D²⁰ 1.4336[BA14]

Prepn.:
Isomerization of methylethyl-2-butynylamine with sodium (28% yield).[BA14]

Derivs.:
Picrate: m. 106–108°[BA14]

C₇H₁₃N

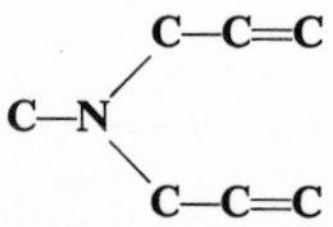

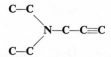

Me
All
All

METHYLDIALLYLAMINE

Phys. Props.:
b. 112°[PA8]

Prepn.:
Methylamine + allyl bromide[PA8]; + allyl chloride.[WE15]

C₇H₁₃N

Et
Et
C₃H₃

3-DIETHYLAMINO-1-PROPYNE

Phys. Props.:
b. 120–121°,[RE7] 119.5–120.1°,[PA5] 120°,[RE11] 119–120°[SA14]; b₈₅ 60–62°[BI1]
d₄²⁵ 0.8042,[PA5] 0.7982[RO7]
n_D²⁵ 1.4296,[PA5] 1.4291,[RO7] 1.4288[SA14]
Dipole moment: 0.80 D[RO7]
Nuclear magnetic resonance[HA26]

Prepn.:
1. Dimethylamine + propargyl bromide (50% yield).[BI1,BI3]
2. 1-Diethylamino-2-bromo-2-butene + sodamide in liquid ammonia (82.5% yield).[PA5]

3. Diethylamine + formaldehyde + acetylene in the presence of copper(II) acetate (60% yield)[RE7,RE11]; in the presence of copper(I) chloride (76% yield).[SA14]
4. Cleavage of 1-diethylamino-4-methyl-2-hexyn-4-ol with sodium (50% yield).[MA42]

$C_7H_{15}N$

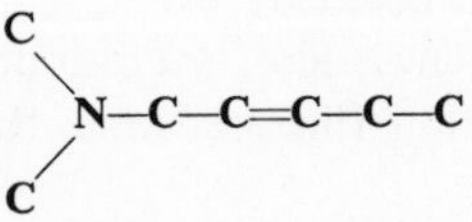

$$\begin{array}{c}C\\ \diagdown\\ N-C-C=C-C-C\\ \diagup\\ C\end{array}$$

Me
Me
C_5H_9

1-DIMETHYLAMINO-2-PENTENE

Phys. Props.:

cis isomer
  b_{120} 68°[OL6]
  d_{20}^{20} 0.7646[OL6]
  n_D^{20} 1.4230[OL6]
trans isomer
  b_{100} 60°[OL6]
  d_{20}^{20} 0.7478[OL6]
  n_D^{20} 1.4170[OL6]
For characteristic absorption (infrared and Raman) of the *cis* and *trans* isomers for this type of compound see 1-dimethylamino-2-heptene[OL6]

Prepn.:

Catalytic hydrogenation of 1-dimethylamino-2-pentyne in the presence of palladium gives the *cis* isomer, whereas reduction with sodium in liquid ammonia produces the *trans* isomer.[OL6]

Derivs.:

cis-Methiodide: m. 159°[OL6]
trans-Methiodide: m. 171–172°[OL6]

$C_7H_{15}N$

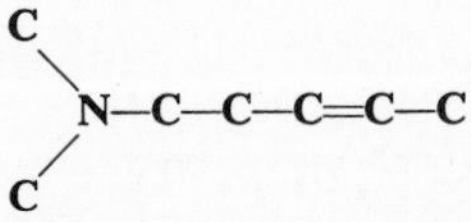

$$\begin{array}{c}C\\ \diagdown\\ N-C-C-C=C-C\\ \diagup\\ C\end{array}$$

Me
Me
C_5H_9

5-DIMETHYLAMINO-2-PENTENE

Phys. Props.:

cis isomer
  b_{80} 60°[OL5,OL6]
  d_{20}^{20} 0.7746[OL5,OL6]
  n_D^{18} 1.4275[OL5,OL6]

pK$_a$ 9.6 (temperature unspecified)[OL5,OL6]

Raman frequency characteristic of *cis* double bond at 1665 cm.$^{-1}$ [OL5]

trans isomer

     b$_{85}$ 61° [OL5,OL6]

     d$_{20}^{20}$ 0.7701 [OL5,OL6]

     n$_D^{18}$ 1.4250 [OL5,OL6]

     pK$_a$ 9.8 (temperature unspecified)[OL5,OL6]

Raman frequency characteristic of *trans* double bond at 1675 cm.$^{-1}$ [OL5]

For characteristic absorption (infrared and Raman) see 1-dimethylamino-2-heptene[OL6]

Prepn.:

1. Catalytic hydrogenation of 5-dimethylamino-2-pentyne in the presence of palladium gives the *cis* isomer. Reduction in the presence of sodium in liquid ammonia gives the *trans* isomer.[OL5,OL6]
2. Isomerization of 5-dimethylamino-1-pentene with potassium amide to unspecified isomer (80% yield).[WI25]

Derivs.:

Picrate: m. 73–76° [WI25] *

cis-Methiodide: m. 214° [OL5,OL6]

trans-Methiodide: m. 267° [OL5,OL6]

Methochloroaurate: m. 116° (dec.) and 89–91° for *cis* and *trans* isomers, but specific stereoisomeric assignment not made.[VA2]

C$_7$H$_{15}$N

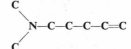

Me
Me
C$_5$H$_9$

5-DIMETHYLAMINO-1-PENTENE†

Phys. Props.:

b. 118°,[HA24,HO7,WI13] 118–120°,[VA2] 117–118°,[BR10,BR27,WI25] 116–118° [LA4];
     b$_{750}$ 118° [KH3]

d$_4^{17.5}$ 0.7548[HA24]; d$_4^{14.9}$ 0.7634[EY1]; d$_4^0$ 0.7705[LA5]

n$_\alpha^{14.9}$ 1.42167[EY1]; n$_\beta^{14.9}$ 1.43118[EY1]; n$_\alpha^{17.5}$ 1.4171[HA24]; n$_D^{17.6}$ 1.4208[WI25];
     n$_D^{17.5}$ 1.4202[HA24,KH3]; n$_\gamma^{17.5}$ 1.4317[HA24]

(Other values: b. 121–122°,[WI25] 117–120° [LA5]; n$_D^{22}$ 1.4226[WI25])

---

* Unspecified isomer.

† In the older literature this compound, obtained by the Hofmann exhaustive methylation of *N*-methylpiperidine, is frequently referred to as dimethylpiperidine. [HA24,LA5,ME14,WI13]

Prepn.:

1. 2-Chloroethyldimethylamine + allylmagnesium chloride (80% yield).[KH3]
2. Degradation of *N,N*-dimethylpiperidinium bromide by potassium amide in liquid ammonia (69.5% yield)[WI25]; by butyllithium in ether (12.7% yield).[WI25]
3. Thermal decomposition of 1,1-dimethylpiperidinium hydroxide (80% yield),[BR27] (77% yield),[WI25] (70% yield),[LA4] (unspecified yield).[HO7]
4. 5-Bromo-1-pentene + dimethylamine.[EP2,MA31]
5. Thermal decomposition of 1,5-bis(trimethylammonium)pentane dihydroxide,[HA24] (24% yield).[BR10]
6. Thermal decomposition of 1,1,3-trimethylpyrrolidinium hydroxide.[LA5]
7. Action of reducing agents (e.g., zinc and sulfuric acid) on 1,1-dimethyl-2-bromoethylpyrrolidinium bromide or 1,1-dimethyl-2-iodomethylpyrrolidinium iodide.[WI13]

Derivs.:

Picrate: m. 79–81°[WI25]
Oxalate: m. 122°[HA24]
Iodine addition product: m. 211–212°[WI13]
Bromine addition product: m. 232° (dec.)[WI13]
Methiodide: m. 200°,[HO7,BR10] 227–229° (dec.)[VA2,KH3]
Methochloroaurate: m. 106–107° (dec.)[VA2]

$C_7H_{15}N$

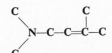

Me
Me
C_5H_9

1-DIMETHYLAMINO-3-METHYL-2-BUTENE

Phys. Props.:

b_{680} 116–118°[BA10]
d_4^{20} 0.7711[BA10]
n_D^{20} 1.4276[BA10]

Prepn.:

1. Pyrolysis of dimethylbis-(3-methyl-2-butenyl)ammonium chloride (68% yield); or heating with 40% sodium hydroxide (85% yield).[BA10]
2. Cleavage by aqueous base of the quaternary ammonium salt derived from 1-dimethylamino-3-methyl-5-methoxy-2-pentene and 1-chloro-3-methyl-2-butene (47.7% yield).[BA2]

Derivs.:

Picrate: m. 99–100°,[BA10] 102–103°[BA2]
Methiodide: m. 160–161°[BA10]
Bis-(3-methyl-2-butenyl)dimethylammonium dichloride: m. 111°[BA8]

$C_7H_{15}N$

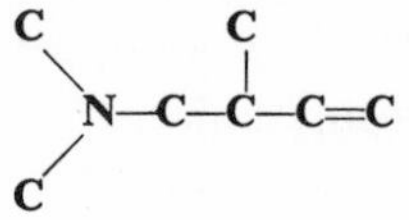

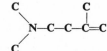

Me
Me
C_5H_9

4-DIMETHYLAMINO-3-METHYL-1-BUTENE

Phys. Props.:

b. 113–116°,[BA14] 112–115°[EU1]

Prepn.:

1. $(CH_3)_2NCH_2CH(CH_3)CH(OH)CH_3$ + sulfuric acid (almost quantitative yield)[BA42] (structure proof depends on subsequent Hofmann degradation to isoprene).
2. $(CH_3)_2NCH_2CH(CH_3)CHBrCH_3$ + sodium carbonate[BA41] (structure proof depends on subsequent Hofmann degradation to isoprene).
3. 1,1,3-Trimethylpyrrolidinium iodide + potassium hydroxide[EU1] [refs. BA41 and BA42 claim to have ruled out an alternate structure, $(CH_3)_2$-$NCH_2CH_2C(CH_3)\!=\!CH_2$, proposed by Euler[EU1]].

$C_7H_{15}N$

Me
Me
C_5H_9

4-DIMETHYLAMINO-2-METHYL-1-BUTENE*

Phys. Props.:

b. 100–105°[SC7]
n_D^{25} 1.4190[SC7]

Prepn.:

Tetramethylmethylenediamine + *t*-butyl alcohol + sulfuric acid (22% yield).[SC7]

---

* One of two possible structures of a compound prepared by Euler,[BA41] but subsequently claimed by ref. BA42 and BA41 to be 4-dimethylamino-3-methyl-1-butene. (*q.v.*) The authors believe the structure of the amine cited in ref. SC7 to be this compound, despite incomplete structure proof. See earlier section 5 on methods of preparation, "*N*-Alkylation of Secondary Amines with Olefins and Formaldehyde."

C₇H₁₅N

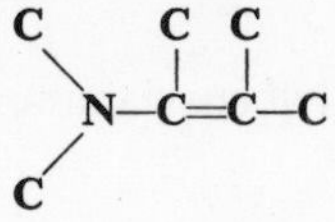

Me
Me
C₅H₉

2-DIMETHYLAMINO-3-METHYL-2-BUTENE

Derivs.:

Methochloroaurate:* m. 193°[SC11]
Methochloroplatinate monohydrate:* m. *ca.* 206°[SC11]

C₇H₁₅N

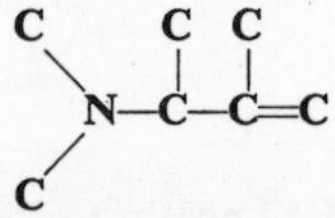

Me
Me
C₅H₉

3-DIMETHYLAMINO-2-METHYL-1-BUTENE

Phys. Props.:

b. 105–106°[BA41]; b_{680} 111.5–117.5°[BA10]†
b_4^{20} 0.7731[BA10]
n_D^{20} 1.4270[BA10]

Prepn.:

1. Decomposition of dimethyl-[3-methyl-2-butenyl]-[1,3-dimethyl-2-prope-nyl]ammonium chloride in the presence of excess 40% sodium hydroxide (75% yield).[BA10]
2. Thermal decomposition of 1,1,2,3-tetramethyltrimethyleniminium hy-droxide.[BA41]

Derivs.:

Picrate: m. 87–88°[BA10]
Methiodide: m. 139–140°[BA10,BA41]

C₇H₁₅N

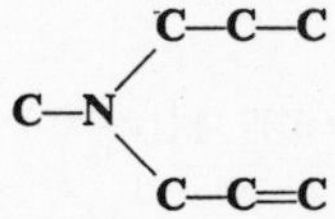

Me
n-Pr
All

METHYLPROPYLALLYLAMINE

Phys. Props.:

b_{765} 171–172°[EM6] ‡

---

* The parent quaternary amine is prepared from trimethylamine and 2-methyl-2,3-dibromobutane with subsequent dehydrobromination. No rigorous structure proof, however, is presented by ref. SC11.

† The boiling point value cited by ref. BA10 appears to be a more reasonable one from comparison of comparable data for isomers of this compound.

‡ This boiling point value appears to be unacceptably high. Comparison with other related structures suggests that a value of about 113° would be more reasonable.

Prepn.:

Reaction of methylpropylallylbenzylammonium chloride with sodium amalgam and water.[EM6]

Derivs.:

Chloroplatinate: m. 144° (dec.)[EM6]
Benzylochloride: m. 279°[EM6]

$C_7H_{15}N$

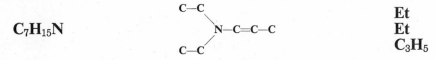

$\begin{array}{l} \text{Et} \\ \text{Et} \\ C_3H_5 \end{array}$

1-DIETHYLAMINO-1-PROPENE

Phys. Props.:

b_{10} 67–69°[GE1]

Prepn.:

Diethylamine + propionaldehyde in the presence of potassium carbonate (*ca.* 13% yield).[GE1]

$C_7H_{15}N$ 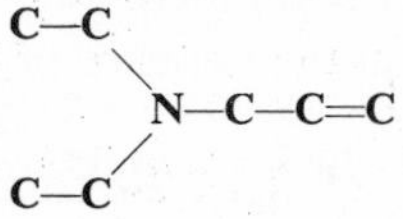
$\begin{array}{c} \text{C—C} \\ \diagdown \\ \text{N—C—C=C} \\ \diagup \\ \text{C—C} \end{array}$
$\begin{array}{l} \text{Et} \\ \text{Et} \\ \text{All} \end{array}$

ALLYLDIETHYLAMINE

Phys. Props.

b. 110–113°,[LI4] 111°,[CO25] 110–111°[ME5]; b_{760} 112°[EM7]; b_{758} 110°[KH4,ME5];
    $b_{22–23}$ 30–31°[KH4]
d_4^{25} 0.7477[CO25]
n_D^{20} 1.4209–1.4213[KH4]
(Other values: b. 100–103°,[R18] 107–110°[EA1,FE1])

Prepn.:

1. Diethylamine + allyl bromide (79–84% yield),[CO25] (52% yield),[FE1] (30% yield).[ME5]
2. Reduction of diethylallylcinnamylammonium iodide with sodium amalgam in water.[EM7]
3. Allylamine + ethyl iodide.[R18]
4. Butyl(diethylaminomethyl) ether + vinylmagnesium bromide.[F12]

Derivs.:

Picrate: m. 94–95.5°,[ME5] 93°[F12]
Amine oxide picrate: m. 138°[ME5]

Chloroplatinite: m. 189–190°,[EM7] 189°[LI4]
Chloroplatinate: m. 166°,[EM7] * 128–130°[LI4] *
Ethochloroplatinate: m. 213° (dec.)[LU1]
Cinnamyloiodide: m. 106°[EM7]
Cinnamylochloroplatinate: m. 157°[EM7]

$C_7H_{17}N$

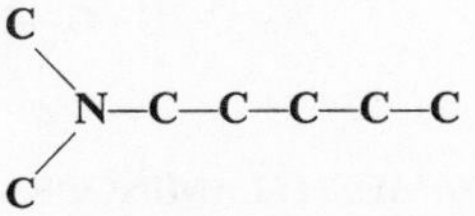

```
    C
     \
      N—C—C—C—C—C
     /
    C
```

Me
Me
n-Pent

PENTYLDIMETHYLAMINE

Phys. Props.:

b. 123°,[BR25] 122–123° (cor.)[BR9]; b_{760} 122°[GA9]; b_{755} 122–123°[CL2,WI17]
d_4^{20} 0.743[WI17]; d_4^0 0.755[WI17]
n_D^{20} 1.4083[WI17]

Prepn.:

1. Catalytic hydrogenation of the "basic product" obtained in the thermal decomposition of 1,1-dimethyl-2-methylenepyrrolidinium hydroxide.[BR25,LU17] (Ref. BR25 claims that the "basic product" is 1-dimethylamino-3,4-pentadiene, whereas reference LU17 claims it to be 1-dimethylamino-3-pentyne.)
2. 1-Butene + dimethylamine + iron pentacarbonyl + carbon monoxide under pressure.[UC1,UC2]
3. Catalytic hydrogenation of 5-dimethylamino-1-pentene.[WI17]
4. Electrochemical reduction of N,N-dimethylvaleramide (80% yield).[SW4]
5. Thermal degradation of pentyltrimethylammonium hydroxide,[IN8] (60% yield).[BR9]
6. Sealed tube reaction of pentylamine hydrochloride with aqueous formaldehyde.[CL2]
7. Pentylamine + formaldehyde + formic acid (80% yield).[GA9]

Derivs.:

Picrate: m. 100°,[BR9,BR25,LU17] 101°[CL2]
Chloroplatinate: m. 128°,[BR9] 127–128°[WI17]
Methobromide: m. 175–176°,[BR22] 174–175°[KA13]
Methiodide: m. 226°,[OL6] 225°,[VA2] 224°,[BR25] 222–223°,[WI17] 215°[BR9]

* Ref. EM7 acknowledges the lower value of ref. LI4 but is unable to explain the discrepancy.

Methopicrate: m. 94–95°[LU17]
Methochloroaurate: m. 139°[VA2]
Methochloroplatinate: m. 249.5° (dec.)[VA2]
Methotriiodide: m. 80°[MU5]

$C_7H_{17}N$

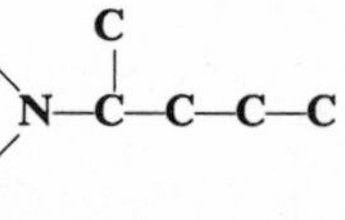

$$
\begin{array}{ccc}
C & C & \\
\diagdown & | & \\
N{-}C{-}C{-}C{-}C \\
\diagup & \\
C & \\
\end{array}
$$

Me
Me
C_5H_{11}

2-DIMETHYLAMINOPENTANE

Prepn.:

Thermal decomposition of 1-methylbutyltrimethylammonium hydroxide (very low yield).[HA11]

Derivs.:

Methobromide (prepared from trimethylamine and 2-bromopentane): m. 224.5–225°[KA13]
Methochloroplatinate: m. 220°[R15]

$C_7H_{17}N$

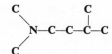

Me
Me
i-Pent

1-DIMETHYLAMINO-3-METHYLBUTANE

Phys. Props.:

b. 110–116°,[SK4] 113–114°[CO8]; b_{770} 113–114°[CL2]; b_{758} 98°[CL4]

Prepn.:

1. Isovaleraldehyde + dimethylamine + hydrogen in the presence of platinum.[SK4]
2. Isoamyl iodide + dimethylamine.[CL2]
3. Methylisoamylamine + methyl iodide.[CL4]
4. Reduction of *N,N*-dimethylisovaleramide with diisobutylaluminum hydride (95% yield).[ZA3]
5. Thermal decomposition of trimethylisoamylammonium hydroxide,[CO8,IN8] or chloride.[CO8]
6. Cleavage in aqueous sodium hydroxide of dimethylisopentyl-(1,2-dimethyl-2-propenyl)ammonium chloride (72% yield)[BA10]; of dimethylisopentyl-(3-methyl-2-butenyl)ammonium chloride (67% yield).[BA10]

Derivs.:

Picrate: m. 135°,[SK4] 132°,[CL2.ZA3] 130°[BA10]
Methochloride: m. *ca.* 200° (dec.)[CO8]
Methobromide: m. 202°,[BR22] 199–200°[KA13]
Methiodide: m. 203–204°[SM9]
Methotriiodide: m. 80°[MU5]

$C_7H_{17}N$

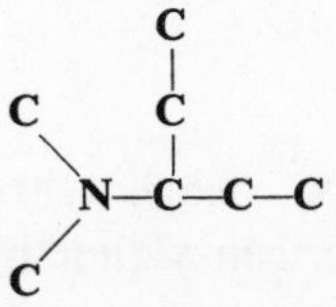

Me
Me
C_5H_{11}

3-DIMETHYLAMINOPENTANE

Phys. Props.:

b. 116–117°[CO23]
d_4^{25} 0.7507[CO23]
n_D^{25} 1.4080[CO23]

Prepn.:

3-Dimethylaminopentane + formaldehyde + formic acid (84% yield).[CO23]

Derivs.:

Amine oxide picrate: m. 180.5–182.5°[CO23]

$C_7H_{17}N$

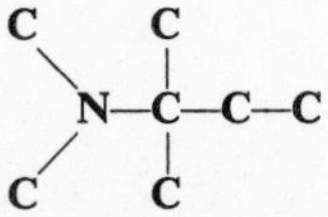

Me
Me
t-Pent

2-DIMETHYLAMINO-2-METHYLBUTANE

Phys. Props.:

b_{761} 117–118°[VE2]; b_{744} 117–118°[BR44]

Prepn.:

1. 2-Amino-2-methylbutane + paraformaldehyde + formic acid.[BR44]
2. 2-Dimethylamino-2-methylpropionitrile + ethylmagnesium bromide (15% yield). The main product in 69% yield is 1,2-bis(dimethylamino)-1,1,2,2-tetramethylethane.[VE2]

Derivs.:

Methiodide: m. 225°[BR44]

$C_7H_{17}N$

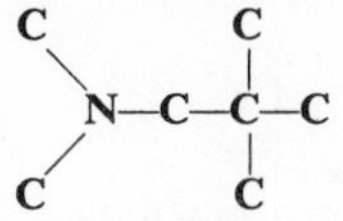

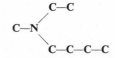

Me
Me
neo-Pent

1-DIMETHYLAMINO-2,2-DIMETHYLPROPANE

Phys. Props.:

b. 96–97° [IN6]; b_{754} 97.5–97.8° [BR41]

n_D^{20} 1.3972 [BR41]

Prepn.:

1. Thermal decomposition of neopentyltrimethylammonium hydroxide (93% yield) [IN6]; of neopentylbenzyldimethylammonium hydroxide (90% yield). [IN6]
2. Paraformaldehyde + 2,2-dimethyl-1-aminopropane. [IN6]
3. N,N-Dimethyl-2,2-dimethylpropionamide + lithium aluminum hydride (50% yield). [BR41]
4. t-Butylmagnesium chloride + butyl dimethylaminomethyl ether. [IN6]

Derivs.:

Hydrochloride: m. 182° [IN6]
Hydrobromide: m. 170° [IN6]
Hydriodide: m. 135° [IN6]
Picrate: m. 193° [IN6]
·$B(CH_3)_3$: m. 13–16.5° [BR43]
Methiodide: m. 240° (dec.) [IN6]
Benzylobromide: m. 200° (dec.) [IN6]

$C_7H_{17}N$

Me
Et
n-Bu

METHYLETHYLBUTYLAMINE

Phys. Props.:

b. 117° [CO23]

d_4^{25} 0.7320 [CO23]

n_D^{25} 1.4048 [CO23]

Prepn.:

Ethylbutylamine + formic acid + formaldehyde (72% yield). [CO23]

Derivs.:

Picrate: m. 77.4–78.4° [CO23]
Amine oxide picrate: m. 90.4–91° [CO23]
Methiodide: 195–195.5° [CO23]

$C_7H_{17}N$

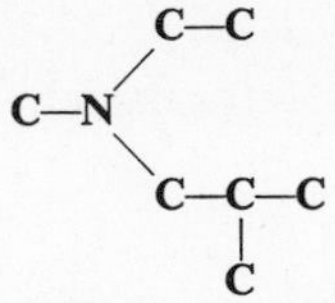

Me
Et
i-Bu

METHYLETHYLISOBUTYLAMINE

Phys. Props.:

b. 106–107°,[CO23] 105°[MA27]
d_4^{25} 0.7293[CO23]
n_D^{25} 1.3990[CO23]

Prepn.:

1. Ethylisobutylamine + formic acid + formaldehyde (62% yield).[CO23]
2. Ethylisobutylamine + sodium methylsulfate.[MA27]

Derivs.:

Hydriodide: m. 132°[WE6]
Chloroaurate: m. 99°[MA27]
Picrate: m. 97–98°[CO23]
Chloroplatinate: m. 197° (dec.)[MA27,WE6]
Propiodide: m. 196.5°[MA27]
Methiodide: m. 184–185°[CO23]
Amine oxide picrate: m. 113–113.8°[CO23]
Chloroaurate: m. 99°[WE6]
Chloroplatinate: m. 197° (dec.)[WE6]
Amine oxide picrate: m. 113–113.8°[CO23]
Methiodide: m. 184–185°[CO23]

$C_7H_{17}N$

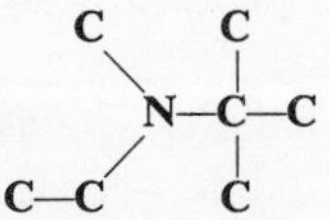

Me
Et
t-Bu

METHYLETHYL-t-BUTYLAMINE

Phys. Props.:

b. 110°[CO23]
d_4^{25} 0.7444[CO23]
n_D^{25} 1.4088[CO23]

Prepn.:

t-Butylethylamine + formic acid + formaldehyde (60% yield).[CO23]

Derivs.:

Picrate: m. 239.5–241° (dec.)[CO23]
Amine oxide picrate: m. 179.2–180.2°[CO23]
Methiodide: m. 212.7–213.6° (dec.)[CO23]

$C_7H_{17}N$

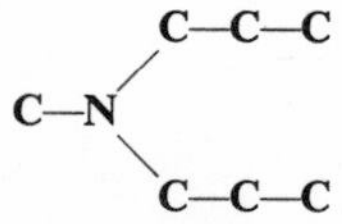

Me
***n*-Pr**
***n*-Pr**

METHYLDIPROPYLAMINE

Phys. Props.:

b. 117°,[PA12] 113–116°,[RE12] 113–114°[BR5]; b_{760} 110–112°[RE6]
d_{20}^{20} 0.743[EM8,EM8a,EM9,EM11]
n_D^{20} 1.4076[EM8,EM8a,EM9,EM11]
(Other values: b. 110–122°,[EM8,EM8a,EM9,EM11] 105–113°[RE14])

Prepn.:

1. Nitromethane + propionaldehyde + hydrogen (platinum-catalyzed) (45% yield).[EM8,EM8a,EM9,EM11]
2. Alkylation of dipropylamine:
   a. With potassium methylsulfate.[PA12]
   b. With methyl iodide (about 40% yield).[BR5]
   c. With methyl sulfate.[WE12]
3. By-product in 10% yield in the reaction of dimethylamine, carbon monoxide, ethylene, and iron pentacarbonyl under pressure.[RE12,RE14] The main product is propyldimethylamine.
4. By-product in 1.6% yield in the reaction of methylamine, carbon monoxide, ethylene, water, and iron pentacarbonyl under pressure. The main product is methylpropylamine.[RE6,RE14]
5. Methyltripropylammonium halide + potassium in liquid ammonia.[HA29]
6. Methyltripropylammonium iodide + sodium in liquid ammonia.[GR14]

Derivs.:

Picrate: m. 92–93°[BO10,EM8,EM8a,EM9,EM11]
Methiodide: m. 181°[BO10]
Methochloroplatinate: m. 250° (dec.),[RI5] 245–250° (dec.)[RI5]
Methopicrate: m. 92°,[RI6] 93°[BO10,WA12]
Methoreineckate: m. 148°[BO10]

$C_7H_{17}N$

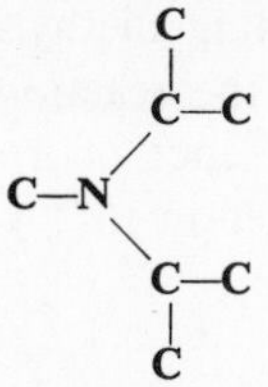

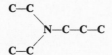

Me
i-Pr
i-Pr

METHYLDIISOPROPYLAMINE

Phys. Props.:

b. 109–112°,[KL2] 111°[RO4]; b_{740} 111.7–112.0[SP2]; b_{739} 112°[WO7]
m. (freezes to a glass at $-196°$)[SP2]
d_4^{27} 0.758[WO7]; d_4^{25} 0.7495[SP2]; d_4^{20} 0.7535[SP2]
n_D^{25} 1.4082,[SP2] 1.4092,[WO7] 1.4100[RO4]; n_D^{20} 1.4109[SP2]
pK_a 11.03 at 25°[SP1]

Prepn.:

1. Diisopropylamine + formaldehyde + formic acid (79% yield).[SP2]
2. Methylamine + isopropyl bromide (6.5% yield).[KL2]

Derivs.:

Picrate: m. 202–203°[KL2]
Methiodide: m. 252–253° (cor.) (dec.)[SP2]
Methotosylate: m. 109–111° (sealed tube)[SP2]
Methochloride: m. 261° (cor.)[RO4]
Ethobromide: m. 247°[RO4]

$C_7H_{17}N$

Et
Et
n-Pr

PROPYLDIETHYLAMINE

Phys. Props.:

b. 112–115°,[RE10,RE12] 111.9–112.2°[EL1]; b_{750} 111.5–112.5°[LE14]
d_4^{20} 0.742[LE14]
n_D^{20} 1.4064[LE14]

Prepn.:

1. Propyl bromide + diethylamine (27% yield),[LE14] (50% yield).[EL1]
2. Thermal decomposition of diethyldipropylammonium iodide[AU1]; of ethyltripropylammonium iodide (*ca.* 65% yield).[AU1]
3. In low yield as a by-product in the catalytic hydrogenation of a mixture of 1-diethylamino-4-pentanone and 6-methoxy-8-aminoquinoline.[EL1,EL2]

4. A mixture of amines including diethylamine, triethylamine, and ethyl-dipropylamine results from the reaction of diethylamine, ethylene, and carbon monoxide in the presence of iron carbonyl under pressure. The diethylpropylamine is obtained in 18% yield,[RE12] 24% yield.[RE10]

Derivs.:

Picrate: m. 82–84° (cor.)[LE14]
Hydrochloride: m. 205.5–206.5°[EL1,EL2]
Picrolonate: m. 140–141° (cor.)[LE14]
Oxide: oil, b_{756} 167–170°[RI4]
Methiodide: m. 243–244°[EL1,EL2]
Ethiodide: m. 255–256°[AU1]
Methochloroplatinate: m. (dec.) 250°[HO4,RI5]
Ethoperchlorate: m. *ca.* 275°[HO10]
Ethochloroplatinate: m. *ca.* 235° (dec.)[RI5]
Ethiodide·2CS(NH$_2$)$_2$: m. 165°[AT1]
Ethiodide·HgI$_2$: m. 85°[BA26]
Ethopicrate: m. 144°,[RI6] 144.2°[WA12]
Propiodide: m. 238–240°[AU1]

C$_7$H$_{17}$N

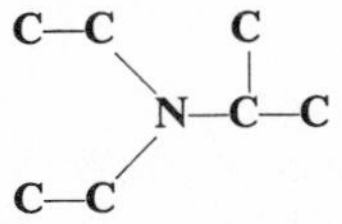

Et
Et
i-Pr

ISOPROPYLDIETHYLAMINE

Phys. Props.:

b. 108–109°,[CA13] 108,[CA12] 107.5[RO4]
d. 0.75[CA12]
n_D^{25} 1.4047[RO4]

Prepn.:

1. Isopropyl bromide + diethylamine (60% yield).[CA12,CA13]
2. As part of a mixture of products in the reaction of 2-cyano-2-diethyl-aminopropane with lithium aluminum hydride.[WE10]
3. Acetonitrile + acetone + hydrogen. A mixture of amines including diethylisopropylamine is obtained.[PR1]

Derivs.:

Oxide: oil, b. 156–161°[BE13]
Hydrochloride: m. 56.8–58° (cor.)[CA14]
Picrate: m. 180.6–181.6° (cor.)[CA14]
Chloroplatinate: m. 210.1–211.1° (cor.) (dec.)[CA14]

·HBCl$_4$: m. 160–163°^{KY2}
Methiodide: m. 269–270° (cor.)^{CA14}
Methobromide: m. 277° (cor.)^{RO4}
Ethobromide: m. 264° (cor.)^{RO4}

C$_8$H$_{13}$N 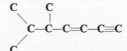 Me Me C$_6$H$_7$

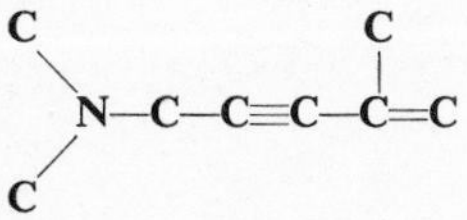

5-DIMETHYLAMINO-2-METHYL-1-PENTEN-3-YNE

Phys. Props.:

b$_{15}$ 53°^{MA32}
n$_D^{19}$ 1.4650^{MA32}

Prepn.:

Sealed tube reaction of 2-methyl-1-buten-3-yne with formaldehyde and
   dimethylamine in the presence of copper(II) acetate (77% yield).^{MA32}

Derivs.:

Methiodide: m. 231–232°^{MA32,MA33}

C$_8$H$_{13}$N C–C–C=C–C≡C Me Me C$_6$H$_7$

trans-**5-DIMETHYLAMINO-3-HEXEN-1-YNE***

Phys. Props.:

b$_{15}$ 45°^{BE4}
Ultraviolet absorption: 2230 A. (ϵ13,600)^{BE4}

Prepn.:

trans-5-Chloro-3-hexene-1-yne + dimethylamine (70% yield).^{BE4}

Derivs.:

Hydrochloride: m. 122–123°^{BE4}

---

* The *trans* configuration is assumed for this compound from the method of synthesis
and because according to ref. BE4 the *cis* isomer would be expected to cyclize to a
pyrrole derivative.

$C_8H_{13}N$

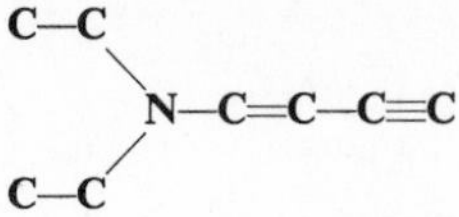

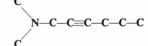

Et
Et
C_4H_3

4-DIETHYLAMINO-3-BUTEN-1-YNE

Phys. Props.:

b_5 53–54°[PE11]; b_3 42–45°[FR4]*
d_4^{20} 0.8556[PE11]
n_D^{20} 1.5208[PE11]

Infrared absorption spectrum: Strong bands at 942, 1610–1620, 2072 and 3288 cm.$^{-1}$ for this compound and the dimethylamino analog.[PE11]

Dipole moment: 2.87D[PE12a]

Prepn.:

Uncatalyzed reaction of diethylamine with 1,3-butadiyne[PE11,PE12,SH4]†; or catalyzed by metallic silver powder (42% yield).[FR4]‡

$C_8H_{15}N$

$$ \overset{\displaystyle C}{\underset{\displaystyle C}{N}} {-} C {-} C \equiv C {-} C {-} C {-} C $$

Me
Me
C_6H_9

1-DIMETHYLAMINO-2-HEXYNE

Phys. Props.:

b_{100} 94°[GU2,MA32]
n_D^{16} 1.4418[GU2,MA32]

Prepn.:

1. Sodio derivative of 3-dimethylamino-1-propyne + propyl bromide (63% yield)[MA32]; + *n*-propyl iodide.[GU2]
2. Sealed tube reaction of 1-pentyne, formaldehyde, and dimethylamine in the presence of copper(II) acetate (75% yield).[MA32]

Derivs.:

Methiodide: m. 147°[GU2,MA32,MA33]

---

* There is some doubt about the structure of the amine prepared by ref. FR4. See note ‡

† Ref. SH4 gives no experimental details but mentions that this type of reaction gives yields of about 60%.

‡ Ref. FR4 describes the product as "diethylaminovinylacetylene" but offers no structure proof. The assigned structure appears to be a reasonable one.

$C_8H_{15}N$

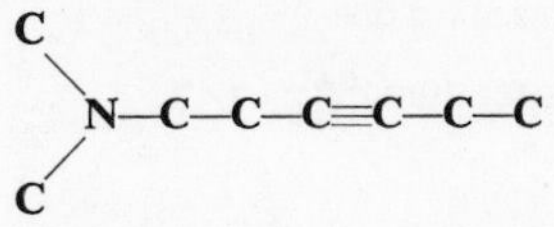

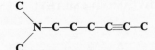

Me
Me
C_6H_9

1-DIMETHYLAMINO-3-HEXYNE

Phys. Props.:

b_{10} 53° [MA30]
$n_D^{14.5}$ 1.4448 [MA30]

Prepn.:

Sodio derivative of 4-dimethylamino-1-butyne + ethyl iodide.[MA30]

Derivs.:

Methiodide: m. 221–223° [JA1,MA30]

$C_8H_{15}N$

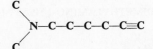

Me
Me
C_6H_9

6-DIMETHYLAMINO-2-HEXYNE

Phys. Props.:

b_{35} 72° [EP2,MA31,OL6]
n_D^{20} 1.4372 [MA31]; n_D^{18} 1.4450 [EP2,OL6]

Prepn.:

Sodio derivative of 5-dimethylamino-1-pentyne + methyl iodide (74% yield).[EP2,MA31,OL6]

Derivs.:

Methiodide: m. 141–142° [EP2,OL6]

$C_8H_{15}N$

C
\
N—C—C—C—C—C≡C
/
C

Me
Me
C_6H_9

6-DIMETHYLAMINO-1-HEXYNE

Phys. Props.:

b_{110} 90° [CA7]; b_{20} 53° [EP2,MA31,OL6]
d_4^{20} 0.8066 [CA7]

n_D^{20} 1.4369[CA7]; n_D^{19} 1.4320[EP2,MA31,OL6]

pK_a 9.24 (temperature unspecified)[CA7]

Prepn.:

Dimethylamine + 6-chloro-1-hexyne   (60%   yield)[CA7]; + 6-iodo-1-hexyne
   (70% yield)[EP2,MA31,OL6]

Derivs.:

Hydrochloride: m. 164–165° [OL6]
Oxalate: m. 118–119° [CA7]
Methiodide: m. 162–163° [EP2,MA31,OL6]

$C_8H_{15}N$ 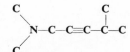   Me
                                          Me
                                          C_6H_9

1-DIMETHYLAMINO-4-METHYL-2-PENTYNE

Phys. Props.:

b_{25} 49° [MA32]
n_D^{21} 1.4310[MA32]

Prepn.:

Sealed tube reaction of 3-methyl-1-butyne, formaldehyde, and dimethylamine in the presence of copper(II) acetate (42% yield).[MA32]

Derivs.:

Methiodide: m. 190° [MA32,MA33]

$C_8H_{15}N$ $\begin{array}{c} C \quad\quad C{\equiv}C \\ \diagdown\quad| \\ N{-}C{-}C{-}C{-}C \\ \diagup \\ C \end{array}$ Me
                                          Me
                                          C_6H_9

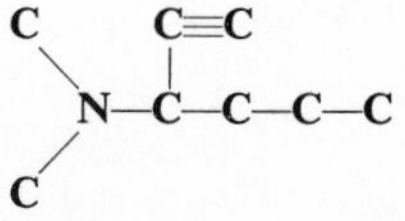

3-DIMETHYLAMINO-1-HEXYNE

Phys. Props.:

b. 135–136°,[RE7] 134–136° [ME13]; b_{755} 135–136° [CO26]

Prepn.:

In "good yield" from dimethylamine, butanal, acetylene, and formic acid in
   the presence of copper(I) chloride.[ME13,RE7]

$C_8H_{15}N$

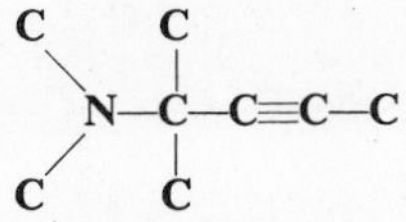

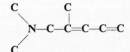

Me
Me
C_6H_9

4-DIMETHYLAMINO-4-METHYL-2-PENTYNE

Phys. Props.:

b_{170} 90–95°[KR11]; b_{90} 78°[KR11]; b_{62} 68°[KR11]; b_{60} 67.5°[KR11]
n_D^{20} 1.4439[KR11]
Infrared absorption: band at 4.5 μ indicates internal triple bond[KR11]

Prepn.:

1. Reaction (under pressure) of dimethylamine with 1-propyne in the presence of zinc and cadmium acetates (71% yield)[KR11]; in the presence of copper(I) chloride (40% yield).[KR11]
2. Sodio derivative of 3-dimethylamino-3-methyl-1-butyne + methyl iodide (44% yield).[KR11]

Derivs.:
Picrate: m. 255° (dec.)[KR11]

$C_8H_{15}N$

Me
Me
C_6H_9

4-(DIMETHYLAMINOMETHYL)-1,3-PENTADIENE

Phys. Props.:

b. 144–146°[LU12,LU13]
d_4^{20} 0.7932[LU13]
n_D^{20} 1.4709[LU13]

Prepn.:

Thermal decomposition of 1,1,3-trimethyl-1,2,5,6-tetrahydropyridinium hydroxide,[LU13] (66% yield)[LU12]

Derivs.:

Acid maleate: m. 106°[LU13]
Picrate: m. 133°[LU12]

$C_8H_{15}N$ 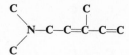 **Me**
Me
C_6H_9

5-DIMETHYLAMINO-3-METHYL-1,3-PENTADIENE

Phys. Props.:
b. 152–156°[LU15]
d_4^{20} 0.7974[LU15]
n_D^{20} 1.4700[LU15]

Prepn.:
Pyrolysis of 1,1,4-trimethyl-1,2,5,6-tetrahydropiperidinium hydroxide (over 76% yield).[LU15]

Derivs.:
Picrate: m. 128°[LU15]

$C_8H_{15}N$ 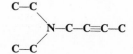 **Et**
Et
C_4H_5

1-DIETHYLAMINO-2-BUTYNE

Phys. Props.:
b. 152.5–153°[PA5]; b_{680} 148–150°[BA14]
d_4^{25} 0.8075[PA5]; d_4^{20} 0.8167[BA14]
n_D^{25} 1.4413[PA5]; n_D^{20} 1.4440[BA14]

Prepn.:
Methyl iodide + the sodio derivative of 3-diethylamino-1-propyne (73.5% yield).[PA5]

$C_8H_{15}N$ 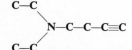 **Et**
Et
C_4H_5

4-DIETHYLAMINO-1-BUTYNE

Phys. Props.:
b_{765} 143–143.5°[PE10]; b_{680} 139–142°[BA14]; b_{110} 85°[EP2,MA31,OL6,PE10]
b_{20} 48°[PE10]
d_4^{20} 0.7987,[BA14] 0.8031[PE10]
n_D^{20} 1.4361,[BA14] 1.4388[PE10]; n_D^{18} 1.4390[EP2,MA31,OL6]
Infrared absorption[PE10]

Prepn.:

1. Isomerization of 1-diethylamino-2-butyne in the presence of sodium (44% yield).[BA14]
2. Benzenesulfonic acid ester of 1-butyn-4-ol + diethylamine (41% yield).[EP2,OL6]
3. Lithiodiethylamine + vinylacetylene (20% yield).[PE10]

Derivs.:

Picrate: m. 107–108.5°[BA14]

$C_8H_{15}N$

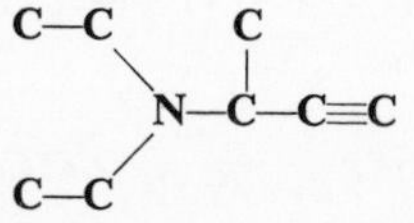

C—C   C
           |
    N—C—C≡C
C—C

Et
Et
C_4H_5

3-DIETHYLAMINO-1-BUTYNE

Phys. Props.:

b. 128°,[RO12] 127–128°,[RE7,RE13] 126–128°,[SA14] 123–126°[GA3]
m. 10°[GA3,RE7,RO12]
n_D^{25} 1.4273[SA14]
Infrared absorption[BR1]
Nuclear magnetic resonance[HA26]

Prepn.:

1. High-pressure reaction of diethylamine with acetylene in the presence of copper(I) chloride (63% yield),[GA3] (65% yield),[RE13] (about 50% yield).[RE7]
2. 1-Diethylamino-1-ethanol + acetylene.[GA3]

Derivs.:

Hydrochloride: m. 178–179.5°[GA3]
Methiodide: m. 108–109.5°[GA3]

$C_8H_{15}N$

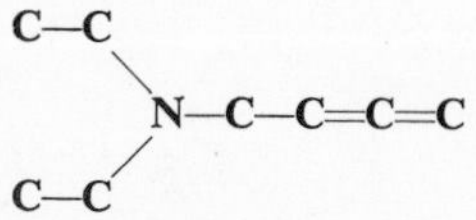

C—C
         \
    N—C—C=C=C
C—C

Et
Et
C_4H_5

4-DIETHYLAMINO-1,2-BUTADIENE

Phys. Props.:

b_{147} 91–92.5°,[EN1] 91–92°[EN2]
n_D^{25} 1.4505[EN2]
Infrared absorption: 5.1 and 11.9 μ confirms terminal allene structure.[EN2,WO8]

Prepn.:

1-Buten-3-yne + diethylamine + water under pressure (20% yield).[EN1,EN2]

Derivs.:

Methiodide: m. 109–110°[EN2]

$C_8H_{15}N$

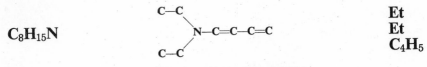

Et
Et
C_4H_5

1-DIETHYLAMINO-1,3-BUTADIENE

Phys. Props.:

b_{31} 85–86°[LA10,LA12]; b_{20} 74°[BO16]; b_{19} 74–76°[LA10,LA12]; b_{10} 64–66°[HU2]
n_D^{19} 1.5232[BO16]
Ultraviolet absorption: 2775 A. (ϵ27,000),[FE4] 2810 A. (ϵ23,500)[BO16]

Prepn.:

1. Diethylamine + crotonaldehyde in the presence of potassium carbonate (50% yield).[BO16]
2. Same reaction as above, except for subsequent use of phenanthrenequinone to help split the intermediate diamine, 1,3-bis(diethylamino)-1-butene, with the loss of diethylamine (yield unspecified),[LA12] (61% yield).[HU2] Various other quinone catalysts have also been used,[LA11] as well as a polycarboxylic product prepared from diaminobenzoic acid and fumaryl chloride.[LA10]

$C_8H_{15}N$

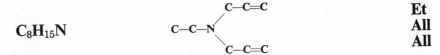

Et
All
All

ETHYLDIALLYLAMINE

Phys. Props.:

b. 129–130°[WE15]
d_{20}^{20} 0.7817[WE15]
n_D^{20} 1.4369[WE15]

Prepn.:

Ethylamine + allyl chloride (12.5% yield).[WE15]

Derivs.:

Allylobromide: m. 159°[BR3]

$C_8H_{17}N$ 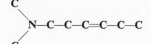 Me
Me
C_6H_{11}

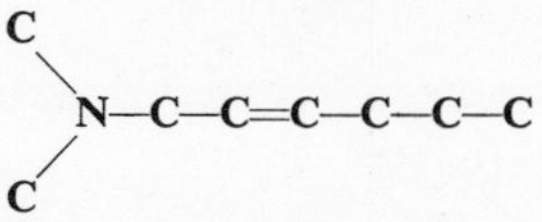

1-DIMETHYLAMINO-2-HEXENE

Phys. Props.:

cis isomer
  b_{105} 84° [OL6]
  d_{20}^{20} 0.7805 [OL6]
  n_D^{20} 1.4290 [OL6]
trans isomer
  b_{100} 83–84° [OL6]
  d_{20}^{20} 0.7706 [OL6]
  n_D^{20} 1.4270 [OL6]

For characteristic absorption maxima (infrared and Raman) of the *cis* and *trans* isomers for this type of compound see 1-dimethylamino-2-heptene. [OL6]

Prepn.:

Catalytic hydrogenation of 1-dimethylamino-2-hexyne in the presence of palladium gives the *cis* isomer in 63% yield, whereas reduction with sodium in liquid ammonia gives the *trans* isomer. [OL6]

Derivs.:

cis-Methiodide: m. 102–103° [OL6]
trans-Methiodide: m. 153° [OL6]

$C_8H_{17}N$ Me
Me
C_6H_{11}

1-DIMETHYLAMINO-3-HEXENE

Phys. Props.:

cis isomer b_{45} 61°, *trans* b_{60} 73° [OL5,OL6]
d_{20}^{20} *cis* 0.7808, *trans* 0.7780 [OL5,OL6]
n_D^{16} *cis* 1.4300, *trans* 1.4310 [OL5,OL6]
pK_a *cis* 9.7, *trans* 10.0 [OL6]

Prepn.:

Catalytic hydrogenation of 1-dimethylamino-3-hexyne in the presence of palladium produces the *cis* isomer, whereas reduction with sodium in liquid ammonia gives the *trans* isomer. [OL5,OL6]

Derivs.:

cis-Methiodide: m. 165° [OL5,OL6]
trans-Methiodide: m. 193–194° [OL5]

C₈H₁₇N   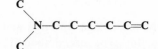   **Me**
Me
C₆H₁₁

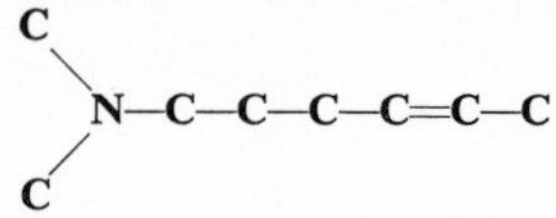

6-DIMETHYLAMINO-2-HEXENE

Derivs.:

Methiodide (from trimethylamine and 6-iodo-2-hexene): m. *ca.* 110° [BR16]

C₈H₁₇N   **Me**
Me
C₆H₁₁

6-DIMETHYLAMINO-1-HEXENE

Phys. Props.:

b. 144–146°, [WI25] 143–144°, [WI25] 143–143.5°, [ME14] 142–144° [WI25]
d_4^{15} 0.767 [ME14]; $d_4^{12.1}$ 0.7730 [EY1]
$n_\alpha^{12.1}$ 1.42797 [EY1]; $n_\beta^{12.1}$ 1.43758 [EY1]; n_D^{23} 1.4248, [WI25] 1.4245 [WI25]

Prepn.:

1. Thermal decomposition of 1,1,2-trimethylpiperidinium hydroxide [ME14]; of
   N,N-dimethylhexamethylenimonium hydroxide (87% yield). [WI25]
2. Degradation of *N,N*-dimethylhexamethylenimonium bromide in the
   presence of potassium amide (61.5% yield) [WI25]; in the presence of butyllithium (59% yield). [WI25]

Derivs.:

Picrate: m. 91–92° [WI25]
Methiodide: m. 126–129° [ME14]

C₈H₁₇N   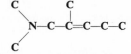   **Me**
Me
C₆H₁₁

1-DIMETHYLAMINO-2-METHYL-2-PENTENE

Phys. Props.:

b₃₀ 76° [FO3]

Prepn.:

Heating ethyl-β-methyl-β-*n*-propylglycidate with aqueous dimethylamine
(8% yield).[FO3]

Derivs.:

Methiodide: m. above 300°[FO3]

C₈H₁₇N $\text{C}_8\text{H}_{17}\text{N}$ 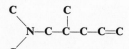 **Me**
Me
C₆H₁₁

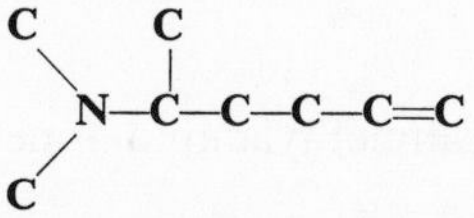

5-DIMETHYLAMINO-1-HEXENE

Phys. Props.:

b. 138–140°[ME14]
d_4^{15} 0.780[ME14]; $d_4^{11.8}$ 0.7834[EY1]
$n_\alpha^{11.8}$ 1.43093[EY1]; $n_\beta^{11.8}$ 1.44027[EY1]

Prepn.:

Thermal decomposition of the methochloride of 5-dimethylamino-1-hexene
(69% yield based on initial primary hexenylamine).[ME14]

Derivs.:

Methiodide: m. 199–200°[ME14]

C₈H₁₇N **Me**
Me
C₆H₁₁

5-DIMETHYLAMINO-4-METHYL-1-PENTENE

Phys. Props.:

b. 129–130°[JA2]
d_4^{15} 0.767[JA2]

Prepn.:

1. In 76% overall yield by the thermal decomposition of 1,1,2,4-tetramethyl-
   pyrrolidinium hydroxide (obtained from the corresponding iodide).[OS2]
2. Thermal decomposition of 1,1,3-trimethylpiperidinium hydroxide.[JA2]

Derivs.:

Picrate: m. 76°[OS2]
Chloroplatinate: m. 148°[OS2]

$C_8H_{17}N$ 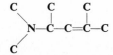 Me
Me
C_6H_{11}

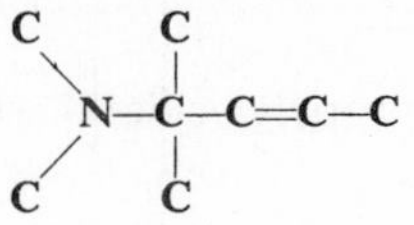

4-DIMETHYLAMINO-4-METHYL-2-PENTENE

Phys. Props.:

Infrared absorption: band at 6.05 μ (characteristic of double bond)[KR11]

Prepn.:

Catalytic hydrogenation of 4-dimethylamino-4-methyl-2-pentyne. The product
was not isolated.[KR11]

$C_8H_{17}N$ 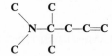 Me
Me
C_6H_{11}

4-DIMETHYLAMINO-2-METHYL-2-PENTENE

Phys. Props.:

b. 136–138°[KO9]; b_{750} 136–139°[KO7]

Prepn.:

Thermal decomposition of 1,1,2,2,4-pentamethyltrimethyleniminium hydroxide.[KO7,KO8,KO9]

Derivs.:

Picrate: m. 121–124°[KO7]

$C_8H_{17}N$ Me
Me
C_6H_{11}

4-DIMETHYLAMINO-4-METHYL-1-PENTENE

Phys. Props.:

b. 138–140°[KO10]

Prepn.:

2-Dimethylamino-4-bromo-2-methylpentane + potassium hydroxide (quantitative yield).[KO10]

Derivs.:

Picrate: m. 175° (dec.)[KO10]
Chloroplatinate: m. 176° (dec.)[KO10]
Methochloroplatinate: m. 177° (dec.)[KO10]

C₈H₁₇N

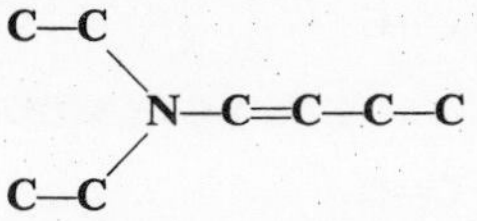

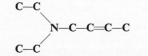

Et
Et
C₄H₇

$$\text{C}_8\text{H}_{17}\text{N}$$

1-DIETHYLAMINO-1-BUTENE*

Phys. Props.:

b_{12} 37–38° OP1

n_D^{20} 1.4471 OP1

Infrared absorption: strong band at 1648 cm.$^{-1}$ OP1

Ultraviolet absorption: 2325 A. (ϵ8110) OP1

Prepn.:

Thermal decomposition of the reaction product of diethylamine with *n*-butyraldehyde in the presence of potassium carbonate (40% overall yield). OP1

C₈H₁₇N

Et
Et
C₄H₇

1-DIETHYLAMINO-2-BUTENE

Phys. Props.:

b. 137–139° YO5; b_{38} 59° FI2

d_4^{22} 0.7873 FI2

$n_D^{22.3}$ 1.4291 YO5; n_D^{22} 1.4310 FI2; n_D^{20} 1.4301 YO5; n_D^{17} 1.4323 YO5; n_D^{14} 1.4332–1.4340 YO5

Prepn.:

1. Reaction of 3-chloro-1-butene with diethylamine *via* allylic rearrangement (82% yield). YO5
2. Cleavage by aqueous alkali of diethyl-[2-butenyl]-[5-methoxy-3-methyl-2-pentenyl]ammonium chloride (60% yield). BA2
3. 1-Chloro-2-butene + diethylamine (85% yield). YO5
4. Butyl(diethylaminomethyl) ether + 1-propenylmagnesium bromide (90% yield). FI2

Derivs.:

Picrate: m. 82–83°, BA2 81.5–83° YO5; 80° FI2

Ethochloride: m. 174.5–175.5° (dec.) YO5

Ethiodide: m. 143.4–144.5° YO5

Ethopicrate: m. 108.5–109.2° YO5

---

* This compound decomposes readily on standing. OP1

C₈H₁₇N

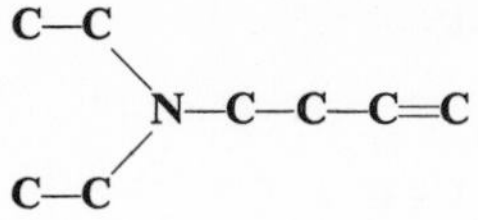

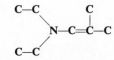

Et
Et
C₄H₇

4-DIETHYLAMINO-1-BUTENE

Phys. Props.:

b_{767} 132°[RO3]

Prepn.:

Allylmagnesium chloride + butyl(diethylaminomethyl)ether.[RO3]

Derivs.:

Picrate: m. 60°[RO3]

C₈H₁₇N

Et
Et
C₄H₇

1-DIETHYLAMINO-2-METHYL-1-PROPENE*

Phys. Props.:

b_{68} 56–57°[OP1]
n_D^{20} 1.4268[OP1]
Infrared absorption: medium band at 1662 cm.$^{-1}$[OP1]
Ultraviolet absorption: 2220 A. (ϵ3500)[OP1]

Prepn.:

Thermal decomposition of the reaction product of diethylamine with isobutyraldehyde in the presence of potassium carbonate (17% overall
yield).[OP1]

C₈H₁₇N

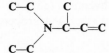

Et
Et
C₄H₇

3-DIETHYLAMINO-1-BUTENE

Phys. Props.:

b. 129.3°[YO5]
n_D^{20} 1.4262[YO5]

---

* This compound decomposes readily on standing.[OP1]

Prepn.:

3-Amino-1-butene + ethyl iodide (66% yield).[YO5]

Derivs.:

Picrate: m. 113.2–113.7° [YO5]
Ethobromide: m. *ca.* 186° (dec.)[YO5]
Ethiodide: m. *ca.* 173° (dec.)[YO5]
Ethopicrate: m. 172–173° (dec.)[YO5]

$C_8H_{17}N$ 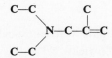 Et
Et
C_4H_7

3-DIETHYLAMINO-2-METHYL-1-PROPENE

Phys. Props.:

b. 129° [KI4]

Prepn.:

1-Chloro-2-methyl-2-propene + diethylamine (52% yield).[KI4]

Derivs.:

Picrate: m. 91–92° [KI4]
Methiodide: m. 171° [KI4]

$C_8H_{17}N$ 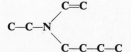 Et
Vin
n-Bu

ETHYLVINYLBUTYLAMINE *

Phys. Props.:

b_{12} 41° [OP1]
n_D^{20} 1.4451 [OP1]
Infrared absorption: strong absorption at 1628 cm.$^{-1}$ [OP1]
Ultraviolet absorption 2310 A. (ϵ4200)[OP1]

Prepn.:

Thermal decomposition of the reaction product of ethylbutylamine with acetaldehyde in the presence of potassium carbonate (18% overall yield).[OP1]

---

* This compound decomposes readily on standing.[OP1]

$C_8H_{19}N$

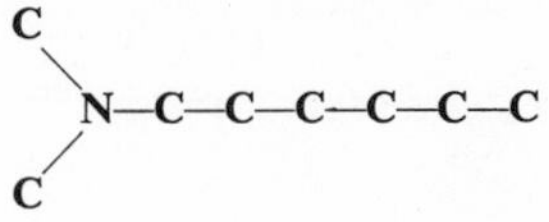

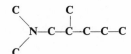

Me
Me
n-Hex

HEXYLDIMETHYLAMINE

Phys. Props.:

b. 146–150°,[AN5] 147°,[BR9] 145–147°,[BA39] 146°[BR13]; b_{766} 146–147°[CL2]; b_{760} 145° [GA9]

Infrared absorption[NA2a]

Prepn.:

1. *N*-Hexylhexaminium bromide + formic acid (13% yield)[AN5]; + formic acid + formaldehyde (60% yield).[AN5]
2. Thermal degradation of hexyltrimethylammonium hydroxide[IN8] (73% yield based on corresponding iodide).[BR9]
3. In about 20% overall yield (starting with hexylamine) by the thermal degradation of hexyltrimethylammonium hydroxide.[BR13]
4. Hexylamine hydrochloride + formaldehyde.[CL2]
5. Hexylamine + formic acid + formaldehyde (81% yield).[GA9]
6. Thermal degradation of hexyltrimethylammonium sulfide.[CL2]
7. Thermal degradation of dimethyl-*N*-hexylphosphoramidate (40% yield).[BA39]

Derivs.:

Picrate: m. 101°,[BR9] 100°[CL2]
Chloroplatinate: m. 126–127°[BR9]
Methiodide: m. 167°,[BR9] 165°,[OL6] 166°[KA13]
Methosulfate: m. 90°[BR13]

$C_8H_{19}N$

Me
Me
C_6H_{13}

1-DIMETHYLAMINO-2-METHYLPENTANE

Phys. Props.:

b. 134°[LU13]

Prepn.:

Catalytic hydrogenation of 1-dimethylamino-2-methyl-2,4-pentadiene.[LU13]

Derivs.:

Picrate: m. 98°[LU13]

$C_8H_{19}N$

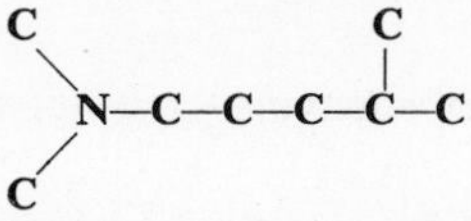

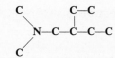

Me
Me
i-Hex

1-DIMETHYLAMINO-4-METHYLPENTANE

Phys. Props.:
b_{766} 139–140° [CL2]

Prepn.:
Isohexylamine hydrochloride + formaldehyde. [CL2]

Derivs.:
Picrate: m. 132° [CL2]
Methiodide: m. 199–201° [KA13]

$C_8H_{19}N$

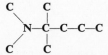

Me
Me
C_6H_{13}

1-DIMETHYLAMINO-2-ETHYLBUTANE

Phys. Props.:
b_{148} 83.5–84.0° [CO24]
n_D^{25} 1.4123 [CO24]

Prepn.:
1. In 57% estimated yield (amine not isolated) based on initial quaternary ammonium bromide in the thermal decomposition of 2-ethylbutyltrimethylammonium hydroxide [HA11]; in 40% yield from the hydroxide. [CO24]
2. Reduction of *N,N*-dimethyl-2-ethylbutyramide (71% yield). [CO24]

Derivs.:
Picrate: m. 94.7–96.2° [CO24]
Methiodide: m. 239.0–240.5° (dec.) [CO24]

$C_8H_{19}N$

Me
Me
C_6H_{13}

2-DIMETHYLAMINO-2-METHYLPENTANE

Phys. Props.:
b. 140–142°, [MO4] 138–139° [VE2]
d_4^{20} 0.7950 [MO4,VE2]

Prepn.:

1. 2-Dimethylamino-2-cyanopropane + propylmagnesium bromide (20% yield).[VE2]
2. *N,N*-Dimethyl-*n*-butyramide + methylmagnesium iodide (8% yield); the main product, in 50% yield, is 2-pentanone.[MO4]
3. Catalytic hydrogenation of 4-dimethylamino-4-methyl-2-pentyne.[KR11]

Derivs.:

Picrate: m. 213°[MO4]
Chloroaurate: m. 103°[MO4]
Chloroplatinate: m. 250°[MO4]

$C_8H_{19}N$

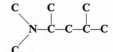

Me
Me
C_6H_{13}

2-DIMETHYLAMINO-4-METHYLPENTANE

Prepn.:

As one of several products resulting from the catalytic hydrogenation of the methyl ester of 2-amino-4-methylpentanoic acid.[OV1]

Derivs.:

Picrate: m. 132–134°[OV1]

$C_8H_{19}N$

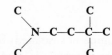

Me
Me
C_6H_{13}

1-DIMETHYLAMINO-3,3-DIMETHYLBUTANE

Derivs.:

Methiodide (from trimethylamine and alkyl iodide): m. 285° (sub.)[SM9]

$C_8H_{19}N$

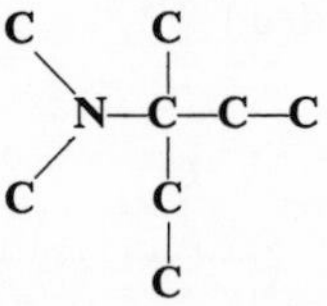

Me
Me
C_6H_{13}

3-DIMETHYLAMINO-3-METHYLPENTANE

Phys. Props.:

b_{769} 146°[BR50]
d_4^{20} 0.7830[BR50]
n_D^{20} 1.4306[BR50]

Prepn.:
2-Dimethylamino-2-cyanobutane + ethylmagnesium bromide.[BR50]

Derivs.:
Chloroplatinate: m. 210° (dec.)[BR50]

$C_8H_{19}N$

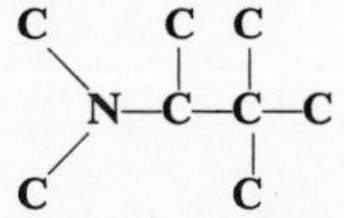

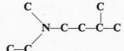

Me
Me
C_6H_{13}

3-DIMETHYLAMINO-2,2-DIMETHYLBUTANE

Phys. Props.:
b_{759} 129–130°[ST10]
d_4^{25} 0.7627[ST10]
n_D^{25} 1.4160[ST10]

Prepn.:
1. 2,2-Dimethyl-3-aminobutane (also called pinacolylamine) + methyl iodide.[ST10]
2. Thermal decomposition of pinacolyltrimethylammonium hydroxide (52% yield).[ST10]

Derivs.:
Hydriodide: m. 260–261°[ST10]
Picrate: m. 214°[ST10]
Methiodide: m. 260°[ST10]

$C_8H_{19}N$

Me
Et
i-Pent

METHYLETHYLISOPENTYLAMINE

Phys. Props.:
b. 135°,[HO4] 133–137°[SK4]

Prepn.:
1. Thermal degradation of methyldiethylisopentylammonium hydroxide.[HO4]*
2. Reductive alkylation of ethylisopentylamine by formaldehyde and hydrogen in the presence of platinum.[SK4]

Derivs.:
Picrate: m. 101–102°[SK4]

---

* Ref. HO4 refers to the product of this reaction as "methylethylamylamine" but it is actually methylethylisopentylamine.

$C_8H_{19}N$

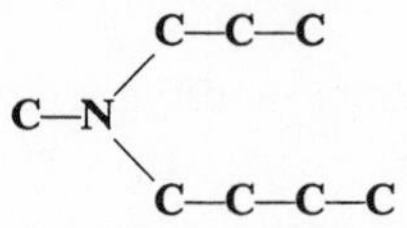

Me
n-Pr
n-Bu

METHYLPROPYLBUTYLAMINE

Phys. Props.:

b. 138° [CO23]
d_4^{25} 0.7420 [CO23]
n_D^{25} 1.4102 [CO23]

Prepn.:

Propylbutylamine + formic acid + formaldehyde (73% yield). [CO23]

Derivs.:

Picrate: m. 69.2–70.2° [CO23]
Amine oxide picrate: m. 65.2–66.2° [CO23]
Methiodide: m. 189–189.4° [CO23]

$C_8H_{19}N$

Me
n-Pr
i-Bu

METHYLPROPYLISOBUTYLAMINE

Phys. Props.:

b. 128–130° [CO23]
d_4^{25} 0.7327 [CO23]
n_D^{25} 1.4047 [CO23]

Prepn.:

Propylisobutylamine + formic acid + formaldehyde (88% yield). [CO23]

Derivs.:

Picrate: m. 100.3–101.8° [CO23]
Amine oxide picrate: m. 86–86.6° [CO23]
Methiodide: m. 194–194.6° [CO23]; *ca.* 170° (dec.) [PO3] *
Ethiodide: m. 196.5° [MA27]

---

* Ref. PO3 claims that dimethylpropylisobutylammonium iodide was obtained instead of the expected methylethylpropylisobutylammonium iodide upon reaction of ethylpropylisobutylamine with methyl iodide.

C$_8$H$_{19}$N

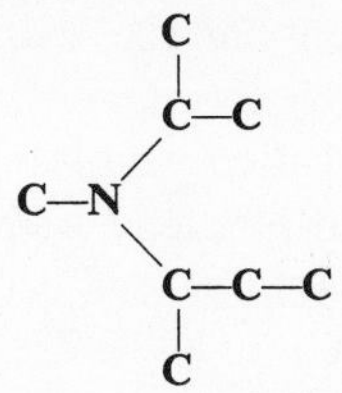

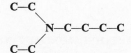

Me
i-Pr
sec-**Bu**

METHYLISOPROPYL-(1-METHYLPROPYL)AMINE

Phys. Props.:

b. 132–133°[SK5]

Prepn.:

Reductive alkylation of methyl-*sec*-butylamine with acetone and hydrogen (47% yield).[SK5]

Derivs.:

Picrate: m. 142–143°[SK5]

C$_8$H$_{19}$N

Et
Et
n-**Bu**

BUTYLDIETHYLAMINE

Phys. Props.:

b. 136–138°,[PE12] 136–137°,[BO16,HA3] 135–137°,[WH4] 136.5°,[YO5] 134–135°[YO5]
n_D^{25} 1.4118[WH4]; n_D^{20} 1.4140,[PE12] 1.4133–1.4135[YO5]
d_4^{20} 0.7522[PE12]; d_0^0 0.7614[HA3]
Infrared absorption: strong 1203, 1294, 1377, 1451 cm.$^{-1}$; medium 724, 766, 927, 962, 1002, 1087, 1139, 1242 cm.$^{-1}$ [PE12]

Prepn.:

1. Lithiodiethylamine + butyl bromide (53% yield).[HO22]
2. Butylamine + acetylene + ammonia + sodium under pressure (74.8% yield),[HO23] (48% yield).[WH4]
3. Raney nickel catalyzed hydrogenation of 1-diethylamino-4-acetoxy-2-butyne or of 1-diethylamino-4-benzoyloxy-2-butyne.[MA34]
4. Catalytic hydrogenation of 1-diethylamino-2-butene (47% yield)[YO5]; of 1-diethylamino-1,3-butadiene.[BO16]
5. Diethylamine + butyl bromide[HA3] (90% yield)[YO5]; + butyl chloride (80% yield).[TO1]
6. Triethylbutylammonium bromide + lithium ethyl or lithium isoamyl.[HA3]

7. High-pressure reaction of butylamine with ethylene in the presence of sodium (48% yield).[WH4]
8. Catalytic hydrogenation of 1-diethylamino-1-buten-3-yne.[PE12]
9. Reduction of 4-diethylamino-1-butene with diisobutylaluminum hydride followed by hydrolysis.[ZA4]

Derivs.:

Picrate: m. 47–48.5°,[YO5] 46°[PE12]
·BH_3: m. −33 to −32°[KO18]; b_{14} 125°[KO18]
Amine oxide picrate: m. 63°[HO21]
4,4′-Dichlorodiphenyldisulfimide salt: m. 91–92°[RU4]
Ethochloroplatinate: m. 220°[RI5]
Ethobromide: m. 212–215° (dec.)[HA3]
Ethiodide: m. 205° (dec.),[HA3] 204.5–205°,[YO5] 203–204°[YO5]
Ethopicrate: m. 110–110.5°[YO5]
$(Et_3NBu)_2$·$NiBr_4$: m. 250°[RE9]
$(Et_3NBu)_2$·$CoBr_4$: m. 255°[RE9]

$C_8H_{19}N$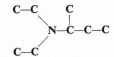

Et
Et
sec-Bu

2-DIETHYLAMINOBUTANE*

Phys. Props.:

b. 132°,[YO5] 131°[LE7]; b_{766} 130–131°[GA3]
d_4^{15} 0.7567[LE7]
n_D^{20} 1.4128,[YO5] 1.4165[GA3]; n_C^{15} 1.41301[LE7]; n_D^{15} 1.41534[LE7]; n_F^{15} 1.42111[LE7]; n_G^{15} 1.42589[LE7]
$[\alpha]_D^{15}$ 89.3°[LE7]

Prepn.:

1. Diethylamine + *sec*-butyl bromide (80% yield).[YO5]
2. *sec*-Butylamine + ethyl iodide (65% yield).[YO5] In *ca.* 30% yield of optically active isomer using *d-sec*-butylamine.[LE7]
3. Catalytic hydrogenation of 3-diethylamino-1-butene,[YO5] or 3-diethylamino-1-butyne.[GA3,RE13]

Derivs.:

Picrate: m. 116–117°[GA3]; 114.5–115.0°[YO5]
Picrate of *d*-amine: m. 117°[LE7]
Ethiodide: m. 234–235° (dec.)[YO5]
Ethopicrate: m. 157.5–158.5°[YO5]

---

* All data obtained by ref. LE7 are for the optically active isomer.

C₈H₁₉N

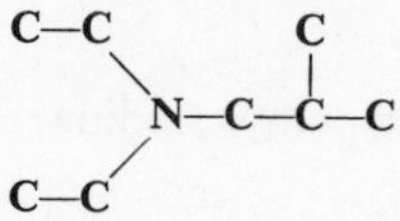

Et
Et
i-Bu

ISOBUTYLDIETHYLAMINE

Phys. Props.:

b. 132°[KI4]

Prepn.:

Reduction of 1-diethylamino-2-methyl-2-propene.[KI4]

Derivs.:

Picrate: m. 87–88°[KI4]
Methiodide: m. 195°[KI4]
Ethochloroplatinate: m. 215°[RI5]

C₈H₁₉N

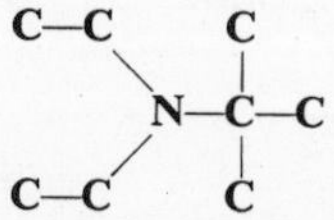

Et
Et
t-Bu

t-BUTYLDIETHYLAMINE

Prepn.:

1. *t*-Butylamine + ethyl iodide.[RE3]
2. Methylmagnesium iodide + isopropylidenedimethylammonium iodide, $(CH_3)_2C{=}N^+(C_2H_5)_2I^-$ (11% yield).[RE3]

Derivs.:

Chloroplatinate: m. 223–225° (dec.)[RE3]

C₈H₁₉N

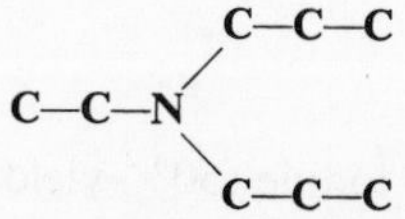

Et
n-Pr
n-Pr

ETHYLDIPROPYLAMINE

Phys. Props.:

b. 133–136°,[RE12] 134°,[PA12] 132–134°,[BR5] 130–132°,[AU1] 128–130°[BR5]; $b_{749.9}$
    137.2°[CO13]
d_4^{24} 0.807[CO13]

Prepn.:

1. From dipropylamine and ethyl iodide[AU1,BR5]; and potassium ethyl sulfate.[PA12]
2. Thermal decomposition of ethyltripropylammonium iodide.[AU1]
3. Ethylamine + propyl chloride.[CO13]
4. A mixture of amines, ethyldipropylamine, diethylpropylamine, and triethylamine is obtained from diethylamine, formic acid, ethylene, and carbon monoxide under pressure in the presence of iron pentacarbonyl.[RE12]
5. Ethyldichloroamine + propylmagnesium chloride (8% yield).[CO4]

Derivs.:

Hydrochloride: m. 113–115° [CO13]
Chloroaurate: m. 96°,[PA12] 93–94° [CO13]
Chloroplatinate: m. 175° [CO13]
Methochloroplatinate: m. 228° (dec.)[RI5]
Methopicrate: m. 72° [RI6]
Ethochloroplatinate: m. 220° (slight dec.)[RI5]
Ethiodide: m. 238–240°[AU1]
Ethopicrate: m. 80–81°,[RI6] 79.8°[WA12]
Propiodide: m. 238°[AU1]
Propiodide·HgCl$_2$: m. 135°[BA26]

$C_8H_{19}N$ 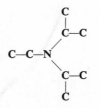 Et
i-Pr
i-Pr

ETHYLDIISOPROPYLAMINE

Phys. Props.:

b. 126.5°[RO4]; b$_{731}$ 119°[WO7]
n$_D^{25}$ 1.4121,[RO4] 1.4112[WO7]
d$_4^{27}$ 0.751[WO7]

Prepn.:

1. Diisopropylamine + ethyl iodide (50% yield)[RO4]; + ethyl bromide.[WO7]
2. Acetonitrile + acetone + hydrogen in the presence of a nickel-aluminum catalyst gives a mixture of several amines, including ethyldiisopropylamine.[PR1]

Derivs.:

Methobromide: m. 247° (cor.)[RO4]
Ethochloride: m. 299° (cor.)[RO4]

C_9H_9N

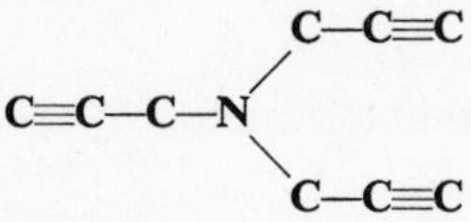

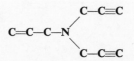

C_3H_3
C_3H_3
C_3H_3

TRI(2-PROPYNYL)AMINE

Phys. Props.:

b_{10} 76° CH1,GA6a
d_4^{16} 0.922 CH1,GA6a
n_D^{16} 1.4875 CH1,GA6a
pK_a 13.0 (temperature unspecified) CH1*
Raman bands: 2108 and 2128 cm.$^{-1}$ PI0

Prepn.:

Propargyl bromide + ammonia gives a mixture of mono-, di-, and tri-propargyl amines. CH1,GA6a

Derivs.:

Picrate: m. 108° CH1,GA6a
Oxalate: m. 135° CH1,GA6a

$C_9H_{11}N$

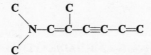

All
C_3H_3
C_3H_3

ALLYLDI(2-PROPYNYL)AMINE

Phys. Props.:

m. *ca.* −60° DO2
Heat of combustion 4480 kcal./lb. DO2

Prepn.:

Allylamine + propargyl bromide or chloride. DO2

$C_9H_{13}N$

C
|
N—C=C—C≡C—C=C
| |
C   C

Me
Me
C_7H_7

1-DIMETHYLAMINO-2-METHYL-1,5-HEXADIEN-3YNE

Phys. Props.:

b_2 55–58° VA6
d_4^{20} 0.9004 VA6
n_D^{20} 1.4824 VA6

---

* This pK_a value appears to be too high. See section entitled "General Properties", p. 9.

Prepn.:

Dehydration of 1-dimethylamino-2-methyl-2-hydroxy-5-hexen-3-yne by sulfuric acid in methanol (*ca.* 50% yield).[VA6]

$C_9H_{13}N$ 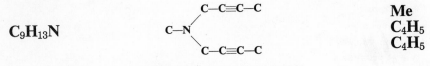 Me
C_4H_5
C_4H_5

METHYLDI(2-BUTYNYL)AMINE

Phys. Props.

b_{680} 190–192° [IN1]

Prepn.:

By-product in the alkylation of *N*-methylaniline with dimethyldi(2-butynyl)-ammonium chloride.[IN1]

$C_9H_{13}N$ 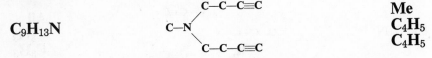 Me
C_4H_5
C_4H_5

METHYLDI(3-BUTYNYL)AMINE

Derivs.:

Methobenzenesulfonate (from 3-butynyldimethylamine and 3-butynylbenzene-sulfonate): m. 118° [EP2,MA31,OL6]

$C_9H_{13}N$ 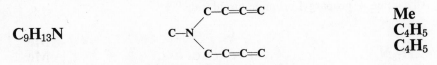 Me
C_4H_5
C_4H_5

METHYLDI(2,3-BUTADIENYL)AMINE

Phys. Props.:

b. 105–107.5° [EN2]; b_{15} 70–71.0° [EN1,EN2]
n_D^{25} 1.4988 [EN1,EN2]
Infrared absorption: maxima at 5.1 and 11.9 μ [EN2]

Prepn.:

Vinylacetylene + methylamine under pressure (11% yield),[EN2] (21% yield).[EN1]

$C_9H_{13}N$

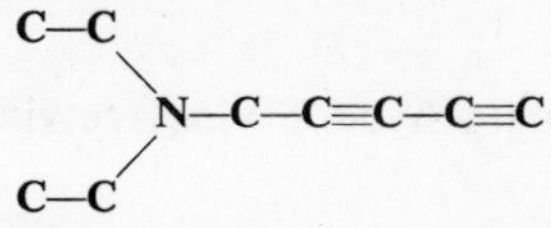

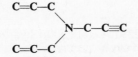

Et
Et
C_5H_3

5-DIETHYLAMINO-1,3-PENTADIYNE

Phys. Props.:

b_8 56–70°[FR5]

Prepn.:

Diethylamine + paraformaldehyde + 1,3-butadiyne (35% yield). The other
   products of the reaction are bis(diethylamino)methane and 1,6-bis(diethylamino)-2,4-hexadiyne. Yields of reaction products vary with
   reaction conditions.[FR5]

$C_9H_{13}N$

All
All
C_3H_3

3-DIALLYLAMINO-1-PROPYNE

Phys. Props.:

$b_{59.3}$ 80–82°[BU17]
d_4^{25} 0.8290[BU17]
n_D^{25} 1.4588[BU17]

Prepn.:

Dehydrobromination of 2-bromoallyldiallylamine with sodamide in liquid
   ammonia (57.2% yield).[BU17]

Derivs.:

Allylobromide: m. 101–104°[BU17]

$C_9H_{15}N$

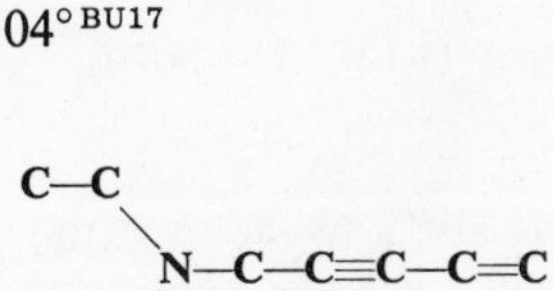

Et
Et
C_5H_5

5-DIETHYLAMINO-1-PENTEN-3-YNE

Phys. Props.:

b_{766} 166–167°[CA11,CO2]; b_{51} 88–89°[CA11]
d_4^{20} 0.8272[CA11,CO2]
n_D^{20} 1.4710[CA11,CO2]

Prepn.:

Diethylamine + paraformaldehyde + vinylacetylene (91% yield).[CA11,CO2]

Derivs.:

Hydrochloride: m. 122–124° [CA11]
Picrate: m. 84–85° [CA11]

$C_9H_{15}N$

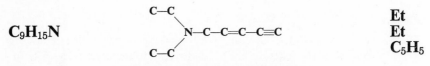

Et
Et
C_5H_5

1-DIETHYLAMINO-2-PENTEN-4-YNE

Phys. Props.

b_{27} 76° [JO5]
n_D^{18} 1.4730 [JO5]
Ultraviolet absorption: 2230 A. (ϵ12,500); hydrochloride 2250 A. (ϵ15,500)
    with inflection at 2340 A. (ϵ12,000) [JO5]

Prepn.:

1-Chloro-2-penten-4-yne + diethylamine (46% yield). [JO5]

Derivs.:

Hydrochloride: m. 172° [JO5]
Picrate: m. 124° [JO5]

$C_9H_{15}N$

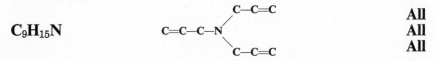

All
All
All

TRIALLYLAMINE

Phys. Props.:

b. 154–156°,[BU13] 150–151°,[PI3] 150°,[LI3] 148–149°,[BU11] 147–148° [MA15]; b_{760}
    155–156° (cor.) [ZA5]
d_4^{20} 0.809 [MA15]; $d_0^{14.3}$ 0.8094 [ZA5]
n_D^{25} 1.4502 [BU11]
Infrared absorption: maxima at 3.38 and 9.32 μ [BU11]

Prepn.:

1. Ammonia + allyl bromide (10% yield),[TS7] (57.2% yield)[BU13]; + allyl
    chloride[MA15,LI3]; + allyl iodide. [MA14]

2. By-product (presumably by disproportionation)* in reaction of 1,4-di(p-toluensulfonoxy)butane with diallylamine[BU11] or of 1,1-diallylpyrrolidinium bromide and diallylamine.[BU11]
3. Thermal decomposition of tetraallylammonium hydroxide.[CA3,GR11]
4. By-product in the reaction of allyl chloride with alcoholic potassium cyanide.[PI5]

Derivs.:

Picrate: m. 94°[TS7]
Methobromide: m. 89–91°[BU16]
Ethobromide: m. 159°[BU14]
Allylobromide:† m. 185°,[BU14] 183–184°[BU11]
Allyloiodide: m. 127–128°[ST9]
Allyloiodide·iodoform: m. 161–162°[ST9]
Butylobromide: m. 175°[BU14]
Benzylochloride: m. 132°[BU14]

$C_9H_{17}N$ 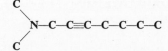 **Me**
Me
C_7H_{11}

1-DIMETHYLAMINO-2-HEPTYNE

Phys. Props.:

b_{90} 111°,[SC20] 110°[CA7]
d_4^{20} 0.7995[CA7]
n_D^{20} 1.4420[CA7]
pK_a 7.70 (in 30% methanol) (temperature unspecified)[CA7]

Prepn.:

1. Dimethylamine + formaldehyde and 1-pentyne (81% yield).[CA7]
2. 2-Heptynylhexaminium bromide + formic acid + formaldehyde (56% yield).[SC20]

Derivs.:

Oxalate: m. 108–109°,[CA7] 107–108°[SC20]
Methiodide: m. 122°[SC20]

---

* Examination of the experimental data in ref. BU11 does not rule out the possibility that the triallylamine isolated originated as a 3–4% impurity in the diallylamine reactant.
† Ref. GR11 claims that tetrallylammonium bromide decomposes at about 80°. This appears to be an obvious error and was not included in the tabulation.

C₉H₁₇N   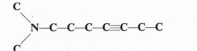   Me
Me
C₇H₁₁

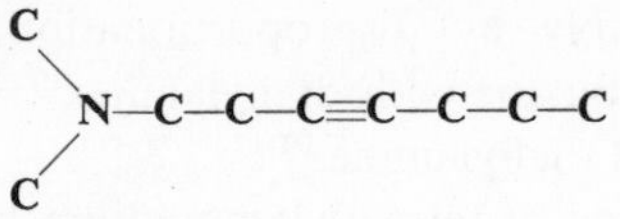

1-DIMETHYLAMINO-3-HEPTYNE

Prepn.:

Sodio derivative of 4-dimethylamino-1-butyne + a propyl halide (unspecified).[JA1]

Derivs.:

Methiodide: m. 216–217°[JA1]

C₉H₁₇N   Me
Me
C₇H₁₁

7-DIMETHYLAMINO-3-HEPTYNE

Phys. Props.

b_{18} 83°,[EP2] 73°[MA31,OL6] *
n_D^{26} 1.4410[EP2,MA31,OL6]

Prepn.:

Sodio derivative of 5-dimethylamino-1-pentyne + ethyl iodide.[EP2,MA31,OL6]

Derivs.:

Methiodide: m. 182–183°,[EP2] 181–182°[OL6]

C₉H₁₇N   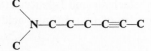   Me
Me
C₇H₁₁

7-DIMETHYLAMINO-2-HEPTYNE

Phys. Props.:

b_{18} 75–76°[EP2,MA31,OL6]
n_D^{19} 1.4420[EP2,MA31,OL6]

---

* The discordant values are given by the same authors. We favor the lower value as being more consistent with those for related compounds.

Prepn.:

Sodio derivative of 6-dimethylamino-1-hexyne + methyl iodide.[EP2,MA31,OL6]

Derivs.:

Methiodide: m. 144°[EP2]

$C_9H_{17}N$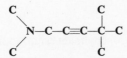

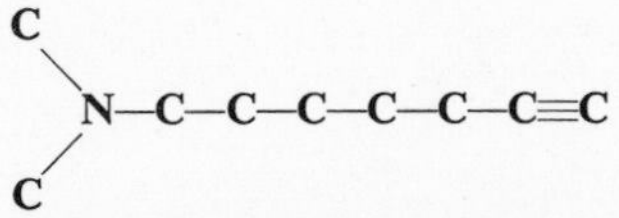

Me
Me
C_7H_{11}

7-DIMETHYLAMINO-1-HEPTYNE

Phys. Props.:

b_{20} 76°[OL6]
n_D^{24} 1.4410[OL6]

Prepn.:

Dimethylamine + 7-iodo-1-heptyne.[OL6]

Derivs.:

Hydrochloride: m. 117°[OL6]
Methiodide: m. 132–133°[OL6]

$C_9H_{17}N$

Me
Me
C_7H_{11}

1-DIMETHYLAMINO-4,4-DIMETHYL-2-PENTYNE

Phys. Props.

b_{25} 55°[MA32,MA33]
n_D^{21} 1.4270[MA32,MA33]

Prepn.:

3,3-Dimethyl-1-butyne + dimethylamine + formaldehyde in the presence of
   copper(II) acetate (62% yield).[MA32]

Derivs.:

Methiodide: m. 183°[MA32,MA33]

$$C_9H_{17}N$$

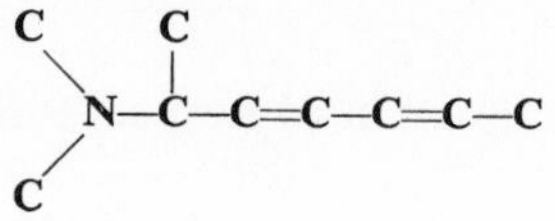

$$
\begin{array}{c}
\text{C}\quad\text{C}\\
\backslash\quad|\\
\text{N--C--C=C--C=C--C}\\
/\\
\text{C}
\end{array}
$$

Me
Me
C_7H_{11}

6-DIMETHYLAMINO-2,4-HEPTADIENE

Phys. Props.
b_{740} 168–169°[LU8]
d_4^{20} 0.8058[LU8]
n_D^{20} 1.4771[LU8]

Prepn.:

Thermal decomposition of 1,1,2,6-tetramethyl-1,2,5,6-tetrahydropyridinium hydroxide[LU8]

Derivs.:
Picrate: m. 127–128°[LU8]

$$C_9H_{17}N$$

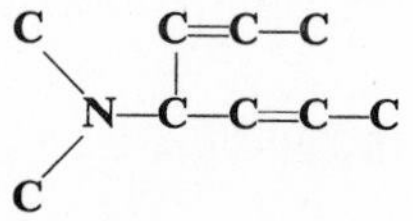

$$
\begin{array}{c}
\text{C}\quad\text{C=C--C}\\
\backslash\quad|\\
\text{N--C--C=C--C}\\
/\\
\text{C}
\end{array}
$$

Me
Me
C_7H_{11}

4-DIMETHYLAMINO-2,5-HEPTADIENE

Phys. Props.:
b_{18} 52°[FI3]
d_4^{20} 0.8012[FI3]
n_D^{20} 1.4527[FI3]

Prepn.:
Dimethylformamide + 1-propenylmagnesium iodide.[FI3]

Derivs.:
Picrate: m. 185°[FI3]

$$C_9H_{17}N$$

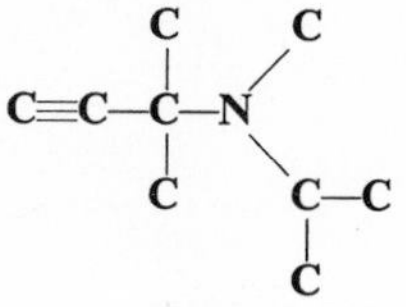

$$
\begin{array}{c}
\quad\quad\text{C}\quad\text{C}\\
\quad\quad|\quad\,/\\
\text{C≡C--C--N}\\
\quad\quad|\quad\backslash\\
\quad\quad\text{C}\quad\text{C--C}\\
\quad\quad\quad\quad|\\
\quad\quad\quad\quad\text{C}
\end{array}
$$

Me
i-Pr
C_5H_7

METHYLISOPROPYL-(1,1-DIMETHYL-2-PROPYNYL)-AMINE

Phys. Props.:
b_{135} 96–98°[AI1]

n_D^{25} 1.4350[AI1]

pK_a 8.7 at 25° (in water), 7.5 (in 66% dimethylformamide)[AI1]

Prepn.:

Methylation of isopropyl-(1,1-dimethyl-2-propynyl)amine with dimethyl sulfate (65% yield).[AI1]

Derivs.:

Hydrochloride: m. 185–186°[AI1]
Methiodide: m. 157–158° (dec.)[AI1]

 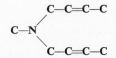

$C_9H_{17}N$ **Me**
          C₄H₇
          C₄H₇

METHYLDI(2-BUTENYL)AMINE*

Prepn.:

Reaction of methylamine with 1,3-butadiene in the presence of the sodium salt of methylamine gives a mixture of methyldi(2-butenyl)amine and methyl-(2-butenyl)-(2,6-octadienyl)amine. The octadienyl group in the latter compound results from dimerization of butadiene.[DA6]

$C_9H_{17}N$ **Me**
          C₄H₇
          C₄H₇

METHYLDI(2-METHYL-2-PROPENYL)AMINE

Phys. Props.:

b. 145–145.5°[WE15]
n_D^{20} 1.4372[WE15]

Prepn.:

Methallyl chloride + methylamine (78% yield).[WE15]

---

* This structure was not definitively proved.

$C_9H_{17}N$

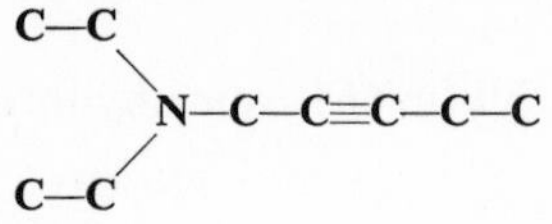

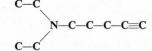

Et
Et
C_5H_7

1-DIETHYLAMINO-2-PENTYNE

Phys. Props.:

b. $168.4-169.9°$[PA5]

d_4^{25} 0.8029[PA5]

n_D^{25} 1.4402[PA5]

Prepn.:

Sodio derivative of 1-diethylamino-2-propyne + ethyl bromide (59% yield).[PA5]

$C_9H_{17}N$

Et
Et
C_5H_7

5-DIETHYLAMINO-1-PENTYNE

Phys. Props.:

b_{40} $76°$[EP2,MA31,OL6,PE10]; b_{20} $60.5-61.5°$[PE10]; b_{10} $54°$[ZA2]

d_4^{20} 0.8061,[ZA2] 0.7901[PE10]

n_D^{22} 1.4380[PE2,MA31,OL6]; n_D^{20} 1.4412,[ZA2] 1.4378[PE10]

Infrared absorption[PE10]

Prepn.:

1. 1-Iodo-4-pentyne + diethylamine.[EP2,MA31,OL6]
2. 1,1,2-Trichloro-5-diethylamino-1-pentene + sodium (88% yield).[ZA2]
3. Lithiodiethylamine + 1-penten-3-yne (5% yield).[PE10]

Derivs.:

Ethiodide: m. $176°$[EP2,MA31,OL6]

$C_9H_{17}N$

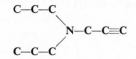

n-Pr
n-Pr
C_3H_3

3-DIPROPYLAMINO-1-PROPYNE

Phys. Props.

b. $157.5-158.5°$[PA6]

d_4^{25} 0.7986[PA6]

n_D^{25} 1.4325[PA6]

Prepn.:

Dehydrobromination of 1-dipropylamino-2-bromo-2-propene with sodamide (81% yield).[PA6]

$C_9H_{17}N$

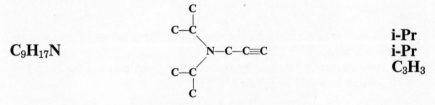

i-Pr
i-Pr
C_3H_3

3-DIISOPROPYLAMINO-1-PROPYNE

Phys. Props.:

b. 152.5–153[PA6]; b_{25} 55–58°[BI1]
d_4^{25} 0.8017[PA6]
n_D^{25} 1.4385[PA6]

Prepn.:

1. Dehydrobromination of 1-diisopropylamino-2-bromopropene with sodamide (81.5% yield).[PA6]
2. 1-Bromo-2-propyne + diisopropylamine (at least 50% yield).[BI1,BI3]

$C_9H_{19}N$

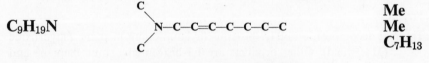

Me
Me
C_7H_{13}

1-DIMETHYLAMINO-2-HEPTENE

Phys. Props.:

cis isomer

b_{38} 77°[OL5,OL6]; b_{18} 58°[CA7]
d_{20}^{20} 0.7760[OL5,OL6]; d_4^{20} 0.7747[CA7]
n_D^{20} 1.4330[CA7,OL6]; n_D^{16} 1.4360[OL5]
pK_a 8.83 (in 30% methanol)[CA7]; 9.4[OL6]
Infrared studies of a series of compounds similar to the subject compound show maxima at about 700 cm.$^{-1}$ and about 1650 cm.$^{-1}$ for the *cis* isomers.[OL6] Raman frequency characteristic of *cis* double bond occurs at 1665 cm.$^{-1}$[OL5,OL6]

trans isomer

b_{90} 103°[CA7]; b_{25} 70–70.5°[OL5,OL6]
d_4^{20} 0.7683[CA7]; d_{20}^{20} 0.7710[OL5,OL6]
n_D^{20} 1.4311,[CA7] 1.4315[OL6]; n_D^{16} 1.4335[OL5]
pK_a 9.10 (in 30% methanol)[CA7]; 9.6[OL6]

Infrared studies of a series of compounds similar to the subject compound
show maxima at about 965 cm.$^{-1}$ and about 1670 cm.$^{-1}$ for the
trans isomers.[OL6] Raman frequency characteristic of trans double
bond occurs at 1675 cm.$^{-1}$[OL5,OL6]

Prepn.:

1. The *cis* isomer is obtained by the catalytic hydrogenation of 1-dimethyl-
   amino-2-heptyne.[CA7,OL5,OL6]
2. The *trans* isomer is obtained by reduction of 1-dimethylamino-2-heptyne
   with sodium in liquid ammonia.[CA7,OL5,OL6]

Derivs.:

cis-Methiodide: m. 119°,[OL6] 116°[OL5]
trans-Methiodide: m. 170°[OL5,OL6]

$C_9H_{19}N$

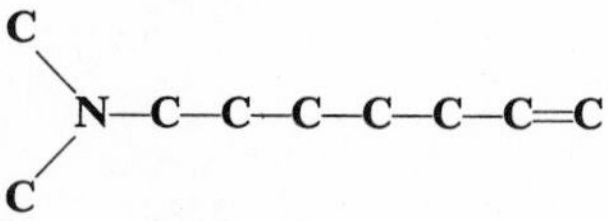

$$\underset{C}{\overset{C}{N}}\!-\!C\!-\!C\!-\!C\!-\!C\!-\!C\!-\!C\!=\!C$$

Me
Me
C_7H_{13}

7-DIMETHYLAMINO-1-HEPTENE

Phys. Props.:

b. 166–169°[BR10]; b_{10} 60–65°[BR10]

Prepn.:

Thermal decomposition of 1,7-bis(trimethylammonium)heptane dihydroxide
(31% yield). Other products are 1,7-bis(dimethylamino)heptane and
1,6-heptadiene.[BR10]

Derivs.:

Picrate: m. 88°[BR10]
Methiodide: m. 120°[BR10]

$C_9H_{19}N$

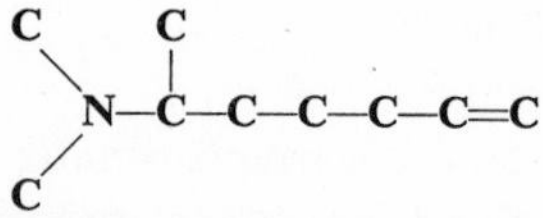

$$\underset{C}{\overset{C \quad\; C}{N}}\!-\!C\!-\!C\!-\!C\!-\!C\!-\!C\!=\!C$$

Me
Me
C_7H_{13}

6-DIMETHYLAMINO-1-HEPTENE

Phys. Props.:

b. 160°[LU8]

Prepn.:

Thermal decomposition of 1,1,2,6-tetramethylpiperidinium hydroxide.[LU8]

Derivs.:

Chloroplatinate: m. 130–131°[LU8]

C₉H₁₉N $C_9H_{19}N$

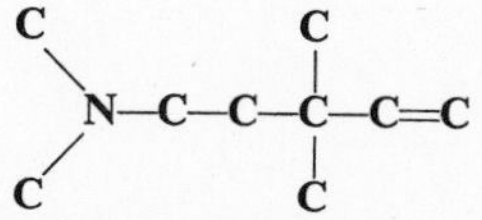

5-DIMETHYLAMINO-3,3-DIMETHYL-1-PENTENE

Me
Me
C₇H₁₃

Phys. Props.:

b. 149°[LU7]

d_4^{20} 0.7739[LU7]

n_D^{20} 1.4313[LU7]

Prepn.:

Thermal decomposition of 1,1,4,4-tetramethylpiperidinium hydroxide (83% yield).[LU7]

Derivs.:

Picrate: m. 164°[LU7]

C₉H₁₉N

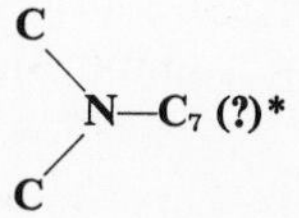

N—C₇ (?)*

DIMETHYLAMINOHEPTENE*

Me
Me
C₇H₁₃

Phys. Props.:

b. 120–130°†[SC7]

Prepn.:

Propylene dimer + tetramethylmethylenediamine + sulfuric acid.[SC7]

C₉H₁₉N

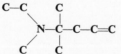

METHYLETHYL-(1,1-DIMETHYL-3-BUTENYL)AMINE

Me
Et
C₆H₁₁

Phys. Props.:

b. 154–156°[KO8]

---

* Structure of this compound in ref. SC7 is undetermined. See "Discussion of Preparative Methods" Section 5.

† This boiling point is significantly lower than would be predicted from comparable isomers; hence might be in error.

Prepn.:

Thermal decomposition of 1,2,2,4-tetramethyl-1-ethyl(trimethyleniminium) hydroxide.[KO8]

Derivs.:

Picrate: m. 85.5–86.5° [KO8]
Picrolonate: m. 137° [KO8]
Chloroplatinate: m. 159–160° (dec. at 163°) [KO8]
Methochloroplatinate: m. 155–156° (dec.) [KO8]

$C_9H_{19}N$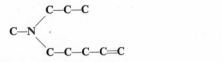

Me
n-Pr
C_5H_9

METHYLPROPYL-(4-PENTENYL)AMINE

Phys. Props.:

b. 168° [BR6]

Prepn.:

Thermal decomposition of N-methyl-N-propylpiperidinium hydroxide yields a trace amount of the subject amine. Major products are N-methyl- and N-propyl-piperidine.[BR6]

Derivs.:

Methiodide: m. 110° [BR6]

$C_9H_{19}N$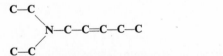

Et
Et
C_5H_9

1-DIETHYLAMINO-2-PENTENE*

Phys. Props.:

b_{735} 156–158° [ME6]

Prepn.:

Diethylamine + 1-chloro-2-pentene (80% yield)[ME6]; + 3-chloro-1-pentene (*via* allylic shift) (67% yield).[ME6]

Derivs.:

Picrate: m. 39–41° [ME6]

---

* There is a nomenclature error for this compound in ref. ME6.

$C_9H_{19}N$

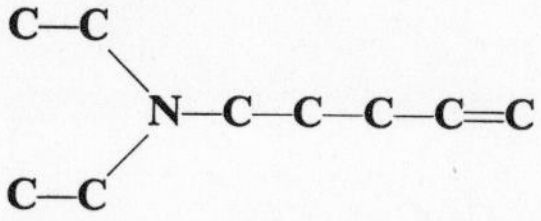

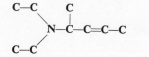

Et
Et
C_5H_9

5-DIETHYLAMINO-1-PENTENE

Phys. Props.:
b. 148–151° ^{BO5}; b$_{746}$ 156.4° ^{KH3}; b$_{68}$ 81.6° ^{KH3}; b$_{32}$ 65–66° ^{KH3}; b$_{31}$ 62.5–64° ^{KH5}; b$_{20}$ 52–55° ^{KH5}
d$_{20}^{20}$ 0.8285^{KH3}
n$_D^{20}$ 1.4310^{KH3,KH5}

Prepn.:
1. 1-Diethylamino-2-chloroethane + allylmagnesium chloride (85% yield),^{KH3} (81% yield)^{KH5}; + allylmagnesium bromide (69% yield).^{KH5}
2. 1,1-Diethyl-2-methylpyrrolidinium chloride + sodium phenylacetylide (68% yield), or sodamide (57% yield), or sodium succinimide (less than 31% yield).^{KH3}

Derivs.:
Ethiodide: m. 147–148°,^{KH3,KH5} 146–147° ^{KH3}

$C_9H_{19}N$

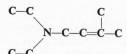

Et
Et
C_5H_9

4-DIETHYLAMINO-2-PENTENE

Phys. Props.:
b. 148–151° ^{BO14a}

Prepn.:
Diethylamine + 4-chloro-2-pentene.^{BO14a}

$C_9H_{19}N$

Et
Et
C_5H_9

4-DIETHYLAMINO-2-METHYL-2-BUTENE

Phys. Props.:
b. 158–160° ^{NA4}
d$_4^{20}$ 0.7911^{NA4}
n$_D^{20}$ 1.4390^{NA4}

Prepn.:
1-Chloro-3-methyl-2-butene + diethylamine (62% yield).^{NA4}

Derivs.:
Picrate: m. 101–102° NA4

$C_9H_{19}N$

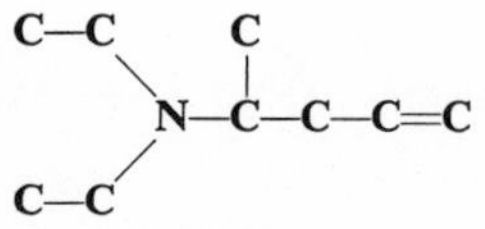

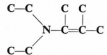

Et
Et
C_5H_9

4-DIETHYLAMINO-1-PENTENE

Phys. Props.:
b_{745} 143–151°KH3; b_{32} 63° KH3
n_D^{20} 1.4307, 1.4313KH3

Prepn.:
Assumed by-product* in the preparation of 5-diethylamino-1-pentene. This
reaction involves heating 1,1-diethylamino-2-methylpyrrolidinium
chloride with sodamide (about 24% yield of by-product), or with
sodium phenylacetylide (about 19% yield of by-product).KH3

Derivs.:
Ethiodide: m. 160–162° KH3

$C_9H_{19}N$

Et
Et
C_5H_9

2-DIETHYLAMINO-3-METHYL-2-BUTENE

Prepn.:
Prepared as the hydrochloride in the reaction of benzoyl chloride with
3-diethylamino-2-methyl-2-butanol.KR3

Derivs.:
Hydrochloride: m. 149° KR3

$C_9H_{19}N$

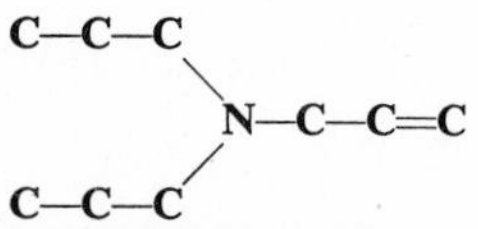

n-Pr
n-Pr
All

ALLYLDIPROPYLAMINE

Phys. Props.:
b. 153.5°,CO25 150–152°,ME12 145–150° LI4
d_4^{25} 0.7633CO25; d_4^{16} 0.7587ME12
n_D^{25} 1.4239CO25

---

* Rigorous structure proof is not given by ref. KH3.

Prepn.:

Reaction of allyl bromide with dipropylamine,[ME12] (76–80% yield).[CO25]

Derivs.:

Amine oxide picrate: m. 97.2–97.6[MA32]
Chloroplatinite: m. 152–153° [LI4]
Chloroaurate dihydrate: m. 88–89° [ME12]

$C_9H_{19}N$

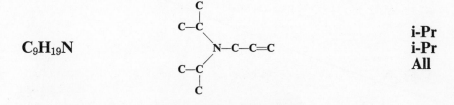

i-Pr
i-Pr
All

ALLYLDIISOPROPYLAMINE

Phys. Props.:

b. 147.5° [CO25]
d_4^{25} 0.7697[CO25]
n_D^{25} 1.4258[CO25]

Prepn.:

Diisopropylamine + allyl bromide (57–66% yield).[CO25]

Derivs.:

Amine oxide picrate: m. 49.6–50.4[CO25]

$C_9H_{21}N$

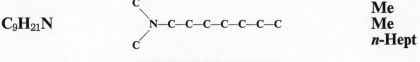

Me
Me
n-Hept

HEPTYLDIMETHYLAMINE

Phys. Props.:

b. 172[BR9]; b_{766} 170° (cor.)[CL2]; b_{760} 170[GA9]; b_{18} 62° [CA7]
d_4^{20} 0.7580[CA7]
n_D^{20} 1.4139[CA7]
pK_a 9.16[CA7]

Prepn.:

1. Catalytic hydrogenation of 1-dimethylamino-2-heptene.[CA7]
2. 1-Bromoheptane + dimethylamine.[CL2]

3. Thermal decomposition of heptyltrimethylammonium hydroxide[IN8] (75% yield based on starting iodide).[BR9]
4. Reduction of *N,N*-dimethylheptanamide with diisobutylaluminum hydride (91% yield).[ZA3]
5. Heptylamine + formic acid + formaldehyde (70% yield).[GA9]

Derivs.:

Picrate: m. 83°,[BR9,ZA3] 75° [CL2]
Chloroplatinate: m. 139° [BR9]
Methiodide: m. 145°,[BR9] 138–141° [KA13]

$C_9H_{21}N$ 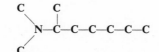   **Me**
Me
C_7H_{15}

2-DIMETHYLAMINOHEPTANE

Phys. Props.:

b_{745} 162–163° [LU8]

Prepn.:

Catalytic hydrogenation of 6-dimethylamino-1-heptene or of 6-dimethyl-amino-2,4-heptadiene.[LU8]

Derivs.:

Chloroplatinate: m. 162–163° [LU8]

$C_9H_{21}N$ 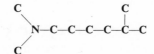   **Me**
Me
i-Hept

1-DIMETHYLAMINO-5-METHYLHEXANE

Phys. Props.:

b_{765} 162° [CL2]; b_7 54° [VA5]
d_4^{20} 0.773[VA5]
n_D^{20} 1.4282[VA5]

Prepn.:

1. Isoheptylamine + formaldehyde.[CL2]
2. Catalytic hydrogenation of 3-chloro-1-dimethylamino-5-methyl-2,4-hexa-diene.[VA5]

Derivs.:

Picrate: m. 86°,[CL2] 84–85° [VA5]

$C_9H_{21}N$

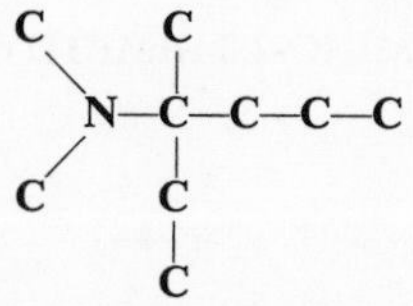

Me
Me
C_7H_{15}

3-DIMETHYLAMINO-3-METHYLHEXANE

Phys. Props.:

b. 163–164° [MO4]

Prepn.:

1. Methyl iodide + 3-amino-3-methylhexane.[MO4]
2. Methylmagnesium iodide + *N,N*-dimethylbutyramide in the presence of methyl iodide (low yield).* The other tertiary amine obtained in this reaction is 2-dimethylamino-2-methylpentane, although the chief reaction product is 2-pentanone.[MO4]

Derivs.:

Picrate: m. 153–154° [MO4]
Chloroaurate: m. 121–122° [MO4]
Chloroplatinate: m. darkens at 230° [MO4]

$C_9H_{21}N$

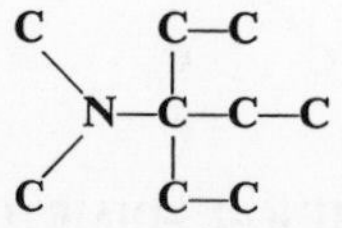

Me
Me
C_7H_{15}

3-DIMETHYLAMINO-3-ETHYLPENTANE

Phys. Props.:

b_{18} 58–59° [LU11]

Prepn.:

N,N-dimethylpropionamide + excess ethylmagnesium iodide.[LU11]

Derivs.:

Picrate: m. 206–207° [LU11]

---

* See section 11 (under "The Methods")—"Bouveault Reaction of *N,N*-Dialkyl-amides with Excess Grignard Reagent"—for the course of this apparently anomalous reaction.

$C_9H_{21}N$

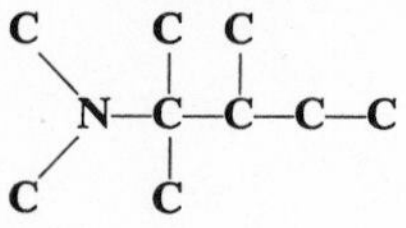

Me
Me
C_7H_{15}

2-DIMETHYLAMINO-2,3-DIMETHYLPENTANE

Phys. Props.:

optically active isomer
  b. 160–162° [LU10]
  d_4^{20} 0.8399[LU10]
  n_D^{20} 1.4360[LU10]
  $[\alpha]_D^{20}$ −11.48° [LU10]
racemic mixture
  b. 161–162° [LU10]
  n_D^{20} 1.4359[LU10]

Prepn.:

N,N-Dimethyl-2-methyl-*n*-butyramide + methylmagnesium bromide (30%
  yield). When an optically active amide is used the amine produced is
  optically active.[LU10]

Derivs.:

Picrate: m. 184° (optically active form),[LU10] 182–183° (racemate)[LU10]

$C_9H_{21}N$

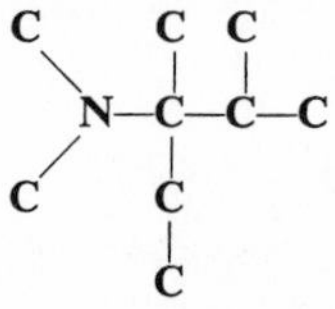

Me
Me
C_7H_{15}

3-DIMETHYLAMINO-2,3-DIMETHYLPENTANE

Phys. Props.:

b. 163–165° [LU11]

Prepn.:

N,N-Dimethylisobutyramide + excess methylmagnesium iodide + methyl
  iodide (25% yield)[LU11]*

Derivs.:

Picrate: m. 212° (dec.)[LU11]

---

* See section 11 (under "The Methods")—"Bouveault Reaction of *N,N*-Dialkyl-
amides with Excess Grignard Reagent"— for the course of this apparently anomalous
reaction.

$C_9H_{21}N$

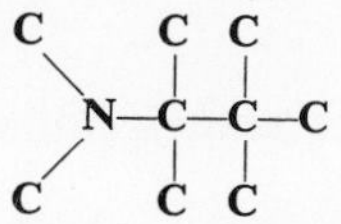

```
    C   C C
    |   | |
    N—C—C—C
    |   | |
    C   C C
```

Me
Me
C_7H_{15}

2-DIMETHYLAMINO-2,3,3-TRIMETHYLBUTANE

Phys. Props.:

b. 160–162°,[LU11] 155–156° [VE1]
m. 12° [LU11]
n. 1.4418[VE1]

Prepn.:

1. *N,N*-Dimethyl-2,2-dimethylpropionamide   (*N,N*-dimethylpivalamide) +
   excess methylmagnesium iodide.[LU11]
2. 2-Amino-2,3,3-trimethylbutane + formic acid + formaldehyde.[VE1]

Derivs.:

Picrate: m. 205–206°,[LU11] 204° (dec.)[VE1]
Hydrobromide: m. 217° [VE1]

$C_9H_{21}N$

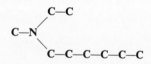

Me
Et
Hex

METHYLETHYLHEXYLAMINE

Prepn.:

2,4,6-Tris-(5′-methylaminopentyl)trithane   trihydrochloride + aqueous ethanol in the presence of Raney nickel (41% yield as the picrolonate).[LE15]

Derivs.:

Picrolonate: m. 79.5–81°[LE15]

$C_9H_{21}N$

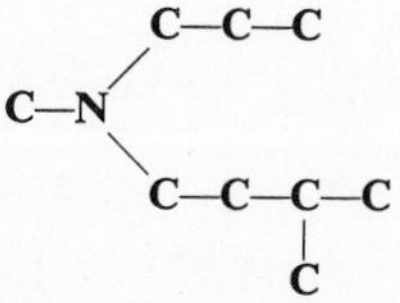

```
       C—C—C
       |
    C—N
       |
       C—C—C—C
           |
           C
```

Me
***n*-Pr**
i-Pent

METHYLPROPYL-(3-METHYLBUTYL)AMINE

Phys. Props.:

b. 153° [CO23]
b_4^{25} 0.7513[CO23]
n_D^{25} 1.4140[CO23]

Prepn.:

Propylisopentylamine + formic acid + formaldehyde (87% yield).[CO23]

Derivs.:

Picrate: m. 96–97° [CO23]

$C_9H_{21}N$

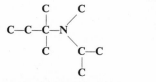

Me
i-Pr
C_5H_{11}

METHYL-(1-METHYLETHYL)-
(1,1-DIMETHYLPROPYL)AMINE

Phys. Props.:

b_{110} 90–91° [AI1]
n_D^{25} 1.4260[AI1]
pK_a 11.2 at 25° (in water), 9.9 (in 66% dimethylformamide)[AI1]

Prepn.:

Nickel-catalyzed hydrogenation of 3-(methylisopropylamino)-3-methyl-1-butyne (10% yield).[AI1]

Derivs.:

Hydrochloride: m. 142–144° [AI1]
Methiodide: m. 147–148° [AI1]

$C_9H_{21}N$

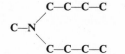

Me
n-Bu
n-Bu

METHYLDIBUTYLAMINE

Phys. Props.:

b.155–163° [EM8,EM8a,EM9,EM11]; b_{757} 156–157° [DA7]; b_{750} 159–160° [WE17]; b_{749} 161.2–162.2° [GR13]; b_{11} 53.5–54.0° [WE17]; b_{10} 50–50.5° [EM13]
d_{20}^{20} 0.782[EM8,EM9,EM11]
n_D^{20} 1.4302,[EM8,EM8a,EM9,EM11]* 1.418,[WE17] 1.4178,[EM13]* 1.4178–1.4179,[EM13]* 1.4172[DA7]

Infrared absorption: maximum at 8.80 mμ used in purity studies[DA7]

---

* The value of n_D^{20} 1.4302 was reported by Emerson.[EM8,EM8a,EM9,EM11] However, Emmons *et al.*[EM13] prepared methyldibutylamine in several different ways and obtained values of n_D^{20} 1.4178–1.4179. Others[DA7,WE17] reported similar values. Based on the evidence the best value is probably about n_d^{20} 1.4179.

Prepn.:

1. Dibutylamine + formic acid + formaldehyde (84% yield).[GR13]
2. Butyl chloride + methylamine (69% yield).[WE17]
3. Reduction of dibutylformamide with lithium aluminum hydride (67% yield).[EM13]
4. Reduction of ethyl-*N*,*N*-dibutylcarbamate with lithium aluminum hydride (85% yield).[DA7]
5. Nitromethane + butyraldehyde + hydrogen in the presence of platinum (56% yield),[EM8,EM8a,EM9,EM11] (39–54% yield).[EM10]
6. Dibutylamine + methyl iodide.[EM13]
7. Methyldichloroamine + butylmagnesium chloride (5% yield).[CO4]
8. Degradation of the following quaternary salts by sodium in the indicated solvents (% yield of methyldibutylamine in parenthesis):
   a. Methyltributylammonium bromide in *t*-butyl alcohol-dioxane (11% yield),[GR13] in dioxane.[GR13]
   b. Methyltributylammonium iodide in dioxane,[GR13] in liquid ammonia.[GR14]
   c. Dimethyldibutylammonium chloride in *t*-butyl alcohol-dioxane (15% yield).[GR13]
   d. Dimethyldibutylammonium iodide in liquid ammonia.[GR14]

Derivs.:

Hydrochloride: m. 131.0–131.5° [EM8,EM8a,EM9,EM11]
Picrate: m. 86–87.5°,[EM8,EM8a,EM9,EM11] 86.6–87.4° [GR13]
Methochloride: m. 148–149° [GR13]
Methobromide: m. 166–166.2° [GR13]
Methiodide: m. 149–150° [EM13]
Butobromide: m. 120.5–121.5° [GR13]
Butothiocyanate: m. 101° [TH3a]

$C_9H_{21}N$

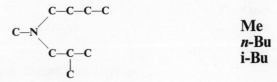

Me
n-Bu
i-Bu

METHYLBUTYLISOBUTYLAMINE

Phys. Props.:

b_{75} 81–81.3° [CO23]
d_4^{25} 0.7432[CO23]
n_D^{25} 1.14109[CO23]

Prepn.:

Butylisobutylamine + formic acid + formaldehyde (97% yield).[CO23]

Derivs.:

Picrate: m. 51–54° [CO23]

$C_9H_{21}N$

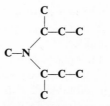

Me
sec-**Bu**
sec-**Bu**

METHYLDI(1-METHYLPROPYL)AMINE

Phys. Props.:

b. 159°,[RO4] 155–157° [SK5]
n_D^{25} 1.4220[RO4]

Prepn.:

1. Di(1-methylpropyl)amine + formic acid + formaldehyde.[RO4]
2. Reductive alkylation of methyl-(1-methylpropyl)amine with 2-butanone and hydrogen (18% yield)[SK5]

Derivs.:

Picrate: m. 92–93°[SK5]

$C_9H_{21}N$

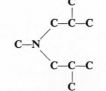

Me
i-Bu
i-Bu

METHYLDIISOBUTYLAMINE

Phys. Props.:

b. 143°[RO4]
n_D^{25} 1.4070[RO4]

Prepn.:

Diisobutylamine + formic acid + formaldehyde.[RO4]

Derivs.:

Methochloroplatinate: m. 174° [R15]
Ethiodide: m. 162° [R04]

$C_9H_{21}N$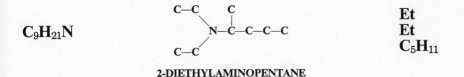

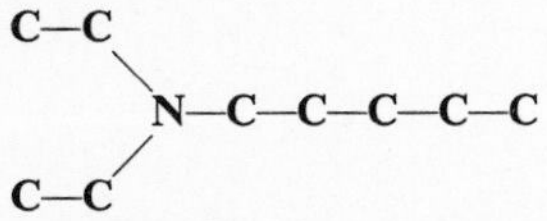

    Et
    Et
    n-Pent

PENTYLDIETHYLAMINE

Phys. Props.:

b. 155–157° [G01]; b_{760} 155–157°, [CA11, CO2] 155° [PR3]; b_{735} 155–158° [ME6] *
b_{76} 85–87° [ST11]; b_{28} 64–65° [CA11]; b_{15} 50–51° [ME6] *
d_4^{20} 0.7663, [CA11, CO2] 0.7702 [G01]
n_D^{20} 1.4250, [CA11, CO2] 1.4197 [G01]

Prepn.:

1. Heating 2-diethylaminomethylthiophene with Raney nickel catalyst (54% yield). [G01]
2. Thermal decomposition of pentyltriethylammonium iodide (44% yield). [ST11]
3. Catalytic hydrogenation of 1-diethylamino-4-pentene-2-yne [CO2, CA11]; of 1-diethylamino-2-pentene. [ME6] *
4. Chloromethyldiethylamine + butylmagnesium chloride. [PR3]

Derivs.:

Picrate: m. 55–56.5°, [ME6] 52–53° [CA11, CO2]

$C_9H_{21}N$

    Et
    Et
    C_5H_{11}

2-DIETHYLAMINOPENTANE

Phys. Props.:

b. 154–158° [WH4]

Prepn.:

Pressure reaction between 2-aminopentane and ethylene in the presence of sodium. [NA4]

---

* In ref. ME6 diethyl-*n*-amylamine is erroneously called dimethyl-*n*-amylamine.

$C_9H_{21}N$ 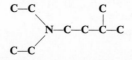   Et
Et
C_5H_{11}

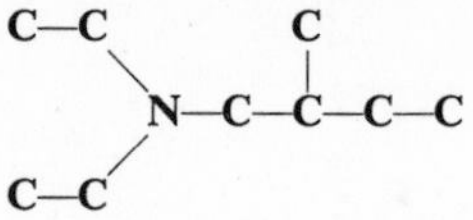

(+)1-DIETHYLAMINO-2-METHYLBUTANE

Phys. Props.:
b_{765} 150–151° [BI5a]
d_4^{20} 0.7515[BI5a]
$[\alpha]_D^{20}$ +17.96° [BI5a]

Prepn.:
Diethylamine plus (+)1-iodo-2-methylbutane.[BI5a]

$C_9H_{21}N$ 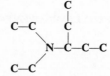   Et
Et
i-Pent

1-DIETHYLAMINO-3-METHYLBUTANE*

Phys. Props.:
b. 153–157°,[SK4] 155° (cor.),[DU7] 154°,[HO4]* 152–153° [NA4]
n_D^{20} 1.4180[NA4]

Prepn.:
1. Reductive alkylation of ethylisopentylamine with acetaldehyde and hydrogen in the presence of platinum (40% yields).[SK4]
2. Hydrogenation of 1-diethylamino-3-methyl-2-butene.[NA4]
3. Isopentylamine + ethyl iodide.[DU7]
4. Thermal decomposition of isopentyltriethylammonium hydroxide.[HO4]

Derivs.:
Picrate: m. 74–75°,[NA4,SK4] 75° [DU7]

$C_9H_{21}N$ Et
Et
C_5H_{11}

3-DIETHYLAMINOPENTANE

Phys. Props.:
b. 143° [MA43]

---

* Ref. HO4 refers to this compound ambiguously as diethylamylamine.

Prepn.:

Diethylformamide + excess ethylmagnesium bromide (51% yield).[MA43]

Derivs.:

Picrate: m. 84°[MA43]

$C_9H_{21}N$

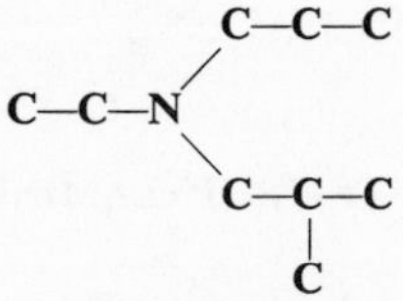

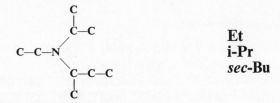

Et
n-Pr
i-Bu

ETHYLPROPYL-(2-METHYLPROPYL)AMINE

Phys. Props.:

b. 146°,[LE3] 145–146°,[WE5] 142–147°[PO3]

Prepn.:

1. Propylisobutylamine + ethyl iodide,[LE3] (74% yield).[PO3]
2. Ethylisobutylamine + propyl iodide.[WE5]

Derivs.:

Chloroplatinate: m. 204–207° (dec.)[PO3]
Methiodide:* m. 197°,[WE5] 196.5°,[MA27] 195°[PO3]
Methochloroaurate: m. 103°[MA27]; 101°[PO3]
Methochloroplatinate: m. 241° (dec.),[PO3] 236° (dec.),[MA27] 233°,[LE3] 212–
    213°[R15] (*sic*)
Metho-*d*-camphorsulfonate: m. 224–225°[PO3]; 223°[WE5]
Metho-*d*-α-bromocamphor-π-sulfonate: m. 182°[PO3]

$C_9H_{21}N$

Et
i-Pr
sec-**Bu**

ETHYLISOPROPYL-(1-METHYLPROPYL)AMINE

Prepn.:

Reductive alkylation of ethyl-(1-methylpropyl)amine with acetone and
    hydrogen (20% yield).[SK5]

---

* Ref. PO3 claims that reaction of ethylpropylisobutylamine with methyl iodide gives
dimethylpropylisobutylammonium iodide (m. 170°) instead of the expected methylethylpropylisobutylammonium iodide.

Derivs.:

Picrate: m. 118° [SK5]

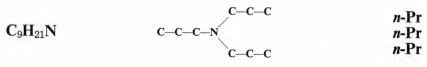

$C_9H_{21}N$ *n*-Pr
                                                     n-Pr
                                                     n-Pr

TRIPROPYLAMINE

Phys. Props.:

b. 156.5° (cor.),[ZA5] 155.5–156.5°,[PE3] 156°[BO13,MA11,OD1,SA5]; b_{765} 157° [JA4]; b_{764} 156.5–157.2° [CO32]; b_{760} 156.5° (cor.),[VO1,ZA5] 156 ± 0.4° [TI3]; $b_{757.5}$ 156° [BR48]; b_{757} 157.3–157.4° [HA16]; b_{756} 156.4° [VI2]; b_{749} 155.5° [CO28]; b_{727} 155° [WO7] (other values: b. 154–157°,[RE6] 153–156°,[SK3] 153°,[GA7] 144–146° [RO6]; b_{760} 154–154.5° [AR1])

m. −100.5°,[TI6] −93.5 ± 1° [TI3]

d_4^{220} 0.5765[CO28]; d_4^{200} 0.5990[CO28]; d_4^{180} 0.6194[CO28]; d_4^{160} 0.6388[CO28]; d_4^{140} 0.6570[CO28]; d_4^{120} 0.6744[CO28]; d_4^{100} 0.6917[CO28]; $d_4^{87.9}$ 0.7056[VO1]; $d_4^{84.3}$ 0.7082; d_4^{80} 0.7084[CO28]; d_4^{75} 0.7130[TU1]; d_4^{62} 0.7258[VO1]; $d_4^{60.1}$ 0.7271[VO1]; d_4^{60} 0.7252,[TU1] 0.7245[CO28]; d_4^{50} 0.733[JA4]; d_4^{45} 0.7373[TU1]; d_4^{42} 0.7411[VO1]; $d_4^{41.3}$ 0.7416[VO1]; d_4^{40} 0.7404[CO28]; d_4^{30} 0.7493[TU1]; d_4^{27} 0.746[WO7]; d_{25}^{25} 0.7539[PE3]; d_4^{25} 0.753[JA4]; $d_4^{24.5}$ 0.7526[VO1]; $d_4^{22.8}$ 0.7535[GL3]; $d_4^{20.08}$ 0.7162[HA16]; d_{20}^{20} 0.7567[PE3]; d_4^{20} 0.7567,[BR48,CO32] 0.7564,[CO28] 0.7558,[VO1] 0.7571[TU1]; d_0^{20} 0.7560[AR1]; $d_4^{19.4}$ 0.7573[BR48]; $d_0^{18.2}$ 0.7563[ZA5]; d_{15}^{15} 0.7600[PE3]; d_{10}^{10} 0.7634[PE3]; $d_4^{4.4}$ 0.7703[GL3]; d_4^{4} 0.7681[PE3]; d_4^{0} 0.773,[JA4] 0.7724,[CO28] 0.771[VI2]; d_0^{0} 0.774[SA5]; d_4^{-20} 0.7882[CO28]; d_4^{-40} 0.8038[CO28]; d_4^{-60} 0.8189[CO28]

Specific volume:

$$V = 1 + 1.3240 \times 10^{-3}\,t + 3.8090 \times 10^{-6}\,t^2 - 8.7983 \times 10^{-9}\,t^3$$
(where t = temperature in °C)[ZA5]

n_D^{25} 1.4142[WO7]; $n_D^{22.8}$ 1.4171[GL3]; n_D^{20} 1.4181,[HA16] 1.4178,[CO32] 1.4159,[AR1] 1.41706[VO1]; $n_D^{19.4}$ 1.41756[BR48]; $n_A^{22.8}$ 1.4121[GL3]; $n_A^{4.4}$ 1.4197[GL3]; n_C^{20} 1.41471[VO1]; $n_F^{22.8}$ 1.4229[GL3]; n_F^{20} 1.42279[VO1]; $n_F^{4.4}$ 1.4306[GL3]; n_G^{20} 1.42718[VO1]; $n_H^{22.8}$ 1.4326[GL3]; $n_H^{4.4}$ 1.4408[GL3]; $n_\alpha^{19.4}$ 1.41515[BR48]; n_α^{19} 1.42814.[BR48]

Infrared absorption: between 1.0 and 12.0 μ[BE3]; 0.59 and 2.40 μ[EL5]; in 3 μ region, absorption maximum 3.48 to 3.52 μ[SA8]

Ultraviolet absorption[BI5]

pK_a 10.74 at 25°,[BR29] 10.65 at 25°,[MO9] 9.0 at 25° (in 70% aqueous methanol)[BO13]; base strength in ethyl acetate and in nitrobenzene[HA5]

Surface tension (dynes/cm.,) at various temperatures (°C): 17.21 (84.3°)[VO1]; 17.87 (75°)[TU1]; 19.28 (60.1°)[VO1]; 19.22 (60°)[TU1]; 20.61 (45°)[TU1]; 20.90 (41.3°)[VO1]; 22.03 (30°)[TU1]; 22.48 (24.5°)[VO1]; 22.96 (20°)[TU1]; 22.85 (20°)[AR1]; values from $-71°$ (30.6 dynes cm.) to 149.5° (11.5 dynes cm.)[JA4]

Apparent polarizability and dipole moment,[AR10,CO32]

Ionization potential (photoionization method): 7.23 e.v.[WA19]

Vapor phase chromatography[BA23a]

Coefficient of expansion[ZA5]

Paper chromatography[KA1]

X-ray spectrum: $a_1 = 7.9_5$, $a_2 = 5.2$, $b = 7.6$[KA15]

Magneto-optic rotation[PE3]: 827[GA1a]

Dipole moment: 0.74 D (benzene solution),[AR10] 0.75 D (benzene solution)[CO32]; 0.65 D (liq.)[CO32]

Dielectric constant: 2.277 at 20° [CO32]

Molar Kerr constant: 8.84 × 10^{-12}[AR10]

Prepn.:

The following reactions produce mixtures of mono-, di- and tri-propylamines: (yields, if available, are given only for tripropylamine):

1. Ammonia + propyl chloride[HO5,MA14]; + propyl bromide[TS6]; + propyl iodide.[MA14,VI2]
2. Ammonia + 1-propanol[BR36] (8% yield)[KR9]; + 1-propanol and hydrogen[DA13,TA12]; + propionaldehyde and hydrogen[SK1] (27% yield).[GU4]
3. Catalytic hydrogenation of propionitrile in the presence of platinum (67% yield)[SK3]; in the presence of nickel (low yield).[SA5]
4. Catalytic hydrogenation of propyl nitrite in the presence of nickel or copper (low yield, main product is dipropylamine).[GA7]
5. Propyl propanoate or propyl butanoate + ammonia at high temperature in the presence of aluminum oxide.[KO21]
6. Ammonia + ethylene + carbon monoxide in the presence of iron carbonyl.[RE6] By using propylamine instead of ammonia, tripropylamine is obtained in 50% yield,[RE10] in 17% yield.[RE6]
7. Disproportionation of propyl- or dipropyl-amine by heat and catalysts.[PL1]

The following reactions do not give a mixture of all three propylamines:

8. High-pressure reaction of propylamine, propionic acid, water, acetylene, and carbon monoxide in the presence of iron carbonyl (52% yield).[RE10]
9. Reaction (under pressure) of propionaldehyde, propylamine, and hydrogen in the presence of Raney nickel.[OL4]
10. Tripropylamine oxide + sulfur dioxide.[MA17]
11. Thermal decomposition of tetrapropylammonium hydroxide.[ZA5]

12. Cleavage of tetrapropylammonium chloride with potassium amide in liquid ammonia. Hydrogen, propylene, and propane also are formed.[HA29] The same reaction with methyltripropylammonium halide also gives tripropylamine and propane. In addition, dipropylamine is also formed.[HA29]

13. Cleavage of methyltripropylammonium iodide or tetrapropylammonium bromide with sodium in liquid ammonia.[GR14]

14. Cleavage of tetrapropylammonium bromide by potassium amide in liquid ammonia.[JO4]

Derivs.:

Hydrochloride: m. 90° [DE6]
Hydrobromide: m. 180° [DE6]
Picrate: m. 116° [MA17,TS6]; 114–115° [AU1,WA12]
Perchlorate: m. 150° [SC24]
Chloroaurate: m. 154–155° [GU4]
Bromoaurate: m. 149° [DE5]
·BH_3: m. 18° [NO3]
·AlH_3: m. 80–81° [RU2]
Amine oxide picrate: m. 130°,[MA17] 129.5°,[ST17] 129°,[DU6] 128–129° (cor.)[CO17]
Amine oxide hydrochloride: m. *ca.* 90° [DU6]
Amine oxide chloroplatinate: m. 174–175° [DU6]
·I_2: m. 65–66°,[SK3] 66° [NO1a]
Methiodide: m. 207–208° (dec.)[WE4]
Methiodide·HgI_2: m. 123° [BA26]
Methopicrate: m. 82–83°,[RI6] 82.2° [WA12]
Methochloroplatinate: m. 220° [RI5]
Ethiodide: m. 238° (dec.)[AU1,WE11]
Ethochloroplatinate: m. 212° [RI5]
Ethiodide·HgI_2: m. 135° [BA26]
4,4'-Dichlorodiphenyldisulfimide salt: m. 130–131° [RU4]
Diphenyldisulfimide salt: m. 55–57° [RU3]
Ethopicrate: m. 108° [RI6]; 107.2° [WA12]
Propiodide: m. *ca.* 280° (dec.)[WE4]
Propiodide·HgI_2: m. 178° [BA26]
Propobromide: m. 252° (cor.)[SU2]
Propopicrate: m. 120°,[RI6] 119.6°,[WA11,WA12] 117.5–118 (cor.)[SU2]
Propochlorate: m. 217° [DA11]
Proponitrate: m. above 200° [WA3]
Proporeineckate: m. 155–156° [HE1]
Propochloroplatinate: m. 198–199° [RI5]

---

* For some less common derivatives see refs. AT1, CO7, DA12, DE5, MA17, ME15, PE6, RU3, SC16, ST9, WE11, and WE15.

$C_9H_{21}N$

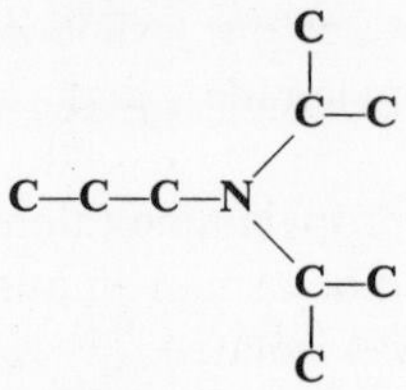

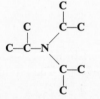

n-Pr
i-Pr
i-Pr

PROPYLDIISOPROPYLAMINE

Phys. Props.:

b. 145–147° [SK5]

Prepn.:

Reductive alkylation of diisopropylamine with propionaldehyde and hydrogen (26% yield). [SK5]

Derivs.:

Picrate: m. 120–121° [SK5]

$C_9H_{21}N$

i-Pr
i-Pr
i-Pr

TRIISOPROPYLAMINE

Phys. Props.:

b. 139° [KU2]
d_4^{20} 0.765 [KU2]
n_D^{20} 1.4142 [KU2]

Prepn.: *

1. Potassium isopropyl + *N*,*N*-diisopropyl-*N*-chloramine (3% yield). [KU2]
2. Vapor phase reaction between isopropyl alcohol and ammonia (trace yield), [WH2] (8% yield), [KR9] (24% yield). [PO6]

---

* Although several claims [KR9,MA8,PO6,SA2,WH2] have been made for the preparation of triisopropylamine, only one is substantiated by analysis and physical properties. This authentic preparation is that of Kuffner and Seifried. [KU2] Also, according to ref. KU2, the citation to triisopropylamine in ref. RI7 arises from a typographic error and refers to tripropylamine (*q.v.*).

3. Catalytic hydrogenation of acetone oxime in the presence of nickel gives isopropylamine, diisopropylamine, and a "trace" of triisopropylamine.[MA8,SA2]

4. Disproportionation of isopropylamine (alone or with ammonia) by heat and catalyst. The formation of a small amount of triisopropylamine might have occurred, but none was isolated.[PL1]

Derivs.:

Hydrochloride: m. 218–220° [KU2]
Picrate: m. 203–205° [KU2]
Reineckate: m. 149–151° [KU2]

$C_{10}H_{11}N$  Me
Me
C_8H_5

1-DIMETHYLAMINO-2,4,6-OCTATRIENE

Phys. Props.:

No boiling point given.[CH6b]

Prepn.:

Propargyldimethylamine + 1-bromo-1,3-pentadiyne in the presence of copper (I) chloride (91% yield).[CH6] The product was analyzed as the hydrochloride.

$C_{10}H_{15}N$ 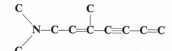 Me
Me
C_8H_9

7-DIMETHYLAMINO-5-METHYL-1,5-HEPTADIEN-3-YNE

Phys. Props.:

b_{24} 92.5–93.5° [TE2]
d_4^{20} 0.8473[TE2]
n_D^{20} 1.5002[TE2]

Prepn.:

Dehydration of 1-dimethylamino-3-methyl-6-hepten-4-yn-3-ol with sulfuric acid (82% yield).[TE2]

$$C_{10}H_{15}N$$

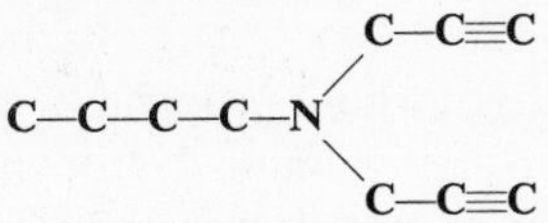

$$C_3H_3$$
$$C_3H_3$$
$$\textit{n-Bu}$$

BUTYLDIPROPARGYLAMINE

Phys. Props.:

$b_{13.7}$ 81–82° [BU17]; b_{10} 73–74° [PA6]
d_4^{25} 0.8512,[PA6] 0.8480[BU17]
n_D^{25} 1.4567,[PA6] 1.4572[BU17]

Prepn.:

In 76.5% yield[PA6] and in 60.8% yield[BU17] by the dehydrohalogenation of
butylbis(2-bromo-2-propenyl)amine.

Derivs.:

Allylobromide: m. 87–91° [BU17]

$$C_{10}H_{17}N$$

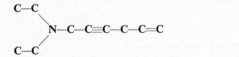

Me
Me
$$C_8H_{11}$$

4-(DIMETHYLAMINOMETHYL)-1,3,6-HEPTATRIENE*

Phys. Props.:

b_{11} 82–83° [KO12]

Prepn.:

Exhaustive methylation and Hofmann degradation of decahydro-1,8-
naphthyridine.[KO12]

$$C_{10}H_{17}N$$

Et
Et
$$C_6H_7$$

6-DIETHYLAMINO-1-HEXEN-4-YNE

Phys. Props.:

b_{11} 52–53° [PA5]
d_4^{25} 0.8085[PA5]
n_D^{25} 1.4452[PA5]

---

* There is some uncertainty about this structure.

Prepn.:

Sodio derivative of 1-diethylamino-2-propyne + allyl bromide. The yield, based on 2-bromo-1-diethylamino-2-propyne from which 1-diethyl-amino-2-propyne was prepared, was 33%.[PA5]

$C_{10}H_{17}N$

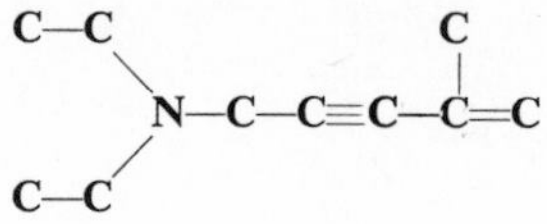

C—C
       \
        N—C—C≡C—C=C
       / |
C—C   C

Et
Et
C_6N_7

5-DIETHYLAMINO-2-METHYL-1-PENTEN-3-YNE

Phys. Props.:

b_7 61–62° [NA3]
n_D^{21} 1.4658[NA3]

Prepn.:

The iron(III) chloride catalyzed reaction of 2-methyl-1-buten-3-yne with the methylolamine derived from paraformaldehyde and diethylamine (83% yield).[NA3]

Derivs.:

Picrate: m. 93–93.5° [NA3]
Hydrochloride: m. 125–126° [NA3]

$C_{10}H_{17}N$

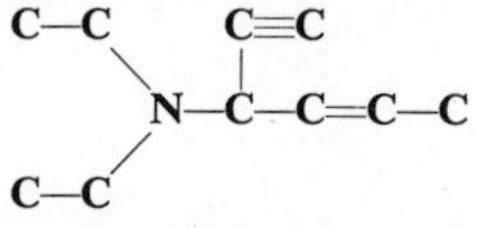

C—C   C≡C
       \ |
        N—C—C=C—C
       /
C—C

Et
Et
C_6H_7

4-DIETHYLAMINO-2-HEXEN-5-YNE

Phys. Props.:

b_{22} 68° [BE4]; b_{19} 69° [JO5]; b_{15} 63–65° [JO5]
$n_D^{21.5}$ 1.4531[BE4]; $n_D^{19.5}$ 1.4552[JO5]; n_D^{18} 1.4568[JO5]; n_D^{14} 1.4589[JO5]
Ultraviolet absorption[JO5]: 2230 A. (ϵ 560) (not a local maximum)[BE4]

Prepn.:

1. 5-Chloro-3-hexen-1-yne + diethylamine (*via* allylic rearrangement) (53% yield).[JO5]
2. 5-Ethylamino-3-hexene-1-yne + ethyl bromide gives a tertiary amine which rearranges spontaneously to the subject amine (30% yield).[JO5]*
3. 3-Ethylamino-4-hexen-1-yne + ethyl bromide (54% yield).[BE4]

---

* Ref. BE4 believes that the starting secondary amine used in this case by ref. JO5 might have contained at least 30% of the actual precursor (3-ethylamino-4-hexen-1-yne) of the subject compound. Conjugated eneyne compounds resinify under the experimental conditions cited according to ref. BE4.

Derivs.:

Hydrochloride: m. 146–147°,[BE4] 144° [JO5]
Methiodide: m. 117–118° (dec.)[JO5]

$C_{10}H_{17}N$

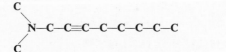

```
C—C    C
    \   |
     N—C—C=C—C≡C
    /
C—C
```

Et
Et
C_6H_7

trans-5-DIETHYLAMINO-3-HEXEN-1-YNE*

Phys. Props.

b_{27} 88–90° [BE4]; b_{15} 74–76° [BE4]
m. −6 to −4° [BE4]
n_D^{26} 1.4706[BE4]; $b_D^{21.5}$ 1.4738[BE4]
Ultraviolet absorption: 2230 A. (ϵ13,400)[BE4]

Prepn.:

1. 5-Ethylamino-3-hexen-1-yne + ethyl bromide[JO5] (59% yield).[BE4]†
2. Diethylamine + *trans*-5-chloro-3-hexene-1-yne (40% yield).[BE4]

Derivs.:

Hydrochloride: m. 147–148° [BE4]
Methiodide: m. 183–184° (dec.)[BE4]

$C_{10}H_{19}N$

```
C
 \
  N—C—C≡C—C—C—C—C—C
 /
C
```

Me
Me
C_8H_{13}

1-DIMETHYLAMINO-2-OCTYNE

Phys. Props.:

b_{16} 89° [GU2,MA32]
n_D^{16} 1.4460[GU2,MA32]

---

* The *trans* configuration is assumed for this compound from the method of synthesis and because according to ref. BE4 the *cis* isomer would be expected to cyclize to a pyrrole derivative.

† 5-Diethylamino-3-hexen-1-yne was postulated as being a transitory intermediate in the reaction of ethyl bromide with 5-ethylamino-3-hexen-1-yne according to ref. JO5. It was claimed that, under experimental conditions, this compound underwent allylic rearrangement to give 3-diethylamino-4-hexen-1-yne, which was isolated in 30% yield. However, another investigator[BE4] believes that ref. JO5 may have used as starting material 5-ethylamino-3-hexen-1-yne containing at least 30% of 3-ethylamino-4-hexene-1-yne. Under alkylation conditions, the conjugated amine was resinified and only the normal unrearranged alkylated product from the latter unconjugated amine was isolated.

Prepn.:

1-Heptyne + dimethylamine + formaldehyde in the presence of copper(II) acetate (74% yield).[GU2,MA32]

Derivs.:

Methiodide: m. 110–111° [GU2,MA32]

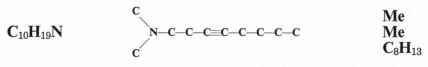

$C_{10}H_{19}N$ C\N–C–C–C≡C–C–C–C–C / C   **Me** **Me** C_8H_{13}

1-DIMETHYLAMINO-3-OCTYNE

Phys. Props.:

b_{90} 131° [CA7]; b_{55} 117° [CA7]; b_{10} 81° [SC20]
d_4^{20} 0.7985[CA7]
n_D^{20} 1.4448[CA7]
pK_a 7.70 (in 30% methanol) (temperature unspecified)[CA7]

Prepn.:

1. Sodio derivative of 1-hexyne + 1-dimethylamino-2-bromoethane in liquid ammonia (27% yield).[CA7]
2. 3-Octyn-1-ylhexaminium bromide + formaldehyde + formic acid (25% yield).[SC20]

Derivs.:

Oxalate: m. 136–137°,[SC20] 134–135° [CA7]
Methiodide: m. 146–147° [JA1]

$C_{10}H_{19}N$ C\N–C–C–C–C≡C–C–C–C / C   **Me** **Me** C_8H_{13}

1-DIMETHYLAMINO-4-OCTYNE

Phys. Props.:

b_{18} 86–87°,[OL6]* 75–76° [EP2]
n_D^{20} 1.4430[OL6]; n_D^{19} 1.4420[EP2]

---

* Both values are due to one group. However, we favor the higher value because it is more compatible with the data and their interrelationships in other acetylenic and dienic isomers.

Prepn.:

Sodio derivative of 5-dimethylamino-1-pentyne + propyl iodide in liquid ammonia.[EP2,OL6]

Derivs.:

Methiodide: m. 151–152° [OL6]

$C_{10}H_{19}N$

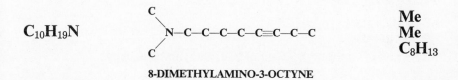

Me
Me
C_8H_{13}

8-DIMETHYLAMINO-3-OCTYNE

Phys. Props.:

b_{13} 85°,[EP2,OL6] 84–84.5° [MA31]
n_D^{18} 1.4450[EP2,MA31,OL6]

Prepn.:

Sodio derivative of 6-dimethylamino-1-hexyne + ethyl iodide in liquid ammonia.[EP2,MA31,OL6]

Derivs.:

Methiodide: m. 156–157° [EP2,OL6]

$C_{10}H_{19}N$

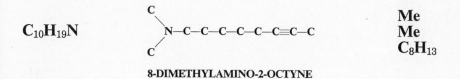

Me
Me
C_8H_{13}

8-DIMETHYLAMINO-2-OCTYNE

Phys. Props.:

b_{18} 90–91° [OL6]
n_D^{18} 1.4500[OL6]

Prepn.:

Sodio derivative of 7-dimethylamino-1-heptyne + methyl iodide in liquid ammonia.[OL6]

Derivs.:

Methiodide: m. 83° [OL6]

$C_{10}H_{19}N$

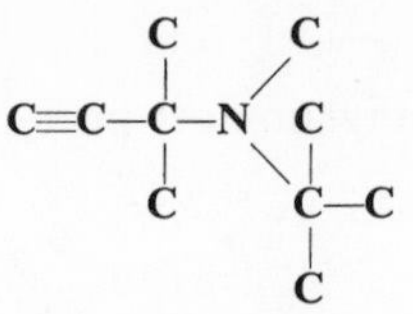

$$C{\equiv}C-\overset{\overset{\displaystyle C}{|}}{\underset{\underset{\displaystyle C}{|}}{C}}-N\overset{C}{\underset{\underset{\displaystyle C}{|}}{C-C}}$$

Me
t-Bu
C_5H_7

METHYL-(*t*-BUTYL)-
(1,1-DIMETHYL-2-PROPYNYL)AMINE

Phys. Props.:

b_{130} 110–112° [AI1]
n_D^{25} 1.4510[AI1]
pK_a 9.3 at 25° (in water), 7.9 (in 66% dimethylformamide)[AI1]

Prepn.:

Methyltion aof *t*-butyl-(1,1-dimethyl-2-propynyl)amine with formic acid and formaldehyde (80% yield), with methyl iodide (20% yield), with dimethyl sulfate (25% yield).[AI1]

Derivs.:

Hydrochloride: m. 138–140° [AI1]
Picrate: m. 155° (dec.)[AI1]
Methiodide: (attempted preparation of the methiodide by reaction of the free base with methyl iodide results in loss of the *t*-butyl group, and the product obtained is 3-dimethylamino-3-methyl-1-butyne methiodide, m. 210°)[AI1]

$C_{10}H_{19}N$

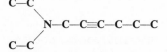

Et
Et
C_6H_9

1-DIETHYLAMINO-2-HEXYNE

Phys. Props.:

b. 187.4–188.4° [PA5]
d_4^{25} 0.8058[PA5]
n_D^{25} 1.4431[PA5]

Prepn.:

Sodio derivative of 3-diethylamino-1-propyne + propyl bromide in liquid ammonia (72.5% yield).[PA5]

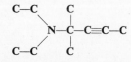

$C_{10}H_{19}N$ Et
                                              Et
                                            C_6H_9

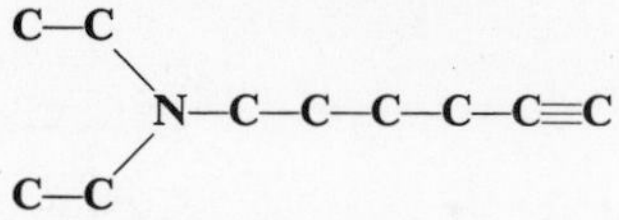

6-DIETHYLAMINO-1-HEXYNE

Phys. Props.:

b_{15} 72° [EP2,MA31,OL6]; b_{12} 73° [NE3a]
n_D^{15} 1.4430[EP2,MA31,OL6]; n_D 1.4450[NE3a]
d. 0.8120[NE3a]

Prepn.:

1. Diethylamine + 6-iodo-1-hexyne in dioxane.[EP2,MA31,OL6]
2. 1,1,2-Trichloro-6-diethylamino-1-hexene + sodium.[NE3a]

Derivs.:

Ethiodide: m. 148° [EP2,OL6]
Hydrochloride: m. 120.5–121° [NE3a]

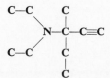

$C_{10}H_{19}N$ Et
                                              Et
                                            C_6H_9

4-DIETHYLAMINO-4-METHYL-2-PENTYNE

Phys. Props.:

b_9 60° [KR11]
n_D^{20} 1.4470[KR11]

Prepn.:

Reaction (under pressure) of diethylamine with 1-propyne in the presence of
zinc and cadmium acetates (80% yield).[KR11]

Derivs.:

Picrate: m. 117–118° (dec.)[KR11]

$C_{10}H_{19}N$ Et
                                              Et
                                            C_6H_9

3-DIETHYLAMINO-3-METHYL-1-PENTYNE

Phys. Props.:

b. 162–164° [HE8]; b_{120} 103–105° [HE11]; b_{11} 88–89.5° [WO4]

d_4^{25} 0.812[HE11]
n_D^{25} 1.4397,[HE11] 1.4398[HE8]

Prepn.:

1. Reaction of 3-amino-3-methyl-1-pentyne with ethyl-*p*-toluenesulfonate (37% yield).[HE11]
2. Reaction of 3-chloro-3-methyl-1-pentyne with diethylamine[WO4]; in the presence of copper bronze and cuprous chloride (21% yield).[HE8]

$C_{10}H_{19}N$

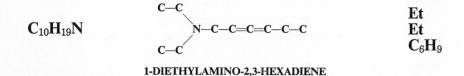

Et
Et
C_6H_9

1-DIETHYLAMINO-2,3-HEXADIENE

Phys. Props.:

b_{20} 85–86° [PE10]
d_4^{20} 0.8111[PE10]
n_4^{20} 1.4554[PE10]
Infrared absorption[PE10]

Prepn.:

Lithiodiethylamine + 1-hexen-3-yne (45–55% yield).[PE10]

$C_{10}H_{19}N$

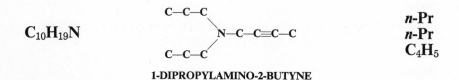

n-Pr
n-Pr
C_4H_5

1-DIPROPYLAMINO-2-BUTYNE

Phys. Props.:

b_{10} 70–70.5° [PA6]
d_4^{25} 0.8090[PA6]
n_D^{25} 1.4431[PA6]

Prepn.:

Sodio derivative of 3-dipropylamino-1-propyne + methyl iodide in liquid ammonia (81% yield).[PA6]

$C_{10}H_{19}N$

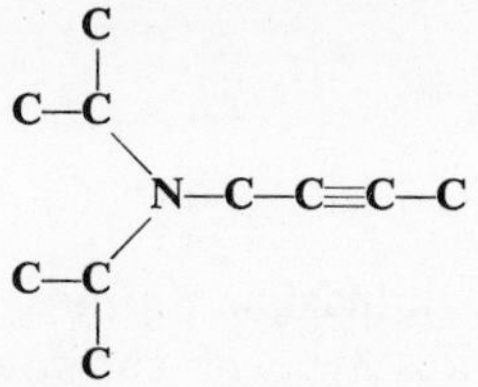

```
        C
        |
      C—C
        |
  C—C—N—C—C≡C—C
        |
      C—C
        |
        C
```

i-Pr
i-Pr
C_4H_5

1-DIISOPROPYLAMINO-2-BUTYNE

Phys. Props.:

b_{10} 64–65° [PA6]
d_4^{25} 0.8209 [PA6]
n_D^{25} 1.4482 [PA6]

Prepn.:

Sodio derivative of 3-diisopropylamino-1-propyne + methyl iodide in liquid
    ammonia (43% yield). [PA6]

$C_{10}H_{19}N$

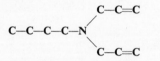

All
All
n-Bu

BUTYLDIALLYLAMINE

Phys. Props.:

b_{760} 170° [BU14]; b_{10} 54–55° [BR3]
d_{25}^{25} 0.7863 [BU14]
n_D^{25} 1.4389 [BU14]

Prepn.:

1. Allyl bromide + butylamine. [BR3]
2. Presumably from allyl chloride and butylamine (53% yield). [BU14]

Derivs.:

Allylobromide: m. 175° [BU14]

$C_{10}H_{21}N$

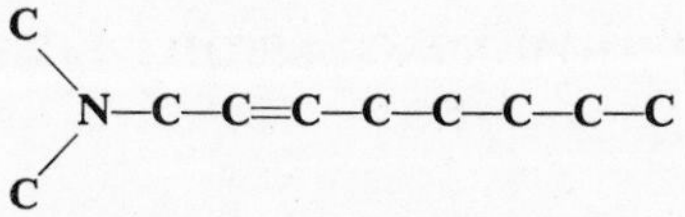

```
  C
   \
    N—C—C=C—C—C—C—C—C
   /
  C
```

Me
Me
C_8H_{15}

1-DIMETHYLAMINO-2-OCTENE

Phys. Props.:

cis isomer
    b_{10} 70° [OL6]
    d_{20}^{20} 0.7877 [OL6]
    n_D^{20} 1.4340 [OL6]

trans isomer

b_{10} 68° [OL6]

d_{20}^{20} 0.7812[OL6]

n_D^{20} 1.4345[OL6]

For characteristic absorption maxima (infrared and Raman) of the *cis* and *trans* isomers for this type of compound see 1-dimethylamino-2-heptene[OL6]

Prepn.:

Catalytic hydrogenation of 1-dimethylamino-2-octyne in the presence of palladium yields the *cis* isomer, whereas reduction with sodium in liquid ammonia yields the *trans* isomer.[OL6]

Derivs.:

cis-Methiodide: m. 148° [OL6]

trans-Methiodide: m. 185° [OL6]

$C_{10}H_{21}N$

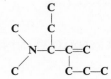

Me
Me
C_8H_{15}

3-DIMETHYLAMINO-2-PROPYL-1-PENTENE

Derivs.:

Methobromide: m. *ca.* 175° (methobromide was prepared from 3-bromo-2-propyl-1-pentene and trimethylamine)[BR21]

$C_{10}H_{21}N$

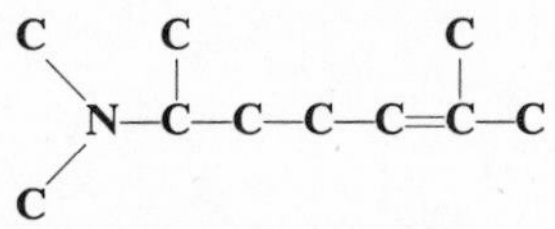

Me
Me
C_8H_{15}

6-DIMETHYLAMINO-2-METHYL-2-HEPTENE

Phys. Props.:

b. 183–185° [KL3]; b_{15} 69° [HE3]

d_4^{18} 0.7965[HE3]

n_4^{18} 1.4440[HE3]

Prepn.:

1. 6-Chloro-2-methyl-2-heptene + dimethylamine (52% yield).[HE3]
2. 6-Amino-2-methyl-2-heptene + formaldehyde.[KL3]

Derivs.:

Picrate: m. 83.5° [KL3]

Hydrochloride: m. 101° [KL3]

$C_{10}H_{21}N$

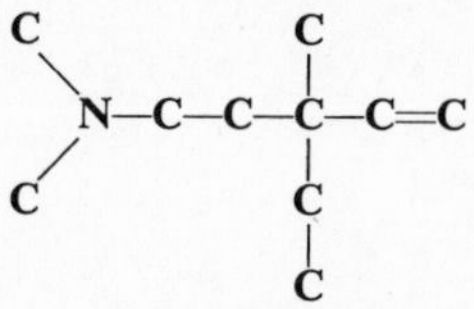

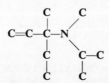

Me
Me
C_8H_{15}

5-DIMETHYLAMINO-3-METHYL-3-ETHYL-1-PENTENE

Phys. Props.:

b_{744} 171–173° [LU5]

Prepn.:

Thermal decomposition of 4-ethyl-1,1,4-trimethylpiperidinium hydroxide.[LU5]

Derivs.:

Picrate: m. 121–123° [LU5]

Methiodide: m. 226–228° [LU5]

$C_{10}H_{21}N$

Me
i-Pr
C_6H_{11}

**3-(METHYLISOPROPYLAMINO)-
3-METHYL-1-PENTENE**

Phys. Props.:

b_{90} 100–101° [AI1]

n_D^{25} 1.4410[AI1]

pK_a 11.3 at 25° (in water), 9.3 (in 66% dimethylformamide)[AI1]

Prepn.:

Methylation of 3-isopropylamino-3-methyl-1-pentene with dimethyl sulfate (50% yield).[AI1]

Derivs.:

Hydrochloride: m. 90–91°[AI1] (*Note:* this compound exploded on analysis, breaking the combustion tube)

$C_{10}H_{21}N$

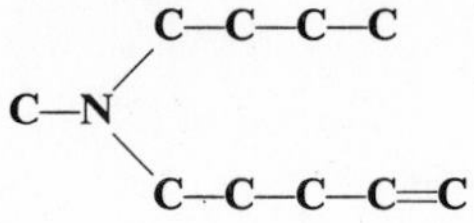

C—C—C—C
C—N
C—C—C—C=C

Me
***n*-Bu**
C_5H_9

METHYLBUTYL-(4-PENTENYL)AMINE

Phys. Props.:

b. 183–184° [BR6]; b_{20} 74–76° [BR14]
d_4^{20} 0.780[BR14]

Prepn.:

Thermal decomposition of 1-butyl-1-methylpiperidinium hydroxide (59%
yield),[BR14] (in unspecified yield).[BR6]

Derivs.:

Picrate: m. 82°,[BR6] 80° [BR14]
Chloroplatinate: m. 137° [BR6]
Methiodide: m. below 100° [BR6]

$C_{10}H_{21}N$

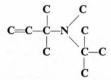

Me
***t*-Bu**
C_5H_9

**METHYL-(*t*-BUTYL)-(1,1-DIMETHYL-
2-PROPENYL)AMINE**

Phys. Props.:

b_{55} 80–85° [AI1]
n_D^{25} 1.4385[AI1]
pK_a 11.3 ± *ca.* 0.2 at 25° (in water), 9.6 (in 66% dimethylformamide)[AI1]

Prepn.:

t-Butyl-(1,1-dimethyl-2-propenyl)amine + dimethyl sulfate (10% yield).[AI1]

Derivs.:

Hydrochloride: m. 127° (dec.)[AI1] (*Note*: this compound exploded on analysis,
breaking the combustion tube)
Picrate: m. 142° (dec.)[AI1]

$C_{10}H_{21}N$

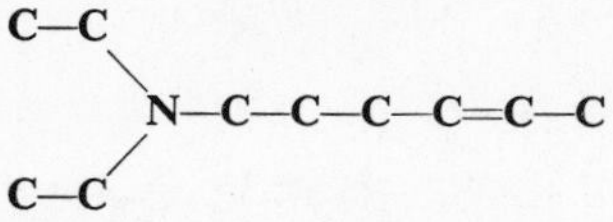

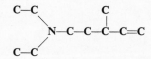

Et
Et
C_6H_{11}

6-DIETHYLAMINO-2-HEXENE

Phys. Props.:

b_{31} 67–68°,[KH3] 73–75° [KH5]*
n_D^{20} 1.4322[KH3]

Prepn.:

2-Chloro-1-diethylaminoethane + 2-butenylmagnesium chloride (75–80%
yield).[KH3,KH5]

$C_{10}H_{21}N$

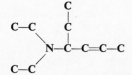

Et
Et
C_6H_{11}

5-DIETHYLAMINO-3-METHYL-1-PENTENE

Phys. Props.:

None given[KH5]

Prepn.:

1-Methylallylmagnesium chloride + 2-chloroethyldiethylamine.[KH5]

$C_{10}H_{21}N$

Et
Et
C_6H_{11}

4-DIETHYLAMINO-2-HEXENE

Phys. Props.:

b. *ca.* 168° [BO14b]

Prepn.:

Diethylamine + 4-chloro-2-hexene.[BO14b]

---

* Both values are cited by the same authors. Comparison with boiling points for other
isomers seems to favor the high value.

$C_{10}H_{21}N$

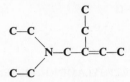

Et
Et
C_6H_{11}

1-DIETHYLAMINO-2-ETHYL-2-BUTENE

Phys. Props.:

b. 169° SO4,SO5

Prepn.:

Dehydration of 1-diethylamino-2-butanol by thionyl chloride or phosphorus
pentachloride or 48% hydrobromic acid[SO5] or (in poor yield) acetic
anhydride.[SO4]

Derivs.:

Picrate: m. 74° SO4,SO5
Chloroplatinate: m. 142–143° SO4,SO5
Chloroaurate: m. 100–102° SO5

$C_{10}H_{21}N$

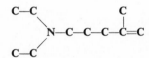

Et
Et
C_6H_{11}

5-DIETHYLAMINO-2-METHYL-1-PENTENE

Phys. Props.:

b_{32} 83° KH3; b_{25} 75–77° KH5
n_D^{20} 1.4377[KH3]

Prepn.:

1-Diethylamino-2-chloroethane + 2-methyl-2-propenylmagnesium   chloride
(75–80% yield).[KH3,KH5]

$C_{10}H_{23}N$

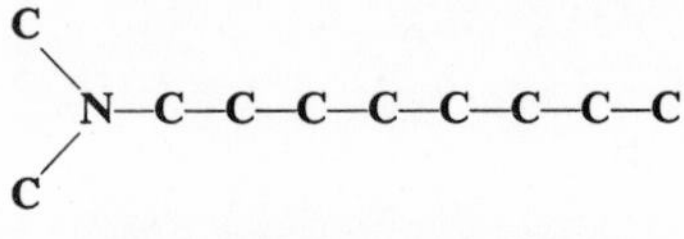

$$\overset{\displaystyle C}{\underset{\displaystyle C}{N}}{-}C{-}C{-}C{-}C{-}C{-}C{-}C{-}C$$

Me
Me
n-Oct

OCTYLDIMETHYLAMINE

Phys. Props.:

b. 194° BR9; b_{760} 191°,BR9 189–190° GA9

Prepn.:

1. Dimethylamine + 1-iodooctane.[CL2]
2. Thermal decomposition of octyltrimethylammonium hydroxide (75% yield, based on starting iodide).[BR9]
3. Thermal degradation of dimethyl-*N*-octylphosphoramidate (33% yield).[BA39]
4. Reduction of *N,N*-dimethyloctanamide with diisobutylaluminum hydride (93% yield).[ZA3]
5. Octylamine + formic acid + formaldehyde (80% yield).[GA9]

Derivs.:

Chloroplatinate: m. 120° [BR9]
Picrate: m. 72°,[CL2] 65°,[ZA3] 62–65° [BR9]
Methobromide: m. 215° [MC5]
Methiodide: m. 141°,[KA13] 138° [BR9]

$C_{10}H_{23}N$

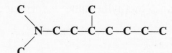

Me
Me
C_8H_{17}

1-DIMETHYLAMINO-3-METHYLHEPTANE

Phys. Props.:

b_{22} 83–84° [TE2]
d_4^{22} 0.7744[TE2]
n_D^{20} 1.4282[TE2]

Prepn.:

Catalytic hydrogenation of 1-dimethylamino-3-methyl-2,6-heptadiene-4-yne (72% yield).[TE2]

Derivs.:

Hydrochloride: m. 175–176° [TE2]
Picrate: m. 35–36° [TE2]

$C_{10}H_{23}N$

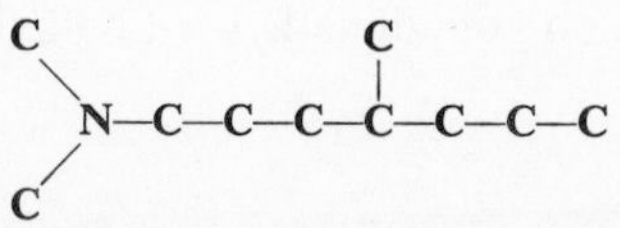

Me
Me
C_8H_{17}

1-DIMETHYLAMINO-4-METHYLHEPTANE

Phys. Props.:

b_{29} 75° [KO12]

Prepn.:

1-Iodo-4-methylheptane + dimethylamine.[KO12]

Derivs.:

Chloroaurate: m. 47–49° [KO12]
Methiodide: m. 185° [KO12]

$C_{10}H_{23}N$ 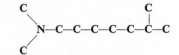   **Me**
    Me
    i-Oct

1-DIMETHYLAMINO-6-METHYLHEPTANE

Phys. Props.:

b_{767} 183–184° [CL2]

Prepn.:

Hydrochloride of 1-amino-6-methylheptane + formaldehyde.[CL2]

Derivs.:

Picrate: m. 69° [CL2]

$C_{10}H_{23}N$ 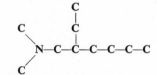   **Me**
    Me
    C_8H_{17}

3-(DIMETHYLAMINOMETHYL)HEPTANE

Phys. Props.:

b. 177–179° [BR21]; b_{20} 88–90° [DE2]; b_{12} 76° [BA39]

Prepn.:

1. 2-Ethylhexanal + the formic acid salt of dimethylamine (60% yield).[DE2]
2. Thermal decomposition of trimethyl-(2-ethylhexyl)ammonium hydroxide (30% yield).[BR21]
3. 1-Bromo-2-ethylhexane + diethylamine.[BR21]
4. Thermal decomposition of dimethyl-*N*-(2-ethylhexyl)phosphoramidate (37% yield).[BA39]

Derivs.:

Methiodide: m. 215° [BR21]
Methobromide: m. above 200° [BR21]
Salt of tetradecafluoroheptane-4,4-diol: m. 57–57.5° [HA26a]
Salt of 5,5′-methylidynebis-(3-methylrhodanine): m. 146–147° [LO1a]

$C_{10}H_{23}N$

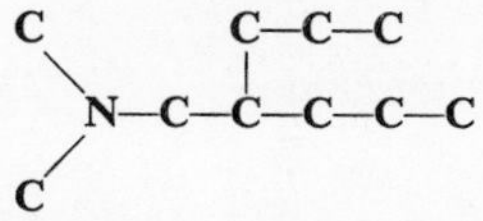

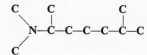

Me
Me
C_8H_{17}

1-DIMETHYLAMINO-2-PROPYLPENTANE

Phys. Props.:

b_{27} 77–80° [KO12]

Prepn.:

1. Thermal decomposition of 2-propylpentyltrimethylammonium hydroxide (69% yield calculated by difference),[HA11] (14% yield).[CO24]
2. Methyl-(2-propylpentyl)amine + formic acid + formaldehyde.[CO24]
3. 4-Iodomethylheptane + dimethylamine.[KO12]
4. Catalytic hydrogenation of product from exhaustive methylation and Hofmann degradation of decahydro-1,8-naphthyridine.[KO12]

Derivs.:

Chloroaurate: m. 160–161° [KO12]
Methiodide: m. 227–229° (dec.),[CO24] 215° (dec.)[KO12]
Picrate: m. 100.6–101.7° [CO24]

$C_{10}H_{23}N$

Me
Me
C_8H_{17}

2-DIMETHYLAMINO-6-METHYLHEPTANE

Phys. Props.:

b_{21} 75–78° [OT1]

Prepn.:

Methyl isohexyl ketone + dimethylamine + formic acid.[OT1]

Derivs.:

Hydrochloride: m. 152–153° [OT1]

$C_{10}H_{23}N$

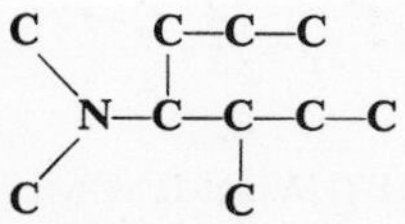

Me
Me
C_8H_{17}

4-DIMETHYLAMINO-3-METHYLHEPTANE*

Phys. Props.:

b. 180–181° [ME13]; b_{700} 180° [WA16]

---

* This compound is also known as tetrahydrode-*N*-methylheliotridane.[ME13]

d_4^{20} 0.948[WA16]
$[\alpha]_D^{20}$ −0.59 °[WA16]

Prepn.:

Two successive Hofmann elimination reactions on heliotridane, each reaction
   followed by reduction.[ME13,WA16]

Derivs.:

Chloroplatinate: m. 133–134° [ME13]
Picrolonate: m. 93–94.5° [ME13]
Methiodide: m. 184° [WA16]; $[\alpha]_D^{26}$ +5.9° (*c.* 1.0, alc.)[WA16]

$C_{10}H_{23}N$

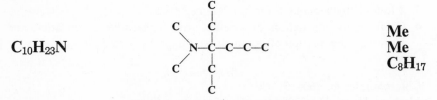

Me
Me
C_8H_{17}

3-DIMETHYLAMINO-3-ETHYLHEXANE

Phys. Props.:

b_{13} 73–74° [MO4]

Prepn.:

N,N-Dimethylbutyramide + ethylmagnesium bromide (33% yield).[MO4]

Derivs.:

Hydrochloride: m. 200–220° (dec.)[MO4]
Picrate: m. 137° [MO4]

$C_{10}H_{23}N$

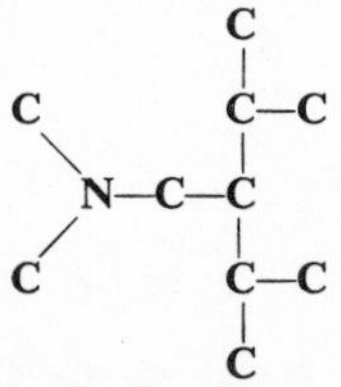

Me
Me
C_8H_{17}

**3-DIMETHYLAMINOMETHYL-
2,4-DIMETHYLPENTANE**

Prepn.:

1. 3-Aminomethyl-2,4-dimethylpentane + formic acid + formaldehyde.[CO24]
2. Thermal decomposition of trimethyl-(2-isopropyl-3-methylbutyl) ammonium hydroxide (25% yield).[CO24]

Derivs.:

Picrate: m. 175.5–176.5° [CO24]
Methiodide: m. 252.5–253.5° (dec.)[CO24]

$C_{10}H_{23}N$

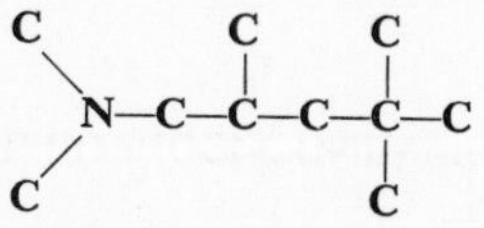

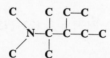

Me
Me
C_8H_{17}

1-DIMETHYLAMINO-2,4,4-TRIMETHYLPENTANE

Phys. Props.:

b_{11} 53–63° [GA6]; b_{10} 47–50° [GA6]
n_D^{20} 1.423[GA6]

Prepn.:

1. Reductive alkylation of dimethylamine with 2,4,4-trimethylpentanal and hydrogen in the presence of Raney nickel (27% yield).[GA6]
2. By-product in the alkylation of di(2,4,4-trimethylpentyl)amine with formic acid and formaldehyde.[GA6]

Derivs.:

Hydrochloride: m. 167–168° [GA6]
Picrate: m. 107° [GA6]*
Methiodide: m. 238° (dec.)[GA6]
Methobromide: m. 275° (dec.)[GA6]

$C_{10}H_{23}N$

Me
Me
C_8H_{17}

2-DIMETHYLAMINO-2-METHYL-3-ETHYLPENTANE

Phys. Props.:

b_{13} 69–70° [LU11]

Prepn.:

N,N-Dimethyl-2-ethylbutanamide + methylmagnesium iodide.[LU11]

Derivs.:

Picrate: m. 171° [LU11]

---

* Ref. GA6 also reports another value (apparently a typographic error) of 105–196°.

$C_{10}H_{23}N$ 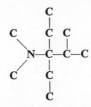 **Me**
Me
C_8H_{17}

3-DIMETHYLAMINO-3-ISOPROPYLPENTANE

Phys. Props.:

b_{12} 63.5–65° [LU11]

Prepn.:

N,N-Dimethylisobutyramide + ethylmagnesium iodide.[LU11]

Derivs.:

Picrate: m. 192–193° [LU11]

$C_{10}H_{23}N$ 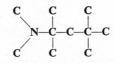 **Me**
Me
C_8H_{17}

2-DIMETHYLAMINO-2,4,4-TRIMETHYLPENTANE

Phys. Props.:

b.174–175° [BO14]; b_{755} 171–172° [BO11]; b_{740} 173–175° [BR44]; b_{110} 107° [PE4]
d_{25}^{25} 0.7900[BO14]
n_D^{25} 1.4330[BO14]

Prepn.:

1. 2-Amino-2,4,4-trimethylpentane + formic acid + formaldehyde.[BO11,BR44][PE4]

2. By-product in the preparation of secondary amine from 2-amino-2,4,4-trimethylbutane and dimethyl sulfate (21.6% yield).[BO14]

Derivs.:

Hydrochloride: m. 182° [PE4]
Methiodide: m. 264° (dec.),[BO14] 255–258° [BR44]
Methobromide: m. 166° [BO11]
Methododecyl sulfate: m. 62° [BO11]

$C_{10}H_{23}N$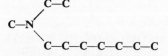

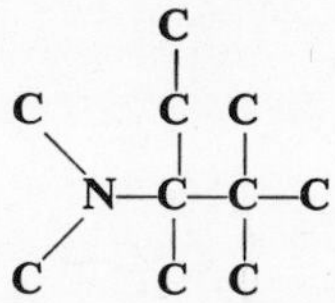

Me
Me
C_8H_{17}

3-DIMETHYLAMINO-2,2,3-TRIMETHYLPENTANE

Phys. Props.:

b_{10} 58–59° [LU7]
n_D^{22} 1.4512[LU7]

Prepn.:

3-Amino-2,3,3-trimethylpentane + formic acid + formaldehyde.[LU7]

Derivs.:

Hydrobromide: m. 199° (dec.)[LU7]

$C_{10}H_{23}N$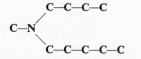

Me
Et
Hept

METHYLETHYLHEPTYLAMINE

Prepn.:

Raney nickel-catalyzed reaction of aqueous ethanol with methylheptylamine
or 2,4,6-tris-(6′-methylaminohexyl)trithane trihydrochloride (49%
yield as the picrate was obtained with the latter reactant).[LE15]

Derivs.:

Picrate: m. 60–62.5° [LE15]

$C_{10}H_{23}N$

Me
n-Bu
n-Pent

METHYLBUTYLPENTYLAMINE

Phys. Props.:

b. 182° [BR14]
d_4^{20} 0.765[BR14]

Prepn.:

Catalytic hydrogenation of methylbutyl-4-pentenylamine.[BR14]

Derivs.:
Picrate: m. 87° BR14
Methiodide: m. 112° BR14

C₁₀H₂₃N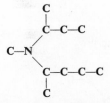

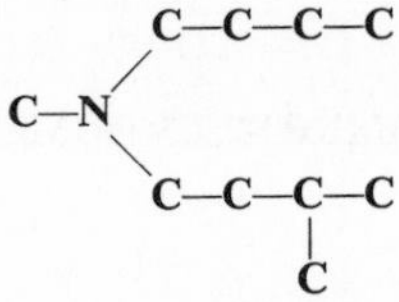

Me
n-Bu
i-Pent

METHYLBUTYL-(3-METHYLBUTYL)AMINE

Derivs.:
Methiodide: m. 150–151° SM9

C₁₀H₂₃N

Me
sec-Bu
C₅H₁₁

METHYL-(1-METHYLPROPYL)-
(1-METHYLBUTYL)AMINE

Phys. Props.:
b. 170–172° SK5

Prepn.:
Reductive alkylation of 2-methylaminobutane with 2-pentanone and hydrogen
      (17% yield).SK5

Derivs.:
Picrate: m. 87–88° SK5
Picrolonate: m. 130–131° SK5

C₁₀H₂₃N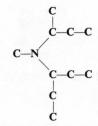

Me
sec-Bu
C₅H₁₁

METHYL-(1-METHYLPROPYL)-
(1-ETHYLPROPYL)AMINE

Phys. Props.:
b₇₄₄ 170–172° SK5

Prepn.:

Reductive alkylation of:

a. 2-Methylaminobutane with 3-pentanone and hydrogen (0.2% yield as the picrolonate). [SK5]

b. 3-Methylaminopentane with 2-butanone and hydrogen (23% yield).[SK5]

c. 3-(*sec*-Butylamino)pentane with formaldehyde and hydrogen (73% yield).[SK5]

Derivs.:

Picrolonate: m. 115–116° [SK5]

$C_{10}H_{23}N$

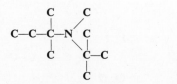

Me
***t*-Bu**
C_5H_{11}

METHYL-(*t*-BUTYL)-(1,1-DIMETHYLPROPYL)AMINE

Phys. Props.:

b_{120} 100–110° [AI1]

n_D^{25} 1.4370[AI1]

pK_a 11.9 at 25° (in water), 10.6 (in 66% dimethylformamide)[AI1]

Prepn.:

Methylation of *t*-butyl-(1,1-dimethylpropyl)amine with dimethyl sulfate (28% yield).[AI1]

Derivs.:

Hydrochloride: m. 107–108° [AI1]

Picrate: m. 148° (dec.)[AI1]

$C_{10}H_{23}N$

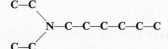

Et
Et
***n*-Hex**

HEXYLDIETHYLAMINE

Phys. Props.:

b. 179–180° [GO1]; b_{750} 179–180° [PE10]; b_{20} 75.5–76.5° [PE10]

d_4^{20} 0.7688,[PE10] 0.7676[PE10]

n_D^{20} 1.4245,[GO1] 1.4242–1.4252[PE10]

Prepn.:

1. Catalytic hydrogenation of 2-diethylaminomethyl-5-methylthiophene in the presence of Raney nickel catalyst (45.7% yield).[GO1]

2. High-pressure alkylation of hexylamine with ethylene in the presence of N-sodiohexylamine (8.5% yield); ethylhexylamine is also formed (26.5% yield).[CL8]

3. Catalytic hydrogenation of 1-diethylamino-2,3-hexadiene over colloidal palladium (*ca.* 100% yield).[PE10]

4. Diethylamine + hexyl bromide.[PE10]

Derivs.:

Oxalate: m. 76.5–77.5° [GO1]
Ethobromide: m. 186° [MC5]

$C_{10}H_{23}N$ 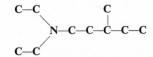 Et
Et
C_6H_{13}

1-DIETHYLAMINO-3-METHYLPENTANE

Phys. Props.:

b_{25} 78° [ZA4]
d_4^{20} 0.7702[ZA4]
n_D^{20} 1.4248[ZA4]

Prepn.:

4-Diethylamino-1-butene + triethylaluminum.[ZA4]

$C_{10}H_{23}N$ 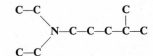 Et
Et
i-Hex

1-DIETHYLAMINO-4-METHYLPENTANE

Phys. Props.:

b. 172° [RO3]

Prepn.:

Isopentylmagnesium bromide + butyl(diethylaminomethyl) ether (50% yield).[RO3]

Derivs.:

Chloroplatinate: m. 101° [RO3]

$C_{10}H_{23}N$

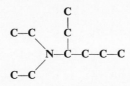

Et
Et
C_6H_{13}

3-DIETHYLAMINOHEXANE

Phys. Props.:

b_{772} 174° [BR49]

d_4^{20} 0.7736[BR49]

n_D^{20} 1.4245[BR49]

Prepn.:

1-Cyano-1-diethylaminobutane + ethylmagnesium bromide (83% yield).[BR49]

$C_{10}H_{23}N$

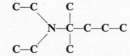

Et
Et
C_6H_{13}

2-DIETHYLAMINO-2-METHYLPENTANE

Phys. Props.:

b. 170–173° [MO5]; b_{760} 171–172° [MO4]; b_{24} 70° [MO4]; b_{14} 60° [MO4]

Prepn.:

1. N,N-Diethylbutyramide + methylmagnesium iodide,[MO5] (28% yield).[MO4]
2. Ethyl iodide + 2-amino-2-methylpentane.[MO4]
3. Catalytic hydrogenation of 4-diethylamino-4-methyl-2-pentyne.[KR11]

Derivs.:

Picrate: m. 124° [MO4]

Chloroplatinate: m. 207° [MO4]

Chloroaurate: m. 82° [MO4]

$C_{10}H_{23}N$

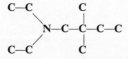

Et
Et
C_6H_{13}

1-DIETHYLAMINO-2,2-DIMETHYLBUTANE

Phys. Props.:

b. 165–166° [BO15]; b_{11} 52° [BO15]

Prepn.:

N,N-Diethylformamide + 2-methyl-2-butylmagnesium chloride (unspecified yield).[BO15]

$C_{10}H_{23}N$

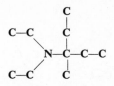

Et
Et
C_6H_{13}

3-DIETHYLAMINO-3-METHYLPENTANE

Phys. Props.:

b_{30} 79–80° [HE11]
n_D^{25} 1.4350 [HE11]

Prepn.:

Catalytic hydrogenation of 3-diethylamino-3-methyl-1-pentyne.[HE11]

$C_{10}H_{23}N$

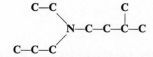

Et
n-Pr
i-Pent

ETHYLPROPYL-3-METHYLBUTYLAMINE

Phys. Props.:

b. 167–168° [SK4]; b_{14} 52–53° [SK4]

Prepn.:

Reductive alkylation of ethylisopentylamine with propionaldehyde and
hydrogen (57% yield).[SK4]

Derivs.:

Picrate: m. 82° [SK4]

$C_{10}H_{23}N$

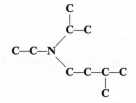

Et
i-Pr
i-Pent

ETHYLISOPROPYL-3-METHYLBUTYLAMINE

Phys. Props.:

b_{762} 163–164° [SK5]

Prepn.:

Reductive alkylation of ethylisopentylamine with acetone and hydrogen (29% yield).[SK5]

Derivs.:

Picrate: m. 60–61° [SK5]

$C_{10}H_{23}N$

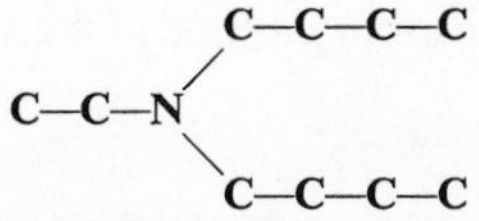

```
              C—C—C—C
             /
    C—C—N
             \
              C—C—C—C
```

ETHYLDIBUTYLAMINE

Et
n-Bu
n-Bu

Phys. Props.:

b. 170–175° [SC12]

Prepn.:

1. *N*-Sodiodibutylamine + ethylene under pressure (68% yield).[CL8]
2. Reductive alkylation of dibutylamine with acetaldehyde and hydrogen.[CH9]
3. Butyldiethylamine + 1-butanol under pressure in the presence of a silicate catalyst.[SC12]
4. Obtained as part of a mixture in the reaction of dibutylamine with 1,1,1-triethoxyethane.[MC6]
5. Ethyldichloroamine + butylmagnesium chloride (9% yield).[CO4]
6. Reaction of ethylamine with butanol in the vapor phase gives 24.8% conversion to ethylbutylamine and 15% conversion to ethyldibutylamine.[OL3]

$C_{10}H_{23}N$

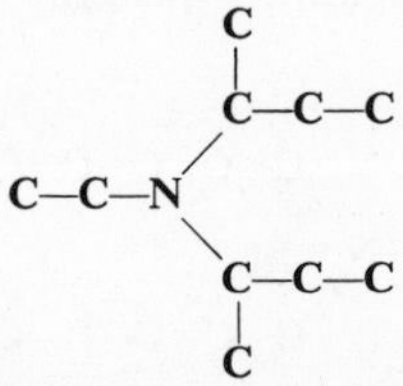

```
              C
              |
              C—C—C
             /
    C—C—N
             \
              C—C—C
              |
              C
```

ETHYLDI(1-METHYLPROPYL)AMINE

Et
sec-Bu
sec-Bu

Derivs.:

Methiodide (from methyldi-*sec*-butylamine and ethyl iodide): m. 199° (cor.)[RO4]

$C_{10}H_{23}N$

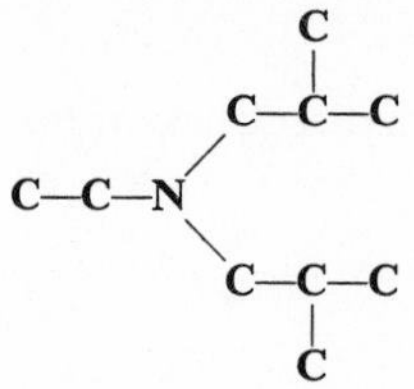

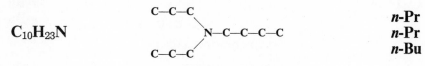

Et
i-Bu
i-Bu

ETHYLDI(2-METHYLPROPYL)AMINE

Derivs.:

Methiodide (from methyldiisobutylamine and ethyl iodide): m. 162° (cor.)[RO4]

$C_{10}H_{23}N$

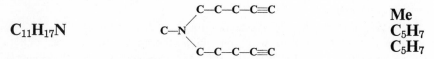

n-Pr
n-Pr
n-Bu

BUTYLDIPROPYLAMINE

Phys. Props.:

b_{743} 172–174° [SM9]; b_{740} 172–174° [DA9]

Prepn.:

Dipropylamine + a butyl halide (78% yield).[SM9]

Derivs.:

Propiodide: m. 260° (dec.)[SM9]

$C_{11}H_{17}N$

```
      C—C—C—C≡C
     /
C—N
     \
      C—C—C—C≡C
```

Me
C_5H_7
C_5H_7

METHYLDI(4-PENTYNYL)AMINE

Derivs.:

Methiodide (from 5-dimethylamino-1-pentyne and 5-iodo-1-pentyne): m. 139–140° [EP2,OL6]

$C_{11}H_{17}N$

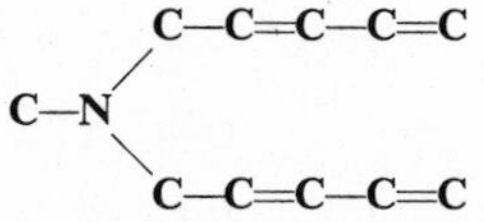

```
      C—C=C—C=C
     /
C—N
     \
      C—C=C—C=C
```

Me
C_5H_7
C_5H_7

METHYLDI(2,4-PENTADIENYL)AMINE

Derivs.:

Methobromide: dec. without melting up to 300°. (This methobromide was one of the products obtained in the cyanogen bromide cleavage of 5-dimethylamino-1,3-pentadiene[LU16]).

$C_{11}H_{17}N$

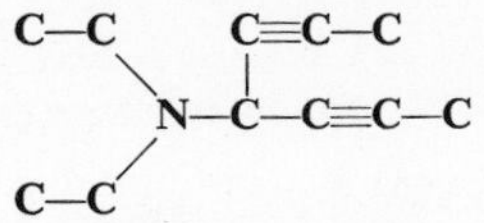

$$\begin{array}{c} C-C \qquad C\equiv C-C \\ \;\;\; N-C-C\equiv C-C \\ C-C \end{array}$$

Et
Et
C_7H_7

4-DIETHYLAMINO-2,5-HEPTADIYNE

Phys. Props.:
b_{14-15} 99–99.5° [VI1]
d_4^{18} 0.871[VI1]
n_D^{18} 1.477[VI1]

Prepn.:
N,N-Diethylformamide + 1-propynylmagnesium bromide.[VI1]

Derivs.:
Chloroplatinate dihydrate: m. 120° (dec.)[VI1]
Picrate: m. 169° [VI1]
Ethiodide: m. 148–150° (dec.)[VI1]

$C_{11}H_{17}N$

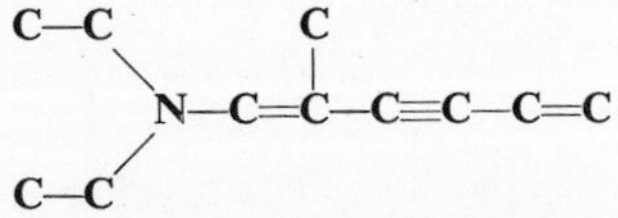

$$\begin{array}{c} C-C \qquad\;\; C \\ \;\; N-C=C-C\equiv C-C=C \\ C-C \end{array}$$

Et
Et
C_7H_7

1-DIETHYLAMINO-2-METHYL-
1,5-HEXADIEN-3-YNE

Phys. Props.:
b_5 70–72° [VA6]
d_4^{20} 0.8835[VA6]
n_D^{20} 1.4807[VA6]

Prepn.:
Dehydration of 1-diethylamino-2-methyl-2-hydroxy-5-hexen-3-yne by sulfuric acid in methanol (*ca.* 50% yield).[VA6]

Derivs.:
Picrate: m. 200° [VA6]

$C_{11}H_{19}N$

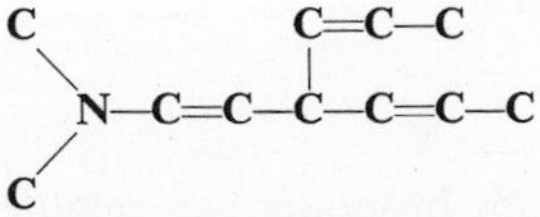

$$\begin{array}{c} C \qquad\quad C=C-C \\ \;\; N-C=C-C-C=C-C \\ C \end{array}$$

Me
Me
C_9H_{13}

1-DIMETHYLAMINO-3-(1-PROPENYL)
-1,4-HEXADIENE

Prepn.:
3-Dimethylamino-2-propen-1-al + 1-propenylmagnesium bromide (80% yield).[FI3]

Derivs.:

Picrate: m. 163° [FI3]

$C_{11}H_{19}N$

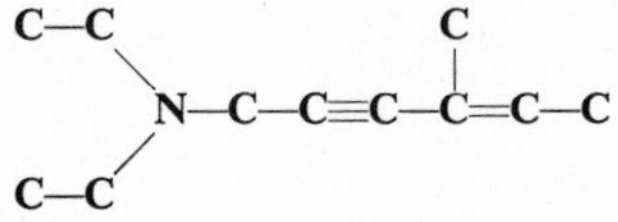

C—C   C
   \
N—C—C≡C—C=C—C
   /
C—C

Et
Et
C_7H_9

6-DIETHYLAMINO-3-METHYL-2-HEXEN-4-YNE

Phys. Props.:

b_{12-13} 86–89° [NA3]
$n_D^{19.5}$ 1.4735[NA3]

Prepn.:

Diethylamine + paraformaldehyde + 3-methyl-2-penten-4-yne in the presence of iron(III) chloride (89% yield).[NA3]

Derivs.:

Picrate: m. 98–99° [NA3]
Hydrochloride: m. 126–127° [NA3]

$C_{11}H_{21}N$

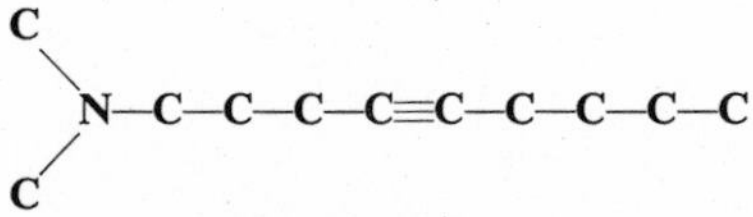

C
   \
N—C—C—C—C≡C—C—C—C—C
   /
C

Me
Me
C_9H_{15}

1-DIMETHYLAMINO-4-NONYNE

Phys. Props.:

b_{33} 118° [CA7]; b_{10} 98° [SC20]
d_4^{20} 0.8103[CA7]
n_D^{20} 1.4488[CA7]
pK_a 8.66 (in 30% methanol)[CA7]

Prepn.:

1. 4-Nonyn-1-ylhexaminium bromide + formaldehyde + formic acid (15% yield). [SC20]
2. 1-Chloro-4-nonyne + dimethylamine. [CA7]

Derivs.:

Oxalate: m. 131–132°, [SC20] 130–131° [CA7]

C₁₁H₂₁N

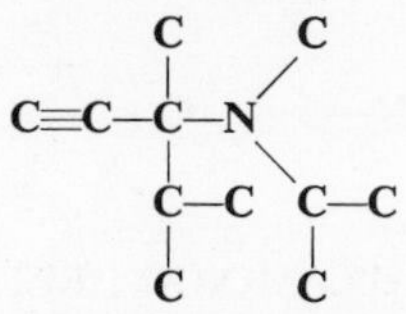

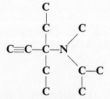

Me
i-Pr
C₇H₁₁

3-(METHYLISOPROPYLAMINO)-
3,4-DIMETHYL-1-PENTYNE

Phys. Props.:

b_{20} 73–75° [A11]
n_D^{25} 1.4450 [A11]
pK_a 8.7 at 25° (in water), 6.8 (in 66% dimethylformamide) [A11]

Prepn.:

Methylation of 3-isopropylamino-3,4-dimethyl-1-pentyne with dimethyl sulfate (60% yield). [A11]

Derivs.:

Hydrochloride: m. 198° (dec.) [A11]

C₁₁H₂₁N

Me
i-Pr
C₇H₁₁

3-(METHYLISOPROPYLAMINO)-3-ETHYL-1-PENTYNE

Phys. Props.:

b_{14} 72–74° [A11]
n_D^{25} 1.4465 [A11]
pK_a 8.8 at 25° (in water), 7.1 (in 66% dimethylformamide) [A11]

Prepn.:

Methylation of 3-isopropylamino-3-ethyl-1-pentyne with dimethyl sulfate (60% yield). [A11]

Derivs.:

Hydrochloride: m. 143–145° [A11]

$C_{11}H_{21}N$

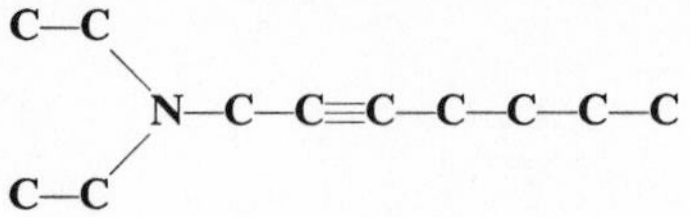

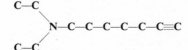

Et
Et
C_7H_{11}

1-DIETHYLAMINO-2-HEPTYNE

Phys. Props.:
b_{20} 100° [JO6]; b_{10} 84–85° [PA5]
d_4^{25} 0.8071[PA5]
n_D^{25} 1.4450[PA5]; n_D^{12} 1.4513[JO6]

Prepn.:
1. Diethylamine + formaldehyde + 1-hexyne (77% yield).[JO6]
2. Sodio derivative of 3-diethylamino-1-propyne + butyl bromide (60% yield).[PA5]

Derivs.:
Picrate: m. 75° [JO6]

$C_{11}H_{21}N$

Et
Et
C_7H_{11}

7-DIETHYLAMINO-1-HEPTYNE

Phys. Props.:
b_{10} 84–85° [ZA2]
n_D^{20} 1.4460[ZA2]
d_4^{20} 0.8128[ZA2]

Prepn.:
Reaction of sodium with 1,1-dichloro-7-diethylamino-1-heptene (78% yield).[ZA2]

Derivs.:
Oxalate: m. 72–73° [ZA2]

$C_{11}H_{21}N$

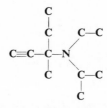

Et
i-Pr
C_6H_9

3-(ETHYLISOPROPYLAMINO)-3-METHYL-1-PENTYNE

Phys. Props.:
pK_a 7.45 at 25° (in 66% dimethylformamide)[A11]

Prepn.:

3-(Isopropylamino)-3-methyl-1-pentyne + ethyl-*p*-toluenesulfonate (7% yield as the hydrochloride).[AI1]

Derivs.:

Hydrochloride: m. 177–179° [AI1]

C₁₁H₂₁N

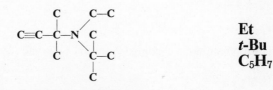

Et
t-Bu
C₅H₇

**ETHYL-(*t*-BUTYL)-(1,1-DIMETHYL-
2-PROPYNYL)AMINE**

Phys. Props.:

b_{130} 110–120° [AI1]
n_D^{25} 1.4440[AI1]
pK_a 9.6 at 25° (in water), 8.0 (in 66% dimethylformamide)[AI1]

Prepn.:

t-Butyl-(1,1-dimethyl-2-propynyl)amine + diethyl sulfate (7% yield).[AI1]

Derivs.:

Hydrochloride: m. 135° (dec.)[AI1]
Picrate: m. 130° (dec.)[AI1]

C₁₁H₂₁N

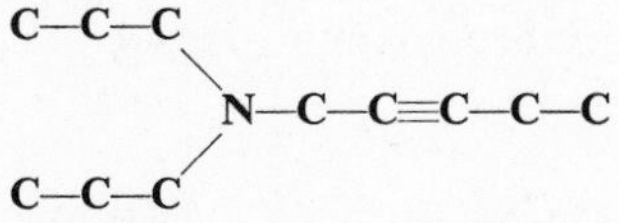

1-DIPROPYLAMINO-2-PENTYNE

n-Pr
n-Pr
C₅H₇

Phys. Props.:

b_{10} 81–81.5° [PA6]
d_4^{25} 0.8040[PA6]
n_D^{25} 1.4423[PA6]

Prepn.:

Sodio derivative of 3-dipropylamino-1-propyne + ethyl bromide (82.5% yield).[PA6]

$C_{11}H_{21}N$

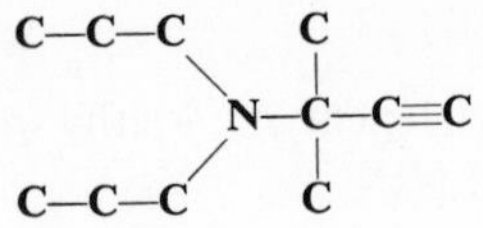

```
C—C—C      C
        \    |
         N—C—C≡C
        /    |
C—C—C      C
```

n-Pr
n-Pr
C_5H_7

3-DIPROPYLAMINO-3-METHYL-1-BUTYNE

Phys. Props.:

b_{19} 74° [HE8]
n_D^{25} 1.4362 [HE8]

Prepn.:

Dipropylamine + 3-chloro-3-methyl-1-butyne (28% yield).[HE8]

Derivs.:

Hydrochloride: m. 208–209° [HE8]

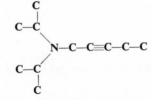

$C_{11}H_{21}N$

i-Pr
i-Pr
C_5H_7

1-DIISOPROPYLAMINO-2-PENTYNE

Phys. Props.:

b_{10} 75.5–76° [PA6]
d_4^{25} 0.8146 [PA6]
n_D^{25} 1.4470 [PA6]

Prepn.:

Sodio derivative of 3-diisopropylamino-1-propyne + ethyl bromide (68% yield).[PA6]

$C_{11}H_{21}N$

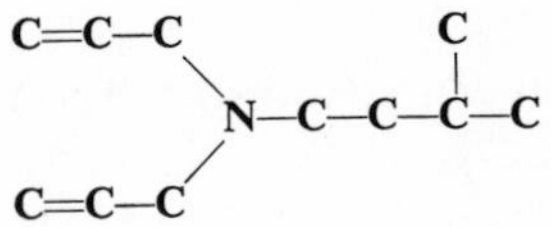

```
C=C—C      C
        \    |
         N—C—C—C—C
        /    
C=C—C      
```

All
All
i-Pent

1-DIALLYLAMINO-3-METHYLBUTANE

Phys. Props.:

b_9 65–66° [BR3]

Prepn.:

Allyl bromide + 1-amino-3-methylbutane.[BR3]

$C_{11}H_{21}N$

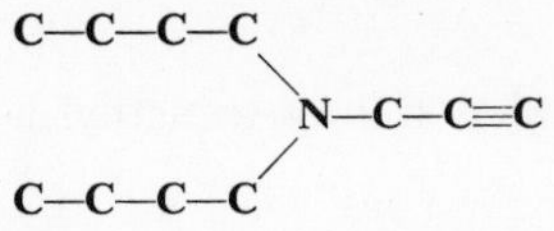

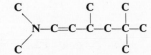

3-DIBUTYLAMINO-1-PROPYNE

n-**Bu**
n-**Bu**
C₃H₃

Phys. Props.:

b_{19} 87–89° [RE7,RE11]; b_{10} 77.5–78.5° [PA6]
d_4^{25} 0.8045[PA6]
n_D^{25} 1.4381[PA6]

Prepn.:

1. Dehydrohalogenation of 2-bromo-3-dibutylamino-1-propene with soda-mide (89% yield).[PA6]
2. Reaction under pressure of dibutylamine with acetylene and formaldehyde in the presence of copper(I) chloride (82% yield),[RE7] (80% yield).[RE11]

$C_{11}H_{23}N$

1-DIMETHYLAMINO-3,5,5-TRIMETHYL-1-HEXENE

Me
Me
C₉H₁₇

Phys. Props.:

b_1 46–50° [DE1,DE2]

Prepn.:

Distillation of the reaction product of 3,5,5-trimethylhexanal with dimethyl-amine (42% yield).[DE1,DE2]

$C_{11}H_{23}N$

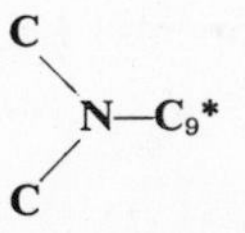

NONENYLDIMETHYLAMINE*

Me
Me
C₉H₁₇

Phys. Props.:

b_{25} 87–92° [SC7]
n_D^{20} 1.4389[SC7]

---

* The authors of the present monograph believe the structure of this compound in ref. SC7 to be $(CH_3)_3CCH_2C(=CH_2)CH_2CH_2N(CH_3)_2$ and/or $(CH_3)_3CCH=C(CH_3)CH_2$ $CH_2N(CH_3)_2$. See section 5 in methods of preparation entitled "*N*-Alkylation of Secondary Amines by Olefins and Formaldehyde."

Prepn.:

Tetramethylmethylenediamine + 2,4,4-trimethyl-1-pentene in the presence of sulfuric acid.[SC7]

$C_{11}H_{23}N$

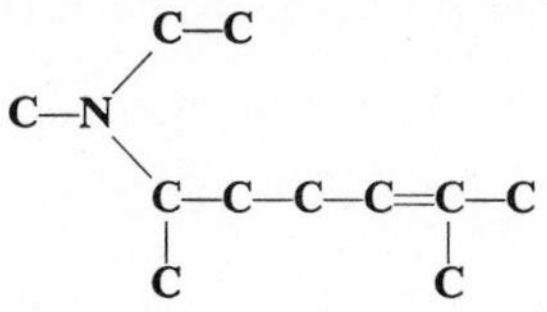

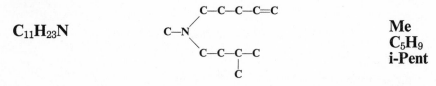

      Me
      Et
      C_8H_{15}

6-(METHYLETHYLAMINO)-2-METHYL-2-HEPTENE

Phys. Props.:

b. 197–199° [KL3]

Prepn.:

Methylation of 6-ethylamino-2-methyl-2-heptene.[KL3]

Derivs.:

Picrate: m. 143° [KL3]

$C_{11}H_{23}N$

      Me
      C_5H_9
      i-Pent

METHYL-(4-PENTENYL)-(3-METHYLBUTYL)AMINE

Phys. Props.:

b. 190–193° [SC18]

Prepn.:

Thermal decomposition of 1-isopentyl-1-methylpiperidinium hydroxide.[SC18]

Derivs.:

Chloroplatinate: m. 140° [SC18]

$C_{11}H_{23}N$

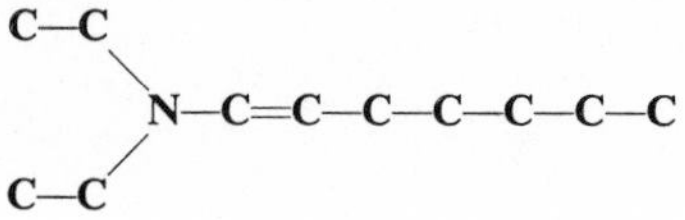

      Et
      Et
      C_7H_{13}

1-DIETHYLAMINO-1-HEPTENE

Phys. Props.:

b_{110} 134–140° [MA21]

pK_a 10.38 at 28° (in 50% methanol)[AD2]

Prepn.:

Distillation of the reaction product between heptanal and diethylamine.[MA21]

$C_{11}H_{23}N$

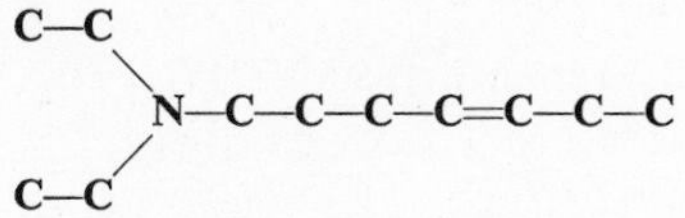

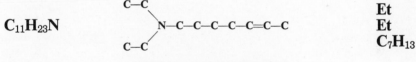

Et
Et
C_7H_{13}

7-DIETHYLAMINO-3-HEPTENE

Phys. Props.:

b_{13} 82.8° [GL1]
$d_4^{16.7}$ 0.788[GL1]
$n_D^{16.7}$ 1.4419[GL1]

Prepn.:

Diethylamine + 1-bromo-4-heptene (92% yield).[GL1]

Derivs.:

Hydrochloride: m. 105.8–106.2° [GL1]

$C_{11}H_{23}N$

Et
Et
C_7H_{13}

7-DIETHYLAMINO-2-HEPTENE

Phys. Props.:

$b_{12.5}$ 83.2° [GL1]
d_4^{16} 0.791[GL1]
n_D^{16} 1.4427[GL1]
Raman absorption at 1672 cm.$^{-1}$[GL1]

Prepn.:

1. Sealed tube reaction of diethylamine with 1-bromo-5-heptene (95% yield).[GL1]
2. By-product (13% yield) in the pyrolysis of the acetate ester of 5-diethylamino-1-heptanol. Main products are 5-diethylamino-1-heptene and 1,2-diethylpiperidine.[GL1]
3. Pyrolysis of various 1,1,2-triethylpiperidinium salts results in low yields of the subject amine, as follows: acetate (18% yield); hydroxide (3% yield); bromide (11% yield). The main product in each case is 1,2-diethylaminopyridine.[GL1]

Derivs.:

Hydrochloride: m. 96.2–96.8° [GL1]

C₁₁H₂₃N

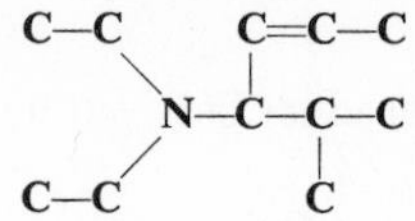

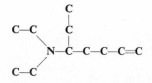

Et
Et
C₇H₁₃

4-DIETHYLAMINO-5-METHYL-2-HEXENE

Phys. Props.:

b. *ca.* 175° [BO14b]

Prepn.:

4-Chloro-5-methyl-2-hexene + diethylamine.[BO14b]

C₁₁H₂₃N

Et
Et
C₇H₁₃

5-DIETHYLAMINO-1-HEPTENE

Phys. Props.:

b_{10} 66–67° [GL1]
d_4^{16} 0.797[GL1]
n_D^{16} 1.4391[GL1]
Raman absorption at 1641 cm.⁻¹ characteristic of terminal alkene[GL1]

Prepn.:

1. Thermal decomposition of the acetate ester of 5-diethylamino-1-heptanol (40% yield).[GL1]

C₁₁H₂₃N

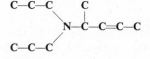

n-Pr
n-Pr
C₅H₉

4-DIPROPYLAMINO-2-PENTENE

Phys. Props.:

b. *ca.* 182–183° [BO14a]

Prepn.:

4-Chloro-2-pentene + dipropylamine.[BA14a]

$C_{11}H_{23}N$

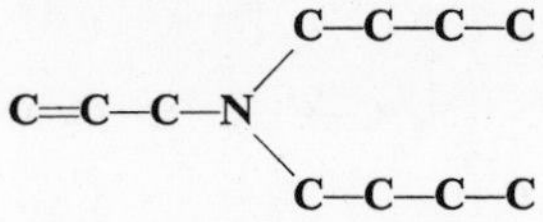

All
***n*-Bu**
***n*-Bu**

ALLYLDIBUTYLAMINE

Phys. Props.:

b. 185–187.5° [BU8]

Prepn.:

Butyl bromide + allylamine (27% yield).[BU8]

$C_{11}H_{25}N$

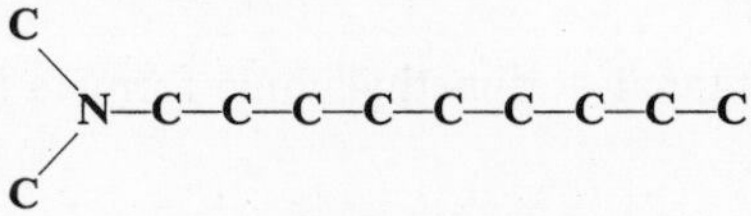

Me
Me
n-C_9H_{19}

NONYLDIMETHYLAMINE

Phys. Props.:

b_{741} 209° [KI3]

Prepn.:

Thermal decomposition of the reaction product of hydrogen sulfide with benzylnonyldimethylammonium hydroxide.[KI3]

Derivs.:

Methiodide: m. 170° [KI3]

$C_{11}H_{25}N$

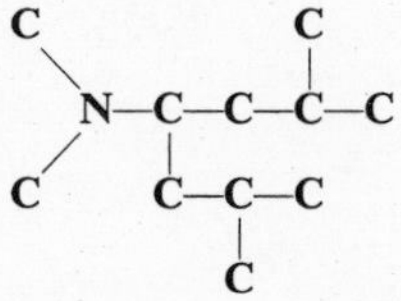

Me
Me
C_9H_{19}

4-DIMETHYLAMINO-2,6-DIMETHYLHEPTANE

Phys. Props.:

b. 176° [MA45]

Prepn.:

Isobutylmagnesium chloride + dimethylformamide (32% yield)[MA45]; in unspecified yield.[BO15]

Derivs.:

Picrate: m. 116° [MA45]

C₁₁H₂₅N

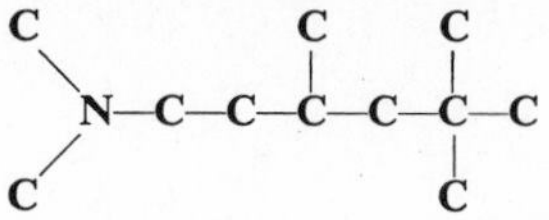

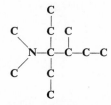

Me
Me
C₉H₁₉

$$C_{11}H_{25}N$$

1-DIMETHYLAMINO-3,5,5,-TRIMETHYLHEXANE

Phys. Props.:

b_6 67–70°[DE1]; b_3 52–55°[DE2]; $b_{1.5}$ 46°[DE2]

Prepn.:

1. Reduction of 1-dimethylamino-3,5,5-trimethyl-1-hexene with formic acid (92% yield).[DE1,DE2]
2. 3,5,5-Trimethylheptanal + dimethylamine formate (84% yield).[DE1,DE2]

C₁₁H₂₅N

Me
Me
C₉H₁₉

3-DIMETHYLAMINO-4-METHYL-3-ETHYLHEXANE

Phys. Props.:

optically active form
   b_{11} 83–84°[LU10]
   d_4^{20} 0.8607*[LU10]
   n_D^{20} 1.4547[LU10]
   $[\alpha]_D^{20}$ −7.80°[LU10]
racemic mixture
   b_{13} 86–88°[LU10]
   n_D^{20} 1.4543[LU10]

Prepn.:

N,N-Dimethyl-2-methylbutyramide + ethylmagnesium bromide. When the amide used is optically active, the resulting amine is optically active (53% yield).[LU10]

Derivs.:

Picrate: m. 148° (for both optically active (−) and for the racemate)[LU10]

---

* Density cited by ref. LU10 seems to be abnormally high.

$C_{11}H_{25}N$

Me
Me
C_9H_{19}

3-DIMETHYLAMINO-3-t-BUTYLPENTANE

Phys. Props.:

b_{12} 75.5–78° [LU11]
m. 35° [LU11]

Prepn.:

N,N-Dimethyl-2,2-dimethylpropanamide + ethylmagnesium iodide.[LU11]

Derivs.:

Picrate: m. 163° [LU11]

$C_{11}H_{25}N$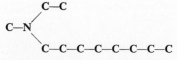

Me
Et
n-Oct

METHYLETHYLOCTYLAMINE

Prepn.:

2,4,6-Tris-(7′-methylaminoheptyl)trithane trihydrochloride with aqueous ethanol in the presence of Raney nickel (52% yield).[LE15]

Derivs.:

Picrolonate: m. 101–102° (dec.)[LE15]

$C_{11}H_{25}N$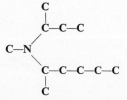

Me
sec-Bu
C_6H_{13}

**METHYL-(1-METHYLPROPYL)-
(1-METHYLPENTYL)AMINE**

Phys. Props.:

b. 192–193° [SK5]

Prepn.:

Reductive alkylation of 2-methylaminobutane with 2-hexanone and hydrogen (8% yield).[SK5]

Derivs.:

Picrolonate: m. 98–99°[SK5]

$C_{11}H_{25}N$ 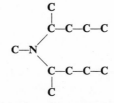 **Me**
C_5H_{11}
C_5H_{11}

METHYLDI(1-METHYLBUTYL)AMINE

Phys. Props.:

b. 196°[RO4]
n_D^{25} 1.4300[RO4]

Prepn.:

Di(1-methylbutyl)amine + formic acid + formaldehyde.[RO4]

Derivs.:

Ethiodide: m. 117–118°[RO4]

$C_{11}H_{25}N$ 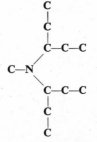 **Me**
C_5H_{11}
C_5H_{11}

METHYLDI(1-ETHYLPROPYL)AMINE

Phys. Props.:

b. 198°[RO4]
n_D^{25} 1.4300[RO4]

Prepn.:

Di(1-ethylpropyl)amine + formic acid + formaldehyde.[RO4]

Derivs.:

Methiodide: m. 114°[RO4]

$C_{11}H_{25}N$

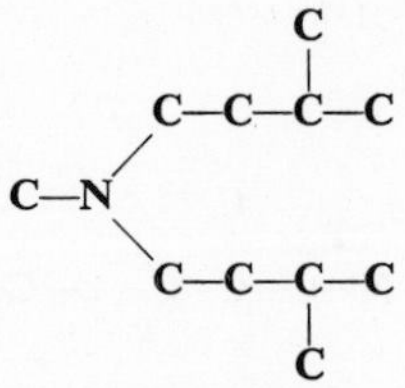

```
            C
            |
      C—C—C—C
     /
C—N
     \
      C—C—C—C
            |
            C
```

Me
i-Pent
i-Pent

METHYLDI(3-METHYLBUTYL)AMINE

Phys. Props.:

b_{21} 83–84°[RO4]
n_D^{25} 1.4219[RO4]

Prepn.:

1. Diisopentylamine + formic acid + formaldehyde.[RO4]
2. Thermal decomposition of dimethyldiisopentylammonium chloride.[CO8]

Derivs.:

Ethobromide: m. 126–128° (cor.)[RO4]

$C_{11}H_{25}N$

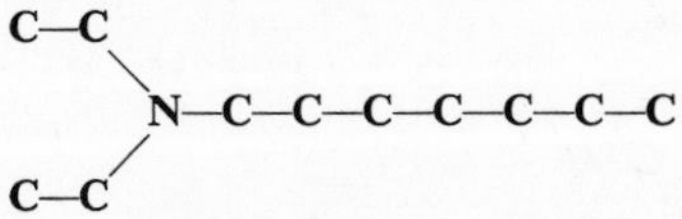

```
 C—C
    \
     N—C—C—C—C—C—C—C
    /
 C—C
```

Et
Et
n-Hept

HEPTYLDIETHYLAMINE

Phys. Props.:

b. 198–200°,[GO1] 198°[MA21]; b_{200} 156°[PE1]; b_{16} 86–87°[WO2]; b_{14} 86°[MA34,MA35]
n_D^{21} 1.4317[MA34,MA35]; n_D^{20} 1.4289[GO1]
pK_a 9.94 at 26° (in 50% methanol)[AD2]

Prepn.:

1. Hydrogenation of 2-diethylaminomethyl-5-ethylthiophene with Raney nickel catalyst (53.7% yield).[GO1]
2. Diethylamine + 1-bromoheptane (84% crude yield).[PE1]
3. In unspecified yield in the catalytic hydrogenation of 1-diethylamino-1-heptene,[MA21] or of 1-diethylamino-5-heptene.[GL1]
4. Catalytic hydrogenation of N,N-diethylheptanamide (4% yield).[WO2]
5. Catalytic hydrogenation of 1-diethylamino-2-heptyne.[MA34,MA35]
6. Raney nickel catalyzed hydrogenation of 1-diethylamino-4-acetoxy-2-heptyne or of 1-diethylamino-4-benzyloxy-2-heptyne.[MA34,MA35]

Derivs.:
Hydrochloride: m. 105–106° [WO2]
Chloroaurate: m. 48°, [MA21] 48.5–48.7° [GL1]
Oxalate: m. 84.7–85.7°, [GO1] 80° [MA34,MA35]
Ethobromide: m. 125–126° [GL1]

$C_{11}H_{25}N$ Et
Et
C_7H_{15}

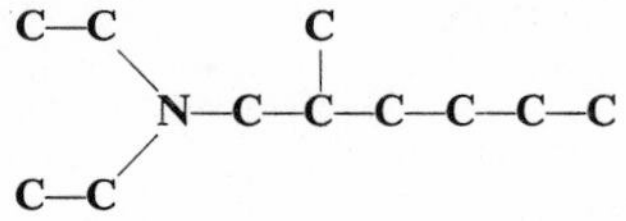

1-DIETHYLAMINO-2-METHYLHEXANE

Phys. Props.:
b_4 73–74° [VA6]
d_4^{20} 0.8492 [VA6]
n_D^{20} 1.4405 [VA6]

Prepn.:
Platinum-catalyzed hydrogenation of 1-diethylamino-2-methyl-1,5-hexadien-3-yne. [VA6]

Derivs.:
Picrate: m. 86° [VA6]

$C_{11}H_{25}N$ 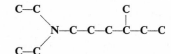   Et
Et
C_7H_{15}

1-DIETHYLAMINO-4-METHYLHEXANE

Phys. Props.:
b_{25} 95–96° [ZA4]
d_4^{20} 0.7817 [ZA4]
n_D^{20} 1.4320 [ZA4]

Prepn.:
5-Diethylamino-1-pentene + triethylaluminum (43% overall yield). [ZA4]

$C_{11}H_{25}N$ 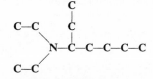   Et
Et
C_7H_{15}

3-DIETHYLAMINOHEPTANE

Phys. Props.:
b_{10} 68–69° [GL1]; b_9 66.5–67° [GL1]

d_4^{14} 0.781[GL1]
n_D^{14} 1.4297[GL1]

Prepn.:

1. Catalytic hydrogenation of 5-diethylamino-1-heptene.[GL1]
2. Sealed tube reaction of diethylamine and 3-bromoheptane (54% yield based on alkyl halide consumed).[GL1]

Derivs.:

Methiodide: m. 111°[GL1]

$C_{11}H_{25}N$

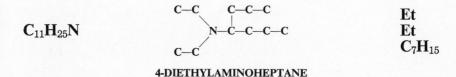

Et
Et
C_7H_{15}

4-DIETHYLAMINOHEPTANE

Phys. Props.:

b_{20} 86°[MA44]

Prepn.:

Diethylformamide + propylmagnesium bromide (22% yield).[MA44]

Derivs.:

Picrate: m. 85°[MA44]

$C_{11}H_{25}N$

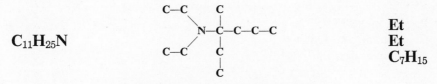

Et
Et
C_7H_{15}

3-DIETHYLAMINO-3-METHYLHEXANE

Phys. Props.:

b. 192–193°[MO4]; b_{20} 84°[MO4]; b_{16} 81°[MO4]
d_4^{27} 0.8034[PA3a]
n_D^{27} 1.4478[PA3a]

Prepn.:

1. 3-Amino-3-methylhexane + ethyl iodide.[MO4]
2. N,N-Diethylbutyramide + methylmagnesium iodide + methyl iodide (60% yield); also obtained is the expected 2-methyl-2-diethylaminopentane in yields as great as 28% depending on conditions,[MO4] (52% yield).[PA3a]

(See earlier section 11, "Bouveault Reaction of *N,N*-Dialkylamides with Excess Grignard Reagent" for explanation of this reaction.)

Derivs.:

Hydrochloride: m. *ca.* 165° (dec.)[MO4]
Chloroplatinate: m. 199° (dec.)[MO4]
Picrate: m. 78–79°,[MO4] 76–77° [PA3a]
Perchlorate: m. 154° [MO4]
Chloroaurate: 84° [MO4]

$C_{11}H_{25}N$

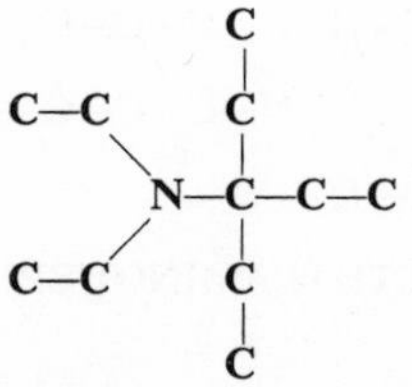

Et
Et
C_7H_{15}

3-DIETHYLAMINO-3-ETHYLPENTANE

Phys. Props.:

b_{13} 81–82.5° [MO4]

Prepn.:

Diethylpropionamide + ethylmagnesium bromide (33% yield).[MO4]

Derivs.:

Picrate: m. 96° [MO4]
Chloroaurate: m. 138° [MO4]
Perchlorate: dec. 180° [MO4]

$C_{11}H_{25}N$

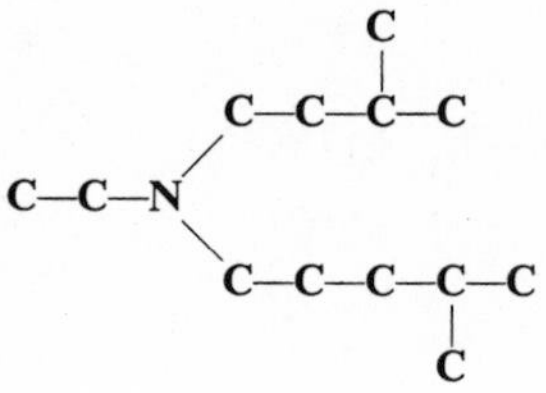

Et
i-Bu
i-Pent

ETHYLISOBUTYLISOPENTYLAMINE

Phys. Props.:

b_{40} 56–57° [SK4]

Prepn.:

Reductive alkylation of ethylisoamylamine with isobutyraldehyde and hydrogen (40% yield).[SK4]

Derivs.:

Picrate: m. 60.5–61°[SK4]

$C_{11}H_{25}N$ 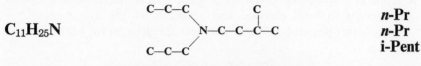 *n*-Pr
n-Pr
i-Pent

1-DIPROPYLAMINO-3-METHYLBUTANE

Phys. Props.:

b. *ca.* 180°[FR9]

Prepn.:

1-Amino-3-methylbutane + 1-iodopropane.[FR9]

$C_{11}H_{25}N$ 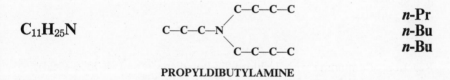 *n*-Pr
n-Bu
n-Bu

PROPYLDIBUTYLAMINE

Derivs.:

Propiodide (from butyldipropylamine and butyl iodide): m. 227° (dec.)[SM9]

$C_{11}H_{25}N$ 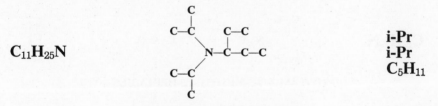 i-Pr
i-Pr
C_5H_{11}

3-DIISOPROPYLAMINOPENTANE

Prepn.:

Ethylmagnesium bromide + diisopropylformamide.[KU1]

Derivs.:

Hydrochloride: m. 127–129°[KU1]
Hydrobromide: m. 178–180°[KU1]

$C_{11}H_{25}N$

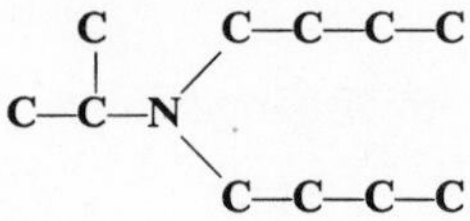

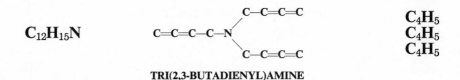

i-Pr
n-Bu
n-Bu

ISOPROPYLDIBUTYLAMINE

Prepn.:

Reaction of 2-cyano-2-dibutylaminopropane with lithium aluminum hydride results in both cleavage and reduction of the cyano group.[WE10] (Neither physical constants nor yield are given for the subject amine.)

$C_{12}H_{15}N$

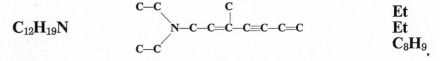

C_4H_5
C_4H_5
C_4H_5

TRI(2,3-BUTADIENYL)AMINE

Phys. Props.:

$b_{7.5}$ 96–98°[FA6]; b_4 84–86°[FA6]; $b_{0.1}$ 81°[CA11a]
d. 0.8934[CA11a]
n_D 1.5320[CA11a]

Prepn.:

Reaction of ammonia with 1-chloro-2,3-butadiene,[CA11a] (55–70% yield),[FA6] or with 1-bromo-2,3-butadiene (65% yield).[FA6]

Derivs.:

Methiodide: m. 111°[CA11a]

$C_{12}H_{19}N$

Et
Et
C_8H_9

7-DIETHYLAMINO-5-METHYL-1,5-HEPTADIEN-3-YNE

Phys. Props.:

b_9 91–92°[TE3]
d_4^{20} 0.8896[TE3]
n_D^{20} 1.5058[TE3]

Prepn.:

Dehydration of 1-diethylamino-3-hydroxy-3-methyl-6-heptene-4-yne with sulfuric acid (74.7% yield).[TE3]

$C_{12}H_{19}N$

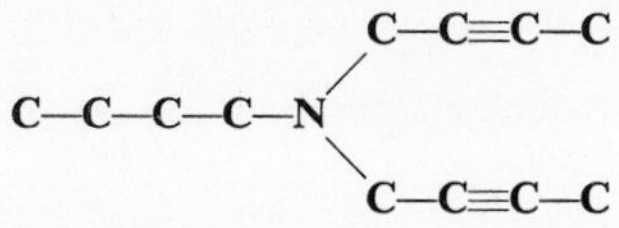

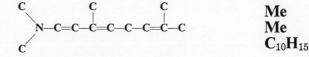

```
                    C—C≡C—C
                   /
    C—C—C—C—N
                   \
                    C—C≡C—C
```

n-Bu
C₄H₅
C₄H₅

n-Bu
C_4H_5
C_4H_5

BUTYLDI(2-BUTYNYL)AMINE

Phys. Props.:

b_{10} 114.5–115.5° PA6
d_4^{25} 0.8616 PA6
n_D^{25} 1.4778 PA6

Prepn.:

Sodio derivative of butyldi(2-propynyl)amine + methyl iodide.[PA6]

$C_{12}H_{21}N$

```
    C         C         C
     \        |         |
      N—C=C—C—C=C—C—C=C—C
     /
    C
```

Me
Me
C₁₀H₁₅

Me
Me
$C_{10}H_{15}$

1-DIMETHYLAMINO-3,7-DIMETHYL-1,3,6-OCTATRIENE*

Phys. Props.:

b_{12} 123–124° MA22

Prepn.:

Dimethylamine + 3,7-dimethyl-2,6-octadienal in the presence of potassium carbonate (50% yield).[MA22]

$C_{12}H_{21}N$

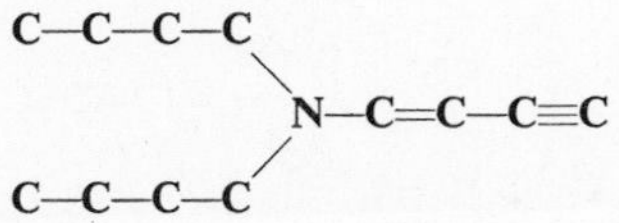

```
    C—C—C—C
            \
             N—C=C—C≡C
            /
    C—C—C—C
```

n-Bu
n-Bu
C₄H₃

n-Bu
n-Bu
C_4H_3

1-DIBUTYLAMINO-1-BUTEN-3-YNE

This is one of three compounds that ref. SH4 cites as being prepared in 60% yield by the uncatalyzed reaction of dipentylamine with diacetylene but gives no experimental details.

---

* This structure was assigned on the basis of studies in ozonolysis,[LA9] ultraviolet absorption,[BO16,CA5] and Diels-Alder reactivity.[BO16,HU2,LA9] Product was initially believed to be 1-diethylamino-3,7-dimethyl-1,2,6-octatriene.[MA22]

$C_{12}H_{21}N$

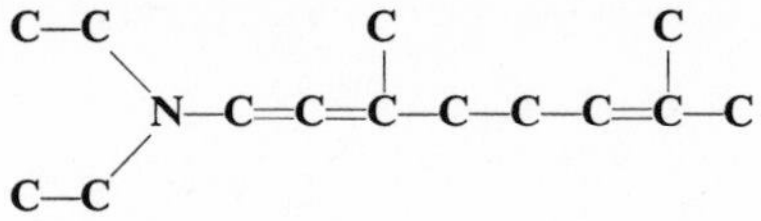

Me
Me
$C_{10}H_{15}$

1-DIETHYLAMINO-3,7-DIMETHYL-1,2,6-OCTATRIENE

This allenic structure was erroneously assigned to the reaction product of dimethylamine with 3,7-dimethyl-2,6-octadienal, or citral.[MA22] It is now believed to be the conjugated isomer, 1-dimethylamino-3,7-dimethyl-1, 3,6-octatriene (*q.v.*).

$C_{12}H_{21}N$

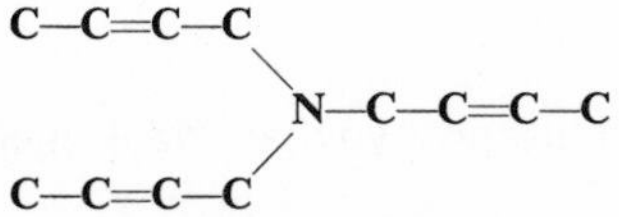

C_4H_7
C_4H_7
C_4H_7

TRI(2-BUTENYL)AMINE

Phys. Props.:

b. 215–217°[BE11]; b_{10} 103–105°[BE11]; b_9 91–92°[HO23]

Prepn.:

1. Aqueous ammonia + 1-bromo-2-butene (40% yield).[BE11]
2. Crotylurea* + aqueous sodium hydroxide (13% yield).[BE11]
3. A compound called "tributenylamine" was obtained as part of a mixture of products from ammonia and butadiene under pressure in the presence of sodium.[HO23] The position of the double bond was unspecified. The authors of the present monograph believe it to be tri(2-butenyl)amine from analogy with other reactions of butadiene.

Derivs.:

Picrate: m. 105–105.5°[HO23]

$C_{12}H_{21}N$

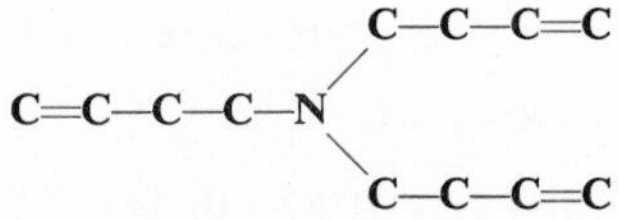

C_4H_7
C_4H_7
C_4H_7

TRI(3-BUTENYL)AMINE

Phys. Props.:

b_1 120°[RE8]

---

* Although monocrotylurea is described in the experimental section as leading to the mixed crotylamines, the pertinent discussion in this paper clearly implies that poly-*N*-crotyl substituted ureas were used.

Prepn.:

In very low yield as a by-product in the preparation of pyrrolidine from
   tetrahydrofuran and ammonia.[RE8]

$C_{12}H_{21}N$ 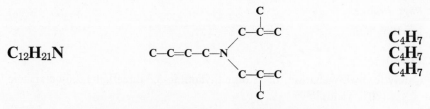 C_4H_7
C_4H_7
C_4H_7

2-BUTENYL-BIS(2-METHYL-2-PROPENYL)AMINE

Phys. Props.:

b. 197–198° [TA5,TA6]

Prepn.:

1-Amino-2-butene + 3-chloro-2-methyl-1-propene.[TA5,TA6]

$C_{12}H_{21}N$ 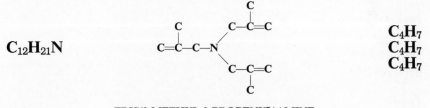 C_4H_7
C_4H_7
C_4H_7

TRIS(2-METHYL-2-PROPENYL)AMINE

Phys. Props.:

b. *ca.* 194–195°,[TA5] 184–189° [BU13]; b_{15} 83–85° [TA6]; b_{10} *ca.* 72° [TA5]
d_4^{20} 0.8256[TA6]
n_D^{20} 1.457[TA6]

Prepn.:

1. 3-Chloro-2-methyl-1-propene + ammonia   under   pressure   (13.7%
   yield),[BU13] (8% yield),[TA6] (2.6% yield).[TA5]
2. 3-Chloro-2-methyl-1-propene + ammonia   under   pressure   (very   low
   yield); main product is di(2-methyl-2-propenyl)amine.[TA5]
3. Bis(2-methyl-2-propenyl)amine + 3-chloro-2-methyl-1-propene ("good
   yield").[TA5]

$C_{12}H_{23}N$

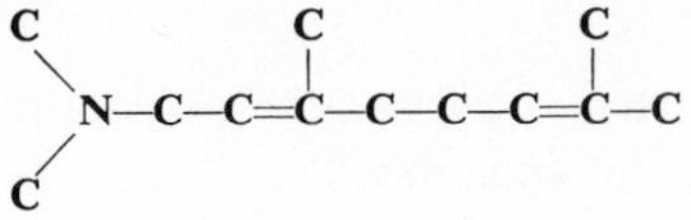

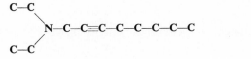

Me
Me
$C_{10}H_{17}$

1-DIMETHYLAMINO-3,7-DIMETHYL-2,6-OCTADIENE

Phys. Props.:

b_{16} 103° MA22

Prepn.:

Catalytic hydrogenation of 1-dimethylamino-3,7-dimethyl-1,2,6-octatriene (80% yield).MA22

Derivs.:

Methiodide: m. 178–180° MA22

$C_{12}H_{23}N$

Et
Et
C_8H_{13}

1-DIETHYLAMINO-2-OCTYNE

Phys. Props.:

b_{10} 100° PA5
n_D^{25} 1.4466PA5
d_4^{25} 0.8097PA5

Prepn.:

Sodio derivative of 3-diethylamino-1-propyne + 1-bromopentane (66% yield).PA5

$C_{12}H_{23}N$

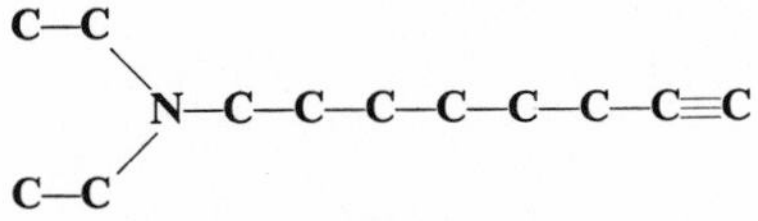

Et
Et
C_8H_{13}

8-DIETHYLAMINO-1-OCTYNE

Phys. Props.:

b_{10} 96° NE3a
n_D 1.4478NE3a
d. 0.8146NE3a

Prepn.:

Reaction of 1,1,2-trichloro-8-diethylamino-1-octene with sodium.[NE3a]

Derivs.:

Hydrochloride: m. 81°[NE3a]

$C_{12}H_{23}N$

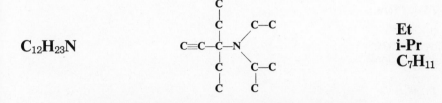

Et
i-Pr
C_7H_{11}

3-(ETHYLISOPROPYLAMINO)-3-ETHYL-1-PENTYNE

Phys. Props.:

b_{25} 93–95°[AI1]
n_D^{25} 1.4485[AI1]
pK_a 8.2 at 25° (in water), 6.8 (in 66% dimethylformamide)[AI1]

Prepn.:

3-Isopropylamino-3-ethyl-1-pentyne + diethyl sulfate (20% yield).[AI1]

Derivs.:

Hydrochloride: m. 165–167°[AI1]

$C_{12}H_{23}N$

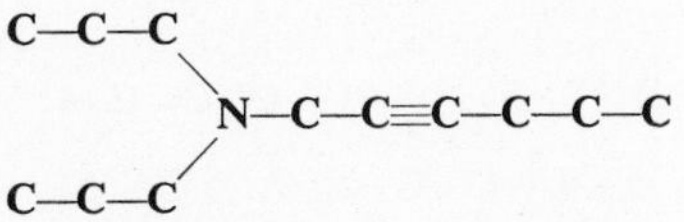

n-Pr
n-Pr
C_6H_9

1-DIPROPYLAMINO-2-HEXYNE

Phys. Props.:

b_{10} 94–95°[PA6]
d_4^{25} 0.8066[PA6]
n_4^{25} 1.4441[PA6]

Prepn.:

Sodio derivative of 3-dipropylamino-1-propyne + propyl bromide (75% yield).[PA6]

$C_{12}H_{23}N$

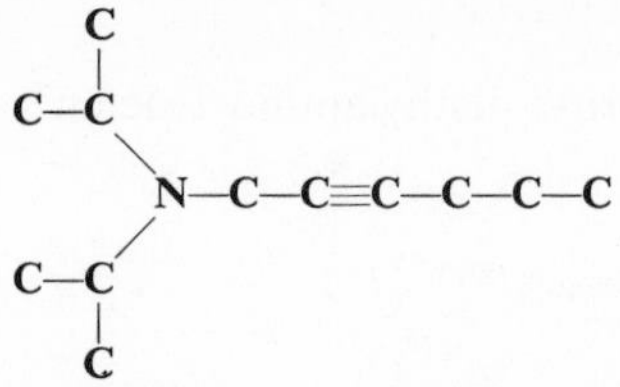

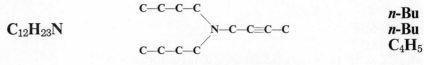

i-Pr
i-Pr
C_6H_9

1-DIISOPROPYLAMINO-2-HEXYNE

Phys. Props.:

b_{10} 80–90° PA6
d_4^{25} 0.8182 PA6
n_4^{25} 1.4490 PA6

Prepn.:

Sodio derivative of 3-diisopropylamino-1-propyne + propyl bromide.[PA6]

$C_{12}H_{23}N$

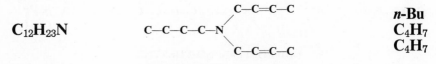

n-Bu
n-Bu
C_4H_5

2-BUTYNYLDIBUTYLAMINE

Phys. Props.:

b_{10} 97.5–97.8° PA6
d_4^{25} 0.8139 PA6
n_D^{25} 1.4465 PA6

Prepn.:

Sodio derivative of 3-dibutylamino-1-propyne + methyl iodide (75% yield).[PA6]

$C_{12}H_{23}N$

C—C=C—C
C—C—C—C—N
C—C=C—C

n-Bu
C_4H_7
C_4H_7

BUTYLDI(2-BUTENYL)AMINE

Phys. Props.:

b_{15} 96° BE11

Prepn.:

1. Butylamine + 1-bromo-2-butene (53% yield).[BE11]
2. Butadiene + butylamine under pressure in the presence of sodium.[DA6]*

---

* The position of the double bonds in the product was not firmly established.

$$\text{C}_{12}\text{H}_{25}\text{N}$$

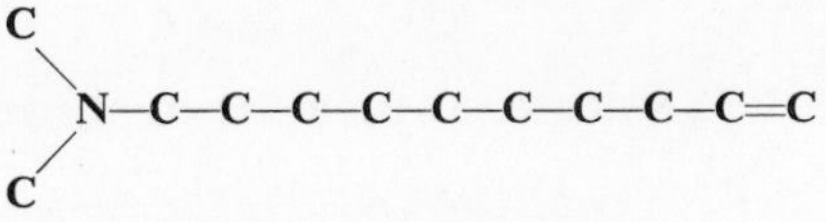

$$\begin{array}{c} \text{C} \\ \diagdown \\ \text{N}-\text{C}-\text{C}-\text{C}-\text{C}-\text{C}-\text{C}-\text{C}-\text{C}-\text{C}=\text{C} \\ \diagup \\ \text{C} \end{array}$$

Me
Me
$$\text{C}_{10}\text{H}_{19}$$

10-DIMETHYLAMINO-1-DECENE

Phys. Props.:

b_{50} 138–139°[BL4a]; b_{17} 118–120°[BR10]; b_6 91–94°[BL4a]; $b_{2.7}$ 80°[BL4a]
n_D^{25} 1.4402,[BL4a] 1.4379[BL4a]
Infrared Absorption[BL4a]

Prepn.:

Thermal decomposition of 1,10-bis(trimethylammonium)decane hydroxide
(14% yield)[BL4a,BR10]; of cyclodecyltrimethylammonium hydroxide (by-
product in 10% yield)[BL4a]; of *N*-methylazacyclohendecane methohydroxide (32% yield).[BL4a]

Derivs.: *

Picrate: m. 53–54°,[BL4a] 137°[BR10]
Methiodide: m. 151–152°,[BL4a] 139–140°[BR10]

$$\text{C}_{12}\text{H}_{25}\text{N}$$

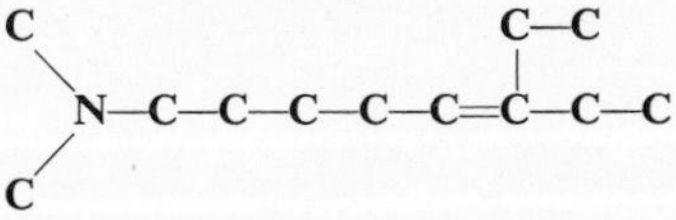

$$\begin{array}{c} \text{C} \qquad\qquad \text{C}-\text{C} \\ \diagdown \qquad\qquad\quad | \\ \text{N}-\text{C}-\text{C}-\text{C}-\text{C}-\text{C}=\text{C}-\text{C}-\text{C} \\ \diagup \\ \text{C} \end{array}$$

Me
Me
$$\text{C}_{10}\text{H}_{19}$$

8-DIMETHYLAMINO-3-ETHYL-3-OCTENE

The pyrolytic product from 1,1-dimethyl-2,2-diethylhexahydroazepinium
hydroxide was initially assigned to this structure or its 2-octene isomer,[LU18a]
It appears more likely to be 6-dimethylamino-6-ethyl-1-octene (*q.v.*).

$$\text{C}_{12}\text{H}_{25}\text{N}$$

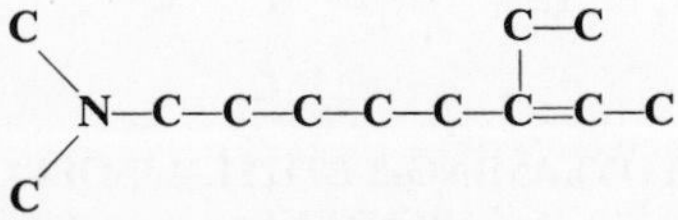

$$\begin{array}{c} \text{C} \qquad\qquad \text{C}-\text{C} \\ \diagdown \qquad\qquad\quad | \\ \text{N}-\text{C}-\text{C}-\text{C}-\text{C}-\text{C}-\text{C}=\text{C}-\text{C} \\ \diagup \\ \text{C} \end{array}$$

Me
Me
$$\text{C}_{10}\text{H}_{19}$$

8-DIMETHYLAMINO-3-ETHYL-2-OCTENE

The pyrolytic product from 1,1-dimethyl-2,2-diethylhydroazepinium
hydroxide, was initially assigned this structure or its 3-octene isomer.[LU18a]
It appears more likely to be 6-dimethylamino-6-ethyl-1-octene (*q.v.*).

---

* The authors are inclined to accept the values of the more recent ref. BL4a who tried
unsuccessfully to duplicate those of ref. BR10.

C₁₂H₂₅N $C_{12}H_{25}N$

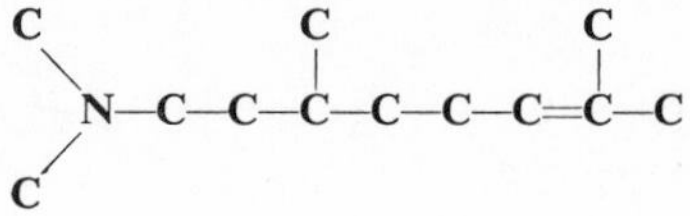

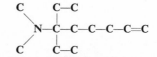

Me
Me
C₁₀H₁₉

8-DIMETHYLAMINO-2,6-DIMETHYL-2-OCTENE

Phys. Props.:

b_{16} 99–100° MA22

Prepn.:

Catalytic hydrogenation of 1-dimethylamino-3,7-dimethyl-2,6-octadiene. MA22

Derivs.:

Hydrochloride: m. 167° MA22
Methiodide: m. 220–222° MA22

$C_{12}H_{25}N$

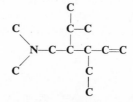

Me
Me
C₁₀H₁₉

6-DIMETHYLAMINO-6-ETHYL-1-OCTENE*

Phys. Props.:

b_{14} 180° LU18a

Prepn.:

Thermal decomposition of aqueous solution of 1,1-dimethyl-2,2-diethyl-hexahydroazepinium hydroxide. LU18a

$C_{12}H_{25}N$

Me
Me
C₁₀H₁₉

5-DIMETHYLAMINO-3-ETHYL-4-ISOPROPYL-1-PENTENE†

Phys. Props.:

b_{20} 80° SA10; b_{16} 84° UE2
$[\alpha]_D^{12}$ 14.5 ± 0.5° UE2

---

* This appears to be the more likely structure, based on Hofmann's rule, although ref. LU18a has postulated 8-dimethylamino-3-ethyl-2-(or 3)-octene.

† This structure is one corrected by ref. UE1 for an erroneous citation in ref. UE2.

Prepn.:

1. Thermal degradation of 1,1,2-trimethyl-4-isopropyl-*x*-ethylpyrrolidinium hydroxide.[UE2]
2. Thermal degradation of 1,1,2-trimethyl-3-ethyl-4-isopropylpyrrolidinium hydroxide.[SA10]

$C_{12}H_{25}N$ 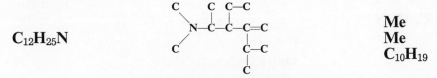 **Me**
Me
$C_{10}H_{19}$

4-DIMETHYLAMINO-3-ETHYL-
2-ISOPROPYL-1-PENTENE

This structure was an erroneous assignment by Ueno *et al.*[UE2] and later corrected by them[UE1] to the isomeric 5-dimethylamino-2-ethyl-3-isopropyl-1-pentene (*q.v.*).

$C_{12}H_{25}N$  **Me**
C_5H_9
n-**Hex**

METHYL-(4-PENTENYL)HEXYLAMINE

Phys. Props.:

b_{21} 108–109°[BR14]
d_4^{20} 0.790[BR14]

Prepn.:

Thermal decomposition of 1-methyl-1-hexylpiperidinium hydroxide (59% yield).[BR14]

Derivs.:

Picrate: m. 61.5°[BR14]

$C_{12}H_{25}N$ 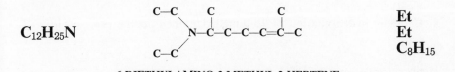 **Et**
Et
C_8H_{15}

6-DIETHYLAMINO-2-METHYL-2-HEPTENE

Phys. Props.:

b_{15} 93°[DO3]
d_4^{15} 0.811[DO3]
n_D^{15} 1.4500[DO3]; n_C^{15} 1.4463[DO3]; n_F^{15} 1.4559[DO3]

Prepn.:

1. Diethylformamide + 2-methyl-2-heptene-6-one (35% yield).[DO3]
2. 2-Methyl-6-bromo-2-heptene + diethylamine.[DO3]

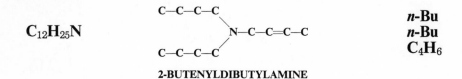

$C_{12}H_{25}N$

2-BUTENYLDIBUTYLAMINE

n-Bu
n-Bu
C_4H_6

Phys. Props.:

b. 215–217°[BE11]

Prepn.:

Dibutylamine + 1-bromo-2-butene (*ca.* 60% yield).[BE11]

$C_{12}H_{27}N$

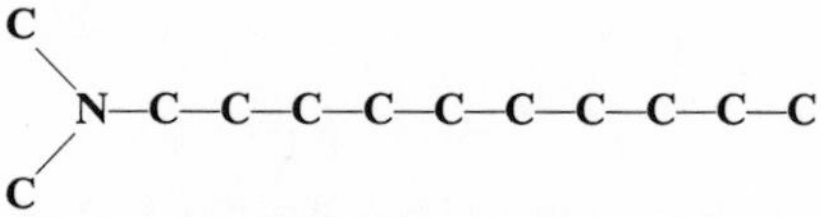

C
\
N—C—C—C—C—C—C—C—C—C—C
/
C

DECYLDIMETHYLAMINE

Me
Me
n-$C_{10}H_{21}$

Phys. Props.:

b. 233–235°[BR27]; b_9 106°[GA9]; $b_{3.2}$ 81°[BL4a]
n_D^{25} 1.4293[BL4a]

Prepn.:

1. Decylamine + formaldehyde + formic acid (73% yield).[GA9]
2. Reduction of *N,N*-dimethylcapramide by lithium aluminum hydride (quantitative yield).[BL4a]
3. Thermal degradation of decyltrimethylammonium hydroxide (76% yield).[BR27]
4. Catalytic hydrogenation of 10-dimethylamino-1-decene (93% yield).[BL4a]

Derivs.:

Hydrochloride: m. 183°[BR27]
Picrate: m. 46°[BL4a]
Methiodide:* m. 200°,[BL4a] 191°[BR25,BR27]
Methobromide:* m. 268–270° (dec.),[BL4a] 239–242°[MC5]

---

* The values reported by ref. BL4a are deemed more reliable.

$C_{12}H_{27}N$

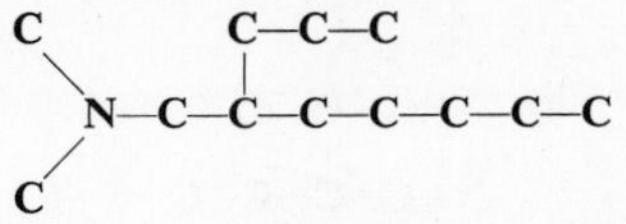

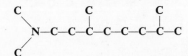

Me
Me
$C_{10}H_{21}$

4-(DIMETHYLAMINOMETHYL)NONANE

Phys. Props.:

b_{11} 88–89° KA12

Prepn.:

Thermal degradation of 2-propylheptyltrimethylammonium hydroxide.KA12

Derivs.:

Methobromide: m. 167–170° ($[\alpha]_D$ + 1.4°) KA12

$C_{12}H_{27}N$

Me
Me
$C_{10}H_{21}$

1-DIMETHYLAMINO-3,7-DIMETHYLOCTANE

Phys. Props.:

b_{15} 96° MA22; b_{14} 94–95° SK4; b_{13} 95–98° BR26
d_4^{20} 0.7757 BR26
n_D^{20} 1.4302 BR26
$[\alpha]_D^{20}$ −4.79° BR26

Prepn.:

1. Thermal degradation of 3,7-dimethyloctyltrimethylammonium hydroxide (20% yield). BR26
2. Dimethylamine + 3,7-dimethyl-2,6-octadienal + hydrogen in the presence of platinum (33% yield). SK4
3. Catalytic hydrogenation of 8-dimethylamino-2,6-dimethyl-2-octene. MA22

Derivs.:

Hydrochloride: m. 186–187° MA22
Oxalate: m. 159° SK4
Methobromide: m. 225° BR26
Methiodide: m. 243°, BR26 242° MA22

$C_{12}H_{27}N$

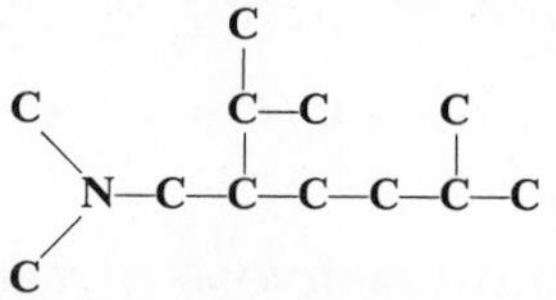

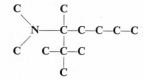

Me
Me
$C_{10}H_{21}$

3-(DIMETHYLAMINOMETHYL)-2, 6-DIMETHYLHEPTANE

Phys. Props.:
b. 196–198° [BR21]

Prepn.:
Thermal decomposition of 5-methyl-2-isopropylhexyltrimethylammonium hydroxide.[BR21]

Derivs.:
Methiodide: m. 132° [BR21]
Methobromide: m. 152° [BR21]

$C_{12}H_{27}N$

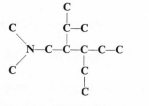

Me
Me
$C_{10}H_{21}$

3-DIMETHYLAMINO-2,2,3-TRIMETHYLHEPTANE

Phys. Props.:
b_{10} 90–91° [VE1]
n_D^{22} 1.4540 [VE1]

Prepn.:
3-Amino-2,2,3-trimethylheptane + formic acid + formaldehyde.[VE1]

Derivs.:
Hydrobromide: m. 179–180° (dec.)[VE1]

$C_{12}H_{27}N$

Me
Me
$C_{10}H_{21}$

3-DIMETHYLAMINOMETHYL-2-METHYL-4-ETHYLHEXANE*

---

* Structure assignment for the subject amine and its methiodide is erroneously given in ref. UE2 and *Chemical Abstracts* citation thereto. It is here corrected based on assumptions derived from ref. UE1 and SA10. The melting point discrepancy of the methiodide is not explicable, unless it is due to racemic compound formation.

Phys. Props.:

b_{16} 85–86° [SA10,UE2]

Prepn.:

Catalytic   hydrogenation   of   5-dimethylamino-3-ethyl-4-isopropyl-1-
pentene.[SA10,UE2]

Derivs.:

Methiodide: m. 207° ($[\alpha]_D^{18}$ − 11.5 ± 0.5°),[UE2]* 186–187° [SA10]

$C_{12}H_{27}N$

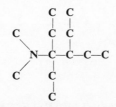

Me
Me
$C_{10}H_{21}$

3-DIMETHYLAMINO-3,4-DIETHYLHEXANE

Phys. Props.:

b_{12} 105° [LU11]

Prepn.:

N,*N*-Dimethyl-2-ethylbutanamide + ethylmagnesium iodide.[LU11]

Derivs.:

Picrate: m. 131° [LU11]

$C_{12}H_{27}N$

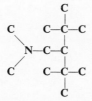

Me
Me
$C_{10}H_{21}$

**3-DIMETHYLAMINOMETHYL-2,2,4,
4-TETRAMETHYLPENTANE**

Phys. Props.:

b_{27} 98–99° [CO24]
n_D^{25} 1.4483 [CO24]

Prepn.:

1. Reductive cleavage of trimethyl-(2-*t*-butyl-3,3-dimethylbutyl)ammonium
   iodide with lithium aluminum hydride (88% yield).[CO20,CO24]

---

* See footnote page 278.

2. Thermal   decomposition   of   trimethyl-(2-*t*-butyl-3,3-dimethylbutyl)-
ammonium hydroxide (12% yield).[CO24]

Derivs.:

Picrate: m. 150.5–152.0° [CO24]
Methiodide: m. 239.0–239.5° (dec.)[CO24]

$C_{12}H_{27}N$

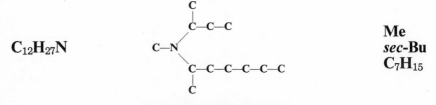

Me
***sec*-Bu**
C_7H_{15}

**METHYL-(1-METHYLPROPYL)-
(1-METHYLHEXYL)AMINE**

Phys. Props.:

b. 211–213° [SK5]

Prepn.:

Reductive alkylation of methyl-(1-methylpropyl)amine with 2-heptanone and
hydrogen (3% yield).[SK5]

Derivs.:

Picrolonate: m. 99–100° [SK5]

$C_{12}H_{27}N$

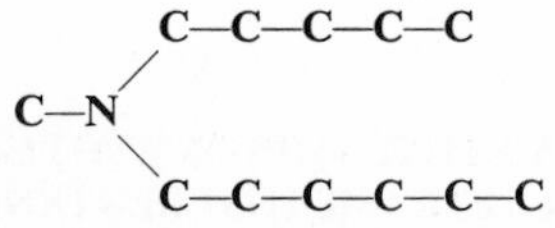

Me
***n*-Pent**
***n*-Hex**

METHYLPENTYLHEXYLAMINE

Phys. Props.:

b_{25} 113–114° [BR14]
d_4^{20} 0.778 [BR14]

Prepn.:

Platinum-catalyzed hydrogenation of methyl-(4-pentenyl)hexylamine.[BR14]

Derivs.:

Picrate: m. 64° [BR14]

$C_{12}H_{27}N$

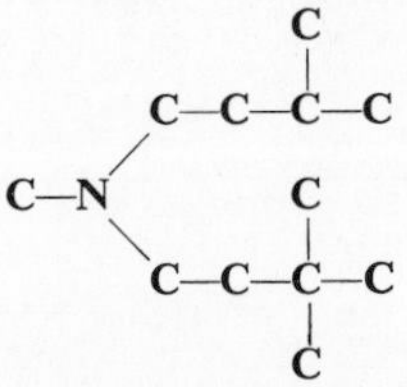

```
              C
              |
        C—C—C—C
        |     |
  C—N        C
        |     |
        C—C—C—C
              |
              C
```

Me
i-Pent
C₆H₁₃

Me
i-Pent
C_6H_{13}

METHYL-(3-METHYLBUTYL)-
(3,3-DIMETHYLBUTYL)AMINE

Derivs.:

Methiodide: m. 185–186° [SM9] (the method of preparation of this quaternary
    salt was not specified; the parent amine is most likely the subject
    amine)

$C_{12}H_{27}N$

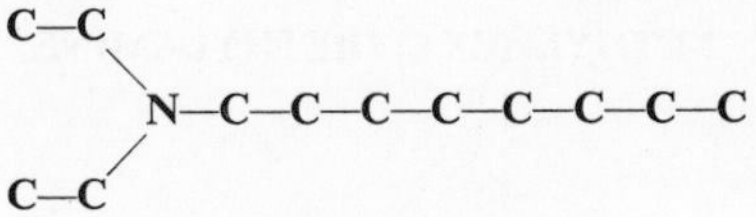

```
  C—C
      \
       N—C—C—C—C—C—C—C—C
      /
  C—C
```

Et
Et
***n*-Oct**

OCTYLDIETHYLAMINE

Phys. Props.:

b_{760} 221–224° [PU2]; b_{18} 110° [WE6a]; b_{17} 105–106° [CO1]; b_{16} 120–130° [FA4]; b_{13}
    98° [BR28]; b_{12} 112–113° [WE17]; b_{10} 93–95° [PU2]; b_1 95–98° [SC14]
n_D^{24} 1.4320 [CO1]; n_D^{21} 1.432 [WE17]; n_D^{20} 1.4228 [SC14]

Prepn.:

1. Reaction of diethylamine
    a. With octyl chloride (91% yield). [WE17]
    b. With octyl bromide [BR28] (36% yield). [CO1]
    c. With octyl iodide (76% yield). [WE6a]
    d. With 1-octanol. [FA4]
2. By the metal oxide catalyzed high-pressure reaction of triethylamine and
    hydrogen:
    a. With 1-octanol (63% yield). [SC14]
    b. With methyl octanoate (25% yield). [SC14]
3. Octyl bromide + lithium diethylamide (89° yield), [PU2] + sodium di-
    ethylamide (30° yield). [PU2]

$C_{12}H_{27}N$

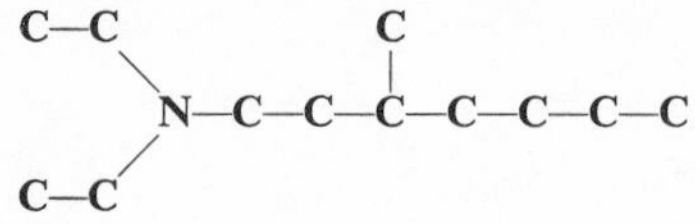

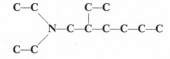

Et
Et
C_8H_{17}

1-DIETHYLAMINO-3-METHYLHEPTANE

Phys. Props.:

b_{11} 80–82° [TE3]
d_4^{20} 0.8172 [TE3]
n_D^{20} 1.4610 [TE3]

Prepn.:

Catalytic hydrogenation of 1-diethylamino-3-methyl-2,6-octadiene-4-yne (80% yield). [TE3]

$C_{12}H_{27}N$

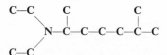

Et
Et
C_8H_{17}

2-ETHYLHEXYLDIETHYLAMINE

Phys. Props.:

b_{760} 205–208° [PU2]

Prepn.:

2-Ethylhexyl bromide + lithium diethylamide (45% yield)[PU2]; + sodium diethylamide (24% yield). [PU2]

$C_{12}H_{27}N$

Et
Et
C_8H_{17}

2-DIETHYLAMINO-6-METHYLHEPTANE

Phys. Props.:

b_{20} 95–97° [OT1]

Prepn.:

Methyl isohexyl ketone + diethylamine + formic acid. [OT1]

Derivs.:

Hydrochloride: m. 58–60° [OT1]

$C_{12}H_{27}N$

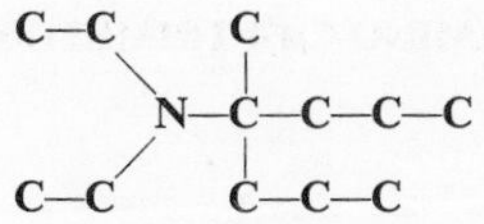

```
    C—C      C
       \     |
        N—C—C—C—C
       /     |
    C—C    C—C—C
```

Et
Et
C_8H_{17}

4-DIETHYLAMINO-4-METHYLHEPTANE

Phys. Props.:

b. 205–207° [MO5]; b_{16} 94° [MO5]

Prepn.:

1. 4-Amino-4-methylheptane + ethyl iodide. [MO5]
2. *N,N*-Diethylbutyramide + methylmagnesium iodide + ethyl iodide. [MO5]*

Derivs.:

Picrate: m. 87° [MO5]
Perchlorate: m. 136.5° [MO5]

$C_{12}H_{27}N$

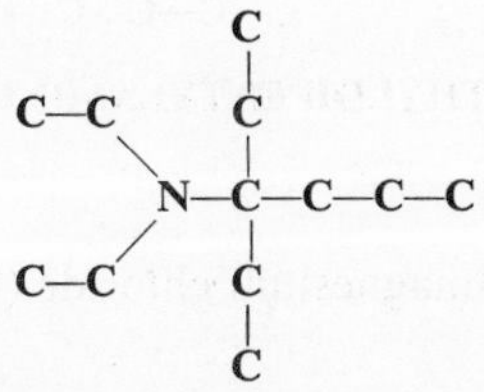

```
            C
            |
    C—C     C
       \    |
        N—C—C—C—C
       /    |
    C—C     C
            |
            C
```

Et
Et
C_8H_{17}

3-DIETHYLAMINO-3-ETHYLHEXANE

Phys. Props.:

b_{18} 98° [MO4]; b_{10} 88–89° [MO4]

Prepn.:

N,N-Diethyl-*n*-butyramide + ethylmagnesium bromide (28% yield). [MO4]

Derivs.:

Picrate: m. 97° [MO4]
Chloroaurate: m. 124° [MO4]
Chloroplatinate: m. 175° [MO4]
Perchlorate: m. 195° [MO4]

---

* See earlier section 11, "Bouveault Reaction of *N,N*-Dialkylamides with Excess Grignard Reagent" for the course proposed for this seemingly anomalous reaction.

$C_{12}H_{27}N$

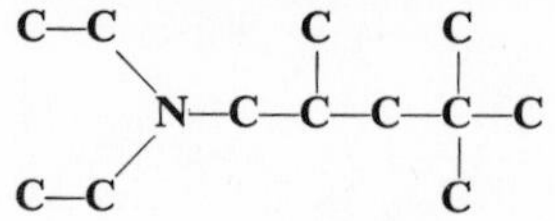

```
        C—C           C     C          Et
          \           |     |          Et
           N—C—C—C—C—C                 C₈H₁₇
          /           |     |
        C—C           C     C
```

Et
Et
C_8H_{17}

1-DIETHYLAMINO-2,4,4-TRIMETHYLPENTANE

Phys. Props.:

b_{10} 70–71°[GA6]

n_D^{20} 1.4272[GA6]

pK_a 10 (temperature unspecified)[GA6]

Prepn.:

Reductive alkylation of diethylamine with 2,4,4-trimethylpentanal and hydrogen in the presence of nickel (16% yield).[GA6]

Derivs.:

Picrate: m. 96–97°[GA6]

$C_{12}H_{27}N$

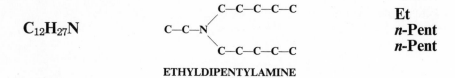

Et
n-Pent
n-Pent

ETHYLDIPENTYLAMINE

Prepn.:

Ethyldichloramine + pentylmagnesium chloride (8% yield).[CO4]

$C_{12}H_{27}N$

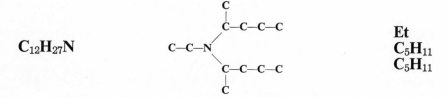

Et
C_5H_{11}
C_5H_{11}

ETHYLDI(1-METHYLBUTYL)AMINE

Prepn.:

The method of preparation of the subject amine was not specified by ref. RO4. From other information in ref. RO4, the implication is that di(1-methylbutyl)amine was ethylated to give the subject amine.

Derivs.:

Methiodide: m. 117–118° (cor.)[RO4]

$$C_{12}H_{27}N$$

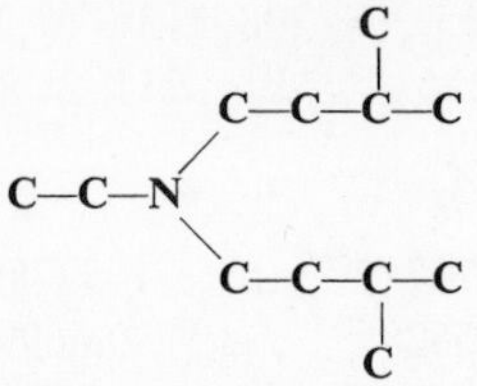

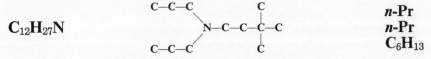

Et
i-Pent
i-Pent

ETHYLDI(3-METHYLBUTYL)AMINE

Phys. Props.:

b_{13} 74–76° [SK4]; b_{11} 75–78° [SK5]

Prepn.:

1. Reductive alkylation of di(3-methylbutyl)amine with acetaldehyde and hydrogen in the presence of colloidal platinum catalyst (34% yield).[SK5]
2. Reductive alkylation of ethylisopentylamine with isovaleraldehyde and hydrogen in the presence of colloidal platinum catalyst (50% yield).[SK4]

Derivs.:

Picrate: m. 95–96° [SK5]
Picrolonate: m. 114–115° [SK5]
Methiodide: m. 148.5–149.5° [SK4,SK5]
Methobromide: m. 126–128° [RO4]

$$C_{12}H_{27}N$$

n-Pr
n-Pr
C_6H_{13}

1-DIPROPYLAMINO-3,3-DIMETHYLBUTANE

Phys. Props.:

b_{15} 80–82° [SM9]
n_D^{20} 1.4275[SM9]

Prepn.:

3,3-Dimethyl-1-halobutane (bromide or iodide?) + dipropylamine.[SM9]

$$C_{12}H_{27}N$$

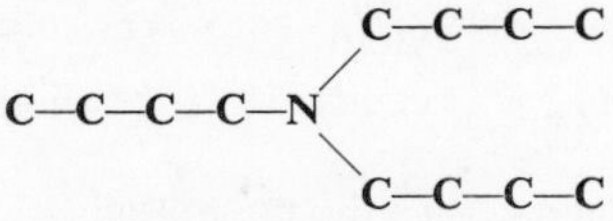

n-Bu
n-Bu
n-Bu

TRIBUTYLAMINE

Phys. Props.:

b. 210–212° [BA43,WE14]; b_{761} 212° (cor.)[VO1]; b_{760} 212–213° [AR1]; b_{754} 211.2° [CO28]; b_{10} 88.5–90° [EA1]; $b_{7.5-8}$ 82–85° [SI6] (other values: b. 214–218°,[CH5]

210–218°,[OL3] 212–215°,[HA3] 208–213°,[FA6] 208°[LI1]; b_{761} 216.5°[LI1]; b_{750} 219°[MO1]; b_{753} 215–216°[PO6]; b_{740} 211–215° (cor.)[LI2])

Vapor pressure from 60–200°[PE2a]

m. −67.5 ± 1°[TI6]

d_4^{280} 0.5559[CO28]; d_4^{260} 0.5774[CO28]; d_4^{240} 0.5978[CO28]; d_4^{220} 0.6171[CO28]; d_4^{200} 0.6353[CO28]; d_4^{180} 0.6528[CO28]; d_4^{160} 0.6699[CO28]; d_4^{140} 0.6861[CO28]; d_4^{120} 0.7020[CO28]; d_4^{100} 0.71731,[BI6] 0.7178[CO28]; $d_4^{89.9}$ 0.7280[VO1]; $d_4^{87.1}$ 0.7300[VO1]; d_4^{80} 0.73331,[BI6] 0.7331[CO28]; $d_4^{61.8}$ 0.7487[VO1]; d_4^{60} 0.7500,[VO1] 0.74827,[BI6] 0.7482[CO28]; $d_4^{42.0}$ 0.7634[VO1]; $d_4^{41.4}$ 0.7638[VO1]; d_{40}^{40} 0.7677[LI2]; d_4^{40} 0.76384,[BI6] 0.7634[CO28]; d_4^{30} 0.77106[BI6]; d_4^{25} 0.7743[MO1]; $d_4^{22.9}$ 0.7761[VO1]; d_{20}^{20} 0.7782[LI2]; d_4^{20} 0.77869,[BI6] 0.7784,[CO28] 0.7781,[VO1] 0.774[KO22]; d_0^{20} 0.7771[AR1]; d_4^{10} 0.78573[BI6]; d_4^{0} 0.79365,[BI6] 0.7935[CO28]; d_0^{0} 0.791[LI2]; d_4^{-20} 0.8086[CO28]; d_4^{-40} 0.8237[CO28]

n_D^{25} 1.4278[MO1]; n_D^{23} 1.428[SI6]; n_D^{20} 1.42967,[VO1] 1.4286,[AR1] 1.425[KO22]; n_C^{20} 1.42727[VO1]; n_F^{20} 1.43547[VO1]; $n_{G'}^{20}$ 1.43975[VO1]

Surface tension (dynes/cm.): 19.00 at 89.9°,[VO1] 21.36 at 61.8°,[VO1] 22.91 at 42.0°,[VO1] 24.60 at 22.9°,[VO1] 24.64 at 20°[AR1]

pK_a* 10.89† at 25°,[DA5] 9.93 at 25°,[HA8] 9.85 at 25°,[HA7] 11.04 at 18°,[DA5] 8.92 at 25° (in 70% ethanol),[BO13] 10.60 (in nitromethane)[ST18a]

Fluidity (rhes): from 216.2 at 100° to 44.70 at 0°[BI6]

Infrared absorption: between 0.59 and 2.40 μ[EL5]; between 1 and 12 μ[BE3]; between 2.75 and 3.75 μ (absorption maximum at 3.46 μ)[SA8]; between 2.5 and 4.5 μ[BR32a]

Vapor phase chromatography[BA23a]

Paper chromatography[KA1,VE1a]

Dipole moment: 0.78 D (from benzene solution)[AR10]

Fluorescence spectrum[BE12]

X-ray spectrum: $a_1 = 7.9_5$, $a_2 = 5.2$, $b = 7.6$[KA15]

Molar Kerr constant: 1.16 × 10⁻¹¹

Prepn.:

1. A mixture of mono-, di-, and tri-butylamines is obtained in the following reactions of ammonia (% yield refers to tributylamine):

   a. With 1-butanol under various conditions of temperature, pressure, and catalyst[BE2,BR36,DA13,KO20,PO6,TA12,] (27.4% yield),[DE3] (22% yield),[VA3] (15 to 25% yield),[KO22] (59% yield),[PO5] (18% yield),[WA1] (11% yield),[KR9] (12.8% yield),[OL3] (17% yield).[LE10]

---

* For other papers of interest, such as those dealing with base strength in organic solvents, effect of hydrogen bonding, correlation studies, etc., see refs. BA43, BE5, GO4, HA5, HA6, PE2, and TA7.

† This value, 10.89 at 25° for the pK_a of tributylamine, seems to be the one most commonly quoted and accepted in recent literature on base strengths of amines (e.g., refs. HA5, HA6, and PE2). It is a calculated value from the one determined experimentally at 18°.[DA5] The other values listed for 25° are unreasonably low.

b. With 1-chlorobutane[BE9] (2.7% yield).[NE2]

c. With 1-bromobutane.[TS6,WE14]

d. With butanal and hydrogen.[GR9,OL1,PO6]

e. With 1,3-butadiene and sodium under pressure.[HO23]

f. With dibutyl ether under pressure (8% yield).[KO19]

g. With butyl acetate, butyl propionate, or butyl butyrate.[KO21]

2. Butyronitrile + n-butyraldehyde + hydrogen in the presence of nickel (42% yield based on nitrile).[PR1]

3. Butylamine + n-butyraldehyde + ammonia + hydrogen,[CH10] (4% yield),[GR9] (7% yield).[VA3]

4. Dibutylamine + n-butyraldehyde + hydrogen in the presence of nickel (34% yield).[CH9]

5. Catalytic hydrogenation of the condensation product of butanal and butylamine (47% yield)[VA3]; of butanal and ammonia (22% yield).[VA3]

6. Heating butylamine in the presence of hydrogen-reduced copper, or cobalt carbonate[NI2]; of Raney nickel.[KA9]

7. Butylamine + carbon monoxide + hydrogen in the presence of iron.[KA1a]

8. n-Butyronitrile + hydrogen in the presence of platinum (16% yield).[SK3]

9. 1-Chlorobutane + potassium cyanate followed by heating with potassium hydroxide.[LI1]

10. Tetrabutylammonium iodide + heptyl lithium,[HA3] + potassium amide in liquid ammonia.[JO4]

11. Reaction of tetrabutyl- or methyltributyl-ammonium bromide or methyltributylammonium iodide with sodium in dioxane[GR13]; of tetrabutylammonium bromide with sodium (55% yield) or with sodium t-amyloxide in t-amyl alcohol-dioxane[GR13]; of methyltributylammonium iodide or bromide with sodium in liquid ammonia.[GR14]

12. By-product (very low yield) in the preparation of valeronitrile from butylamine, 2-butene, and ammonia.[OL2]

13. Dibutylchloramine + butylmagnesium chloride (4% yield).[CO4]

14. Catalytic hydrogenation of tri(2-butenyl)amine.[HO23]

Derivs.:

Picrate: m. 107°,[TS6] 106.9°,[EL4] 106.6°,[WI23] 106°,[RO17] 104–105°,[SK3] 101–102°,[HO23] 100.5°[WA7]

Hydriodide: m. 103°,[WI23] 102°[RO17]

Hydrochloride·FeCl$_3$: m. 171°[SC16]

Amine oxide picrate: m. 110.5–111° (cor.),[CO17] 110°,[MA3] 109°[HO21]

Disulfimide salt, Bu$_3$N·(C$_6$H$_5$SO$_2$)$_2$NH: m. 51–53°[RU3]

·SO$_3$: m. 94°[MO1]

d-Camphor-10-sulfonic acid salt: m. 128–130°[SC19]

·BH$_3$: m. −28°[NO3]; b$_{0.1}$ 103–105°[AS1]; b$_{0.001}$ 87°[KO18]; b$_{10^{-5}}$ 80°[NO3]

Methobromide: m. 120.5–121.5°[GR13]

Butobromide: m. 116–120°,[EA1] 118°,[WI23] 103.1–103.3°[MC7]

Butiodide: m. 144–145°,[HA3,SM9] 142°[LU3]
Butoacetate: m. 118 ± 2°,[WI23] 116°[LU3]
Butopicrate: m. 89.5°,[SE8] 89.4°[SE7]
Butonitrate: m. 120°[WI23]
Butoperchlorate: m. 207°[LU3,RO17]
Butofluoride·BF_3: m. 161.8°[WI23]
Propiodide: m. 198–199°[SM9]; 195–196°[EA1]
Benzylochloride: m. 185°[MA37]
Reineckate: m. 131–133°[AY1]

$C_{12}H_{27}N$

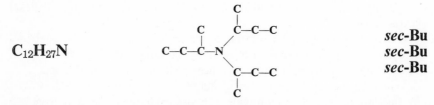

sec-Bu
sec-Bu
sec-Bu

TRI(1-METHYLPROPYL)AMINE

Phys. Props.:

b. 135–160°,[MA8*,SA2*] 130–160°[MA9*]

Prepn.:

1. Catalytic hydrogenation of the oxime of 2-butanone in the presence of nickel gives *sec*-butylamine, di(*sec*-butyl)amine and, by inference, a trace of tri(*sec*-butyl)amine.[MA8*,SA2*]
2. *sec*-Butyl alcohol + ammonia (40% yield)[PO5]†; (1% yield).[TA12]†

$C_{12}H_{27}N$

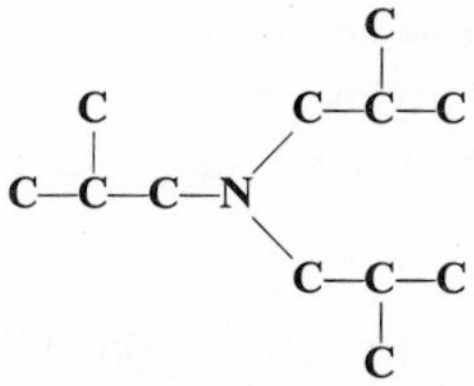

i-Bu
i-Bu
i-Bu

TRIISOBUTYLAMINE

Phys. Props.:

b. 191.5 ± 0.2°,[TI3] 186–188°,[MA14] 184–186°,[SA6] 182–186°,[GA7] 180–186°,[LA2] 185°,[ME15] 177–180°[HO9]; b_{760} 191.5°[KA15]; b_{15} 84°[BR48]

---

* The boiling point reported seems to be too low based on analogy with other isomers.
† It is doubtful that tri-*sec*-butylamine was obtained in these reactions. The compound was not characterized. Moreover, no one has unequivocally succeeded in obtaining R_3N, where R is a secondary alkyl group, by direct alkylation of ammonia or amines.

m. $-25.8°,$[PI1] $-24°,$[JA4] $-21.8 \pm 0.2°$[TI3]

d_4^{50} 0.745[JA4]; d_4^{25} 0.764[JA4]; d_{21}^{21} 0.785[SA6]; d_4^{20} 0.7684[BR48]; $d_4^{17.3}$ 0.7711[BR48]; d_4^{0} 0.782[JA4]

$n_D^{17.3}$ 1.42519[BR48]; $n_\alpha^{17.3}$ 1.42280[BR48]; $n_\gamma^{17.3}$ 1.43571[BR48]

pK_a 10.32 at 25°[BR29]

Surface tension between 85° (11.0 dynes/cm.) and $-21°$ (24.5 dynes/cm.)[JA4]

X-ray spectrum: $a_1 = 8.5_5$, $a_2 = 5.5_5$, $b = 8.2$[KA15]

Heat of combustion (kcal./mole) at constant pressure 1971.6,[LE12] 1973.6,[KH1a] and at constant volume 1969[LE12]; heat of formation 91.5 kcal/mole.[LE12]

Diamagnetic susceptibility[AN1,PA10]

Prepn.:

1. A mixture of primary, secondary, and tertiary isobutylamines results from the reaction of ammonia:
   a. With isobutyl chloride,[MA14] bromide,[HO9] or iodide.[MA14]
   b. With isobutyl alcohol under various conditions of temperature, pressure, and catalyst[WH2,TA12,ME15] (7–14% yield),[KO20] (27% yield),[PO5] (6.8% yield).[KR9]
   c. With diisobutylether (8% yield),[KO19] or with isobutyl acetate.[KO21]
2. Hydrogenation of isobutyl nitrite in the presence of copper or nickel gives a mixture of the three isobutylamines, with diisobutylamine predominating.[GA7]
3. Hydrogenation of diisobutylidene azine in the presence of nickel results in the formation of trace amounts of triisobutylamine. The main product of the reaction is a mixture of isobutyl- and diisobutyl-amines.[MA13]

Derivs.:

Methochloroplatinate: m. 174°[RI5]
Ethochloroplatinate: m. 170°[RI5]
Propochloroplatinate: m. 168°[RI5]
Isobutochloroplatinate: m. 162°[RI5]

$C_{13}H_{21}N$

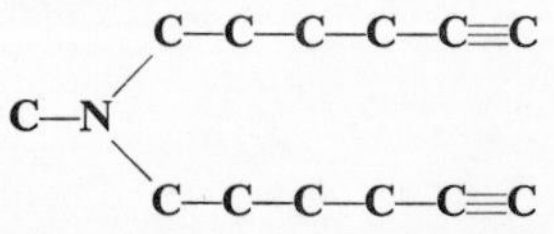

C—C—C—C—C≡C
C—N
C—C—C—C—C≡C

Me
C_6H_9
C_6H_9

METHYLDI(5-HEXYNL)AMINE

Derivs.:

Methiodide (prepared from 6-dimethylamino-1-hexyne and 5-hexynyl iodide): m. 139–140°[MA31,OL6]

$C_{13}H_{23}N$

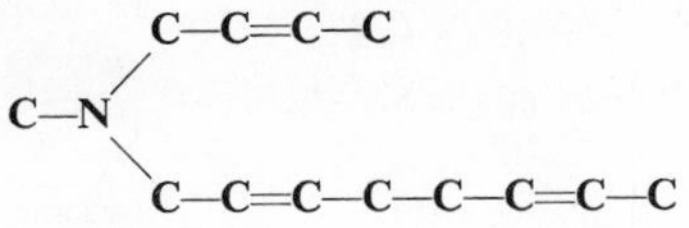

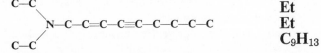

Me
C_4H_7
C_8H_{13}

METHYL-(2-BUTENYL)-(2,6-OCTADIENYL)AMINE*

Prepn.:

Reaction of methylamine with 1,3-butadiene in the presence of the sodium
salt of methylamine gives a mixture of methyldi(2-butenyl)amine and
methyl-(2-butenyl)-(2,6-octadienyl)amine. In the latter compound the
octadienyl radical results from initial dimerization of some of the
butadiene.[DA6]

$C_{13}H_{23}N$

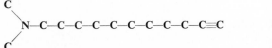

Et
Et
C_9H_{13}

1-DIETHYLAMINO-2-NONEN-4-YNE

Phys. Props.:

b_4 72–74° [J05]
n_D^{19} 1.4800[J05]
Ultraviolet absorption: 2280 A. (ϵ 16,000), 2370 A. (inflection; ϵ 15,500)[J05]

Prepn.:

Diethylamine + 1-chloro-2-nonen-4-yne (70% yield).[J05]

$C_{13}H_{25}N$

C
\
N—C—C—C—C—C—C—C—C—C—C≡C
/
C

Me
Me
$C_{11}H_{19}$

11-DIMETHYLAMINO-1-UNDECYNE

Phys. Props.:

$b_{0.1}$ 83° [OL6]
n_D^{21} 1.4460 [OL6]

Prepn.:

Dimethylamine + 11-iodo-1-undecyne.[OL6]

Derivs.:

Methiodide: m. 129° [OL6]

---

* This structure was not definitively proved.

$C_{13}H_{25}N$

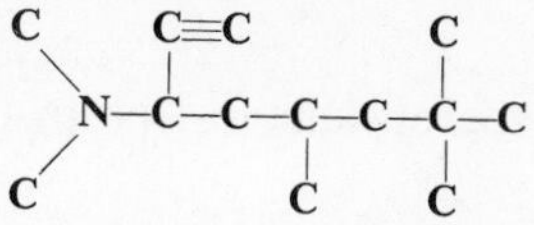

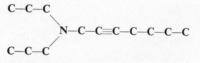

Me
Me
$C_{11}H_{19}$

3-DIMETHYLAMINO-5,7,7-TRIMETHYL-1-OCTYNE

Phys. Props.:

b_7 105–107° CR3
d_D^{20} 1.4391 CR3

Prepn.:

Dimethylamine + 3,5,5-trimethylhexanal + acetylene in the presence copper(I) chloride, CR3 (80% yield). FE2

$C_{13}H_{25}N$

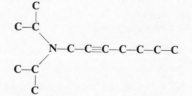

n-Pr
n-Pr
C_7H_{11}

1-DIPROPYLAMINO-2-HEPTYNE

Phys. Props.:

b_{10} 108–9° PA6
d_4^{25} 0.8087 PA6
n_D^{25} 1.4459 PA6

Prepn.:

Sodio derivative of 3-dipropylamino-1-propyne + 1-bromobutane (76% yield). PA6

$C_{13}H_{25}N$

i-Pr
i-Pr
C_7H_{11}

1-DIISOPROPYLAMINO-2-HEPTYNE

Phys. Props.:

b_{10} 103° PA6
d_4^{25} 0.8200 PA6
n_D^{25} 1.4505 PA6

Prepn.:

Sodio derivative of 3-diisopropylamino-1-propyne + 1-bromobutane (62% yield).[PA6]

$C_{13}H_{25}N$

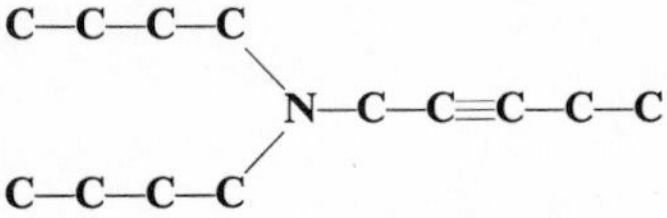

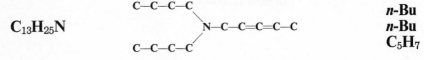

1-DIBUTYLAMINE-2-PENTYNE

*n-*Bu
*n-*Bu
C_5H_7

Phys. Props.:

b_{10} 107–107.2° [PA6]
d_4^{25} 0.8090[PA6]
n_D^{25} 1.4455[PA6]

Prepn.:

Sodio derivative of 3-dibutylamino-1-propyne + ethyl bromide.[PA6]

$C_{13}H_{25}N$

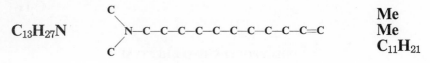

1-DIBUTYLAMINO-2,3-PENTADIENE

*n-*Bu
*n-*Bu
C_5H_7

Phys. Props.:

b_{20} 123–124° [PE10]
d_4^{20} 0.8119[PE10]
n_D^{20} 1.4588[PE10]
Infrared absorption[PE10]

Prepn.:

Lithiodibutylamine + 1-penten-3-yne, followed by hydrolysis (5% yield).[PE10]

$C_{13}H_{27}N$

C
\
  N—C—C—C—C—C—C—C—C—C—C=C
/
C

Me
Me
$C_{11}H_{21}$

11-DIMETHYLAMINO-1-UNDECENE

Phys. Props.:

b_2 89–91° [CO1]
n_D^{24} 1.4416[CO1]

Prepn.:

Reduction of *N,N*-dimethyl-10-undecenamide with lithium aluminum hydride (59.2% yield).[CO1]

$C_{13}H_{29}N$

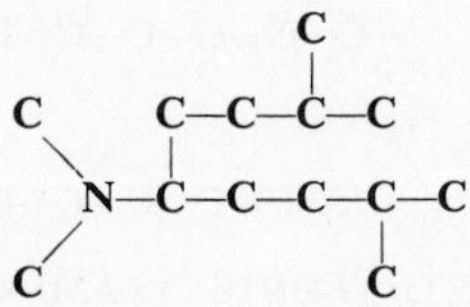

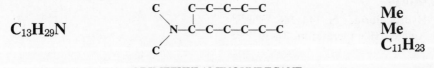

Me
Me
$C_{11}H_{23}$

5-DIMETHYLAMINO-2,8-DIMETHYLNONANE

Phys. Props.:

b. 198°[MA45]; b_{15} 110°[BO15]

Prepn.:

3-Methylbutylmagnesium bromide + dimethylformamide (37% yield)[MA45]; in unspecified yield.[BO15]

Derivs.:

Picrate: m. 104°,[MA45] 103°[BO15]

$C_{13}H_{29}N$

Me
Me
$C_{11}H_{23}$

6-DIMETHYLAMINOUNDECANE

Phys. Props.:

b_{16} 115°[IC1]

Prepn.:

6-Aminoundecane + formaldehyde + formic acid.[IC1]

$C_{13}H_{29}N$

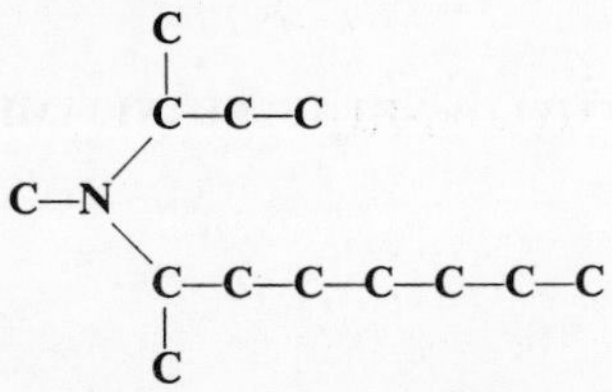

Me
***sec*-Bu**
C_8H_{17}

**METHYL-(1-METHYLPROPYL)-
(1-METHYLHEPTYL)AMINE**

Phys. Props.:

b. 224–226°[SK5]

Prepn.:

Reductive alkylation of methyl-(1-methylpropyl)amine with 2-octanone and hydrogen (0.5% yield).[SK5]

$C_{13}H_{29}N$

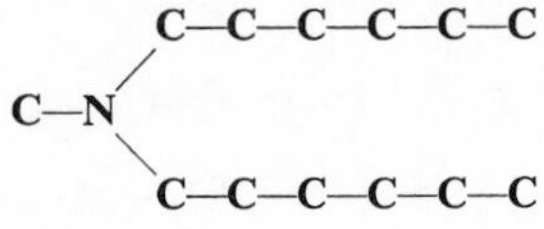

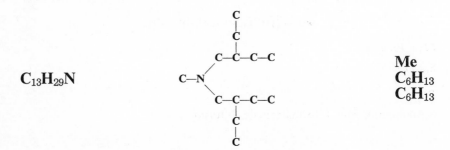

$$\text{C—N} \underset{\text{C—C—C—C—C—C}}{\overset{\text{C—C—C—C—C—C}}{\Big<}}$$

Me
n-C_6H_{13}
n-C_6H_{13}

METHYLDIHEXYLAMINE

Phys. Props.:

b_{755} 228–233° [WE17]; b_{19} 121–122° [BO13,BL4]; b_{12} 118° [WE17]; $b_{4.6}$ 97–98° [CO22]
n_D^{25} 1.4315 [CO22]; n_D^{20} 1.434 [WE17]

Prepn.:

1. Methylamine + 1-chlorohexane (40% yield),[WE17] + 1-bromohexane.[BL4, BO13]
2. Methylamine + formic acid + formaldehyde (86% yield).[CO22]
3. Platinum-catalyzed hydrogenation of a mixture of nitromethane and hexanal (30% yield).[EM10]

Derivs.:

Hydrochloride: m. 144–145° [BL4,BO13]
Amine oxide picrate: m. 77–79° [CO22]

$C_{13}H_{29}N$

$$\text{C—N} \underset{\text{C—C—C—C}}{\overset{\text{C—C—C—C}}{\Big<}}$$

Me
C_6H_{13}
C_6H_{13}

METHYLDI(2-ETHYLBUTYL)AMINE

Phys. Props.:

b_{13} 100–101° [BL4]

Prepn.:

Methylamine + 2-ethylbutyl bromide.[BL4]

Derivs.:

Hydrochloride: m. 154–155° [BL4]

$C_{13}H_{29}N$

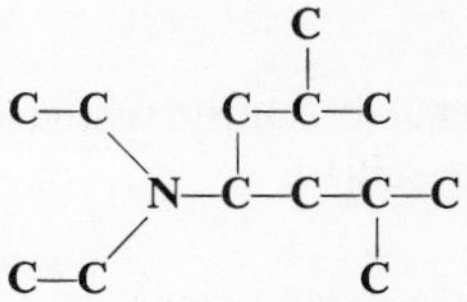

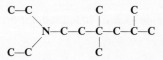

Et
Et
C_9H_{19}

4-DIETHYLAMINO-2,6-DIMETHYLHEPTANE

Phys. Props.:

b_{760} 206° MA43; b_{19} 95° MA43

Prepn.:

Diethylformamide + 2-methylpropylmagnesium bromide (22% yield).MA43
A yield of 29% of 4-methylpentanal was also obtained.

Derivs.:

Picrate: m. 89–90° MA43

$C_{13}H_{29}N$

Et
Et
C_9H_{19}

1-DIETHYLAMINO-3,3,5-TRIMETHYLHEXANE

Phys. Props.:

b_{20} 104–106° WH4
n_D^{20} 1.4311WH4

Prepn.:

1-Amino-3,3,5-trimethylhexane + acetylene + sodium at 500 atm. pressure
(26% yield).WH4

$C_{13}H_{29}N$

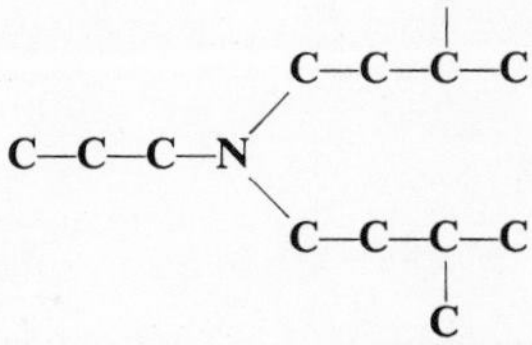

n-**Pr**
i-Pent
i-Pent

PROPYLDI(3-METHYLBUTYL)AMINE

Phys. Props.:

b_{24} 109–110° SM9

Prepn.:

Diisoamylamine + 1-iodo or 1-bromo-propane (68% yield).[SM9] The exact halide used was not specified.

Derivs.:

Methiodide: m. 142–143°[SM9]
Propiodide: m. 108° (dec.)[SM9]

$C_{13}H_{29}N$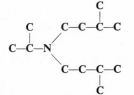

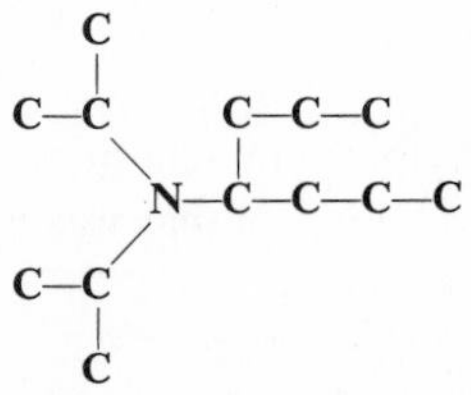

i-Pr
i-Pr
C_7H_{15}

4-DIISOPROPYLAMINOHEPTANE

Prepn.:

N,N-Diisopropylformamide + propylmagnesium bromide (46% yield).[KU1]

Derivs.:

Hydrochloride: m. 143–145°[KU1]
Hydrobromide: m. 189–191°[KU1]

$C_{13}H_{29}N$

i-Pr
i-Pent
i-Pent

ISOPROPYLDI(3-METHYLBUTYL)AMINE

Phys. Props.:

b. 206°[SK5]

Prepn.:

Reductive alkylation of diisopentylamine with acetone and hydrogen (14% yield).[SK5]

Derivs.:

Picrate: m. 80–81°[SK5]

$C_{13}H_{29}N$

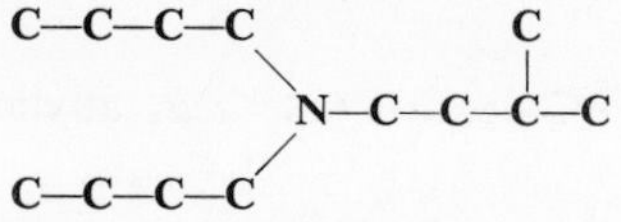

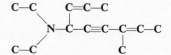

C—C—C—C   C
       N—C—C—C—C
C—C—C—C

n-Bu
n-Bu
i-Pent

3-METHYLBUTYLDIBUTYLAMINE

Phys. Props.:

b_{18} 107–108°[SM9]; b_{13} 96–98°[DA9]

Prepn.:

Dibutylamine + isopentyl bromide or iodide (exact halide unspecified).[SM9]

Derivs.:

Butiodide: m. 120–120.5°[SM9]

$C_{14}H_{23}N$

C—C   C=C—C
   N—C—C≡C—C=C—C
C—C   C

Et
Et
$C_{10}H_{13}$

6-DIETHYLAMINO-3-METHYL-2,7-NONADIEN-4-YNE

Phys. Props.:

$b_{0.5}$ 57–59°[JO5]
d_D^{19} 1.4855[JO5]

Prepn.:

Diethylamine + 2-chloro-7-methyl-3,7-nonadien-5-yne* *via* allylic rearrangement (59% yield).[JO5]

$C_{14}H_{25}N$

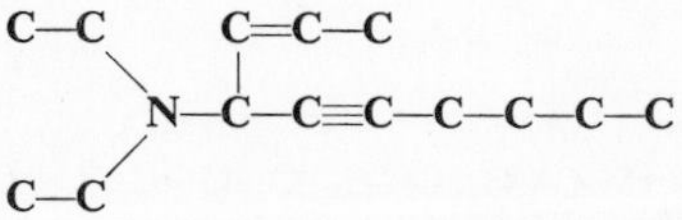

C—C   C=C—C
   N—C—C≡C—C—C—C—C
C—C

Et
Et
$C_{10}H_{15}$

4-DIETHYLAMINO-2-DECEN-5-YNE

Phys. Props.:

b_4 70–71°[JO5]
n_D^{18} 1.4634[JO5]
Ultraviolet absorption[JO5]

---

* In the experimental section of ref. JO5 this chloro compound is called a 2,7-diene, but according to the formulas in the article the 3,7-diene was used.

Prepn.:

Diethylamine + 2-chloro-3-decen-5-yne *via* allylic rearrangement (83% yield).[JO5]

Derivs.:

Picrate: m. 88° [JO5]

$$C_{14}H_{25}N$$

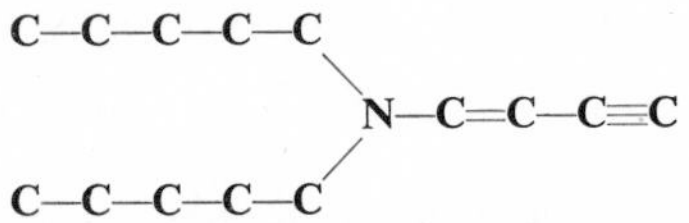

```
        C—C—C—C—C
                   \                      n-Pent
                    N—C=C—C≡C            n-Pent
                   /                      C_4H_3
        C—C—C—C—C
```

1-DIPENTYLAMINO-1-BUTEN-3-YNE

This is one of three compounds that ref. SH4 cites as being prepared in 60% yield by the uncatalyzed reaction of dipentylamine with diacetylene but gives no experimental details.

$$C_{14}H_{27}N$$

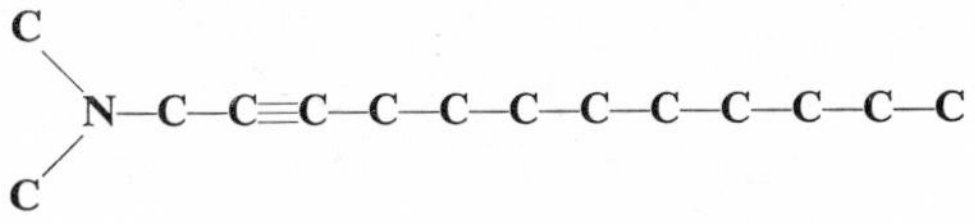

```
    C
     \                                      Me
      N—C—C≡C—C—C—C—C—C—C—C—C—C           Me
     /                                      C_12H_21
    C
```

1-DIMETHYLAMINO-2-DODECYNE

Phys. Props.:

$b_{1.2}$ 90° [EP1]
n_D^{14} 1.4540[EP1]

Prepn.:

Dimethylamine + formaldehyde + 1-undecyne in the presence of copper(I) acetate.[EP1]

Derivs.:

Methiodide: m. 145–146° [EP1]

$$C_{14}H_{27}N$$

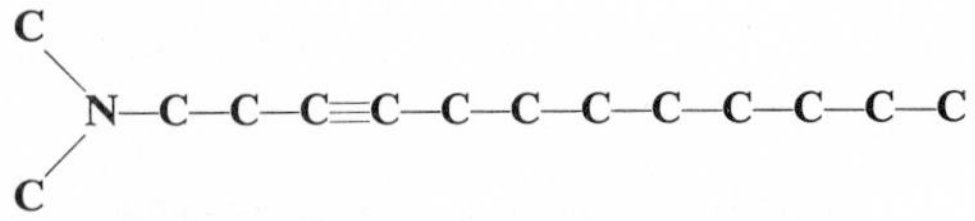

```
    C
     \                                      Me
      N—C—C—C≡C—C—C—C—C—C—C—C—C           Me
     /                                      C_12H_21
    C
```

1-DIMETHYLAMINO-3-DODECYNE

Phys. Props.:

$b_{0.2}$ 90° [EP1]
n_D^{16} 1.4545[EP1]

Prepn.:

Sodio derivative of 1-dimethylamino-3-butyne + octyl bromide.[EP1]

Derivs.:

Methiodide: m. 144° [EP1]

$$C_{14}H_{27}N$$

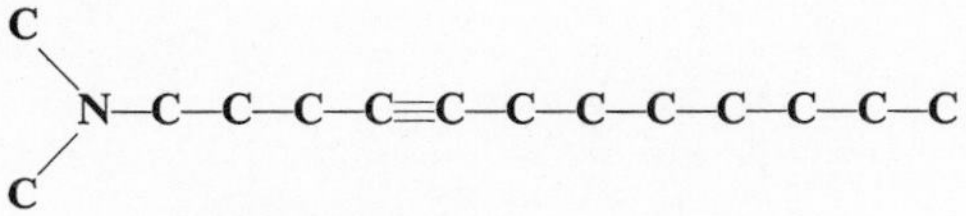

$$
\begin{array}{c}
\text{C} \\
\diagdown \\
\text{N---C---C---C---C}\!\equiv\!\text{C---C---C---C---C---C---C} \\
\diagup \\
\text{C}
\end{array}
$$

Me
Me
$C_{12}H_{21}$

1-DIMETHYLAMINO-4-DODECYNE

Phys. Props.:

$b_{0.05}$ 81° [EP1]

n_D^{22} 1.4520[EP1]

Prepn.:

Sodio derivative of 5-dimethylamino-1-pentyne + heptyl bromide.[EP1]

Derivs.:

Methiodide: m. 121–122° [EP1]

$$C_{14}H_{27}N$$

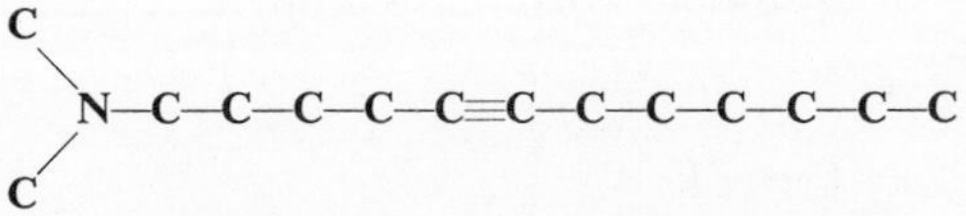

$$
\begin{array}{c}
\text{C} \\
\diagdown \\
\text{N---C---C---C---C---C}\!\equiv\!\text{C---C---C---C---C---C} \\
\diagup \\
\text{C}
\end{array}
$$

Me
Me
$C_{12}H_{21}$

1-DIMETHYLAMINO-5-DODECYNE

Phys. Props.:

$b_{0.1}$ 95° [OL6]

n_D^{18} 1.4530[OL6]

Prepn.:

Sodio derivative of 6-dimethylamino-1-hexyne + hexyl iodide.[OL6]

Derivs.:

Methiodide: m. 108° [OL6]

$$C_{14}H_{27}N$$

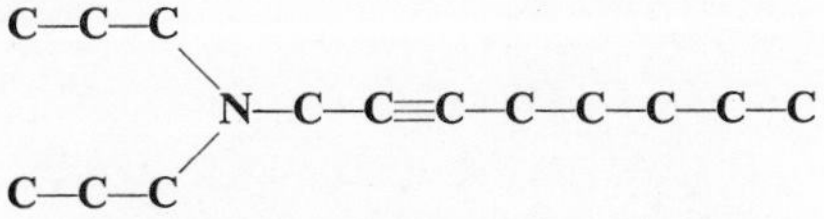

$$
\begin{array}{c}
\text{C---C---C} \\
\diagdown \\
\text{N---C---C}\!\equiv\!\text{C---C---C---C---C---C} \\
\diagup \\
\text{C---C---C}
\end{array}
$$

n-Pr
n-Pr
C_8H_{13}

1-DIPROPYLAMINO-2-OCTYNE

Phys. Props.:

b_{10} 120.5–121.5° [PA6]

d_4^{25} 0.8115[PA6]

n_D^{25} 1.4471[PA6]

Prepn.:

Sodio derivative of 3-dipropylamino-1-propyne + pentyl bromide (77% yield).[PA6]

$C_{14}H_{27}N$

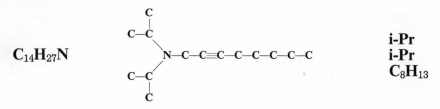

i-Pr
i-Pr
C_8H_{13}

1-DIISOPROPYLAMINO-2-OCTYNE

Phys. Props.:

b_{10} 115.5–116.5° [PA6]
d_4^{25} 0.8203[PA6]
n_D^{25} 1.4515[PA6]

Prepn.:

Sodio derivative of 3-diisopropylamino-1-propyne + pentyl bromide (60% yield).[PA6]

$C_{14}H_{27}N$

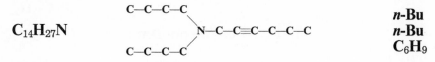

n-Bu
n-Bu
C_6H_9

1-DIBUTYLAMINO-2-HEXYNE

Phys. Props.:

b_{10} 119.5–119.8° [PA6]
d_4^{25} 0.8813[PA6]
n_D^{25} 1.4472[PA6]

Prepn.:

Sodio derivative of 3-dibutylamino-1-propyne + propyl bromide (72% yield).[PA6]

$C_{14}H_{27}N$

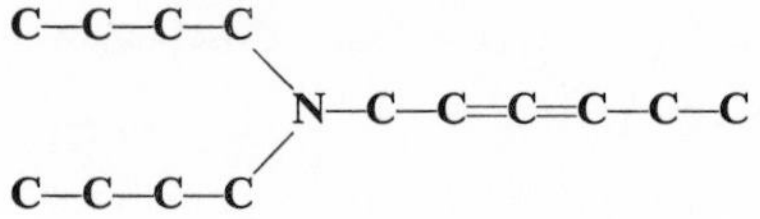

n-Bu
n-Bu
C_6H_9

1-DIBUTYLAMINO-2,3-HEXADIENE

Phys. Props.:

b_{20} 136–136.5° [PE10]
d_{20} 0.8150[PE10]

n_D^{20} 1.4558[PE10]
Infrared absorption[PE10]

Prepn.:

Reaction of lithiodibutylamine with 1-hexen-3-yne, followed by hydrolysis (45–55% yield).[PE10]

$C_{14}H_{29}N$

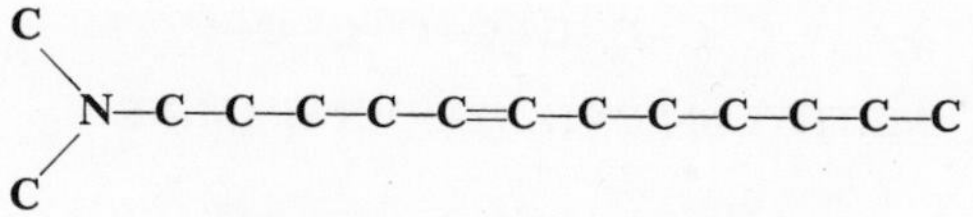

C
$\backslash$
N—C—C—C—C—C=C—C—C—C—C—C—C
/
C

Me
Me
$C_{12}H_{23}$

1-DIMETHYLAMINO-5-DODECENE

Phys. Props.:

cis isomer
  $b_{0.1}$ 83° [OL6]
  d_{20}^{20} 0.8064[OL6]
  n_D^{18} 1.4480[OL6]
trans isomer
  $b_{0.1}$ 81–82° [OL6]
  d_{20}^{20} 0.8048[OL6]
  n_D^{15} 1.4490[OL6]

Prepn.:

Catalytic hydrogenation of 1-dimethylamino-5-dodecyne in the presence of palladium yields the *cis* isomer. Reduction by means of sodium in liquid ammonia gives the *trans* isomer.[OL6]

Derivs.:

cis-Methiodide: m. 195–196° [OL6]
trans-Methiodide: m. 189–190[OL6]

$C_{14}H_{29}N$

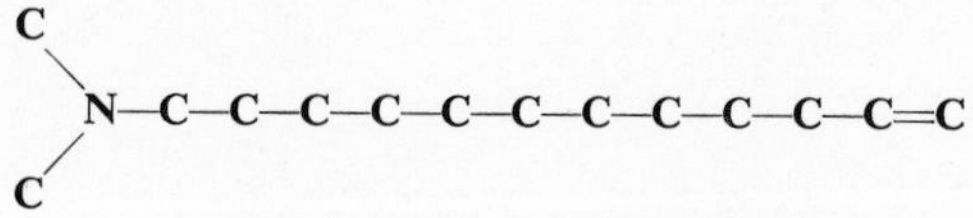

C
$\backslash$
N—C—C—C—C—C—C—C—C—C—C—C=C
/
C

Me
Me
$C_{12}H_{23}$

12-DIMETHYLAMINO-1-DODECENE

Phys. Props.:

b_{16} 132–135° [BR13]

Prepn.:

Thermal decomposition of dodecamethylene-1,12-bis-trimethylammonium hydroxide (overall yield based on dodecamethylenediamine was 25%).[BR13]

Derivs.:

Picrate: m. 127° BR13

$C_{14}H_{29}N$ **Me**
C_5H_9
***n*-Oct**

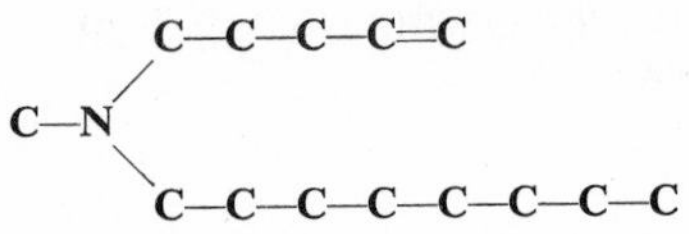

METHYL-(4-PENTENYL)OCTYLAMINE

Phys. Props.:

b_{22} 139–140° BR14
d_4^{20} 0.796 BR14

Prepn.:

Thermal degradation of 1-methyl-1-octylpiperidinium hydroxide (60% yield). BR14

$C_{14}H_{29}N$ ***n*-Bu**
***n*-Bu**
C_6H_{11}

6-DIBUTYLAMINO-1-HEXENE

Phys. Props.:

$b_{0.5}$ 63–64° PE5
n_D^{26} 1.4410 PE5

Prepn.:

3-Dibutylaminopropylmagnesium chloride + allyl bromide. PE5

$C_{14}H_{31}N$ 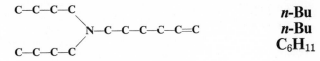   **Me**
Me
***n*-$C_{12}H_{25}$**

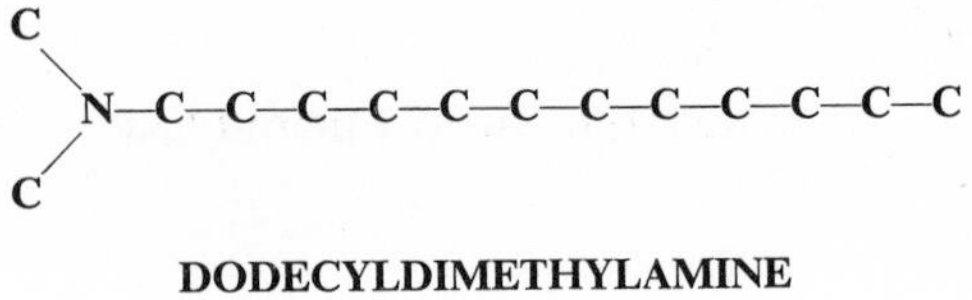

DODECYLDIMETHYLAMINE

Phys. Props.:

b_{20} 147–148° FA4; b_{15} 144–149° SC12; b_8 133°, GA9 127–128° BO12; b_5 121–122° KI5; $b_{0.1}$ 80–100° ER2; $b_{0.07-0.15}$ 80–105° ER2
m. −20.30°, RE1 −21 to −11° EA1

Prepn.:

1. 1-Aminododecane + formic acid + formaldehyde (86.5% yield),[KI5] (60% yield),[RE1] (98% yield),[ER2] (84% yield).[GA9]
2. Dimethylamine + 1-bromododecane.[BO12]
3. Trimethylamine + 1-chlorododecane at 180° (the expected quaternary ammonium salt evidently decomposes to dodecyldimethylamine and methyl chloride).[WE17]
4. Transalkylation reaction between trimethylamine and dodecyl alcohol.[SC12]
5. Dimethylamine + dodecyl alcohol in the vapor phase (90% yield). Reaction with methylamine gives methyldodecylamine plus a small amount of dodecyldimethylamine.[SM4]

*Derivs.:**

Hydrochloride: m. *ca.* 132° [WE17]

Methochloride: m. *ca.* 37° [WE17]

Methobromide: m. 243° [MC5]

Propiodide: m. 135° [BO12]

Allylochloride: m. 58° [BO12]

Propargylochloride: m. 148° [BO12]

Methopicrate: m. 115° [GA8]

Methoformate: m. 136–138° [GA8]

Methoacetate: m. 182° [GA8]

Methopropionate: m. 188° [GA8]

Methobutyrate: m. 159–161° [GA8]

Methovalerate: m. 167° [GA8]

Methocaproate: m. 170° [GA8]

Methocaprylate: m. 170° [GA8]

Metholaurate: m. 157–158° [GA8]

Methostearate: m. 148–149° [GA8]

Methocrotonate: m. 195° [GA8]

Metho-10-undecylenate: m. 157–158° [GA8]

Methooleate: m. 146–147° [GA8]

Methobenzoate: m. 199° [GA8]

Methophenyl acetate: m. 92° [GA8]

Methobutyl sulfate: m. 166° [BO11]

Methooctyl sulfate: m. 157° [BO11]

Methododecyl sulfate: m. 164° [BO11]

---

* See refs. BO11, BO12, and GA8 for a significant number of less common quaternary salts.

$C_{14}H_{31}N$

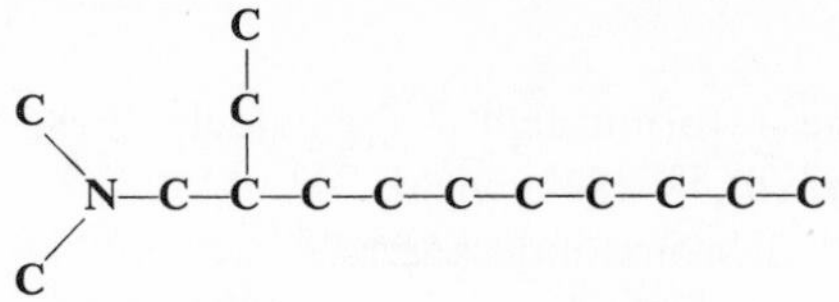

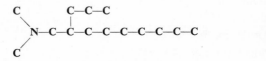

Me
Me
$C_{12}H_{25}$

1-DIMETHYLAMINO-2-ETHYLDECANE

Phys. Props.:

b_{13} 124°[BR26]

n_4^{20} 0.7913[BR26]

Prepn.:

Thermal decomposition of 2-ethyldecyltrimethylammonium hydroxide.[BR26]

Derivs.:

Methobromide: m. 225–227°[BR26]

$C_{14}H_{31}N$

Me
Me
$C_{12}H_{25}$

1-DIMETHYLAMINO-2-PROPYLNONANE

Phys. Props.:

b_{13} 114–116°[BR19]

Prepn.:

Thermal degradation of 2-propylnonyltrimethylammonium hydroxide.[BR19]

Derivs.:

Methiodide: m. 175°[BR19]

$C_{14}H_{31}N$

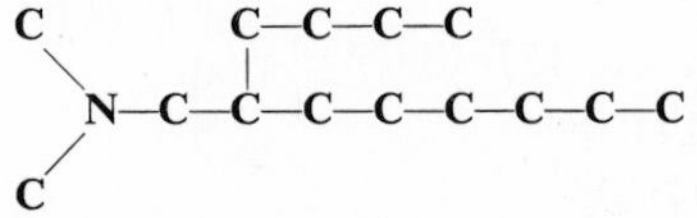

Me
Me
$C_{12}H_{25}$

1-DIMETHYLAMINO-2-BUTYLOCTANE

Phys. Props.:

b_{15} 125°[BR19]

Prepn.:

Thermal degradation of 2-butyloctyltrimethylammonium hydroxide.[BR19]

Derivs.:

Methiodide: m. 145°[BR19]

$C_{14}H_{31}N$ 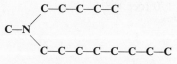 Me
                                      n-Pr
                                      n-$C_{10}H_{21}$

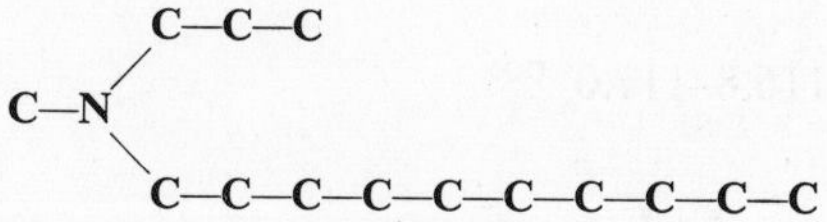

METHYLPROPYLDECYLAMINE

Phys. Props.:

b_1 89–90° [CO23]
d_4^{25} 0.7808[CO23]
n_D^{25} 1.4340[CO23]

Prepn.:

Methylpropylamine + decyl chloride (72% yield).[CO23]

Derivs.:

Oxalate: m. 108.8–109.8° [CO23]
Methiodide: m. 56–57.3° [CO23]

$C_{14}H_{31}N$ Me
                                      n-Pent
                                      n-Oct

METHYLPENTYLOCTYLAMINE

Phys. Props.:

b_{15} 132°[BR14]
d_4^{20} 0.790[BR14]

Prepn.:

Catalytic hydrogenation of methyl-(4-pentenyl)octylamine.[BR14]

$C_{14}H_{31}N$ Et
                                      Et
                                      n-$C_{10}H_{21}$

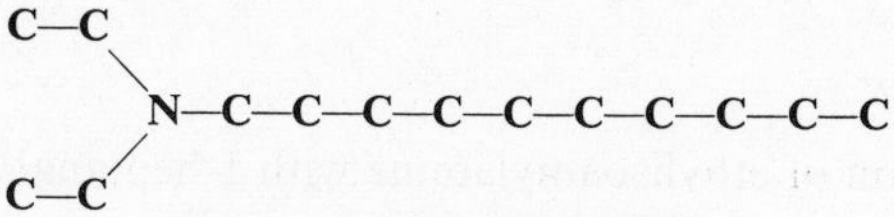

DECYLDIETHYLAMINE

Phys. Props.:

b_1 75–80° [CO1]
n_D^{24} 1.4362[CO1]

Prepn.:

Diethylamine + 1-bromodecane (80% yield).[CO1]

Derivs.:

Hydrochloride: m. 116.8–117.0° [CO1]

$C_{14}H_{31}N$

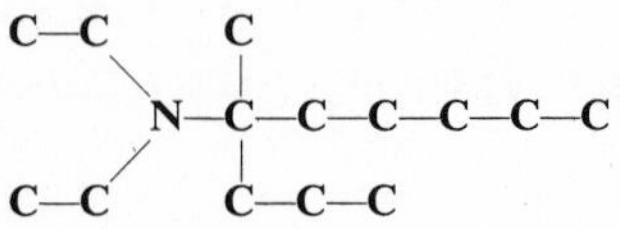

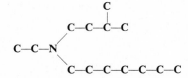

Et
Et
$C_{10}H_{21}$

4-DIETHYLAMINO-4-METHYLNONANE

Phys. Props.:

b_{24} 132° [MO4]; b_{20} 128–129° [MO4]

Prepn.:

N,N-Diethylbutyramide + methylmagnesium iodide + butyl iodide or bromide. Also obtained is an equivalent quantity of 2-methyl-2-diethylaminopentane.[MO4] *

Derivs.:

Hydrochloride: m. *ca.* 170°(dec.)[MO4]
Chloroaurate: m. 54° [MO4]
Picrate: m. 78–79° [MO4]

$C_{14}H_{31}N$

Et
i-Pent
n-C_7H_{15}

ETHYL-(3-METHYLBUTYL)HEPTYLAMINE

Phys. Props.:

b_{11} 112–113° [SK5]

Prepn.:

Reductive alkylation of ethylisoamylamine with 1-heptanal and hydrogen.[SK5]

Derivs.:

Oxalate: m. 75–76° [SK5]

---

* The proposed course for this seemingly anomalous reaction is presented in section 11, "Bouveault Reaction of *N,N*-Dialkylamides with Excess Grignard Reagent."

$C_{14}H_{31}N$

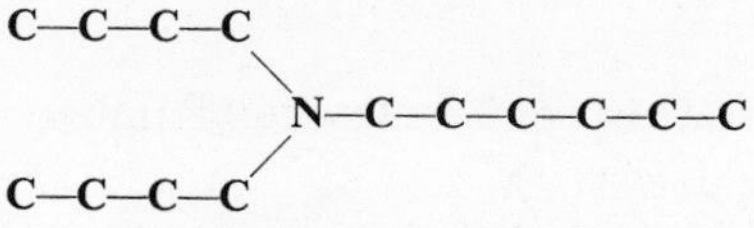

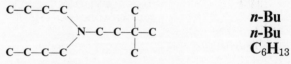

n-Bu
n-Bu
n-Hex

HEXYLDIBUTYLAMINE

Phys. Props.:

b_{20} 129–130° PE10

d_4^{20} 0.7864,PE10 0.7853PE10

n_D^{20} 1.4360,PE10 1.4350PE10

Prepn.:

1. Catalytic hydrogenation of 1-dibutylamino-2,3-hexadiene over colloidal palladium (*ca.* 100% yield).PE10
2. Dibutylamine + hexyl bromide.PE10

$C_{14}H_{31}N$

n-Bu
n-Bu
C_6H_{13}

DIBUTYL-(3,3-DIMETHYLBUTYL)AMINE

Phys. Props.:

b_{18} 116–118° LE13

n_D^{20} 1.4291–1.4310LE13

Prepn.:

Reduction of 1-dibutylamino-3,3-dimethyl-2-butanone with hydrazine and potassium hydroxide (21% yield).LE13

Derivs.:

p-Hydroxybenzenesulfonate: m. 191.5–193.5° LE13

$C_{14}H_{31}N$

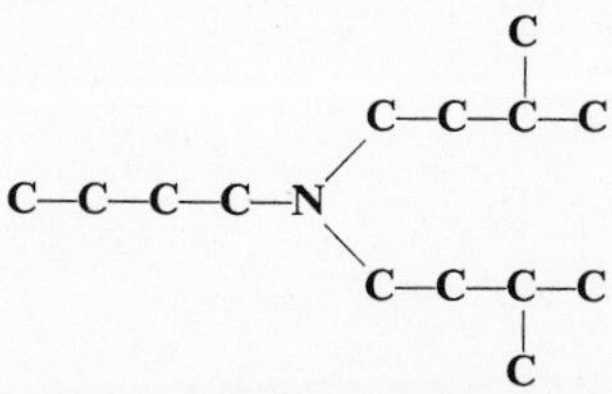

n-Bu
i-Pent
i-Pent

BUTYLDI(3-METHYLBUTYL)AMINE

Phys. Props.:

b_{11} 100–103° SK5

Prepn.:

1. Reductive alkylation of di(3-methylbutyl)amine with 2-butenal and hydrogen (44% yield).[SK5]
2. Reductive alkylation of di(3-methylbutyl)amine with acetaldehyde and hydrogen (15% yield).* This reaction also yields 34% of the expected ethyldi(3-methylbutyl)amine.[SK5]

Derivs.:

Picrate: m. 117–118°[HO4]
Butiodide: m. 120–120.5°[SM9]

$C_{15}H_{27}N$

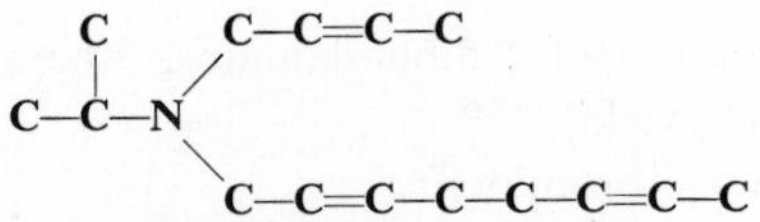

i-Pr
C_4H_7
C_8H_{13}

**ISOPROPYL-(2-BUTENYL)-
(2,6-OCTADIENYL)-AMINE†**

Phys. Props.:

b_{10} 113°[DA6]
d 0.8209[DA6]
n_D^{20} 1.4605[DA6]

Prepn.:

N-Sodioisopropylamine + 1,3-butadiene + isopropylamine. The octadienyl group results from the initial dimerization of some of the butadiene.[DA6]

$C_{15}H_{27}N$

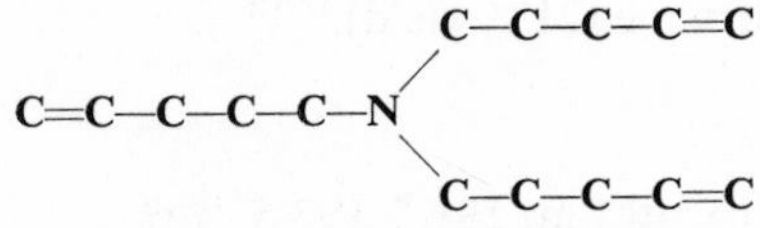

C_5H_9
C_5H_9
C_5H_9

TRI(4-PENTENYL)AMINE

Phys. Props.:

b_4 90–91°[KH3]
n_D^{20} 1.4618[KH3]

Prepn.:

Allylmagnesium chloride + tri(2-chloroethyl)amine (90% yield).[KH3]

---

* The formation of the product obtained is explained by aldolization of some of the acetaldehyde prior to reductive alkylation.

† Some doubt exists as to the position of the double bonds in the octadienyl radical.[DA6]

$C_{15}H_{29}N$

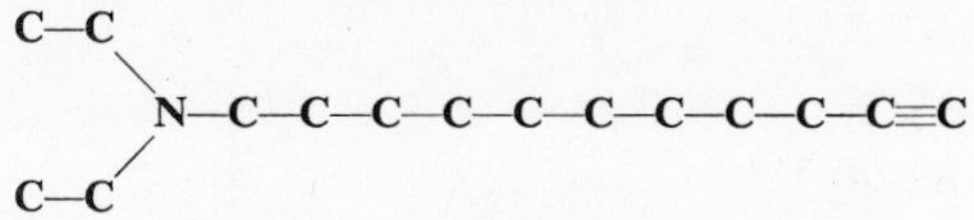

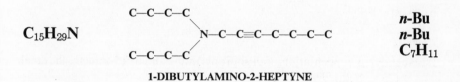

Et
Et
$C_{11}H_{19}$

11-DIETHYLAMINO-1-UNDECYNE

Phys. Props.:

b_3 112–115° [CO1]
n_D^{24} 1.4506 [CO1]

Prepn.:

Reduction of *N,N*-diethyl-10-undecynoamide with lithium aluminum hydride
(70% yield). [CO1]

$C_{15}H_{29}N$

```
C—C—C—C
         \
          N—C—C≡C—C—C—C—C
         /
C—C—C—C
```

n-Bu
n-Bu
C_7H_{11}

1-DIBUTYLAMINO-2-HEPTYNE

Phys. Props.:

b_{10} 131.6–132.2° [PA6]
d_4^{25} 0.8127 [PA6]
n_D^{25} 1.4483 [PA6]

Prepn.:

Butyl bromide + the sodio derivative of 3-dibutylamino-1-propyne (75.5%
yield). [PA6]

$C_{15}H_{31}N$

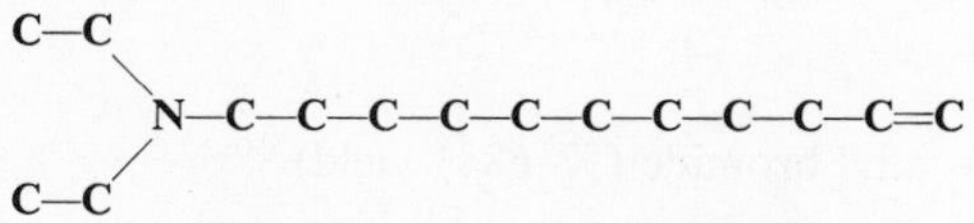

```
C—C
    \
     N—C—C—C—C—C—C—C—C—C—C—C=C
    /
C—C
```

Et
Et
$C_{11}H_{21}$

11-DIETHYLAMINO-1-UNDECENE

Phys. Props.:

b_{11} 136–138° [CO1]
n_D^{24} 1.4473 [CO1]

Prepn.:

Reduction of *N,N*-diethyl-10-undecenoamide with lithium aluminum hydride
(66.2% yield). [CO1]

Derivs.:

Maleate: m. 34–35° [CO1]
Methiodide: m. 89–90° [CO1]

$C_{15}H_{31}N$ 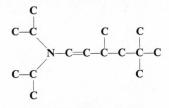 i-Pr
i-Pr
C_9H_{17}

**1-DIISOPROPYLAMINO-
3,5,5-TRIMETHYL-1-HEXENE**

Phys. Props.:

b_2 79–81° [DE1,DE2]

Prepn.:

Base-catalyzed condensation of diisopropylamine and 3,5,5-trimethylhexanal
(23% yield). [DE1,DE2]

$C_{15}H_{31}N$ 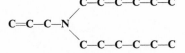 All
n-Hex
n-Hex

ALLYLDIHEXYLAMINE

Phys. Props.:

b_8 126° [CO25]
d_4^{25} 0.7935 [CO25]
n_D^{25} 1.4411 [CO25]

Prepn.:

Dihexylamine + allyl bromide (57–68% yield). [CO25]

$C_{15}H_{31}N$ *n*-Bu
n-Bu
C_7H_{13}

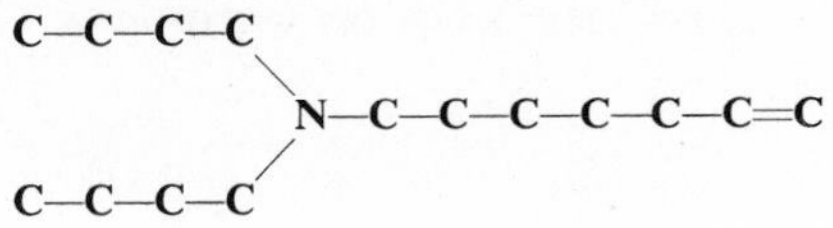

7-DIBUTYLAMINO-1-HEPTENE

Phys. Props.:

$b_{0.4}$ 92–94° [PE5]; $b_{0.2}$ 78° [PE5]
n_D^{25} 1.4427 [PE5]

Prepn.:

Dibutylamine + 7-chloro-1-heptene (60% yield).[PE5]

Derivs.:

Chloroplatinate: m. 169–171° [PE5]

$C_{15}H_{33}N$

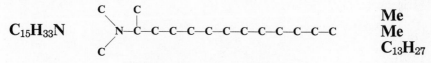

Me
Me
$C_{13}H_{27}$

2-DIMETHYLAMINOTRIDECANE

Phys. Props.:

b_{22} 160–162° [FA4]

Prepn.:

Dimethylamine + hydrogen + 2-tridecanol under pressure in the presence of a hydrogenation catalyst.[FA4]

$C_{15}H_{33}N$

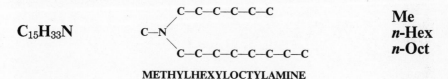

Me
n-Hex
n-Oct

METHYLHEXYLOCTYLAMINE

Phys. Props.:

b_{22} 140–145° [BO13]

Prepn.:

Methyloctylamine + hexyl bromide.[BO13]

Derivs.:

Oxalate: m. 227–228° (dec.)[BO13]

$C_{15}H_{33}N$

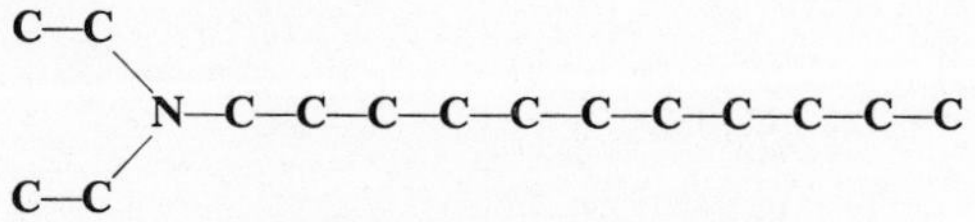

Et
Et
n-Undec

UNDECYLDIETHYLAMINE

Phys. Props.:

b_3 107–111° [CO1]; b_2 85–88° [PE1] *

---

* The higher value cited by ref. CO1 seems more reasonable than that reported by ref. PE1, as judged by comparison with data for other diethylaminoalkanes.

Prepn.:

1. 1-Bromoundecane + diethylamine (80% yield).[PE1]
2. Hydrogenation of 11-diethylamino-1-undecene in the presence of platinum oxide (90% yield).[CO1]

Derivs.:

Reineckate: m. 71°[PE1]

$C_{15}H_{33}N$

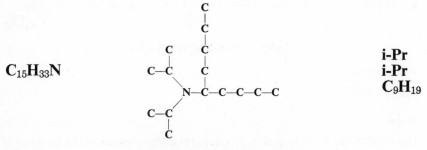

i-Pr
i-Pr
C_9H_{19}

5-DIISOPROPYLAMINONONANE

Phys. Props.:

b_{760} 243°[KU1]; b_{15} 121°[KU1]
d_{20}^{20} 0.8053[KU1]
n_D^{20} 1.4405[KU1]

Prepn.:

N,N-Diisopropylformamide + butylmagnesium bromide (67% yield).[KU1]

Derivs.:

Hydrochloride: m. 130–132°[KU1]
Hydrobromide: m. 179–181°[KU1]
Hydroiodide: m. 202–204°[KU1]*

$C_{15}H_{33}N$

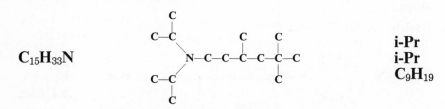

i-Pr
i-Pr
C_9H_{19}

1-DIISOPROPYLAMINO-3,5,5-TRIMETHYLHEXANE

Phys. Props.:

b_4 98–100°[DE1,DE2]; b_2 85–88°[DE2]

---

* According to ref. KU1 the hydriodide forms instead of the methiodide when the amine is treated with methyl iodide.

Prepn.:

1. Reduction of 1-diisopropylamino-3,5,5-trimethyl-1-hexene with formic acid (62% yield).[DE1,DE2] The aforementioned enamine was obtained in 23% overall yield by distilling 1,1-bis(diisopropylamino)-3,5,5-trimethyl-hexane, which in turn was derived from the reaction product of 3,5,5-tri-methylhexanal with diisopropylamine.[DE1,DE2]

2. From diisopropylamine formate and 3,5,5-trimethylhexanal (47% yield).[DE1,DE2]

$C_{15}H_{33}N$

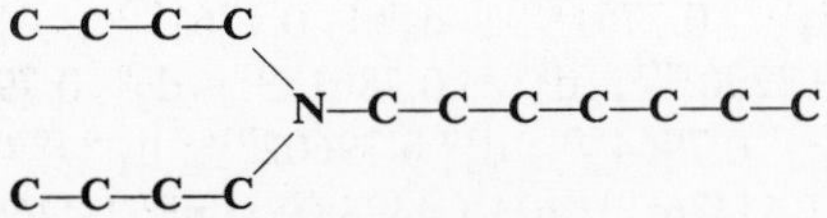

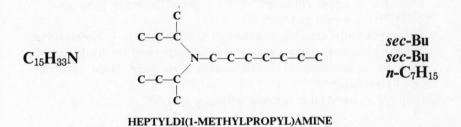

n-Bu
n-Bu
n-Hept

1-DIBUTYLAMINOHEPTANE

Phys. Props.:

b_7 119–120°[HA3]
d_0^0 0.8088[HA3]
n_D^{15} 1.4389[HA3]

Prepn.:

1. Dibutylamine + 1-bromoheptane.[HA3]
2. Heptyltributylammonium iodide + butyllithium.[HA3]

$C_{15}H_{33}N$

sec-Bu
sec-Bu
n-C_7H_{15}

HEPTYLDI(1-METHYLPROPYL)AMINE

Phys. Props.:

b. 249–252°[SK5]

Prepn.:

Reductive alkylation of di(1-methylpropyl)amine with 1-heptanal and hydrogen (67% yield).[SK5]

Derivs.:

Picrolonate: m. 105–106°[SK5]

$C_{15}H_{33}N$

$$C-C-C-C-C$$
$$\diagup$$
$$C-C-C-C-C-N$$
$$\diagdown$$
$$C-C-C-C-C$$

n-Pent
n-Pent
n-Pent

TRIPENTYLAMINE*

Phys. Props.:

b. 240–245°[MA11]; b_{14} 130°[SK3]; b_{12} 125–128°[EA1]; b_{11} 127°[BO13]; b_5 109°[VO1]
d_4^{100} 0.73023[BI6]; $d_4^{87.5}$ 0.7423[VO1]; $d_4^{86.8}$ 0.7428[VO1]; d_4^{80} 0.74562[BI6]; d_4^{75} 0.7461[TU1];
    $d_4^{61.1}$ 0.7611[VO1]; $d_4^{60.7}$ 0.7614[VO1]; d_4^{60} 0.76004,[BI6] 0.7568[TU1]; d_4^{45}
    0.7676[TU1]; $d_4^{41.5}$ 0.7751[VO1]; $d_4^{40.1}$ 0.7761[VO1]; d_4^{40} 0.77458[BI6]; d_4^{30}
    0.78252,[BI6] 0.7790[TU1]; $d_4^{26.4}$ 0.7861[VO1]; d_4^{20} 0.7907,[VO1] 0.78985,[BI6]
    0.7859[TU1]; $d_4^{12.1}$ 0.7964[VO1]; d_4^{10} 0.79602[BI6]; $d_4^{-0.10}$ 0.80342[BI6]
n_D^{20} 1.43665[VO1]; n_F^{20} 1.43426[VO1]; n_F^{20} 1.44238[VO1]; $n_{G'}^{20}$ 1.44666[VO1]
Surface tension (dynes/cm.): 26.86 at 12.1°, 25.80 at 26.4°, 24.41 at 41.5°,
    22.70 at 61.1°, 20.53 at 87.5°[VO1]; 24.25 at 20°, 23.41 at 30°, 22.11 at
    45°, 20.85 at 60°, 19.59 at 75°[TU1]
pK_a 8.79 at 25° (in 70% ethanol)[BO13]; base strength in ethyl acetate[HA5]
Raman spectrum[TH5]
X-ray diffraction: Bragg spacing 4.70 Å[TH5]
Flash point: 88° (190°F)[PE2a]
Fluidity (rhes); from 146.9 at 100° to 21.14 at 0°[BI6]
Magneto-optic rotation: 1263[GA1a]

Prepn.:

1. Ammonia + pentyl chloride[BE9,MA14]; + pentyl bromide (very low
   yield)[BR11]; + 1-pentanol.[SM12]
2. Mixture of pentyl chlorides (including 1-chloropentane) + dipentylamine.
   The mixed tertiary amines presumably are separated by distillation.[HU3a]
3. Catalytic hydrogenation of valeronitrile (low yield, main product is
   dipentylamine).[SA1,SK3]
4. Pentanal + ammonium formate + formic acid.[WA15]

Derivs.:

Picrate: m. 119°[TS6]
Picrate of amine oxide: m. 61.6–63°, 57.8–58.8°[CO17]†
Pentiodide: m. 133–135°,[EA1] 127.6–127.8°[MI2]
Methotosylate: m. 76–78°[MA37]

---

* Tripentylamine may also be called triamylamine. However, in the older literature
(such as refs. HO5, MA14, and WA15) the term "amyl" applies to a mixture of pentyl
isomers, predominantly isopentyl, derived from fermentation amyl alcohol (fusel oil).

† Both values are listed by ref. CO17, the higher being found in the experimental part
and the lower in one of the tables.

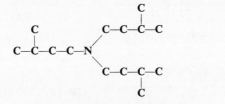

$C_{15}H_{33}N$

```
        C
        |
 C—C—C—C        C
        \       |
         N—C—C—C—C
        /
 C—C—C—C
        |
        C
```

pri. act. **Pent**
pri. act. **Pent**
pri. act. **Pent**

(+) TRI(2-METHYLBUTYL)AMINE

Phys. Props.:

b. 230–237° [PL4]
d_4^{13} 0.7964[PL4]
Strongly dextrorotatory[PL4]

Prepn.:

From *d*-(2-methylbutyl)amine and *d*-(2-methylbutyl) bromide.[PL4]

$C_{15}H_{33}N$

```
          C          C
          |          |
 C—C—C—C—N    C—C—C—C
          \
           C—C—C—C
                |
                C
```

i-Pent
i-Pent
i-Pent

TRI(3-METHYLBUTYL)AMINE

Phys. Props.:*

b. 237°,[PL4] 235° [MA11]; b_{10} 111–113° [EA1]; b_4 94° [VO1]

d_4^{100} 0.72305[BI6]; $d_4^{86.7}$ 0.7364[VO1]; d_4^{80} 0.73981[BI6]; $d_4^{60.5}$ 0.7557[VO1]; d_4^{60}
0.75409[BI6]; $d_4^{40.6}$ 0.7700[VO1]; d_4^{40} 0.76818[BI6]; d_4^{30} 0.77527[BI6]; d_4^{20}
0.7848,[VO1] 0.78279[BI6]; $d_4^{14.7}$ 0.7886[VO1]; d_4^{13} 0.7882[PL4]; d_4^{10} 0.78995[BI6];
d_4^0 0.79748[BI6]

n_D^{20} 1.43305[VO1]; n_C^{20} 1.43066[VO1]; n_F^{20} 1.43875[VO1]; $n_{G'}^{20}$ 1.44308[VO1]

Surface tension (dynes/cm.): 24.85 at 14.7°, 22.58 at 40.8°, 20.92 at 60.7°,
18.98 at 86.5° [VO1]

Infrared absorption: between 0.59 and 2.40 μ[EL5]; between 1 and 12 μ[BE3];
between 2.75 and 3.75 μ, with absorption maximum at 3.47[SA8]

X-ray spectrum: a_1 = 10.5, a_2 = 5.9, b = 9.7$_5$[KA15]

Heat of combustion (kcal./mole) at constant volume 2452.1,[LE12] 2459.3,[KH1a]
at constant pressure 2456.3[LE12]; heat of formation (kcal./mole)
96.7[LE12]

---

* In the older literature (such as refs. HO5, MA14, and WA15) the term "amyl" was
used to describe a mixture of pentyl isomers, predominantly isopentyl, derived from
fermentation amyl alcohol (fusel oil). Physical properties determined on products
derived from these mixtures are, therefore, not reliable and are not included in the
present monograph.

Fluidity (rhes): from 148.5 at 100° to 20.07 at 0°[BI6]
Diamagnetic susceptibility[PA10]

Prepn.:

1. Reaction of ammonia with isopentyl chloride[PL3,MA14]; with isopentyl bromide[TS6]; with isopentyl alcohol (8.5% yield)[KR9]; with isopentyl bromide in the presence of sodamide (87% yield).[SH5]
2. Diisopentylamine + isopentyl bromide.[HO5]
3. Thermal decomposition of tetraisopentylammonium hydroxide.[HO5]
4. Heating the reaction mixture composed of 3-methylbutanal, ammonium formate, and formic acid.[WA15]
5. Heating isopentylamine in the presence of copper[MA12]; or diisopentylamine in the presence of nickel.[MA11]
6. Heating isopentyl chloride with sodamide.[MA41a]
7. Hydrogenation of isopentyl nitrite in the presence of manganese oxide or zinc oxide[SA1]; in the presence of nickel or copper.[GA7] All give low yields. Mono- and di-isopentylamines are also obtained, with diisopentylamine being the main product in each case. With nickel catalyst others report isovaleronitrile as the main product.[MA10,MA11]

Derivs.:

Hydriodide: m. 105°[WA11]
Picrate: m. 124–126°,[WA11] 124.6°,[WA12] 119–120°,[WA6] 119°[TS6]
Hydrothiocyanate: m. 62–63°[WA4]
Amine oxide picrate: m. 99–100°[CO17]
Isopentiodide:* m. 143–144.5°,[WA5,WA7] 144°,[WA8] 132°,[WA11] 127°[WA5]
Isopentopicrate: m. 90°,[WA11] 87–87.2°[WA12]
Isopentoperchlorate: m. 199°[WA11]
Isopentonitrate: m. 83°[WA4]
Isopentothiocyanate: m. 106°[WA11]

$$C_{16}H_{29}N \qquad C-C-C-C-N \Big\langle \begin{matrix} C-C=C-C \\ C-C=C-C-C-C=C-C \end{matrix} \qquad \begin{matrix} \textit{n-Bu} \\ C_4H_7 \\ C_8H_{13} \end{matrix}$$

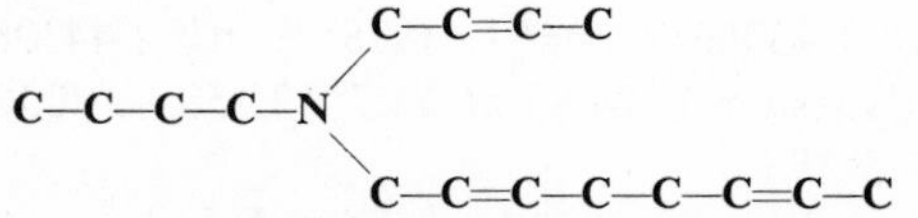

BUTYL-(2-BUTENYL)-(2,6-OCTADIENYL)AMINE†

Prepn.:

Reaction of butylamine with 1,3-butadiene in the presence of the sodium salt of butylamine gives butyldi(2-butenyl)amine and butyl-(2-butenyl)-(2,6-octadienyl)amine. The octadienyl group results from initial dimerization of butadiene.[DA6]

---

* See ref. WA5 for discussion of anomalous behavior of the melting point of tetra-isopentylammonium iodide.

† This structure was not definitively proved.

$C_{16}H_{31}N$

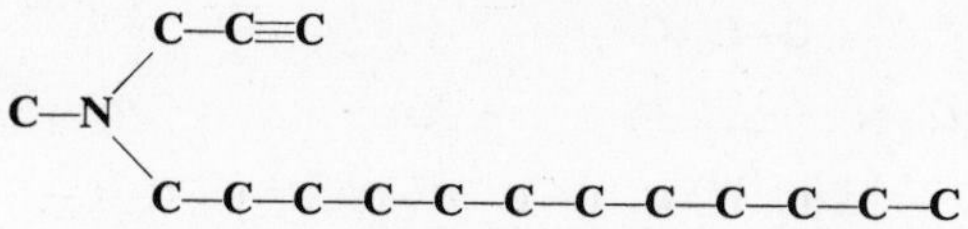

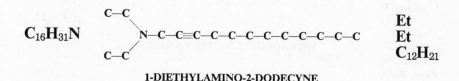

Me
C_3H_3
$n\text{-}C_{12}H_{25}$

METHYLPROPARGYLDODECYLAMINE

Derivs.:

Methochloride (from dodecyldimethylamine and propargyl chloride): m. 148° B012

$C_{16}H_{31}N$

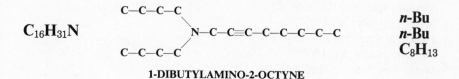

Et
Et
$C_{12}H_{21}$

1-DIETHYLAMINO-2-DODECYNE

Phys. Props.:

$b_{0.5}$ 115–116° EP1
n_D^{17} 1.4523 EP1

Prepn.:

Diethylamine + 1-undecyne + paraformaldehyde in the presence of copper(I) acetate. EP1

Derivs.:

Ethiodide: m. 144–145° EP1

$C_{16}H_{31}N$

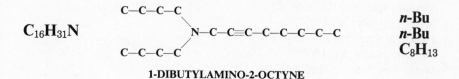

n-Bu
n-Bu
C_8H_{13}

1-DIBUTYLAMINO-2-OCTYNE

Phys. Props.:

b_{10} 143.5–143.8° PA6
d_4^{25} 0.8144 PA6
n_D^{25} 1.4498 PA6

Prepn.:

Sodio derivative of dibutyl(2-propynyl)amine + 1-bromopentane (77% yield). PA6

$C_{16}H_{33}N$

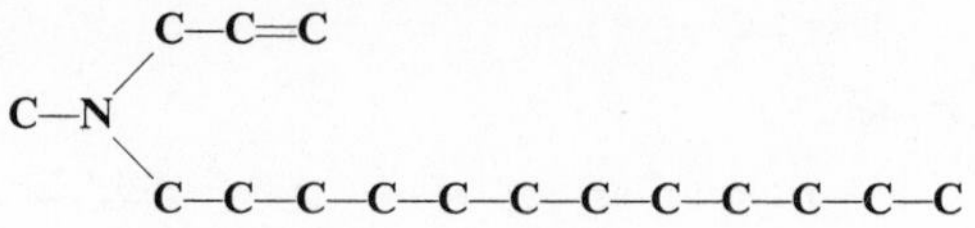

```
            C—C=C
             \
    C—N
             \
            C—C—C—C—C—C—C—C—C—C—C—C
```

Me
All
$n\text{-}C_{12}H_{25}$

METHYLALLYLDODECYLAMINE

Derivs.:

Methochloride (from dodecyldimethylamine and allyl chloride): m. 58° BO12

$C_{16}H_{35}N$

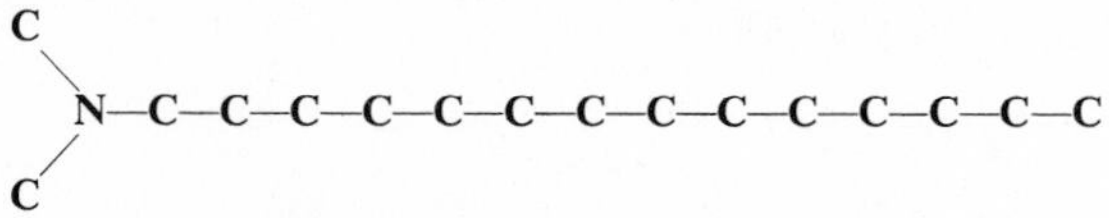

```
      C
       \
        N—C—C—C—C—C—C—C—C—C—C—C—C—C—C
       /
      C
```

Me
Me
$n\text{-}C_{14}H_{29}$

TETRADECYLDIMETHYLAMINE

Phys. Props.:

b_{11} 159–161° ST4; $b_{0.5}$ 103–105° GA9
m. below 0° ST4
Viscosity of solutions ST4

Prepn.:

1. Tetradecylamine + formaldehyde + formic acid (92% yield). GA9
2. Dimethylamine + tetradecyl bromide in a sealed tube. ST4

Derivs.:*

Methopicrate: m. 118° GA8
Methonitrate: m. 205–207° MC5
Methoformate: m. 168° GA8
Methoacetate: m. 192° GA8
Methopropionate: 187–188° GA8
Methobutyrate: m. 178° GA8
Methovalerate: m. 168–169° GA8
Methocaproate: m. 186° GA8
Methocaprylate: m. 162° GA8
Metholaurate: m. 161–162° GA8
Methostearate: m. 145–147° GA8
Methocrotonate: m. 184–185° GA8
Metho-10-undecylenate: m. 154–156° GA8
Methooleate: m. 139–140° GA8
Methobenzoate: m. 203° GA8
Methophenyl acetate: m. 87–89° GA8

---

* See ref. GA8 for a significant number of additional, but uncommon, quaternary ammonium salts.

$C_{16}H_{35}N$

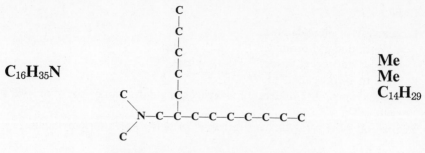

Me
Me
$C_{14}H_{29}$

1-DIMETHYLAMINO-2-PENTYLNONANE

Phys. Props.:

b_{11} 143–145°[BR21]

Prepn.:

Thermal degradation of 2-pentylnonyltrimethylammonium hydroxide (50% yield).[BR21]

Derivs.:

Methochloroplatinate: m. 218° (dec.)[BR21]

$C_{16}H_{35}N$

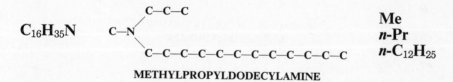

Me
n-Pr
n-$C_{12}H_{25}$

METHYLPROPYLDODECYLAMINE

Derivs.:

Methochloride (made from dodecyldimethylamine and propyl chloride): m. 135°[BO12]

$C_{16}H_{35}N$

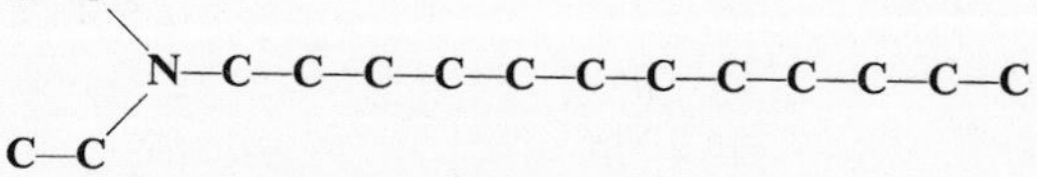

Et
Et
n-$C_{12}H_{25}$

DODECYLDIETHYLAMINE

Phys. Props.:

b_{11} 148–151°[BO12]; b_3 120–125°[CO1]; b_2 132–134°,[EA1]; b^2 122–124°,[WE17]; 121–123°[SC14]

n_D^{25} 1.4392[SC14]; n_D^{20} 1.4410[CO1]; n_D^{19} 1.443[WE17]

Prepn.:

1. Reaction of diethylamine:
   a. With dodecyl bromide,[BO12] (76.5% yield).[CO1]
   b. With dodecyl chloride,[SC14] (90% yield).[WE17]
   c. With 1-dodecanol.[FA4,SM4]
2. Triethylamine + 1-dodecanol + hydrogen under high pressure (42% yield).[SC14]
3. High-pressure catalytic hydrogenation of lauric acid in triethylamine.[SC14]

Derivs.:

Hydrochloride: m. 119.5°,[WE17] 117–119°[SC14]
Styphnate: m. 57.1–58.1°[SC14]
Methiodide: m. 122–123°[SC14]
Methotosylate: m. 128.5–129.7°[SC14]
Benzylochloride: m. 59°[BO12]
p-Nitrobenzylochloride: m. 139–140°[BO12]

$C_{16}H_{35}N$

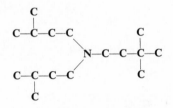

i-Pent
i-Pent
C_6H_{13}

1-BIS-(3-METHYLBUTYL)AMINO-3,3-DIMETHYLBUTANE

Phys. Props.:

b_{15} 121–122°[SM9]

Prepn.:

Diisopentylamine + 3,3-dimethyl-1-bromobutane (or possibly the corresponding iodide, the exact halide was not specified) (49% yield).[SM9]

Derivs.:

Picrate: m. 77–79°[SM9]

$C_{17}H_{37}N$

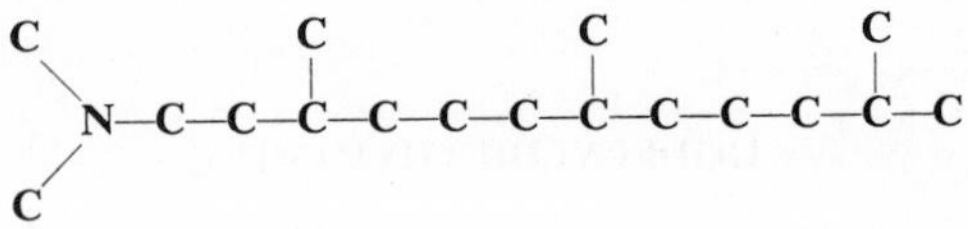

Me
Me
$C_{15}H_{31}$

1-DIMETHYLAMINO-3,7,11-TRIMETHYLDODECANE

Phys. Props.:

b_{10} 155–157°[BR12]

Prepn.:

Thermal decomposition of 3,7,11-trimethyldodecyltrimethylammonium hydroxide.[BR12]

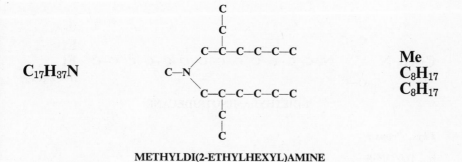

$C_{17}H_{37}N$ Me   n-Oct   n-Oct

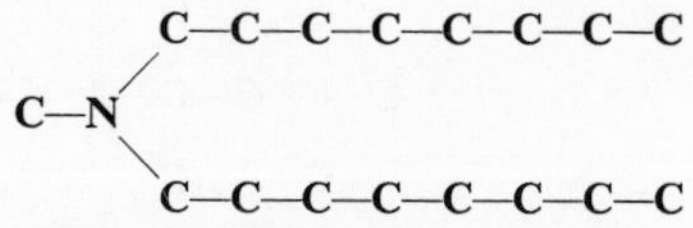

METHYLDIOCTYLAMINE

Phys. Props.:

b_{15} 162–165°[BO13]; b_{10} 158°[BO13]; b_5 136–138°[BL4]; b_3 143–145°[WE17]
$n_D^{20.5}$ 1.443[WE17]
pK_a 8.56 at 25° (in 70% ethanol)[BO13]

Prepn.:

1. Reaction of methylamine:
   a. With octyl bromide[BL4] (42% yield).[BO13]
   b. With octyl chloride (30% yield).[WE17]
2. Dioctylamine + formic acid + formaldehyde.[RA4]

Derivs.:

Hydrochloride: m. 149–150° [BL4,BO13]

$C_{17}H_{37}N$ Me C_8H_{17} C_8H_{17}

METHYLDI(2-ETHYLHEXYL)AMINE

Phys. Props.:

b_6 113–114°[BL4]

Prepn.:

Methylamine + 3-(bromomethyl)heptane.[BL4]

Derivs.:

Chloroaurate: m. 103–104°[BL4]

$C_{17}H_{37}N$

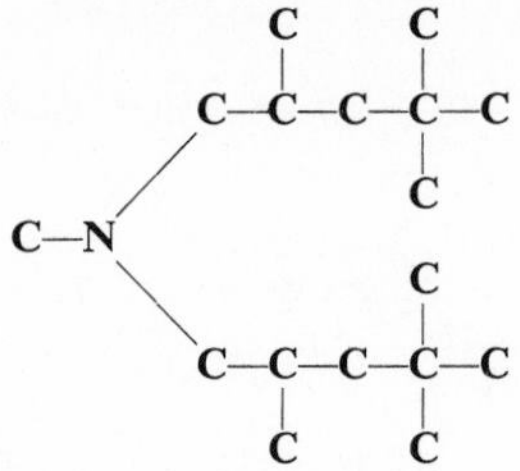

Me
C_8H_{17}
C_8H_{17}

METHYLBIS-(2,4,4-TRIMETHYLPENTYL)AMINE

Phys. Props.:

b_{13} 127–128° GA6
n_D^{20} 1.4377 GA6

Prepn.:

Bis-(2,4,4-trimethylpentyl)amine + formaldehyde + formic   acid   (66%
     yield). GA6

Derivs.:

Picrate: m. 128–129° GA6
Hydrobromide: m. 238° GA6
Methobromide: m. 209–210° GA6
Methiodide: m. 198° (dec.) GA6

$C_{17}H_{37}N$

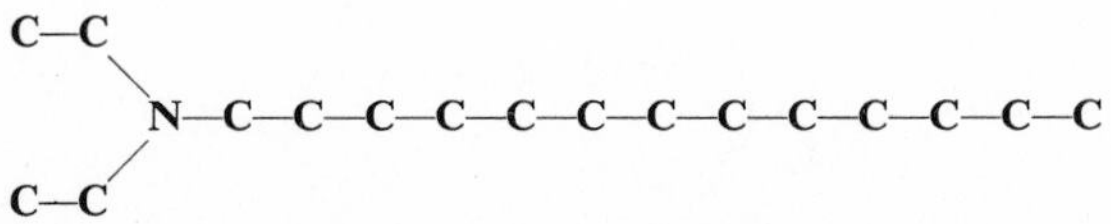

Et
Et
$n\text{-}C_{13}H_{27}$

1-DIETHYLAMINOTRIDECANE

Phys. Props.:

b_{12} 169° WE16
n_D^{19} 1.448 WE16

Prepn.:

Diethylaminoacetonitrile + dodecylmagnesium   chloride   (41%   yield   of
     hydrochloride based on the original 1-chlorododecane used). WE16

Derivs.:

Hydrochloride: m. 77–79° WE16

$C_{17}H_{37}N$

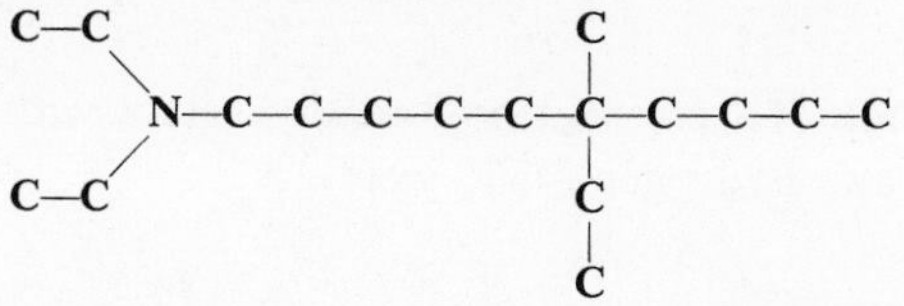

Et
Et
$C_{13}H_{27}$

1-DIETHYLAMINO-6-METHYL-6-ETHYLDECANE

Phys. Props.:

b_{18} 159–162°[G01]

n_D^{22} 1.4473[G01]

Prepn.:

Reduction of 2-(2'-thienyl)-2-[2''-(5''-diethylaminomethyl)thienyl]butane with
hydrogen in the presence of Raney nickel catalyst (66% yield).[G01]

Derivs.:

Oxalate: m. 111–112°[G01]

$C_{17}H_{37}N$

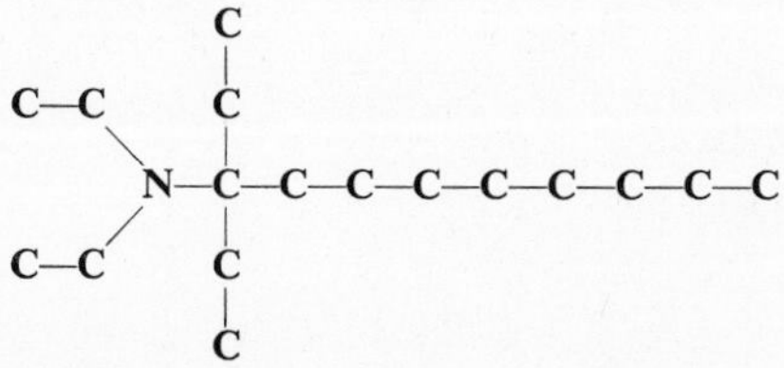

Et
Et
$C_{13}H_{27}$

3-DIETHYLAMINO-3-ETHYLUNDECANE

Phys. Props.:

b_{15} 161–163°[M04]

Prepn.:

N,N-Diethylnonanoamide + ethylmagnesium bromide (43% yield). A 25%
yield of 3-undecanone is also obtained.[M04]

Derivs.:

Picrate: m. 57°[M04]

$C_{17}H_{37}N$

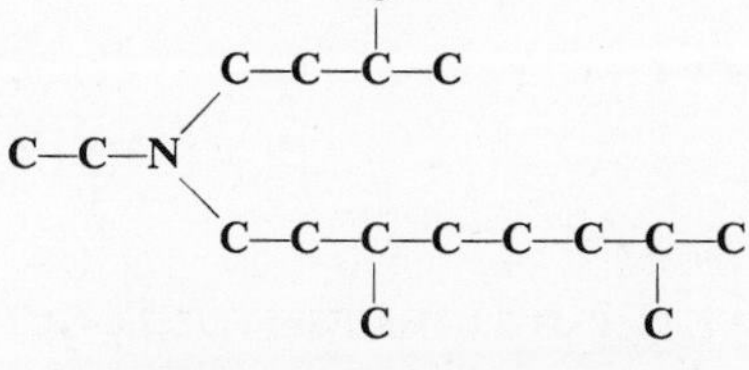

Et
i-Pent
$C_{10}H_{21}$

ETHYL-(3-METHYLBUTYL)-
(3,7-DIMETHYLOCTYL)AMINE

Phys. Props.:

b_{11} 136–137°[SK5]

Prepn.:

Reductive alkylation of 1-ethylamino-3-methylbutane with 3,7-dimethyl-2,6-octadienal and hydrogen (47% yield).[SK5]

Derivs.:

Oxalate: m. 81–82°[SK5]

$C_{17}H_{37}N$

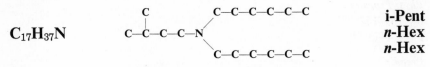

i-Pent
n-Hex
n-Hex

3-METHYLBUTYLDIHEXYLAMINE

Prepn.:

b_{22} 140–145°[BO13]

Prepn.:

1-Amino-3-methylbutane + 1-bromohexane (5% yield).[BO13]

Derivs.:

Oxalate: m. 128–130°[BO13]

$C_{17}H_{37}N$

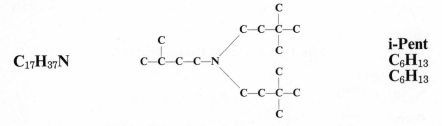

i-Pent
C_6H_{13}
C_6H_{13}

3-METHYLBUTYLBIS(3,3-DIMETHYLBUTYL)AMINE

Derivs.:

Isopentyloiodide (made from 1-diisopentylamino-3,3-dimethylbutane and 1-iodo-3,3-dimethylbutane): m. 182–182.5°[SM9]

$C_{18}H_{33}N$

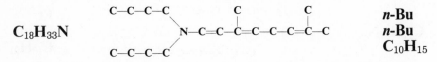

n-Bu
n-Bu
$C_{10}H_{15}$

1-DIBUTYLAMINO-3,7-DIMETHYL-1,3,6-OCTATRIENE

Phys. Props.:

b_4 144–145°[CA5]

n_D^{20} 1.5129[CA5]

Ultraviolet absorption: 2820 and 2920 A. (ϵ 23,500)[CA5]

Prepn.:

Citral + dibutylamine in the presence of potassium carbonate (61% yield).[CA5]

$C_{18}H_{35}N$

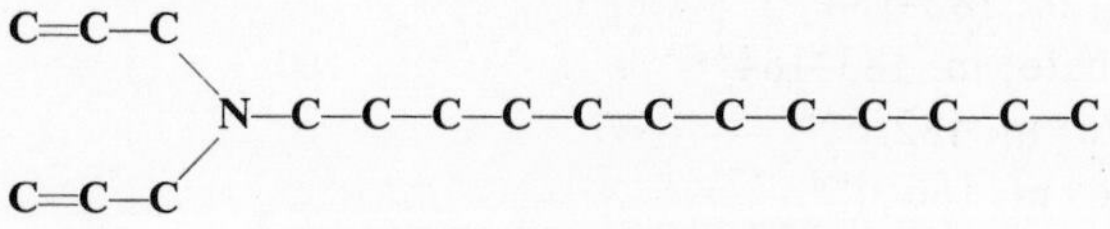

All
All
$n\text{-}C_{12}H_{25}$

DODECYLDIALLYLAMINE

Prepn.:

Dodecyl bromide + diallylamine.[FA12]

$C_{18}H_{39}N$

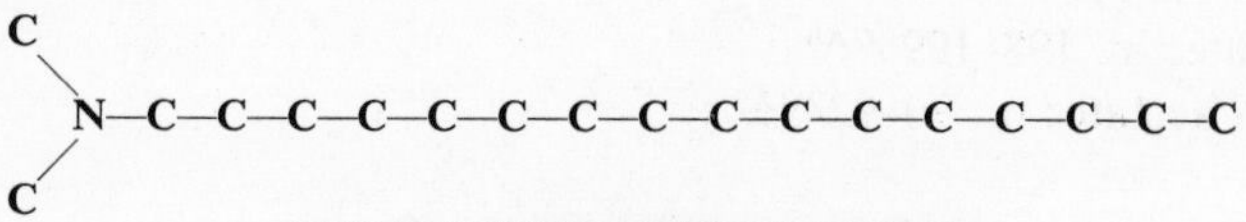

Me
Me
$n\text{-}C_{16}H_{33}$

HEXADECYLDIMETHYLAMINE

Phys. Props.:

b_{17} 203–205° [BR9]; b_6 175° [KI5]; b_3 158° [WE17]; $b_{2.5}$ 159–162° [GA9]; b_1 138° [WE17]; $b_{0.1}$ 137–138° [ST4]

m. *ca.* 12° [ST4]

n_D^{23} 1.445 [WE17]

Viscosity of solutions[ST4]

Prepn.:

1. Hexadecyl chloride + dimethylamine,[ST4] (91.5% yield),[KY3] (82% yield).[WE17]
2. Hexadecylamine + formaldehyde + formic acid,[KI5] (80% yield).[GA9]
3. Thermal degradation of hexadecyltrimethylammonium hydroxide (71% yield).[BR9]

Derivs.:*

Hydrochloride: m. 198° [WE17]

Picrate: m. 69° [BR9]

Chloroplatinate: m. 83° [BR9]

Methiodide: m. 222°,[BR9] 247° [MA2] †

Methochloride: m. *ca.* 70°,[WE17] 240° [MA2] †

---

* Ref. GA8 contains a significant number of uncommon quaternary ammonium salts in addition to those cited in this section.

† Ref. MA2 gives melting point values differing substantially from those reported by an earlier reference on one derivative and a later one on another. All list good analytical data and each reference takes note of the discrepancy with prior literature with no comment. We can only suggest that isomeric cetyl intermediates may have been responsible.

Methopicrate: m. 128°[GA8]
Benzylochloride: m. 58°[WE17]
Methoformate: m. 178–180°[GA8]
Methoacetate: m. 182–184°[GA8]
Methopropionate: m. 183–184°[GA8]
Methobutyrate: m. 182°[GA8]
Methovalerate: m. 166°[GA8]
Methocaproate: m. 145–147°[GA8]
Methocaprylate: m. 171°[GA8]
Metholaurate: m. 161°[GA8]
Methostearate: m. 142–143°,[GA8] 78–82°[EA1]
Methocrotonate: m. 198°[GA8]
Metho-10-undecylenate: m. 149–151°[GA8]
Methooleate: m. 142–143°[GA8]
Methobenzoate: m. 198–199°[GA8]
Methophenyl acetate: m. 90–92°[GA8]

$C_{18}H_{39}N$
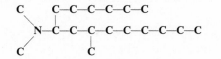
Me
Me
$C_{16}H_{33}$

7-DIMETHYLAMINO-9-METHYLPENTADECANE

Phys. Props.:

b_5 170–180°[CO31a]

Prepn.:

Reductive alkylation of 9-methyl-7-pentadecanone (or the corresponding alcohol) with dimethylamine and hydrogen.[CO31a]

$C_{18}H_{39}N$

Et
Et
n-$C_{14}H_{29}$

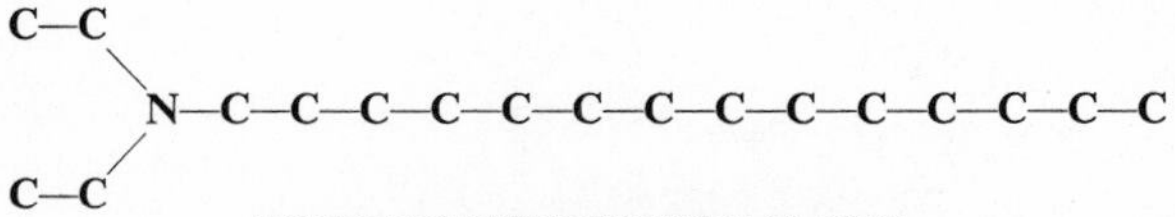

TETRADECYLDIETHYLAMINE

Prepn.:

1-Aminotetradecane + ethyl iodide.[CO1]

Derivs.:

Hydrochloride: m. 119–120°[CO1]

$C_{18}H_{39}N$

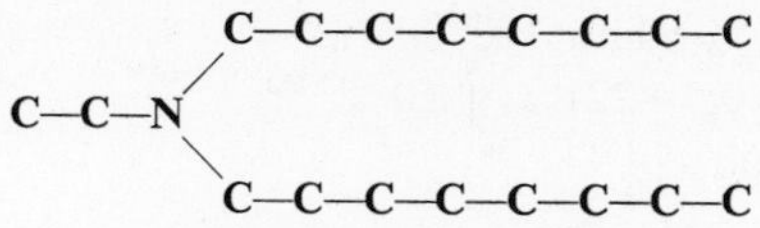

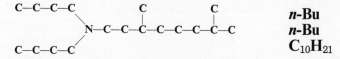

Et
n-Oct
n-Oct

ETHYLDIOCTYLAMINE

Phys. Props.:

b_{10} 166–167°[BO13]; $b_{0.7}$ 123–128°[SC14]
n_D^{25} 1.4411[SC14]
pK_a 8.70 at 25° (in 70% ethanol)[BO13]

Prepn.:

1. Ethylamine + octyl bromide.[BO13]
2. Transalkylation reaction between triethylamine and 1-octanol in the presence of hydrogen and Raney nickel catalyst (7% yield) (the main product, in 63% yield, was octyldiethylamine).[SC14]

$C_{18}H_{39}N$

n-Bu
n-Bu
$C_{10}H_{21}$

1-DIBUTYLAMINO-3,7-DIMETHYLOCTANE

Phys. Props.:

b_4 116–117°[CA5]
n_D^{18} 1.4431[CA5]

Prepn.:

Catalytic hydrogenation of 1-dibutylamino-3,7-dimethyl-1,3,6-octatriene.[CA5]

$C_{18}H_{39}N$

C—C—C—C—C—C—N
C—C—C—C—C—C
C—C—C—C—C—C

n-Hex
n-Hex
n-Hex

TRIHEXYLAMINE

Phys. Props.:

b. 263–265°,[MA11] 260°[PE9]; b_{16} 165–170°[BO13]; b_{15} 119° (*sic*)[SH5]*; b_{12} 150–159°[BO13]; b_5 155–157°[EA1]

---

* The conflict in the boiling point and the inconclusiveness of the experimental work cast doubt on the reliability of the data cited.

pK$_a$ 8.53 at 25° (in 70% ethanol)[BO13]
Magnetic susceptibility: -221.7×10^{-6} [FR2]
Magneto-optic rotation: 1478[GA1a]

Prepn.:

1. Reaction of ammonia with hexyl bromide (28% yield)[BO13]; with hexyl chloride (2.5% yield)[NE2]; with hexyl bromide in the presence of sodamide (11.3% yield; 48.8% yield on subsequent treatment with water)[SH5]*; with 1-hexanol (3% yield).[KR9]
2. By-product in the catalytic hydrogenation of hexanenitrile.[MA11,SA1]
3. Pyrolysis of the ammonia-heptanal bisulfite addition product.[PE7,PE9]†

Derivs.:

Hexiodide: m. 104–105° [EA1]
Oxalate: m. 120° [BO13]
Chloroplatinate: m. above 200° (dec.)[PE7]
m-Nitrobenzenesulfonate: m. 107–108° [BO13]
Amine oxide picrate: m. 51–52°,[CO17] 34–36° [MA3]

$C_{18}H_{39}N$ i-Hex i-Hex i-Hex

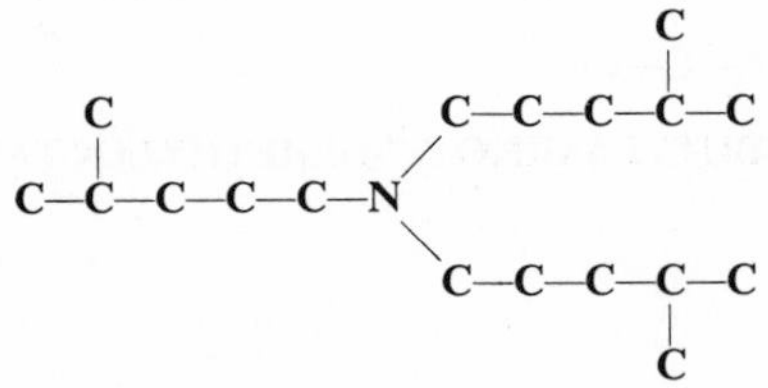

TRI(4-METHYLPENTYL)AMINE

Phys. Props.:

b$_{762}$ 283° (dec.)[SA5]; b$_{35}$ 178° [SA5]
d$_0^0$ 0.807[SA5]

Prepn.:

By-product in the catalytic hydrogenation of 4-methylpentanenitrile. The main product is diisohexylamine.[SA5]

Derivs.:

Oxalate: m. 250° (dec.)[SA5]

---

* See footnote page 327.

† Although analysis and physical constants in refs. PE7 and PE9 agree with the cited structure, why this procedure works is not clear to us. Ref. PE8 by the same worker offers some support and claims that loss of a carbon atom from the aldehyde is a general occurrence.

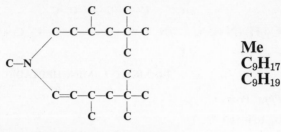

$C_{19}H_{39}N$

Me
C_9H_{17}
C_9H_{19}

**METHYL-(3,5,5-TRIMETHYLHEXYL)-
(3,5,5-TRIMETHYL-1-HEXENYL)AMINE**

Phys. Props.:

b_1 117–121° [DE2]; $b_{0.95-1.3}$ 117–121° [DE1]

Prepn.:

Distillation of the base-catalyzed reaction product between 3,5,5-trimethyl-hexanal and 1-methylamino-3,5,5-trimethylhexane (70% yield).[DE1,DE2]

$C_{19}H_{39}N$

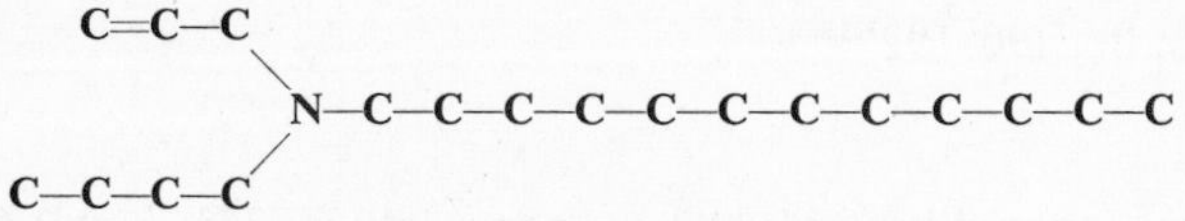

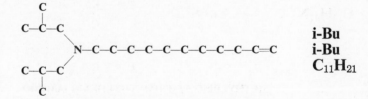

All
n-Bu
n-$C_{12}H_{25}$

ALLYLBUTYLDODECYLAMINE

Phys. Props.:

b_3 140–143° [LE5a]

Prepn.:

Allyl bromide + butyldodecylamine.[LE5a]

$C_{19}H_{39}N$

i-Bu
i-Bu
$C_{11}H_{21}$

11-BIS(2-METHYLPROPYL)AMINO-1-UNDECENE

Phys. Props.:

b_2 133–140° [CO1]
n_D^{24} 1.4464 [CO1]

Prepn.:

Reduction of *N,N*-diisobutyl-10-undecenoamide with lithium aluminum hydride (57% yield).[CO1]

C₁₉H₄₁N

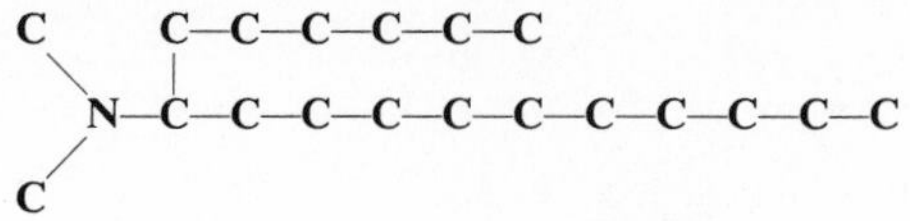

$C_{19}H_{41}N$

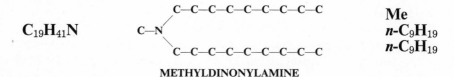

Me
Me
C₁₇H₃₅

Me
Me
$C_{17}H_{35}$

7-DIMETHYLAMINOHEPTADECANE

Phys. Props.:

b_4 164–166° [K15]

Prepn.:

7-Aminoheptadecane + formaldehyde + formic acid (90% yield). [K15]

$C_{19}H_{41}N$

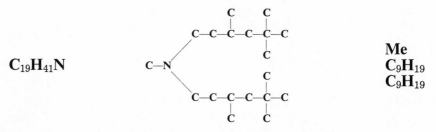

Me
n-C₉H₁₉
n-C₉H₁₉

Me
$n\text{-}C_9H_{19}$
$n\text{-}C_9H_{19}$

METHYLDINONYLAMINE

Phys. Props.:

b_{25} 204° [BO13]; b_{15} 190–192 [KI3]

Prepn.:

Methylamine + nonyl bromide[BO13]; + nonyl iodide (75% yield). [KI3]

Derivs.:

Hydrochloride: m. 149–150° [BO13]

$C_{19}H_{41}N$

Me
C₉H₁₉
C₉H₁₉

Me
C_9H_{19}
C_9H_{19}

METHYLBIS(3,5,5-TRIMETHYLHEXYL)AMINE*

Phys. Props.:

$b_{1.5}$ 124–133° [DE1,DE2]†; $b_{1.5}$ 115–121° [DE2]†

---

* In ref. DE1 (a patent) one gets the impression that all substituents on the nitrogen are straight chain alkyl groups. This is not the case when judging from the same author's article in ref. DE2.

† Ref. DE2 (same author as in DE1) lists these two divergent boiling point values but gives no explanation. There are no independent data by which one can decide which value is more likely to be correct.

Prepn.:

1. Reduction of methyl-(3,5,5-trimethylhexyl)-3,5,5-trimethyl-1-hexenyl)-amine by formic acid (57% yield).[DE1,DE2] This enamine was obtained in 70% yield by distilling the product of the base-catalyzed reaction between 3,5,5-trimethylhexanal and 1-methylamino-3,5,5-trimethylhexane.[DE1,DE2]

2. 3,5,5-Trimethylhexanal + the formic acid salt of 1-methylamino-3,5,5-trimethylhexane (54% yield).[DE1,DE2]

$C_{19}H_{41}N$

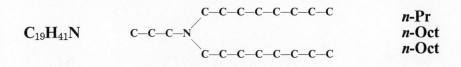

n-Pr
n-Oct
n-Oct

PROPYLDIOCTYLAMINE

Phys. Props.:

b_{10} 174°[BO13]
pK_a 8.51 at 25° (in 70% ethanol)[BO13]

Prepn.:

Octyl bromide + propylamine.[BO13]

$C_{20}H_{41}N$

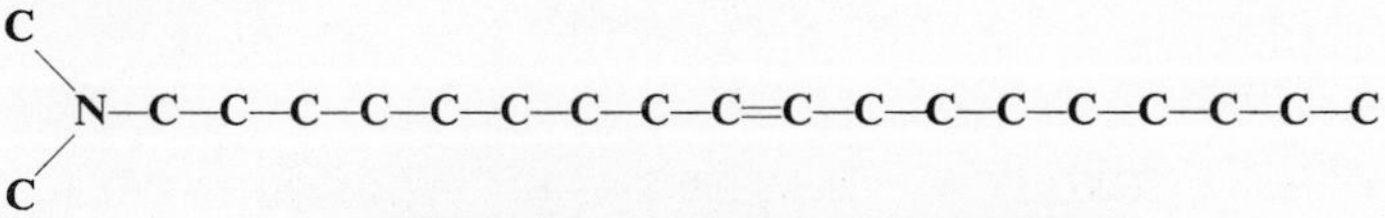

C
    \
     N—C—C—C—C—C—C—C—C—C—C=C—C—C—C—C—C—C—C—C—C
    /
C

Me
Me
$C_{18}H_{35}$

***cis*-1-DIMETHYLAMINO-9-OCTADECENE**

Prepn.:

Reaction under high pressure of oleyl alcohol (*cis*-9-octadecen-1-ol) with methylamine produces methyloleylamine and a small amount of subject compound.[SM4]

$C_{20}H_{43}N$

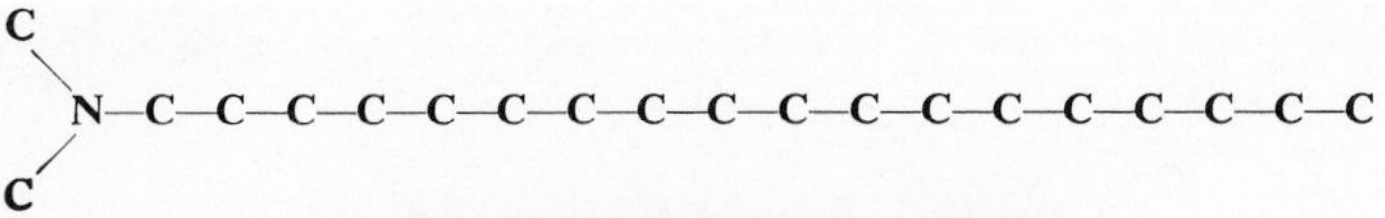

C
    \
     N—C—C—C—C—C—C—C—C—C—C—C—C—C—C—C—C—C—C—C—C
    /
C

Me
Me
n-$C_{18}H_{37}$

OCTADECYLDIMETHYLAMINE

Phys. Props.:

b_6 194°[KI5]; b_5 190°[KI5]; $b_{0.5}$ 161–163°[ST4]
m. 22.89°,[RE1] *ca.* 25°[ST4]
Viscosity of solutions[ST4]

Prepn.:

1. As part of a mixture of amines in the reaction of technical-grade stearyl-amine with formic acid and formaldehyde.[KI5]
2. Octadecylamine + formic acid + formaldehyde.[RE1]
3. Stearyl chloride + dimethylamine,[ST4] (almost quantitative yield).[FA5]
4. Octadecyl alcohol + dimethylamine under pressure (90% yield). (When methylamine is used instead of dimethylamine, methyloctadecylamine and a small amount of octadecyldimethylamine are obtained.)[SM4]

Derivs.:

Methochloride: m. softens at 70°, dec. at 180°[RE1]
Methiodide: m. 234.5–236°[TH3a]
Methonitrate: m. 210°[TH3a]
Methooctadecyl sulfate: m. 147°[TH3a]

$C_{20}H_{43}N$

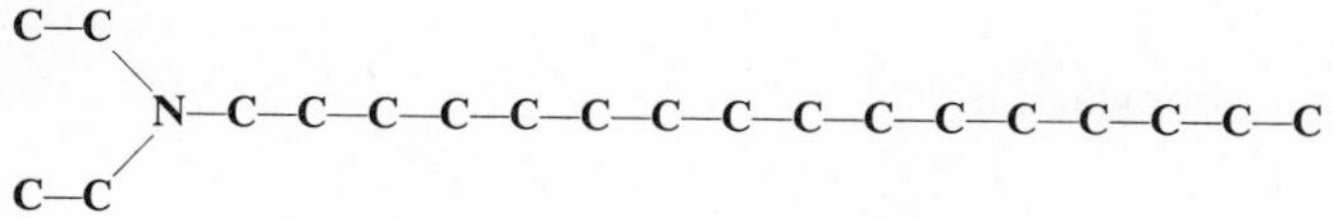

HEXADECYLDIETHYLAMINE

Phys. Props.:

b. 355° (cor.)[KR1]; b_{15} 204–206°[KR1]; b_{15} 200°[VA2]; b_{10-12} 198–201°[RE15]; $b_{2.5}$ 200° (bath temp.)[SA15]*; $b_{0.4}$ 161°[BR18]
m. 6–8°,[KR1] 4°[RE15]

Prepn.:

1. Thermal decomposition of hexadecyltriethylammonium hydroxide.[RE15]
2. Pressure reaction of diethylamine with 1-hexadecanol (44% yield).[SA15,VA2]
3. Obtained along with octadecyldimethylamine in the reaction of technical-grade stearylamine with formic acid and formaldehyde.[KI5,RE1]
4. Diethylamine + cetyl iodide[KR1]; + cetyl bromide (quantitative yield)[BR18]; + cetyl chloride.[SA15]

Derivs.:

Hydrochloride: m. 118–119°[YA2]
Ethiodide: m. 180–181° (dec.),[YA2] 179–181°[RE5]

---

* The reliability of this boiling point value seems poor since this author, as a co-worker in ref. YA2, cites the more reasonable value also listed.

$C_{20}H_{43}N$

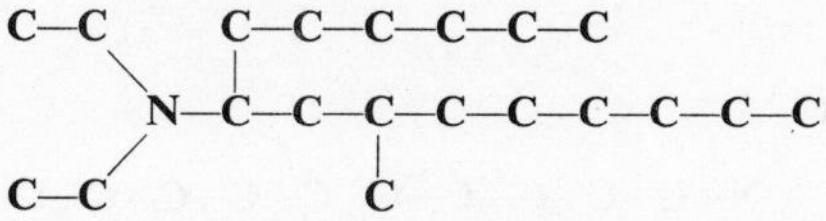

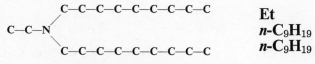

Et
Et
$C_{16}H_{33}$

7-DIETHYLAMINO-9-METHYLPENTADECANE

Phys. Props.:

b_2 146.5–150° [CO31a]

Prepn.:

Diethylamine + 7-bromo-9-methylpentadecane. [CO31a]

$C_{20}H_{43}N$

Et
n-C_9H_{19}
n-C_9H_{19}

ETHYLDINONYLAMINE

Phys. Props.:

b_{20} 208° [BO13]

Prepn.:

Nonyl bromide + ethylamine. [BO13]

Derivs.:

Hydrochloride: m. 78–79° [BO13]

$C_{20}H_{43}N$

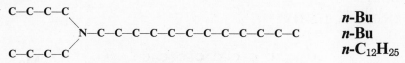

n-Bu
n-Bu
n-$C_{12}H_{25}$

DODECYLDIBUTYLAMINE

Phys. Props.:

b_{12} 188–190° [BO12]; b_{11} 186–190° [SC12]; b_3 158–160° [MA40]
d_{20}^{20} 0.8073 [MA40]
n_D^{20} 1.4471 [MA40]

Prepn.:

1. Dibutylamine + dodecyl bromide (68% yield). [BO12]
2. Transalkylation reaction by heating tributylamine with dodecyl alcohol. [SC12]

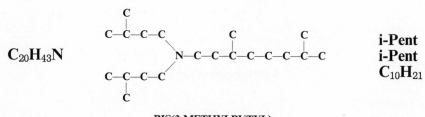

$C_{20}H_{43}N$ **i-Bu**
                   i-Bu
                   n-C$_{12}$H$_{25}$

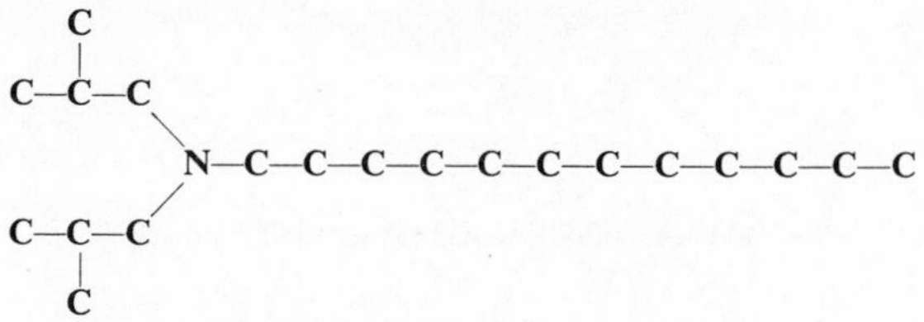

DODECYLDIISOBUTYLAMINE

Prepn.:

Reaction of isobutylamine with dodecyl alcohol gives isobutyldodecylamine and a small amount of dodecyldiisobutylamine.[SM4]

$C_{20}H_{43}N$ **i-Pent**
                   i-Pent
                   $C_{10}H_{21}$

**BIS(3-METHYLBUTYL)-
(3,7-DIMETHYLOCTYL)AMINE**

Phys. Props.:

b_{12} 161–162° [SK5]

Prepn.:

Reductive alkylation of diisopentylamine with citral and hydrogen (34% yield as the oxalate).[SK5]

Derivs.:

Oxalate: m. 112–113° [SK5]

$C_{21}H_{45}N$ **Me**
                   n-Oct
                   n-C$_{12}$H$_{25}$

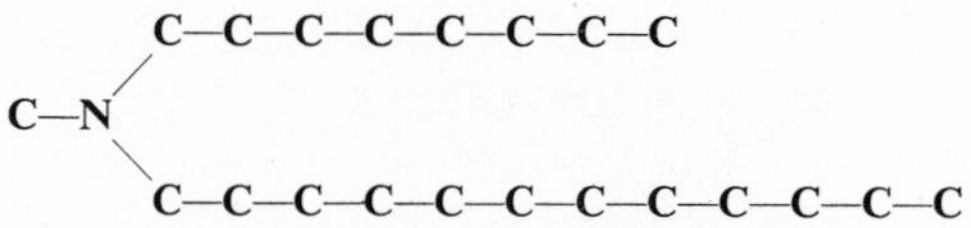

METHYLOCTYLDODECYLAMINE

Phys. Props.:

$b_{0.25}$ 170° [RA4]

Prepn.:

Methyldodecylamine + octyl bromide.[RA4]

$C_{21}H_{45}N$

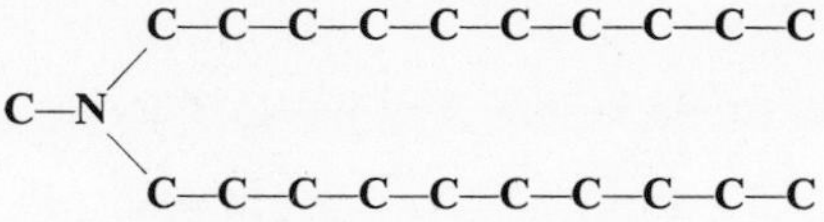

$$C-N\begin{cases}C-C-C-C-C-C-C-C-C-C\\C-C-C-C-C-C-C-C-C-C\end{cases}$$

Me
$n\text{-}C_{10}H_{21}$
$n\text{-}C_{10}H_{21}$

METHYLDIDECYLAMINE

Prepn.:

Didecylamine + formic acid + formaldehyde.[RA4]

$C_{21}H_{45}N$

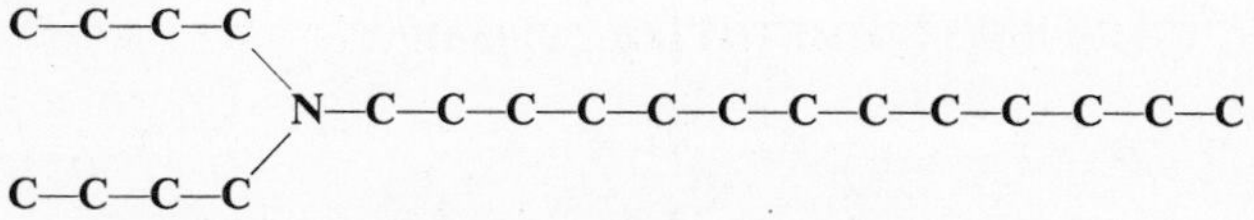

$$\begin{matrix}C-C-C-C\\ \quad\quad\quad N-C-C-C-C-C-C-C-C-C-C-C-C-C\\ C-C-C-C\end{matrix}$$

n-Bu
n-Bu
$n\text{-}C_{13}H_{27}$

TRIDECYLDIBUTYLAMINE

Phys. Props.:

$b_{0.1}$ 120–122° [MA40]
d_{20}^{20} 0.809[MA40]
n_D^{20} 1.448[MA40]

Prepn.:

Butyl(dibutylaminomethyl) ether + dodecylmagnesium bromide (52% yield).[MA40]

Derivs.:

Methiodide: m. 52–52.5° [MA40]

$C_{21}H_{45}N$

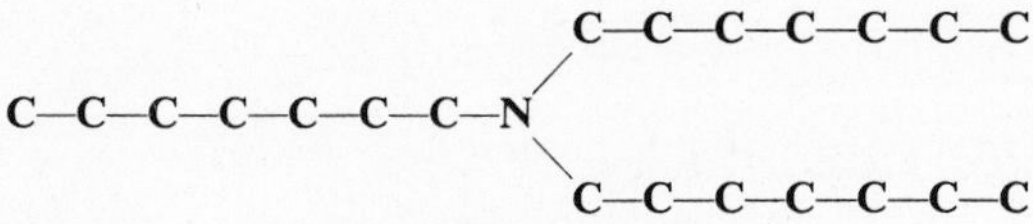

$$C-C-C-C-C-C-C-N\begin{cases}C-C-C-C-C-C-C\\C-C-C-C-C-C-C\end{cases}$$

n-Hept
n-Hept
n-Hept

TRIHEPTYLAMINE

Phys. Props.:

b_{762} *ca.* 330° [MA8,MA9,SA2]; b_6 185–195° [CO14]; b_1 151–154° [EA1]
Magnetic susceptibility: -251.3×10^{-6} [FR2]
Magneto-optic rotation: 1697[GA1a]

Prepn.:

1. Ammonia + heptyl bromide,[CO14] (trace yield)[DA14]; + heptyl chloride (1.5% yield).[DA14]
2. Catalytic hydrogenation of heptanaldoxime[MA8,MA9,SA2]

Derivs.:

Amine oxide picrate: m. 48.2–48.8°,[CO17] 44–46°[MA3]
Heptiodide: m. 121–122°[ER3]

$C_{22}H_{47}N$

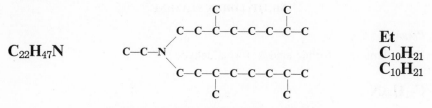

Et
$C_{10}H_{21}$
$C_{10}H_{21}$

ETHYLBIS(3,7-DIMETHYLOCTYL)AMINE

Phys. Props.:
b_{10} 186–188°[SK5]

Prepn.:

Reductive alkylation of di(3,7-dimethyloctyl)amine with acetaldehyde and
hydrogen (33% yield as the oxalate).[SK5]

Derivs.:
Oxalate: m. 94–95°[SK5]

$C_{22}H_{47}N$

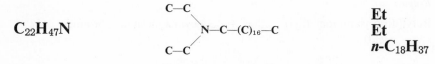

Et
Et
$n\text{-}C_{18}H_{37}$

OCTADECYLDIETHYLAMINE

Phys. Props.:
b_1 178–180°[SO3a]

Prepn.:
Octadecyl bromide + diethylamine.[SO3a]

$C_{22}H_{47}N$

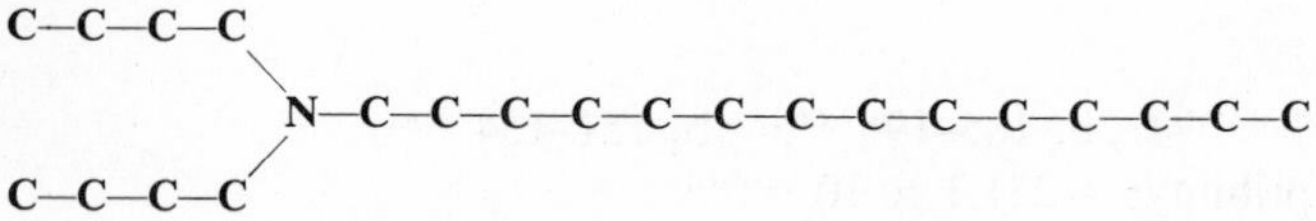

C—C—C—C
          N—C—C—C—C—C—C—C—C—C—C—C—C—C—C—C
C—C—C—C

n-Bu
n-Bu
$n\text{-}C_{14}H_{29}$

TETRADECYLDIBUTYLAMINE

Phys. Props.:
b_3 178–180°[MA40]
d_{20}^{20} 0.8046[MA40]
n_D^{20} 1.4480[MA40]

Prepn.:

Dibutylamine + 1-bromotetradecane (76% yield).[MA40]

$C_{22}H_{47}N$

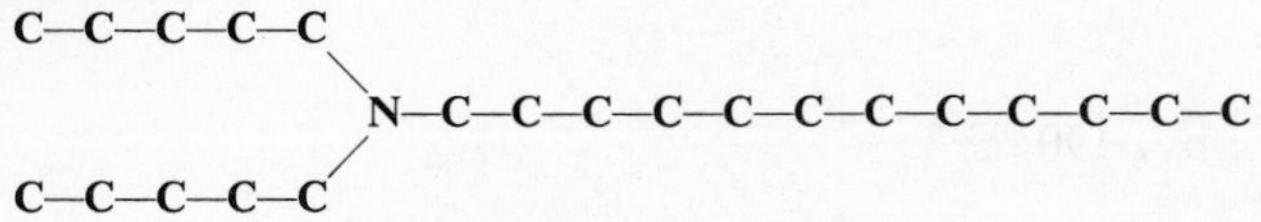

n-Pent
n-Pent
n-$C_{12}H_{25}$

DODECYLDIPENTYLAMINE

Phys. Props.:

b_3 174–175° [WO2]
d_4^{25} 0.8094[WO2]
n_D^{25} 1.4460[WO2]

Prepn.:

Copper chromite catalyzed hydrogenation of N,N-dipentyllauramide.[WO2]

$C_{23}H_{47}N$

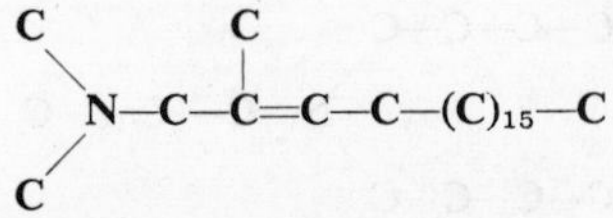

Me
Me
$C_{21}H_{41}$

1-DIMETHYLAMINO-2-METHYL-2-EICOSENE

Prepn.:

Reduction of N,N-dimethyl-2-methyl-2-eicosenoamide with lithium aluminum hydride.[BA19]

Derivs.:

Hydrochloride: m. 168–169°[BA19]

$C_{23}H_{49}N$

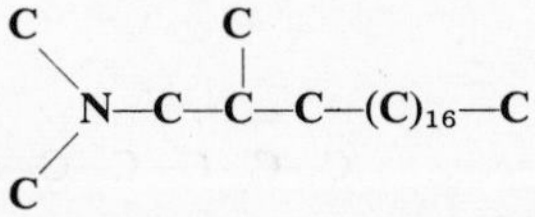

Me
Me
$C_{21}H_{43}$

1-DIMETHYLAMINO-2-METHYLEICOSANE

Prepn.:

Reduction of N,N-dimethyl-2-methyleicosanoamide with lithium aluminum hydride.[BA19]

Derivs.:

Hydrochloride: m. 176–178°[BA19]

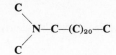

$C_{24}H_{51}N$

Me
Me
n-C$_{22}$H$_{45}$

DOCOSYLDIMETHYLAMINE

Phys. Props.:

$b_{0.6}$ *ca.* 190°[BR27]; $b_{0.6}$ 190°[BR18]
m. 44°,[BR18] 41°[BR27]

Prepn.:

1. Dimethylamine + 1-bromodocosane ("quantitative yield").[BR18]
2. Thermal decomposition of docosyltrimethylammonium hydroxide[BR18] (84% yield).[BR27]

Derivs.:

Hydrochloride: m. 180°[BR27]
Picrate: m. 84°[BR27]
Methobromide: m. *ca.* 240° (dec.)[BR27]

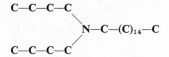

$C_{24}H_{51}N$

n-Bu
n-Bu
n-C$_{16}$H$_{33}$

HEXADECYLDIBUTYLAMINE

Phys. Props.:

b_4 203–205°[MA40]
d_{20}^{20} 0.8150[MA40]
n_D^{20} 1.4500[MA40]

Prepn.:

Dibutylamine + hexadecyl bromide (81% yield).[MA40]

$C_{24}H_{51}N$

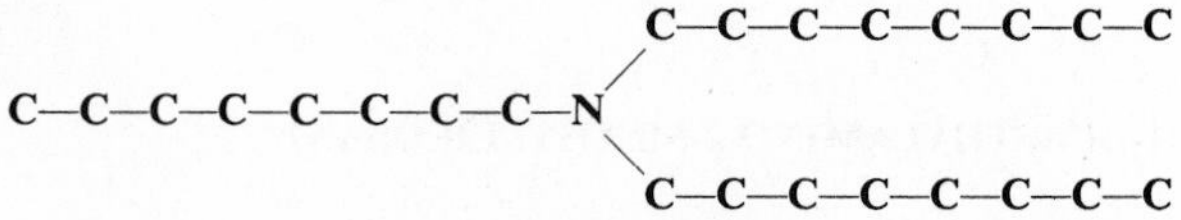

C—C—C—C—C—C—C—C

C—C—C—C—C—C—C—C—N

C—C—C—C—C—C—C—C

n-C$_8$H$_{17}$
n-C$_8$H$_{17}$
n-C$_8$H$_{17}$

TRIOCTYLAMINE

Phys. Props.:

b. 365–367°[ME15]; b_{12} 212–218°[BO13]; b_{10} 215.5–216°[AR1]; b_3 183–185.5°[WE17]; b_1 167–169°[EA1]; $b_{0.7}$ 164–168°[BO13]
m. −34.6°[RA3]

d_0^{20} 0.8110[AR1]

n_D^{20} 1.4499[AR1]; $n_D^{19.5}$ 1.450[WE17]

pK_a 8.35 at 25° (in 70% aqueous ethanol)[BO13]

Surface tension (dynes/cm.): 28.35 at 20°[AR1]

Dipole moment: 0.80 D (from benzene solution)[AR10]

Molar Kerr constant: 3.02 × 10⁻¹¹[AR10]

Prepn.:

1. Reaction of ammonia with octyl bromide (36% yield)[BO13]; with octyl chloride[MA14] (22% yield),[WE17] (0.8% yield)[NE2]; with 1-octanol,[AR7] in the presence of zinc chloride.[ME15]
2. Dioctylamine + octyl iodide.[RA3]

Derivs.:

Hydrochloride: m. 72–74°[EA1]

Propobromide: m. 72–75°[EA1]

Octyloiodide: m. 127–128°[ER3]

4,4'-Dichlorodiphenyldisulfimide salt: m. 137–138°[RU4]

$C_{24}H_{51}N$

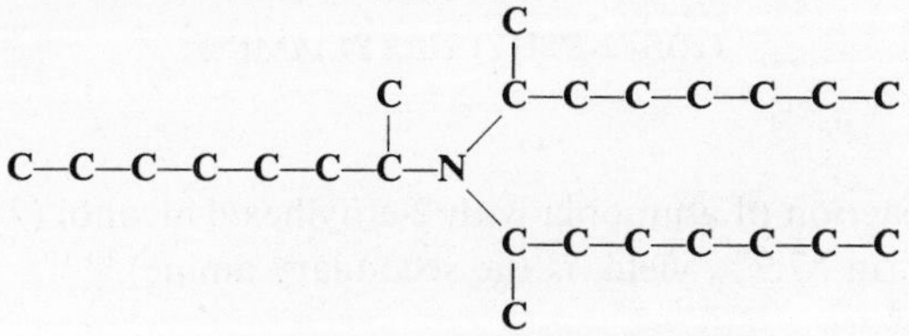

C_8H_{17}
C_8H_{17}
C_8H_{17}

TRI(1-METHYLHEPTYL)AMINE

Phys. Props.:

b. 370°[ME15]

Prepn.:

2-Octanol + ammonia in the presence of zinc chloride.[ME15]

$C_{24}H_{51}N$

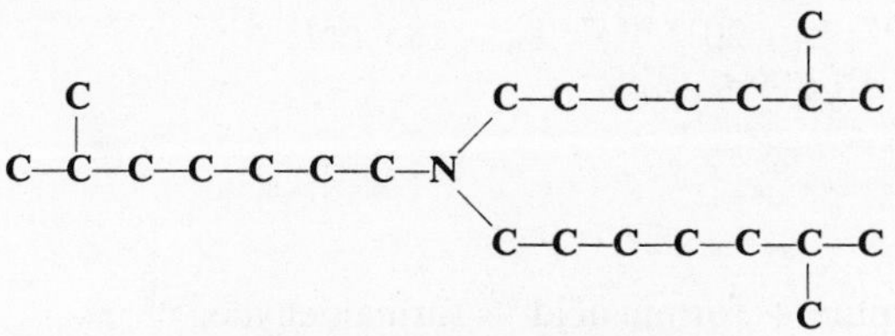

i-Oct
i-Oct
i-Oct

TRI(6-METHYLHEPTYL)AMINE

Phys. Props.:

b_{100} 275°[UN2]; b_{50} 253°[UN2]; b_{10} 209°[UN2]; $b_{0.1}$ 132–137°[UN2]

m. sets to a glass below −70°[UN2]

d_{20}^{20} 0.8195[UN2]
n_D^{20} 1.4519[UN2]
Viscosity (cp.): 14.4 at 20°[UN2]
Surface tension (dynes/cm.): 23.1 at 20°[UN2]
Flash point (Cleveland open cup): 325°F[UN2]

Prepn.:

Method of preparation was not cited by ref. UN2.

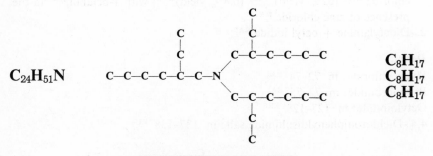

$C_{24}H_{51}N$

C_8H_{17}
C_8H_{17}
C_8H_{17}

TRIS-(2-ETHYLHEXYL)AMINE

Prepn.:

Vapor phase reaction of ammonia with 2-ethylhexyl alcohol (2% yield; main product, in 57.9% yield, is the secondary amine).[LE10]

$C_{25}H_{53}N$

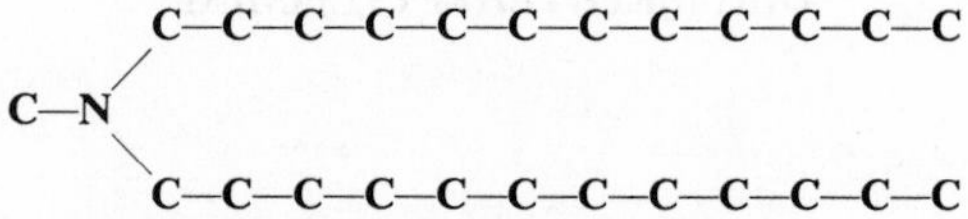

Me
$n\text{-}C_{12}H_{25}$
$n\text{-}C_{12}H_{25}$

METHYLDIDODECYLAMINE

Phys. Props.:

b_2 203–204°[WE17]; $b_{1.5}$ 201°[WE17]; $b_{0.35}$ 183°[RA4]
m. 15–16°,[WE17] 10.4°[RA4]
n_D^{22} 1.453[WE17]

Prepn.:

1. Didodecylamine + formic acid + formaldehyde.[RA4]
2. Decyl chloride + methylamine (51.5% yield).[WE17]
3. Methyldodecylamine + dodecyl chloride (51% yield).[WE17]

Derivs.:

Hydrochloride: m. 138°[WE17]

$C_{25}H_{53}N$

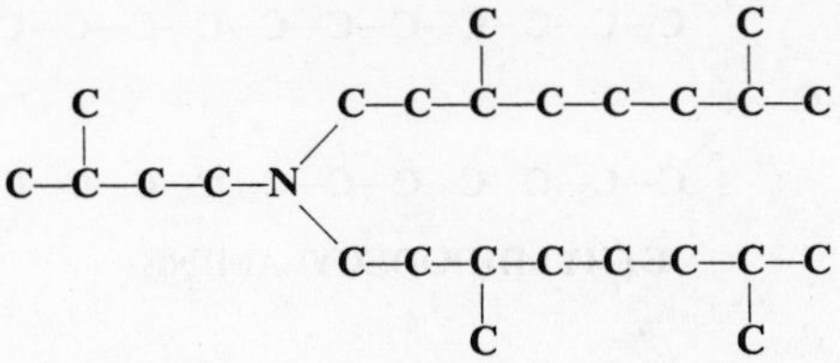

```
              C           C
              |           |
      C-C-C-C-C-C-C-C-C
      |
C-C-C-C-N
      |
      C-C-C-C-C-C-C-C-C
            |           |
            C           C
```

i-Pent
$C_{10}H_{21}$
$C_{10}H_{21}$

3-METHYLBUTYL-BIS(3,7-DIMETHYLOCTYL)AMINE

Phys. Props.:

b_{13} 208° [SK5]

Prepn.:

1. Reductive alkylation of 3-methylbutyl-(3,7-dimethyloctyl)amine with 3,7-dimethyloctanal (74% yield as the oxalate).[SK5]
2. Reductive alkylation of bis-(3,7-dimethyloctyl)amine with 3-methylbutanal (67% yield as the oxalate).[SK5]

Derivs.:

Oxalate: m. 100–101° [SK5]

$C_{26}H_{53}N$

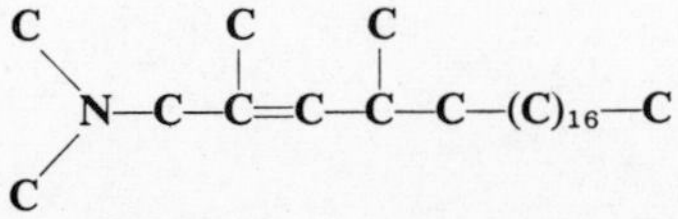

```
C
 \       C   C
  N-C-C=C-C-C-(C)₁₆-C
 /       |
C
```

Me
Me
$C_{24}H_{47}$

1-DIMETHYLAMINO-2,4-DIMETHYL-2-DOCOSENE

Prepn.:

Reduction of *N,N*-dimethyl-2,4-dimethyl-2-docosenoamide with lithium aluminum hydride.[BA19]

Derivs.:

Hydrochloride: m. 147–150° [BA19]

$C_{26}H_{55}N$

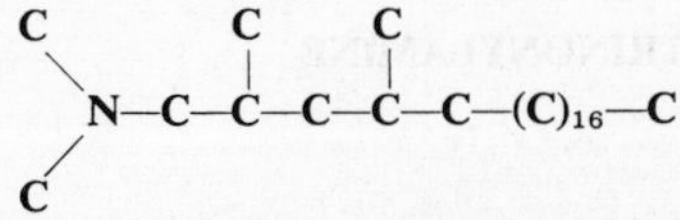

```
C
 \       C   C
  N-C-C-C-C-C-(C)₁₆-C
 /       |   |
C
```

Me
Me
$C_{24}H_{49}$

1-DIMETHYLAMINO-2,4-DIMETHYLDOCOSANE

Prepn.:

Reduction of *N,N*-dimethyl-2,4-dimethyldocosanoamide with lithium aluminum hydride.[BA19]

Derivs.:

Hydrochloride: m. 151–153° [BA19]

$C_{26}H_{55}N$ 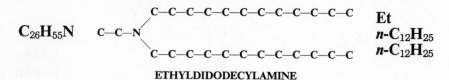 **Et**
n-$C_{12}H_{25}$
n-$C_{12}H_{25}$

ETHYLDIDODECYLAMINE

Phys. Props.:

$b_{0.03}$ 176–180° SC14
n_D^{25} 1.4516 SC14

Prepn.:

Triethylamine + 1-dodecanol + hydrogen under pressure (20% yield).SC14

$C_{26}H_{55}N$ 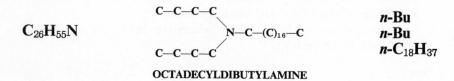 **n-Bu**
n-Bu
n-$C_{18}H_{37}$

OCTADECYLDIBUTYLAMINE

Phys. Props.:

b_3 204–207° MA40
d_{20}^{20} 0.8192 MA40
n_D^{20} 1.4513 MA40

Prepn.:

Dibutylamine + octadecyl bromide (79% yield).MA4

$C_{27}H_{57}N$

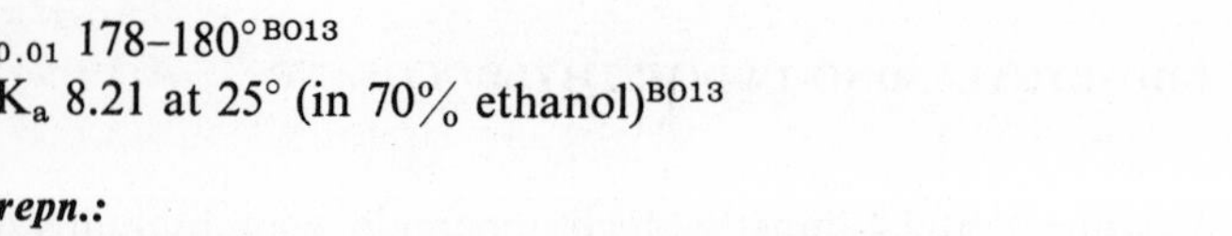

C—C—C—C—C—C—C—C—C **n-C_9H_{19}**
C—C—C—C—C—C—C—C—C—N **n-C_9H_{19}**
C—C—C—C—C—C—C—C—C **n-C_9H_{19}**

TRINONYLAMINE

Phys. Props.:

$b_{0.01}$ 178–180° BO13
pK_a 8.21 at 25° (in 70% ethanol)BO13

Prepn.:

Dinonylamine + nonyl bromide (47% yield).BO13

Derivs.:

Oxalate: m. 107–108° BO13

$C_{28}H_{59}N$

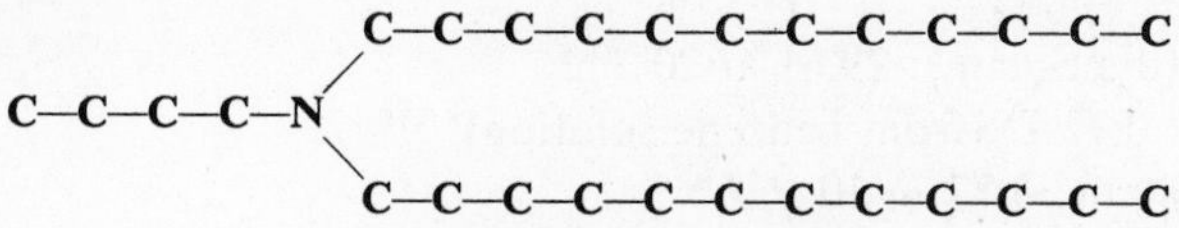

C—C—C—C—C—C—C—C—C—C—C—C—C
C—C—C—C—N
C—C—C—C—C—C—C—C—C—C—C—C—C

n-Bu
n-$C_{12}H_{25}$
n-$C_{12}H_{25}$

BUTYLDIDODECYLAMINE

Phys. Props.:

b_6 224–226° [SE3]
d_4^{20} 0.8281 [SE3]
n_D^{20} 1.4582 [SE3]

Prepn.:

1. Dodecyl *p*-toluenesulfonate + butylamine (29% yield). [SE3]
2. Dodecanonitrile + 1-butanol + hydrogen under pressure in the presence of nickel (3% yield). [SU1]

$C_{29}H_{61}N$ C—N
C—C—C—C—C—C—C—C—C—C—C—C—C—C
C—C—C—C—C—C—C—C—C—C—C—C—C—C

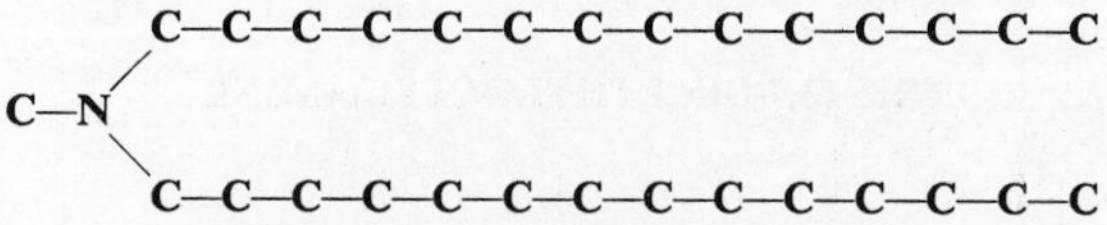

Me
n-$C_{14}H_{29}$
n-$C_{14}H_{29}$

METHYLBIS(TETRADECYL)AMINE

Phys. Props.:

$b_{0.03}$ 200–206° [ST4]
m. 24–25° [ST4]
Viscosity of solutions [ST4]

Prepn.:

1. Methylamine + tetradecyl bromide in a sealed tube. [ST4]
2. Di(tetradecyl)amine + formaldehyde + formic acid. [RA4]

$C_{30}H_{63}N$

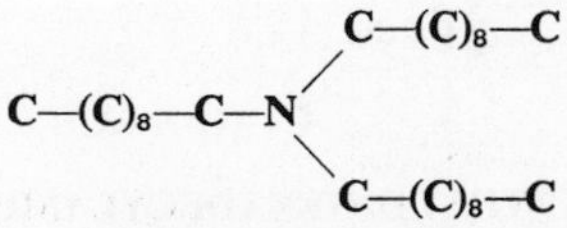

C—(C)$_8$—C
C—(C)$_8$—C—N
C—(C)$_8$—C

n-$C_{10}H_{21}$
n-$C_{10}H_{21}$
n-$C_{10}H_{21}$

TRIDECYLAMINE

Phys. Props.:

b_1 224.5–245° [AR1]
m. −5 to −3° [EA1]

d_0^{20} 0.8197[AR1]
n_D^{20} 1.4531
Surface tension (dynes/cm.): 29.61 at 20°[AR1]
Dipole moment: 0.72 D (from benzene solution)[AR10]
Molar Kerr constant: 3.77×10^{-11}[AR10]

Prepn.:

No preparative details were given in any of the above references cited.

Derivs.:

Decyloiodide: m. 118–120°[ER3]

$C_{30}H_{63}N$

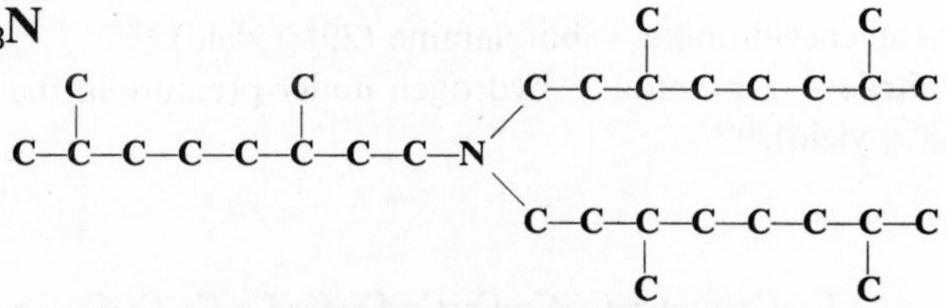

TRIS-(3,7-DIMETHYLOCTYL)AMINE

$C_{10}H_{21}$
$C_{10}H_{21}$
$C_{10}H_{21}$

Phys. Props.:

b_{12} 237–239°[SK5]

Prepn.:

1. Reductive alkylation of bis-(3,7-dimethyloctyl)amine with citral and hydrogen (64% yield); in 84% yield when tetrahydrocitral is used instead of citral.[SK5]

Derivs.:

Oxalate: m. 105–106°[SK5]

$C_{33}H_{69}N$

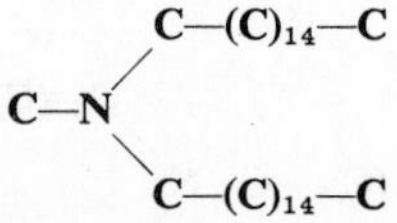

METHYLDIHEXADECYLAMINE

Me
n-$C_{16}H_{33}$
n-$C_{16}H_{33}$

Phys. Props.:

b_1 269–271°[WE17]; $b_{0.02}$ 238–244°[ST4]
m. 36–37°,[WE17] 34–35°[ST4]
Viscosity of solutions[ST4]

Prepn.:

1. Methylamine + hexadecyl chloride (68% yield)[WE17]; + hexadecyl bromide.[ST4]
2. Dihexadecylamine + formic acid + formaldehyde.[RA4]

$C_{36}H_{75}N$

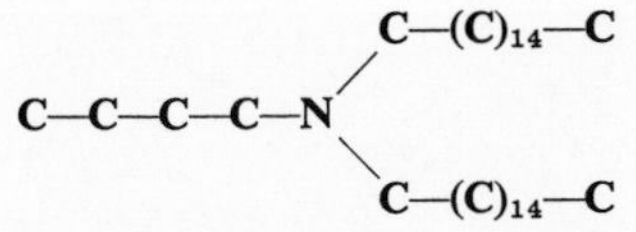

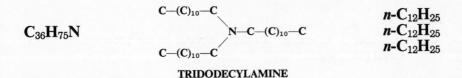

n-Bu
n-$C_{16}H_{33}$
n-$C_{16}H_{33}$

BUTYLDIHEXADECYLAMINE

Phys. Props.:

b_6 295–297° [SE3]
m. 44–46° [SE3]

Prepn.:

Butylamine + hexadecyl-*p*-toluenesulfonate (33% yield).[SE3]

$C_{36}H_{75}N$

n-$C_{12}H_{25}$
n-$C_{12}H_{25}$
n-$C_{12}H_{25}$

TRIDODECYLAMINE

Phys. Props.:

$b_{0.03}$ 220–228° [SC14]
m. 15–17°,[EA1] 15.7° [RA3]
n_D^{25} 1.4567 [SC14]

Prepn.:

1. Didodecylamine + dodecyl chloride [MC1]; + dodecyl iodide.[RA3,SC14]
2. By-product (17% yield) in the reaction of dodecanonitrile, 1-butanol, and hydrogen under pressure to give mainly 1-butylaminododecane.[SU1]
3. Dodecyl iodide + aqueous ammonia (52% yield).[BO13]
4. Vapor phase reaction of ammonia with dodecyl alcohol.[AR7]

Derivs.:

Hydrochloride: m. 78–79° [BO13,MC1]
Dodecyloiodide: m. 116–117° [ER3]

$C_{37}H_{77}N$

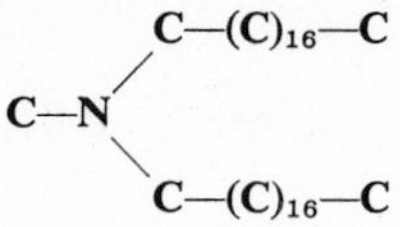

C—N
C—(C)$_{16}$—C
C—(C)$_{16}$—C

Me
n-C$_{18}$H$_{37}$
n-C$_{18}$H$_{37}$

METHYLDIOCTADECYLAMINE

Phys. Props.:

$b_{0.05}$ 252–259° [ST4]
m. 40° [ST4]
Viscosity of solutions[ST4]

Prepn.:

Methylamine + octadecyl bromide in a sealed tube.[ST4]

$C_{39}H_{81}N$

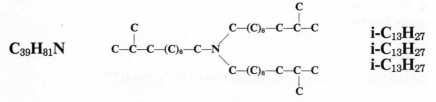

i-C$_{13}$H$_{27}$
i-C$_{13}$H$_{27}$
i-C$_{13}$H$_{27}$

TRIS-(11-METHYLDODECYL)AMINE

Prepn.:

Ammonia vapor + refluxing isotridecyl alcohol in the presence of Raney
nickel (58% yield).[WH1]

$C_{42}H_{87}N$

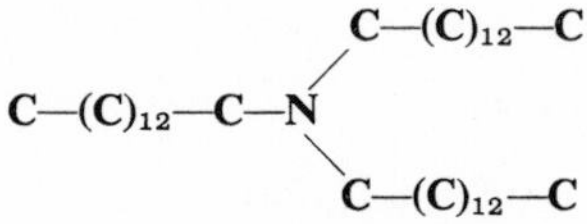

C—(C)$_{12}$—C—N
C—(C)$_{12}$—C
C—(C)$_{12}$—C

n-C$_{14}$H$_{29}$
n-C$_{14}$H$_{29}$
n-C$_{14}$H$_{29}$

TRI(TETRADECYL)AMINE

Phys. Props.:

$b_{0.1}$ 273–278° [ST4]
m. 33–34° [ST4]
Viscosity of solutions[ST4]

Prepn.:

Ammonia + tetradecyl bromide.[ST4]

Derivs.:

Tetradecyloiodide: m. 114.5–115° [ER3]

$C_{48}H_{99}N$

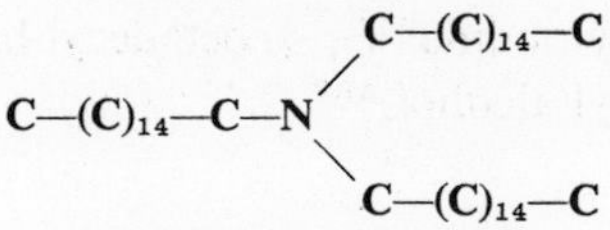

$$C-(C)_{14}-C-N \begin{array}{c} C-(C)_{14}-C \\ \\ C-(C)_{14}-C \end{array}$$

$n\text{-}C_{16}H_{33}$
$n\text{-}C_{16}H_{33}$
$n\text{-}C_{16}H_{33}$

TRIHEXADECYLAMINE

Phys. Props.:

$b_{0.03}$ 277–282°[ST4]
m. 42–43.5°,[ST4] 39°,[FR10] 38–40°[AR1]
Viscosity of solutions[ST4]

Prepn.:

Ammonia + hexadecyl iodide[FR10,GI5]; + hexadecyl bromide.[ST4]

Derivs.:

Hexadecyloiodide: m. 80°,[GI5] 110–111°[ER3]

$C_{54}H_{105}N$

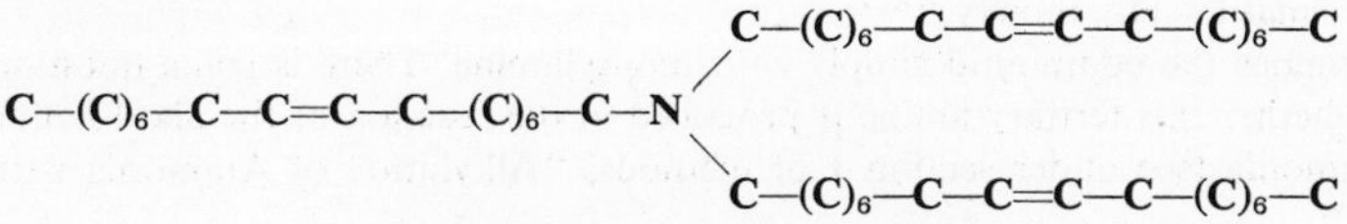

$$C-(C)_6-C-C=C-C-(C)_6-C-N \begin{array}{c} C-(C)_6-C-C=C-C-(C)_6-C \\ \\ C-(C)_6-C-C=C-C-(C)_6-C \end{array}$$

$C_{18}H_{35}$
$C_{18}H_{35}$
$C_{18}H_{35}$

TRI(9-OCTADECENYL)AMINE

Prepn.:

Reaction of oleyl alcohol with ammonia in the vapor phase over alumina gives a mixture (uncharacterized) of mono-, di-, and tri-oleylamines.[AR7]

$C_{54}H_{111}N$

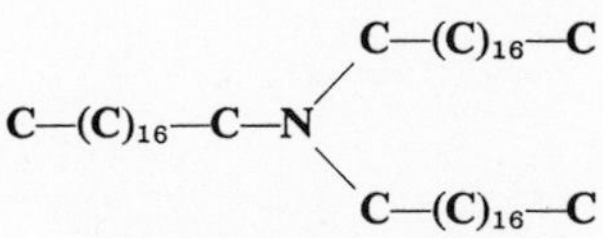

$$C-(C)_{16}-C-N \begin{array}{c} C-(C)_{16}-C \\ \\ C-(C)_{16}-C \end{array}$$

$n\text{-}C_{18}H_{37}$
$n\text{-}C_{18}H_{37}$
$n\text{-}C_{18}H_{37}$

TRIOCTADECYLAMINE

Phys. Props.:

m. 54–55°,[MC1] 54.6°,[ST4] 54.0°[RA3]; 47.6°,[WE9] 38–40°[AR1]
Viscosity of solutions [ST4]

Prepn.:

1. Dioctadecylamine + octadecyl chloride,[MA40,MC1] (52% yield)[MA40]; + octadecyl iodide.[RA3]

2. Ammonia + octadecyl iodide[WE9]; + octadecyl bromide.[ST4]
3. Ammonia + octadecyl alcohol.[AR7]

Derivs.:

Hydriodide: m. 79.5–81°[HO26] (the hydriodide was formed instead of the
quaternary salt upon reaction of octadecyl iodide with trioctadecyl-
amine)

$C_{87}H_{177}N$

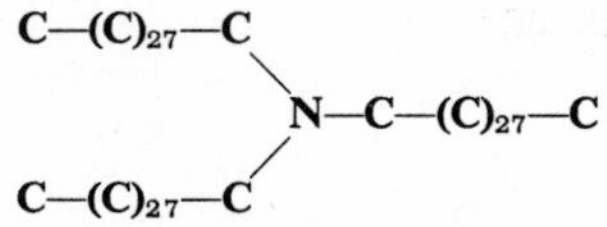

$$
\begin{array}{l}
C-(C)_{27}-C \\
\phantom{C-(C)_{27}-C} \diagdown \\
\phantom{C-(C)_{27}-C-}N-C-(C)_{27}-C \\
\phantom{C-(C)_{27}-C} \diagup \\
C-(C)_{27}-C
\end{array}
$$

n-$C_{29}H_{59}$
n-$C_{29}H_{59}$
n-$C_{29}H_{59}$

TRIMONTANYLAMINE*

Prepn.:

Purported to be formed along with the primary and secondary amines by the
reaction of liquid ammonia, under pressure at 100°, with the product
from montanyl alcohol and thionyl chloride.[FA8]†

---

* The montanyl group, derived from the compounds in montan wax, appears to be
basically the normal $C_{29}H_{59}$ moiety.[WA17]

† Ref. FA8 names the compound simply as trimontylamine. There is some question
in our minds whether this tertiary amine is produced in the reaction of the alkyl halide
with liquid ammonia (see under section 1 of methods, "Alkylation of Ammonia with
Alkyl Halides").

Polyamines

$C_5H_{14}N_2$

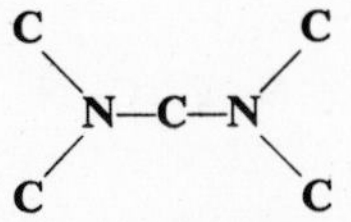

$$\begin{array}{ccc} C & & C \\ & \diagdown & \diagup \\ & N{-}C{-}N & \\ & \diagup & \diagdown \\ C & & C \end{array}$$

Me
Me
—CH$_2$—
Me
Me

BIS(DIMETHYLAMINO)METHANE

Phys. Props.:

b. 90–95°,[KL2]* 86°,[BO9] 85°,[BR23,HE15,HE16] 83–84°,[AT2] 82–83°,[DZ1] 82.5°[PI3]; b$_{760}$ 82–84°[DA4]

d$_4^{20}$ 0.7494[AT2]; d$_4^{18.7}$ 0.7491[HE16]

Raman spectrum[KA5]

Prepn.:

1. Dimethylamine + formaldehyde,[HE15,IS1] (59% yield).[DZ1]
2. Heating dimethylaminomethanol.[HE16,MC1]
3. Dimethylamine + methylene chloride.[JO8]
4. Treatment of chlorodimethylamine with finely divided silver[KA4]; with copper bronze (14% yield)[KL2]*; with magnesium dimethylamide (6% yield).[KL2]*
5. By-product in thermal decomposition of 1,1,1-trimethylhydrazonium hydroxide (2.5% yield).[KL1]

---

* Ref. KL2 reported that dimethylchloramine reacts with either copper bronze or magnesium dimethylamide to give the present product (although the boiling point is high and, in the absence of analytical data, decomposition reactions are given as structure proof). That the expected tetramethylhydrazine was not obtained was attributed to elimination of hydrogen chloride from the chloramine to give N-methylmethylenimine (the Schiff base derivable from methylamine and formaldehyde), which could react further to the observed product. In partial support for this hypothesis, Class, Aston, and Oakwood[CL6] subsequently synthesized tetramethylhydrazine and found its boiling point to be 73°.

6. Thermal decomposition of 1-dimethylaminomethylpiperidine produces bis(dimethylamino)methane and bis(piperidino)methane.[BO9]
7. By-product in the photolysis or pyrolysis of 1,1,4,4-tetramethyl-2-tetrazene (trace yield).[WA20a]
8. Irradiation of trimethylamine with γ-rays gives about 1% yield of a mixture of bis(dimethylamino)methane and 1,2-bis(dimethylamino)-ethane.[SM11]

*Derivs.:**

Bis-picrate: m. 95°[SN1]

$C_6H_{12}N_2$

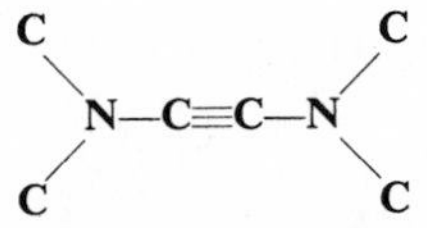

1,2-BIS(DIMETHYLAMINO)ETHYNE

Derivs.:

Bis-methoperchlorate: m. above 350°[OT2]
Bis-methochloroplatinate: m. 285°[OT2]
These salts were prepared *via* the methochloride, which in turn was prepared from 1,2-dichloroethyne and trimethylamine.

$C_6H_{14}N_2$

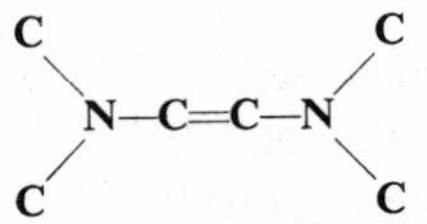

1,2-BIS(DIMETHYLAMINO)ETHENE

Phys. Props.:

b_{15} 38–40°[DO5,MA4]
n. 1.4643–1.4658[MA4] (measurement conditions unspecified); n_D 1.4648[DO5]

---

* The usual derivatives of bis(dialkylamino)methanes are difficult to prepare because of the ease of cleavage of these molecules.[BO9,BO10,HU3] For example, Hunt and Wagner[HU3] showed that most of the acid salts of bis(dialkylamino)methanes reported in the literature are in fact salts of the corresponding secondary amines. Ref. TS2 found that reaction of bis(dimethylamino)methane with methyl iodide in dry ether gives tetramethyl-ammonium iodide. Ref. BO10 prepared the monomethobromide of bis(dimethylamino)-methane by reaction with methyl bromide under rigorously anhydrous conditions. No melting point was given.

Prepn.:

Dimethylamine + chloroacetaldehyde,[DO5] (38% yield).[MA4]

$C_6H_{16}N_2$

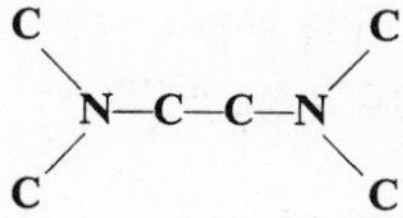

Me Me —CH₂CH₂— Me Me

1,2-BIS(DIMETHYLAMINO)ETHANE

Phys. Props.:

b. 120–122°,[BR6] 119–122°,[EA1,RE17] 121–121.5°[HA11]; b_{760} 121°[CL1]; b_{760} 120°[GR4]; b_{748} 121.0–121.6°[SP1]; b_{745} 120–122°[KN4]; b_{724} 119.4–119.5[SP3]

m. −57°,[RE17] −55.1°[SP3]

d_4^{25} 0.7711[SP1]; d_4^{20} 0.77654,[CL1] 0.7753[RE17]; d_4^{15} 0.78107[CL1]

n_D^{25} 1.4180,[MA4] 1.4170,[MA4] 1.4159[SP1]; n_D^{20} 1.4167[RE17]; n_D^{18} 1.4196[SP3]; n_α^{20} 1.41480[CL1]; n_γ^{20} 1.42984[CL1]

pK_{a_1} 5.85, pK_{a_2} 8.97 (at 30°)[SP3]; pK_{a_1} 5.75, pK_{a_2} 9.18 (at 25°)[SP1]; pK_{a_1} 5.7, pK_{a_2} 9.1 (at 22°)[RO10]

Infrared absorption: maxima at 3.41 and 3.61 μ[WR2]

Viscosity (cs.): 0.74 at 75°F, 2.02 at −40°F, 3.00 at −65°F[RE17]

Prepn.:

1. 1,2-Ethylenediamine + formaldehyde (40% yield)[HA11]; + formic acid and formaldehyde.[GR6]
2. Dimethylamine + 1,2-dibromoethane,[FR8] (nearly quantitative yield),[FA5] (65% yield)[HA11]; similar reaction with 1,2-dichloroethane.[FA5]
3. Dimethylamine + 2-chloroethyldimethylamine.[G44]
4. Thermal decomposition of ethylene-1,2-bis-trimethylammonium hydroxide[SK6]; of (2-dimethylaminoethyl)ethyldimethylammonium hydroxide (30% yield)[HA11]; of 1,1,4,4-tetramethylpiperazinium hydroxide.[HR1]
5. N-Benzhydryl-N',N'-dimethylethylenediamine + formaldehyde.[FO4]
6. Cleavage of α-methylmorphimethine with hydrogen chloride[KN2]; of thebaine methiodide with sodium methoxide.[KN3]
7. Hydrogenolysis of ethylene-1,2-bis(aminodimethylammonium)dibromide.[EV1]
8. Irradiation of trimethylamine with γ-rays gives about 1% yield of a mixture of bases, 1,2-bis(dimethylamino)ethane and bis(dimethylamino)methane.[SM11]

Derivs.:

Bis-hydrochloride: m. 303° (dec.),[HR1] 300° (dec.),[KN2,SM11] dec. at 300° (sinters at 280°),[FO4] dec. at 288°,[FO4] (sinters at 280°)[FR8]

Bis-picrate: m. 263°,[SM11] 263° (dec. at 250°),[HA11] 255° (dec.),[KN4] 253–254° (dec.),[HR1] *ca.* 252° (dec.)[KN4]

Bis-chloroplatinate: m. 252° (dec.),[FR8] 250° (dec.),[KN2,KN3] 246° (dec.)[MA19]

Bis-chloroaurate: 212° (dec.),[KN2,KN3] 205° (dec.),[FR8] 200° (dec.)[HR1]

Bis-(2,4-dinitrophenolate): m. 171.5°[HR1]

Bis-methochloride: m. 252–254° (dec.)[LE16]

Bis-methobromide*

Bis-methiodide: m. 282° (dec.),[GR6] 265° (dec.),[ZA1] 250° (dec.)[MO14,SK6]

Bis-methopicrate: m. 285° (dec.)[HA11]

Bis-methochloroaurate: m. 223–225°[SC11]

Bis-methochloroplatinate: m. 275–276°[SC11]

Bis-methochloroplatinate monohydrate: m. 80° (resolidifies at 100° then dec. at 220°)[FR6]

Bis-methochloride·CdCl$_2$: m. > 320°[FR6]

Bis-ethiodide: m. 233° (dec.)[HA11]

Bis-ethopicrate: m. 216° (dec.)[HA11]

Monoethopicrate: m. 212–214°[HA11]

·PdCl$_2$: m. 245–247°[MA19]

·PdBr$_2$: m. 226°[MA19]

·PtCl$_2$: m. 303°[MA19]

·IrCl$_2$: m. 288°[MA19]

·Cu(SCN)$_2$: m. 107°[MA19]

·Cu(II) picrate: m. 240°[MA19]

·CdCl$_2$: m. 254–255° (resolidifies to a white solid mass at 260°)[MA19]

Bis(diamine) μ,μ'-dihydroxydicopper (II) dinitrate: both the trihydrate and the monohydrate of this compound have the same m.p., 178–179°[MA19]

$C_7H_{16}N_2$ 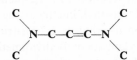   Me
Me
$+C_3H_4+$
Me
Me

1,3-BIS(DIMETHYLAMINO)PROPENE

Phys. Props.:

b_{13} 52–54°[MA22]; $b_{10.3}$ 48°[MA4]; b_5 37–43°,[DO6] 35–45°[RE17]

m. −90°[RE17]

d_4^{20} 0.8223[RE17]

n_D^{20} 1.4600,[MA4] 1.4589°[MA4]; n 1.4650 (conditions unspecified)[DO6]

---

* According to ref. GR6 the reaction of trimethylamine with 1,2-dibromoethane results in a mixture of products, among which is tetramethylammonium bromide. Ref. GR6 claims that other investigators (e.g., ref. BA28) erroneously reported the product of the foregoing reaction to be ethylene-bis-trimethylammonium bromide, but actually obtained tetramethylammonium bromide.

Ultraviolet absorption[TS3]
Viscosity (cs.): 1.30 at 75°F, 6.96 at -40°F, 15.06 at -65°F[RE17]

Prepn.:

Reaction of acrolein with dimethylamine in the presence of magnesium sulfate (73.6% yield)[DO6]; of sodium carbonate (55.8% yield)[DO6]; of potassium carbonate (*ca.* 60% yield)[MA22]; (50% yield),[DO6] (30% yield).[MA4]

$C_7H_{18}N_2$

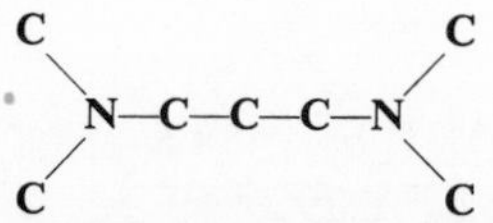

C\ /C
 N—C—C—C—N
C/ \C

Me
Me
$-(CH_2)_3$
Me
Me

1,3-BIS(DIMETHLAMINO)PROPANE

Phys. Props.:

b. 146°,[RE17] 143–145°[MA22]; b_{760} 144°[CL2]; b_{755} 145–146°,[KN6] 143–145°[MA22]; b_{747} 143.8–144.2°[SP1]
m. -82°[RE17]
d_4^{25} 0.7783[SP1]; d_4^{20} 0.7822[RE17]; $d_4^{18.7}$ 0.7837[CL2]
n_D^{25} 1.4213[SP1]; n_D^{20} 1.4236[RE17]; $n_\alpha^{18.7}$ 1.4215[CL2]; $n_\gamma^{18.7}$ 1.4362[CL2]
pK_{a_1} 9.79, pK_{a_2} 7.69 at 25°[SP1]; pK_{a_1} 9.8, pK_{a_2} 7.7 at 22°[RO10]
Viscosity (cs.): 0.97 at 75°F, 3.35 at -40°F, 5.54 at -65°F[RE17]

Prepn.:

1. Dimethylamine + 1,3-dibromopropane.[CL2,KN6]
2. Thermal decomposition of propylene-1,3-bis(trimethylammonium) hydroxide (1% yield),[BR10] (0% yield).[LU23]
3. By-product in the thermal decomposition of decamethylspermine sulfide.[DU3]
4. Hofmann degradation of 1,5-dimethyl-1,5-diaza-octane[KN6]; of methylated pithecolobine.[W16]

Derivs.:

Bis-picrate: m. 207° (dec.),[CL2] 206–207°,[DU3] 205°[BR10,KN6]
Bis-chloroaurate: m. 214–215°[DU3]
Bis-chloroplatinate: m. 247°,[MA22] 246–247° (dec.),[KN6] 240–244°[DU3]
Bis-methobromide: m. 285° (dec.)[LU23]
Bis-methobromide·4Br: m. 163°[PA7]
Bis-methochloride: m. 252–254° (dec.)[LE16]
Bis-methochloride·2HgCl$_2$: 268–270° (dec.)[DU3]
Bis-methiodide·4I: m. 205°[ST19]; ·8I: m. *ca.* 150°[ST19]; ·16I: m. *ca.* 100°[ST19]
Bis-methopicrate: m. 284–286° (dec.)[DU3]
Bis-methochloroaurate: m. 280–282 (dec.),[DU3] 245°[PA7]

Bis-methochloroplatinate monohydrate: m. 282–286° (dec.)[DU3]
Bis-methoperchlorate: stable to 250°[HO10]
Bis-methochloroplatinate: m. 274–275° (dec.)[LU1]

$C_7H_{18}N_2$

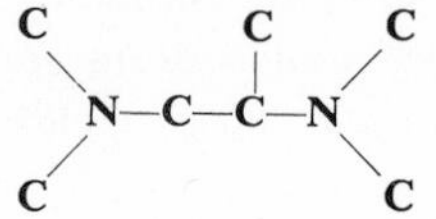

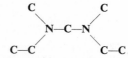

1,2-BIS(DIMETHYLAMINO)PROPANE

Me
Me
$\text{+C}_3\text{H}_6\text{+}$
Me
Me

Phys. Props.:

b. 140–142°,[PA15] 133–137°[RE17]; b_{748} 138.6–138.8°[SP1]; b_{745} 138–139°[MO16]
d_4^{25} 0.7900,[MO16] 0.7896[SP1]; d_4^{20} 0.7950[RE17]
n_D^{25} 1.4241,[SP1] 1.4230[MO16]; n_D^{20} 1.4248[RE17]
pK_{a_1} 5.40, pK_{a_2} 9.49 (at 30°)[SP3]; pK_{a_1} 5.33, pK_{a_2} 9.76 (at 25°)[SP1]
Dielectric constant: 2.4[SP3]
Viscosity (cs.): 0.94 at 75°F, 3.42 at −40°F, 5.78 at −65°F[RE17]

Prepn.:

1. 1,2-Propanediamine + formaldehyde + formic acid (76% yield).[MO16]
2. By-product (in 7% yield) in the reaction of 2-chloro-1-dimethylamino-propane with sodium.[PA15]

Derivs.:

Bis-hydrochloride: m. 177–179°[MO16]
Bis-picrate: m. 190°[PA15]
Monopicrate: m. 112–114°[MO16]
Bis-methiodide: m. 223–225° (dec.)[MO16]
Bis-methotosylate: m. 228–229°[MO16]

$C_7H_{18}N_2$

BIS(METHYLETHYLAMINO)METHANE

Me
Et
—CH_2—
Me
Et

Phys. Props.:

b. 131°[GR8]
d_4^{18} 0.7888[GR8]

Prepn.:

Hydrolysis of the monomethiodide of N,N',N''-triethyltrimethylenetri-amine.[GR8]

$C_8H_{16}N_2$

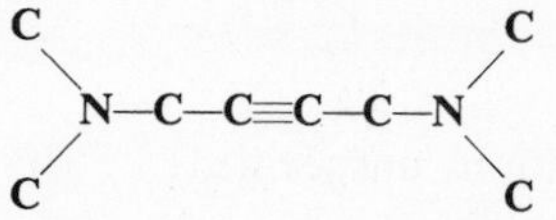

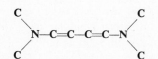

Me
Me
$\overline{)C_4H_4)}$
Me
Me

1,4-BIS(DIMETHYLAMINO)-2-BUTYNE

Phys. Props.:

b. 181–183°,[FE2] 180°,[RE11] 178–180°[RE7]; b_{31} 92°[BA17,JO1,JO2] (ref. BI3 reports $b_{0.4}$ 95–98°; this is obviously in error)
n_D^{20} 1.4561,[JO1] 1.4550[FE2]

Prepn.:

1. 1,4-Bis(dimethylamino)-2-chloro-2-butene + potassium hydroxide (87% yield),[BA11] (68% yield).[BA17]
2. 1,1-Bis(dimethylamino)methane + formaldehyde + acetylene in the presence of copper(I) chloride (73% yield).[FE2]
3. Dimethylamine + formaldehyde + acetylene in the presence of copper(II) acetate (about 10% yield).[RE7,RE11] Main product (70% yield) is propargyldimethylamine.
4. 1,4-Dichlore-2-butyne + dimethylamine[BI1] (31% yield).[JO1,JO2]

Derivs.:

Bis-picrate: m. 240–242° (dec.)[JO1]
Bis-methobromide: m. 235° (dec.)[BA11]
Bis-ethobromide: m. 210° (dec.)[BA11]
Bis-propobromide: m. 190° (dec.)[BA11]
Bis-butobromide: m. 89° (dec.)[BA11]

$C_8H_{16}N_2$

Me
Me
$\overline{)C_4H_4)}$
Me
Me

1,4-BIS(DIMETHYLAMINO)-1,3-BUTADIENE

Phys. Props.:

cis,trans isomer
  b_{760} 205°[FE4]; b_{27} 112°[FE5]; b_{20} 100–109°[FE5]; b_{15} 108°[FE2]; b_7 75–80°[FE2];
    $b_{1.1–0.65}$ 63–73°[FE5]
  m. below −100°[FE4]
  n_D^{20} 1.5500[FE2,FE4]; n (conditions unspecified) 1.5492[FE5]
  Infrared absorption[FE2]
  Ultraviolet absorption: 2940 A. (ε 19,300)[FE2,FE4]

trans,trans isomer

b_{760} 215° [FE4]; b_2 80° [FE2]; b_1 61–62° [MC8]*

m. −4° [FE2,FE4]

n_D^{20} 1.5569[FE4]; n (conditions unspecified) 1.5550[MC8]*

Infrared absorption[FE2]

Ultraviolet absorption: 2875 A. (ϵ 23,200)[FE2,FE4]

Prepn.:

1. Isomerization of 1,3-bis(dimethylamino)-2-butyne yields the *cis,trans* isomer† when the following catalysts are used: sodium (89% yield),[FE5] (85% yield)[FE2]; lithium (70% yield),[FE5] (81% yield)[FE2]; phenylsodium (85% yield)[FE5]; Alfin catalyst (55% yield)[FE2]; sodamide (12% yield)[FE2]; potassium (9% yield).[FE2]

2. The *cis,trans* isomer is converted to the *trans,trans* isomer on standing, especially if catalyzed by traces of acids or water.[FE2]

3. Isomerization of 1,3-bis(dimethylamino)-2-butyne vapor in the presence of chromic oxide (78% yield) or chromia-alumina catalyst (38% yield).[MC8]

$C_8H_{18}N_2$

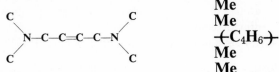

1,4-BIS(DIMETHYLAMINO)-2-BUTENE

Phys. Props.:

b. 166–169° (cor.)[WI16]; b_{735} 171–172° [CR2]; b_{723} 171–172° [WI18]; b_{24-25} 39–40° [WI16]; b_{22} 70° [CR2]‡; b_{17} 65–65.5°,[WI18] 65° [CR2]‡

d_4^0 0.8198[WI18]

n_D^{28} 1.437[CR2]‡

Prepn.:

1. Dimethylamine + 1,4-dichloro-2-butene (66% yield).[CR2]‡

2. Dimethylamine + 1,4-dibromo-2-butene,[WI16] (62% yield),[WI18] (58% yield).[BR20]

3. Interaction of a mixture of the following substances: 1,4-dibromo-2-butene, dimethylcyanamide, cyanogen bromide, and a quaternary salt which is possibly the bis-methobromide of 1,6-diaza-1,6-dimethyl-cyclo-3,8-decadiene.[BR20]

---

* Although ref. MC8 does not identify the configuration of this compound, ref. FE2 assigns the *trans,trans* configuration to this isomer.

† Ref. FE5 does not specify which geometric isomer was obtained. However, later ref. FE2 and FE4 by some of the same authors show that the *cis,trans* isomer is formed in this type of reaction.

‡ See footnote on page 357.

Derivs.:

Bis-hydrochloride: m. 279°[CR2]*
Bis-picrate: m. 222–223°,[WI18] 220–222°[CR2]*
Bis-chloroaurate: m. 201° (dec.)[WI18]
Chloroplatinate dihydrate: m. 227–228°[WI18]
Bis-methiodide: m. 270° (dec.)[WI18]
cis-Bis-methobromide: m. 278–280°[BI3]
Bis-methobromide: m. 295–300°[BR20]
Bis-allylobromide: m. 183–184°[BU16]
Bis-methochloroplatinate: m. 246°[BR20]

$C_8H_{18}N_2$

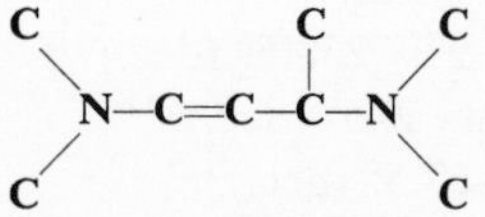

$$\underset{C}{\overset{C}{N}}-C=C-\underset{C}{\overset{C\quad C}{N}}$$

Me
Me
$+C_4H_6+$
Me
Me

1,3-BIS(DIMETHYLAMINO)-1-BUTENE

Phys. Props.:

b_{17} 64°[MA22]; b_{14} 58–62°[LA8]; b_7 49–50°[AR8]; b_5 45–48°[DO6,RE17]
m. −88°[RE17]
d_4^{20} 0.818°[RE17]
n_D^{20} 1.4660[RE17]; n 1.4666 (unspecified conditions)[DO6]
Viscosity (cs.): 1.34 at 75°F, 7.35 at −40°F, 16.86 at −65°F[RE17]

Prepn.:

Reaction of dimethylamine with crotonaldehyde in the presence of sodium
carbonate[LA8]; in the presence of potassium carbonate (72% yield),[AR8]
(70% yield),[DO6] (65% yield)[MA22]; in the presence of magnesium sulfate
(92% yield).[DO6]

$C_8H_{18}N_2$

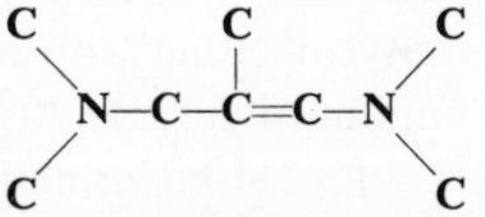

$$\underset{C}{\overset{C}{N}}-C-C=C-\underset{C}{\overset{C}{N}}$$

Me
Me
$+C_4H_6+$
Me
Me

1,3-BIS(DIMETHYLAMINO)-2-METHYLPROPENE

Phys. Props.:

b. 150–154°[GI2]; b_{12} 50–54°[GI2]

---

* Ref. CR2 calls the diamine he has prepared the *trans* isomer. It was prepared from
dimethylamine and a mixture of 76.5% *trans*- and 23.5% *cis*-1,4-dichloro-2-butenes.
There is no proof that the resultant diamine is exclusively the *trans* isomer.

Prepn.:

Thermal decomposition of tetrakis(dimethylaminomethyl)methane tetra-hydrochloride.[G12]

Derivs.:

Bis-hydrochloride: m. 260° (dec.)[G12]
Bis-hydrobromide: m. 243° (dec.)[G12]
Bis-hydriodide: m. 203–205°[G12]
Bis-picrate: m. 185.5–187.5°[G12]
Bis[α-bromocamphor-π-sulfonate]: m. 174–178°[G12]
Bis-Methiodide: m. 216–217° (dec.)[G12]
Bis-Methochloride monohydrate: m. 184–186° (dec.)[G12]
Bis-Methochloride: m. 224° (dec.)[G12]
Bis-Methochloroaurate: m. 237–238.5° (dec.)[G12]
Bis-Methochloroplatinate: m. 245° (dec.)[G12]
Bis-Methopicrate: m. 257–257.5° (dec.)[G12]
Bis-Metho-d-camphorsulphonate: m. 261–263°[G12]

$C_8H_{20}N_2$

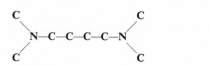

1,4-BIS(DIMETHYLAMINO)BUTANE

Phys. Props.:

b. 169°,[BR20] 169° (cor.),[WI14] 167–170°,[KE2] 167°,[CL3] 164–166°[AM2]; b_{762} 168° (uncor.)[CL2]; b_{740} 168°[PR2]; b_{28} 78–80°[LU24]
d_4^{27} 0.7864[LU24]; $d_4^{18.9}$ 0.8041[CL2]; d_4^{15} 0.7941[WI14]
n_D^{25} 1.4261[LU24]; $n_\alpha^{18.9}$ 1.4316[CL2]; $n_\gamma^{18.9}$ 1.4463[CL2]

Prepn.:

1. 1,4-Butanediamine + formic acid + formaldehyde (92% yield).[CL3]
2. 1,4-Butanediamine hydrochloride + formaldehyde.[KE1,KE2]
3. Sealed tube reaction of γ-butyrolactone with dimethylamine, followed by reduction with lithium aluminum hydride (30% overall yield).[LU24]
4. Catalytic hydrogenation of 1,4-bis(dimethylamino)-2-butene (53% yield).[AM2]
5. Thermal degradation of 1,4-tetramethylene-bis-trimethylammonium hydroxide (5% yield)[BR20]; or of its reaction product with hydrogen sulfide.[CL2]
6. Electrolytic reduction of N,N,N',N'-tetramethylsuccinamide (ca. 10% overall yield based on dimethylamine and succinic acid used to make succinamide).[PR2]
7. Hofmann degradation of desoxypithecolobine.[WI6]
8. Isolated in very low yield from Hyoscyamus reticulus L.[KO16]

Derivs.:

Bis-hydrochloride: m. 280–283°, [PR2] 273° (dec.),[WI14]

Bis-picrate: m. 203–205°,[LU24] 202.8–203.2° (cor.),[AM2] 199–200°,[KO16] 198–199°,[CL3,PR2] 197°,[CL2] 196–197°[KE2]

Bis-chloroaurate: m. 210°,[KE2] 207°,[PR2] 206–207° (dec.),[WI14] 200–205°[KO16]

Chloroplatinate: m. 236–237°,[KE2] 233.5° (dec.),[PR2] 224°[KO16]

Chloroplatinate dihydrate: m. 238–239° (dec.),[CL2] 234° (dec.),[WI14] 233.5° (dec.)[PR2]*

Bis-methochloride: m. 295° (dec.) [LE16]

Bis-methochloride dihydrate: m. 116–117° [WI14]

Bis-methobromide: m. 295°[BR20]

Bis-methiodide: m. 305–308° (dec.)[WI14]

Bis-methopicrate: unchanged by heating up to 294°,[DU3] m. 285° (dec.)[WI14]

Bis-methochloroaurate: m. 304–309° (dec.)[WI14]

Bis-methochloroplatinate: m. 284–286°,[DU3] 279° (dec.)[WI14]

Bis-methochloride·2HgCl$_2$: m. 266–277° (dec.)[DU3]

Bis-ethobromide: m. 301–304° (dec.)[BA23]

Monochloroaurate monomethochloroaurate: m. 244–245° (dec.)[KE2]

Monopicrate monomethopicrate: m. 260°[KE2]

$C_8H_{20}N_2$

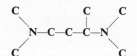

Me
Me
$-C_4H_8-$
Me
Me

1,3- BIS(DIMETHYLAMINO)BUTANE

Phys. Props.:

b. 159–160°[RE17]; b$_{760}$ 165.0°[UN1]; b$_{747}$ 162.4–162.6°[SP1]; b$_{50}$ 82°[UN1]; b$_{12}$ 55–56°[MA23]; b$_{10}$ 49°[UN1]; b$_{1.64}$ 20°[UN1]

m. −91°[RE17]; below −100°[UN1]

d$_4^{25}$ 0.7966[SP1]; d$_4^{20}$ 0.8008,[UN1] 0.795[RE17]

n$_D^{25}$ 1.4290[SP1]; n$_D^{20}$ 1.4311,[UN1] 1.4300[RE17]

pK$_{a_1}$ 10.01, pK$_{a_2}$ 7.56[UN1]; pK$_{a_1}$ 10.21, pK$_{a_2}$ 7.81 at 25°[SP1]

Viscosity (cp.): 1.5 at 0°, 1.0 at 20°, 0.75 at 40°[UN1]

Viscosity (in cs.): 1.25 at 75°F, 5.68 at −40°F, 11.24 at −65°F[RE17]

Coefficient of expansion at 20°: 0.00101/°C[UN1]

Flash point (Cleveland open cup): 114°F[UN1]

Prepn.:

3-Chloro-1-dimethylaminobutane + dimethylamine (nearly 100% yield).[MA23]

---

* Although the analysis reported is for the anhydrous salt, the experimental conditions suggest that the cited melting point is for the dihydrate.

Derivs.:

Bis-methiodide: m. *ca.* 250° MA23

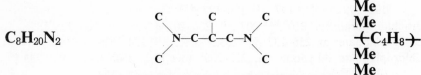

C$_8$H$_{20}$N$_2$

Me
Me
$+C_4H_8+$
Me
Me

1,3-BIS(DIMETHYLAMINO)-2-METHYLPROPANE*

Phys. Props.:

b. 151–152° G12

Prepn.:

Dimethylamine + 1,3-dibromo-2-methylpropane (35% yield).G12

Derivs.:

Bis-hydrochloride: m. 233–234° G12
Bis-methiodide: m. 267–268° G12
Bis-benzylopicrate: m. 169–171° G12

C$_8$H$_{20}$N$_2$

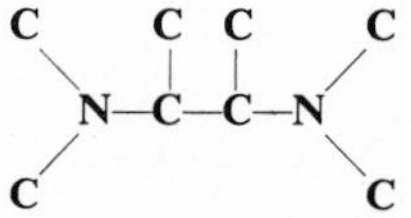

Me
Me
$+C_4H_8+$
Me
Me

2,3-BIS(DIMETHYLAMINO)BUTANE

Derivs.:

Bis-methochloroplatinate:† m. 221–222° SC11
Bis-methochloroaurate† (contaminated with "pseudocrotyltrimethyl-ammonium chloride"): m. 138–140° SC11

C$_8$H$_{20}$N$_2$

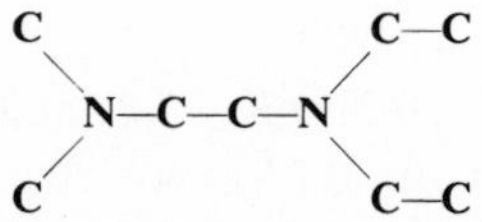

Me
Me
—CH$_2$CH$_2$—
Et
Et

1-DIMETHYLAMINO-2-DIETHYLAMINOETHANE

Phys. Props.:

b$_{760}$ 163–165° GR4; b. 156–157° ME16

* Elemental analysis reported by ref. G12 for this amine was quite poor. The nitrogen content is supposed to be 19.4%, but the observed value was 16.8%.

† This derivative was prepared from the corresponding bis-methobromide, which in turn was prepared from 2,3-dibromobutane and trimethylamine.

Prepn.:

1. 1-Diethylamino-2-bromoethane + dimethylamine.[ME16]
2. 1-Dimethylamino-2-chloroethane + diethylamine.[GR4]
3. Thermal degradation of (2-diethylaminoethyl)trimethylammonium hydroxide (49% yield).[ME16]

Derivs.:

Bis-hydrobromide m. 207–208°[ME16]
Monohydrobromide: m. 180–181°[ME16]
Bis-picrate: m. 240°[ME16]
Chloroplatinate: m. 220°[ME16]
Monomethobromide ($Et_2NCH_2CH_2NMe_3Br$): m. 208°[ME16]

$C_9H_{18}N_2$

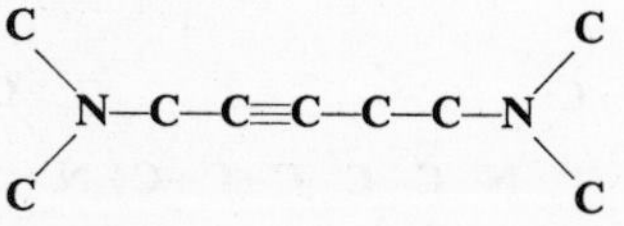

```
        C                      C      Me
         \                    /       Me
          N—C—C≡C—C—C—N              ─(C5H6)─
         /                    \       Me
        C                      C      Me
```

1,5-BIS(DIMETHYLAMINO)-2-PENTYNE

Phys. Props.:

b_8 87–90°[BI1,BI3]

Prepn.:

Sodio derivative of 1-dimethylamino-2-propyne + 1-chloro-2-dimethylaminoethane (yield at least 50%).[BI1,BI3]

Derivs.:

Bis-methobromide: m. 238–240°[BI3]

$C_9H_{20}N_2$

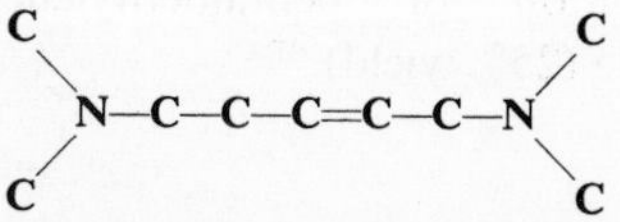

```
        C                      C      Me
         \                    /       Me
          N—C—C—C=C—C—N               ─(C5H8)─
         /                    \       Me
        C                      C      Me
```

1,5-BIS(DIMETHYLAMINO)-2-PENTENE

Derivs.:

cis-Bis-methobromide (prepared from the corresponding acetylenic bis-methobromide by catalytic hydrogenation): m. 233–235°[BI4]

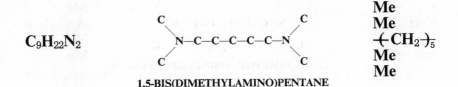

C₉H₂₀N₂

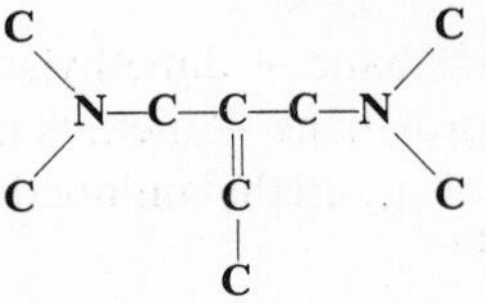

1-DIMETHYLAMINO-2-DIMETHYLAMINOMETHYL-2-BUTENE

Derivs.:

Monochloroaurate monomethochloroaurate [obtained from reaction of
(2-dimethylaminomethyl-2-butenyl)trimethylammonium hydroxide
with hydrochloric acid and gold(III) chloride]: m. 212° MA26

Monochloroplatinate monomethochloroplatinate [obtained from reaction
of (2-dimethylaminomethyl-2-butenyl)trimethylammonium hydroxide
with hydrochloric acid and platinum(IV) chloride]: m. 220° MA26

C₉H₂₂N₂

1,5-BIS(DIMETHYLAMINO)PENTANE

Phys. Props.:

b. 193–194°, BR10,BR15 192–194° BO2; b₇₆₆ 190–191° CL2
d₄¹⁹·³ 0.8033 BR10
n α¹⁹·³ 1.4327 BR10; n γ¹⁹·³ 1.4475 BR10

Prepn.:

1. 1,5-Diaminopentane + formaldehyde + formic acid (50–55% yield). BO2
2. Catalytic hydrogenation of 1,5-bis(dimethylamino)-2-pentene. BI4
3. Thermal decomposition of pentamethylene-1,5-bis-trimethylammonium
   hydroxide (36% yield) BR10; thermal decomposition of the product
   obtained from the foregoing hydroxide and hydrogen sulfide. CL2
4. Thermal decomposition of pentamethylene-1,5-bis-dimethylphenyl-
   ammonium hydroxide (25% yield). BR15

Derivs.:

Bis-picrate: m. 149° BR10,BR15,CL2
Chloroplatinate: m. 250° (dec.), CL2 218° (dec.) BR10 *
Bis-methiodide: m. 268–273° (dec.) BR9

---

* The structure of the cited "platinsalz" is not given although the platinum analysis
suggests the chloroplatinate monohydrate.

Bis-methobromide: m. above 300° [HA24]
Bis-methochloride: m. 285° (dec.) [LE16]
Bis-methohydrogen tartrate: m. 197° (dec.) [BA23]
Bis-benzobromide: m. 218–220° [SM10]

$C_9H_{22}N_2$

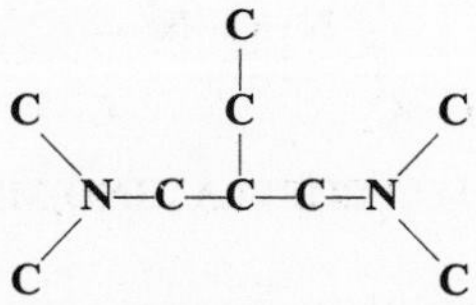

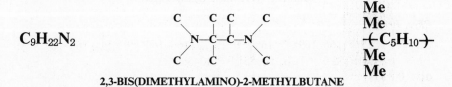

$\begin{matrix} Me \\ Me \\ +C_5H_{10}+ \\ Me \\ Me \end{matrix}$

1-DIMETHYLAMINO-2-(DIMETHYLAMINOMETHYL)BUTANE

Phys. Props.:

b. 184°; b_{12} 82° [MA26]

Prepn.:

Hydrogen iodide + red phosphorus + 1-dimethylamino-2-(dimethylamino-methyl)-2-butanol ("almost quantitative yield"). [MA26]

Derivs.:

Bis-hydrobromide: m. 243° [MA26]

$C_9H_{22}N_2$

$\begin{matrix} Me \\ Me \\ +C_5H_{10}+ \\ Me \\ Me \end{matrix}$

2,3-BIS(DIMETHYLAMINO)-2-METHYLBUTANE

Derivs.:

Bis-methochloroplatinate: m. 203° [SC11] (the bis-methochloroplatinate was prepared from the corresponding bis-methobromide, which in turn was prepared from 2,3-dibromo-2-methylbutane and trimethylamine)

$C_9H_{22}N_2$

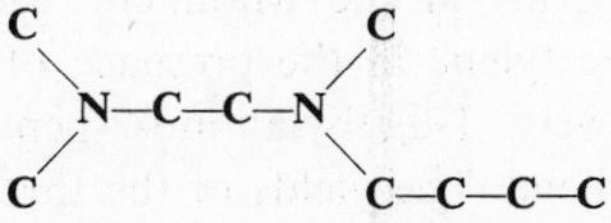

$\begin{matrix} Me \\ Me \\ -CH_2CH_2- \\ Me \\ n\text{-}Bu \end{matrix}$

1-DIMETHYLAMINO-2-(METHYLBUTYLAMINO)ETHANE

Phys. Props.:

b_{760} 181–183° [GR4]

Prepn.:

1-Chloro-2-diethylaminoethane + methylbutylamine.[GR4]

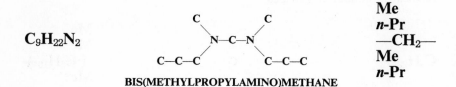

$C_9H_{22}N_2$ BIS(METHYLPROPYLAMINO)METHANE

Me
n-Pr
—CH_2—
Me
n-Pr

Phys. Props.:

b. 170–171°[BL5]
d_4^{19} 0.795[BL5]

Prepn.:

Methylpropylamine + formaldehyde.[BL5]

$C_9H_{22}N_2$ BIS(DIETHYLAMINO)METHANE

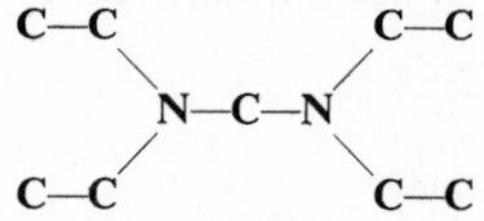

Et
Et
—CH_2—
Et
Et

Phys. Props.:

b. 167–169°,[MA24] 166–169°,[TS2] 168°[HE15]; $b_{760.7}$ 166–169°[KO15]; b_{760} 163–167°[DA4];
b_{15} 54.5–55.0°[NO1]; b_8 54–55°,[HU3] 40–56°[FR5]
$d_4^{18.7}$ 0.8105[KA5]
Raman spectrum[KA5]

Prepn.:

1. Sealed tube reaction of diethylamine and formaldehyde.[EH1,KO15,TS2]
2. Diethylamine + aqueous formaldehyde,[DA4,HE15] (64% yield).[TS2]
3. Diethylamine + diethylaminomethanol.[HE16]
4. By-product (in 32% yield) in the Mannich reaction of diethylamine, formaldehyde, and diacetylene in the presence of copper(I) chloride.[FR5] The other products were 1-diethylamino-2-penten-4-yne and 1,6-bis-diethylamino-2,4-hexadiene. The yields of the three products varied with reaction conditions.
5. By-product in the reaction of ethyl or other half esters of malonic acid with diethylamine and formaldehyde.[MA24]
6. By-product (very low yield) in the catalytic hydrogenation of 1,3-bis-(diethylamino)-2-methyl-2-nitropropane.[LA6]

Derivs.:*

Bis-ethobromide: m. 235° (dec.)^{TS2} *

$C_{10}H_{16}N_2$

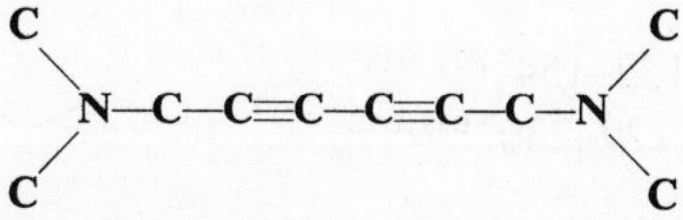

$$\underset{C}{\overset{C}{|}}N-C-C\equiv C-C\equiv C-C-\underset{C}{\overset{C}{|}}N$$

Me
Me
$+C_6H_4+$
Me
Me

1,6-BIS(DIMETHYLAMINO)-2,4-HEXADIYNE

Phys. Props.:

b_{20} 134–135°^{KA7}; b_{15} 125–130°^{KA8}; $b_{0.01}$ 65°^{AR5}
m. 33.2–33.8°,^{KA7} 28–29° ^{AR5}
n_D^{20} 1.5085^{AR5}
Ultraviolet absorption^{AR5}

Prepn.:

1. Dimethylamine + 1,6-dibromo-2,4-hexadiyne (50% yield)^{AR5}; + 1,6-dichloro-2,4-hexadiyne (45% yield).^{AR5}
2. Air oxidation of 3-dimethylamino-1-propyne in the presence of copper(II) chloride^{KA7}; oxidation of the copper(I) salt of 3-dimethylamino-1-propyne with copper(II) chloride (85% yield).^{KA8}

Derivs.:

Bis-picrate: m. 262°,^{AR5} 256°^{AR5}

$C_{10}H_{20}N_2$

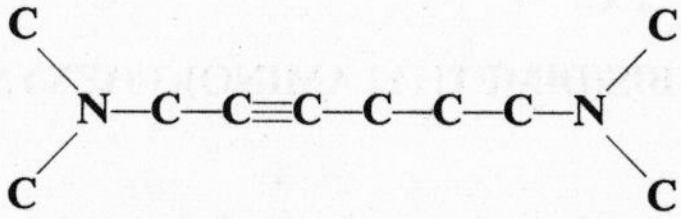

$$\underset{C}{\overset{C}{|}}N-C-C\equiv C-C-C-C-\underset{C}{\overset{C}{|}}N$$

Me
Me
$+C_6H_8+$
Me
Me

1,6-BIS(DIMETHYLAMINO)-2-HEXYNE

Phys. Props.:

b_1 60–61°^{BI1,BI3}

---

* Attempts to prepare acid salts of bis(dialkylamino)methanes can result in the formation of dialkylamine salts.^{HU3} Attempts to prepare the ethiodide of bis(diethylamino)methane by reaction with ethyl iodide result in cleavage with formation of tetraethylammonium iodide$^{EH1, TS2}$ and diethylamine hydriodide.^{TS2} Rigorously anhydrous conditions are needed to prepare quaternary salts of bis(dialkylamino)methanes.^{BO10} However, reaction of ethyl bromide with bis(diethylamino)methane gives the expected methylene-bis(triethylammonium) bromide without observing any special precautions.^{TS2}

Prepn.:

Sodio derivative of 1-dimethylamino-2-propyne + 1-chloro-3-dimethyl-aminopropane,[BI1] (unspecified yield in the range of 50–90%).[BI3]

Derivs.:

Bis-hydrochloride: m. 152–154° [BI1,BI3]
Bis-methobromide: m. 229–230° [BI1,BI3]

$C_{10}H_{20}N_2$

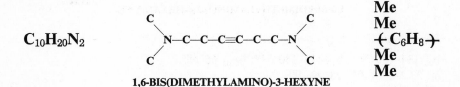

1,6-BIS(DIMETHYLAMINO)-3-HEXYNE

Me
Me
(C_6H_8)
Me
Me

Phys. Props.:

b_1 59–60° [BI3]

Prepn.:

Disodium acetylide + 1-dimethylamino-2-haloethane.[BI3]

Derivs.:

Bis-methobromide: m. 245–247° [BI3]

$C_{10}H_{20}N_2$

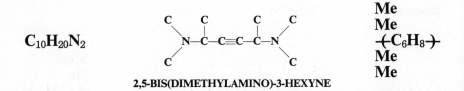

2,5-BIS(DIMETHYLAMINO)-3-HEXYNE

Me
Me
(C_6H_8)
Me
Me

Prepn.:

By-product in the reaction of dimethylamine, formic acid, acetaldehyde, and acetylene in the presence of copper(I) chloride.[RE7,RE11]

$C_{10}H_{20}N_2$

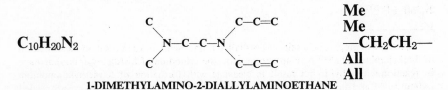

1-DIMETHYLAMINO-2-DIALLYLAMINOETHANE

Me
Me
—CH_2CH_2—
All
All

Phys. Props.:

b_{18} 70–73° [GR4]

Prepn.:

1-Chloro-2-diethylaminoethane + diallylamine.[GR4]

$C_{10}H_{20}N_2$

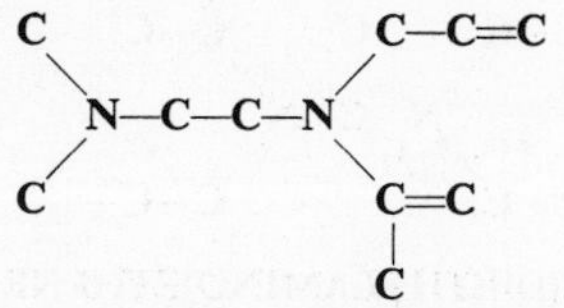

	Me
	Me
	—CH₂CH₂—
	All
	C₃H₅

Me
Me
—CH$_2$CH$_2$—
All
C$_3$H$_5$

1-DIMETHYLAMINO-2-[ALLYL(1-METHYLVINYL)AMINO]ETHANE

Phys. Props.:

b_{13} 90–93°[GR4]

Prepn.:

1-Chloro-2-dimethylaminoethane + allyl(1-methylvinyl)amine.[GR4]

$C_{10}H_{22}N_2$

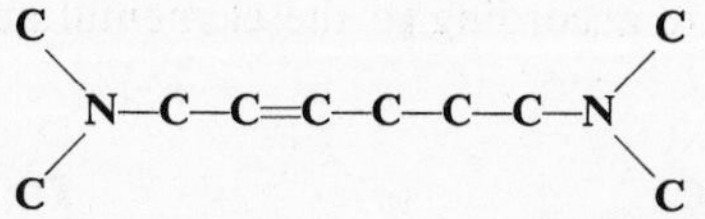

Me
Me
(C_6H_{10})
Me
Me

1,6-BIS(DIMETHYLAMINO)-2-HEXENE

Phys. Props.:

cis isomer
b_1 58–60°[BI4]

Prepn.:

Catalytic hydrogenation of 1,6-bis(dimethylamino)-2-hexyne in the presence of palladium gives the *cis* isomer.[BI4]

Derivs.:

cis-Bis-methobromide: m. 218–219°[BI4]

$C_{10}H_{22}N_2$

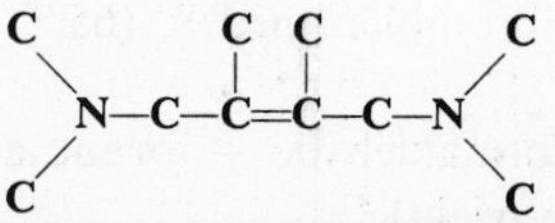

Me
Me
(C_6H_{10})
Me
Me

1,4-BIS(DIMETHYLAMINO)-2,3-DIMETHYL-2-BUTENE

Prepn.:

Dimethylamine + 1,4-dibromo-2,3-dimethyl-2-butene.[MA1]

Derivs.:

Bis-chloroaurate: m. 188–189°[MA1]

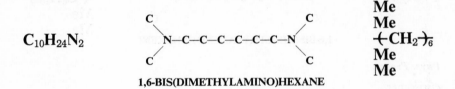

$C_{10}H_{22}N_2$

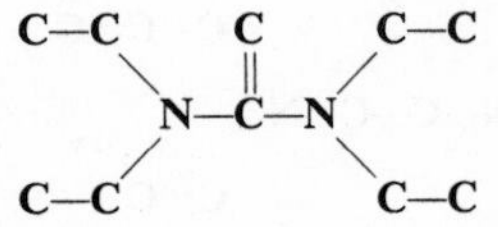

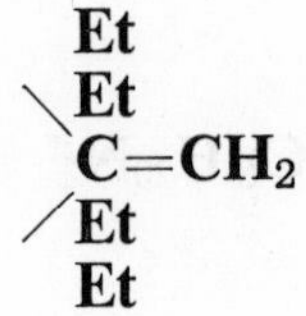

1,1-BIS(DIETHYLAMINO)ETHENE

Phys. Props.:

b_{40} 89–93°,[MC6] 91.5–92.5°[AR2]
d_4^{20} 0.8226[MC6]
n_D^{20} 1.4520,[MC6] 1.4532[AR2]

Prepn.:

1. Diethylamine + 1,1-diethoxyethene (41% yield).[MC6]
2. Diethylamine + ethoxyacetylene.[AR2,AR3] (The product obtained by ref. AR3 was very impure according to the elemental analysis.)

$C_{10}H_{24}N_2$

1,6-BIS(DIMETHYLAMINO)HEXANE

Phys. Props.:

b_{765} 209–210°[CL2]; b_{760} 209–211°,[BA22] 206–208°[PH1]; b_{732} 208.5°[PR2]; b_{25} 112–113°[BO2]; b_{20} 103°[CL2]; b_{15} 96–98°,[BA22] 87–89°[CA19]; b_{11} 86.5°[SP1]; b_2 60°[RE17]; $b_{1.0}$ 58–61°[BI4]
d_4^{25} 0.7960[SP1]; d_4^{20} 0.8056[RE17]; $d_4^{14.5}$ 0.8064[CL2]
n_D^{25} 1.4347[SP1]; n_D^{20} 1.4360[SP1]; $n_\alpha^{14.5}$ 1.4366[CL2]; $n_\gamma^{14.5}$ 1.4512[CL2]
pK_{a_1} 10.46, pK_{a_2} 9.25 at 25°[SP1]

Prepn.:

1. Dimethylamine + 1,6-dibromohexane,[BA30] (65% yield)[CA19]; + 1,6-diiodohexane.[BR7]
2. 1,6-Diaminohexane + formaldehyde + formic acid,[KU4] (66% yield),[BA22] (60–65% yield),[BO2] (80% yield).[KU3]
3. Catalytic hydrogenation of 1,6-dimethylamino-2-hexyne.[BI4]
4. Thermal decomposition of the reaction product of 1,6-hexamethylene-bis-trimethylammonium hydroxide with hydrogen sulfide.[CL2]
5. Electrolytic reduction of *N,N,N',N'*-tetramethyladipamide.[PR2]

Derivs.:

Bis-hydrochloride: m. 248°,[BA22] 245–246°[PH1]
Bis-hydrobromide: m. 224–225°,[CA19] 223°[BA30]
Bis-picrate: m. 164°,[PR2] 162°,[BR7] 160°[CL2]
Chloroplatinate: m. 222°[PR2]
Bis-chloroaurate: m. 169°[PR2]
Bis-methochloride dihydrate: m. 284°[BR7]
Monomethobromide: m. 175–178°[LO3]
Monomethobromide monohydrobromide monohydrate: m. *ca.* 175–178°[LO3]
Bis-methobromide: m. 274–276°[BI4]
Bis-methiodide: m. (does not melt up to 270°)[BR7]
Bis-methosulfate dihydrate: m. 247° (dec.)[BR7]
Bis-methosulfate: m. 184–186° (dec.)[BR7]
Bis-ethobromide: m. 258° (dec.)[BA22]
Bis-ethohydrogen tartrate: m. 169–170° (dec.)[BA23]
Bis-propobromide: m. 234° (dec.)[BA22]
Bis-isopropobromide: m. 255–257°[BA22]
Bis-allylobromide dihydrate: m. 185°[BA22]
Bis-butobromide hydrate: m. 253° (dec.)[BA22]
Bis-isobutobromide: m. 185° (dec.)[BA22]
Bis-benzobromide: m. 226°[SM10]

$$C_{10}H_{24}N_2$$

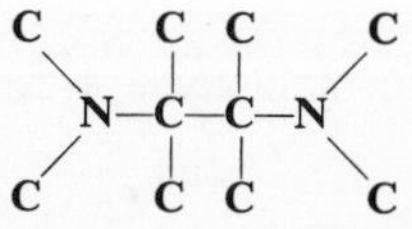

$$\begin{array}{ccccc} C & C & C & & C \\ & | & | & & \\ N & - C & - C & - N & \\ | & & | & & | \\ C & C & C & & C \end{array}$$

2,3-BIS(DIMETHYLAMINO)-2,3-DIMETHYLBUTANE

Me
Me
$\left(C_6H_{12} \right)$
Me
Me

Phys. Props.:

b_{767} 149°[VE2]

Prepn.:

2-Dimethylamino-2-cyanopropane + ethylmagnesium bromide (69% yield)[VE2];
+ methylmagnesium bromide (67% yield)[VE2]; + propylmagnesium
bromide (low yield).[VE2] In each of these reactions a small amount of
monoamine is obtained. For example, in the reaction with ethylmagnesium bromide a 15% yield of 2-dimethylamino-2-methylbutane
is also obtained.

---

* For other less common quaternary ammonium salts see refs. BA22, BA23, CA19,
and SM10.

$C_{10}H_{24}N_2$

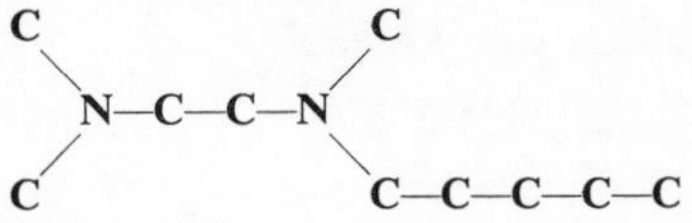

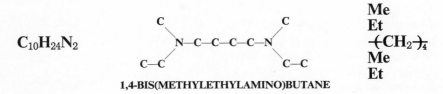

$$\begin{array}{ccc}
& C & & & C \\
& \diagdown & & & \diagup \\
& N-C-C-N & & \\
& \diagup & & & \diagdown \\
& C & & & C-C-C-C-C
\end{array}$$

Me
Me
—CH₂CH₂—
Me
n-Pent

1-DIMETHYLAMINO-2-(METHYLPENTYLAMINO)ETHANE

Phys. Props.:

b_{20} 93–95°[GR4]

Prepn.:

1-Chloro-2-dimethylaminoethane + methylpentylamine.[GR4]

$C_{10}H_{24}N_2$

$$\begin{array}{cccc}
C & & & C \\
\diagdown & & & \diagup \\
N-C-C-C-C-N & \\
\diagup & & & \diagdown \\
C-C & & & C-C
\end{array}$$

Me
Et
—(CH₂)₄—
Me
Et

1,4-BIS(METHYLETHYLAMINO)BUTANE

Phys. Props.:

b_{10} 76–78°[BA24]

Prepn.:

1,4-Bis(ethylamino)butane + formaldehyde + formic acid (49% yield).[BA24]

Derivs.:

Bis-hydrobromide: m. 233–235°[BA24]
Bis-methohydrogen tartrate: m. 169–170° (dec.)[BA23]
Bis-ethobromide: m. 284–287° (dec.)[BA24]
Bis-ethiodide: m. 293–295° (dec.)[BA24]

$C_{10}H_{24}N_2$

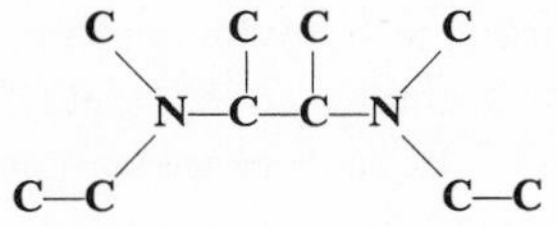

$$\begin{array}{cccc}
C & C \; C & & C \\
\diagdown & | \; | & & \diagup \\
N-C-C-N & \\
\diagup & & & \diagdown \\
C-C & & & C-C
\end{array}$$

Me
Et
—(C₄H₈)—
Me
Et

2,3-BIS(METHYLETHYLAMINO)BUTANE

Phys. Props.:

meso isomer
  b_{15} 70–80° (bath temp.)[SM11]

dl mixture
 b_{14} 65–80° (bath temp.)[SM11]

Prepn.:

meso-N,N'-Diethylbutane-2,3-diamine + formic acid + formaldehyde (*meso* isomer in about 73% yield).[SM11] Similar methylation of the corresponding racemic compound gave about 79% yield of racemic mixture of 2,3-bis(methylethylamino)butane.[SM11]

Derivs.:

meso-Bis-hydrochloride: m. 240°[SM11]
meso-Bis-picrate: m. 203° (dec.)[SM11]
meso-Bis-perchlorate: m. 159°[SM11]
dl-Bis-picrate: m. 168° (dec.)[SM11]

$C_{10}H_{24}N_2$

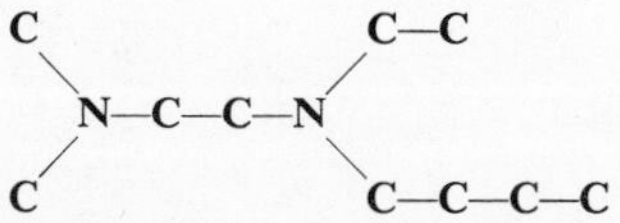

Me
Me
—CH₂CH₂—
Et
***n*-Bu**

1-DIMETHYLAMINO-2-(ETHYLBUTYLAMINO)ETHANE

Phys. Props.:
 b_{18} 87–89°[GR4]

Prepn.:

1-Dimethylamino-2-chloroethane + ethylbutylamine.[GR4]

$C_{10}H_{24}N_2$

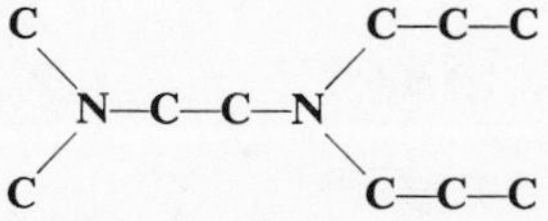

Me
Me
—CH₂CH₂—
***n*-Pr**
***n*-Pr**

1-DIMETHYLAMINO-2-DIPROPYLAMINOETHANE

Phys. Props.:
 b_{27} 93–97°[GR4]

Prepn.:

1-Chloro-2-dimethylaminoethane + dipropylamine.[GR4]

$C_{10}H_{24}N_2$

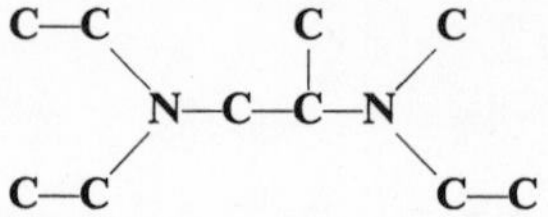

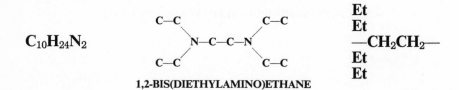

Et
Et
$\{C_3H_6\}$
Me
Et

1-DIETHYLAMINO-2-(ETHYLMETHYLAMINO)PROPANE

Phys. Props.:

b_{15} 85–125° (bath temp.)[SM11] (the C,H analysis was satisfactory for the indicated amine in spite of the extended distillation range cited)

Prepn.:

1. Reduction of *N,N*-diethyl-2-(ethylmethylamino)propionamide with lithium aluminum hydride (*ca.* 86% yield).[SM11]
2. As part of a mixture of three diamines (total yield *ca.* 1%) resulting from the irradiation of methyldiethylamine with γ-rays.[SM11]

Derivs.:

Bis-picrate: m. 165–168°[SM11]

$C_{10}H_{24}N_2$

Et
Et
—CH$_2$CH$_2$—
Et
Et

1,2-BIS(DIETHYLAMINO)ETHANE

Phys. Props.:

b. 194°[GE3]; b_{760} 178–184°[AR4]; b_{758} 186°[SM11]; b_{42} 100°[PO1]; $b_{31.5}$ 89°[LA1,RE16]; b_{20} 80–82°,[PA15] 78–80°[JO7]; b_{18} 82–85°[TS2]; b_{10} 72°,[PO1] 70–72°[GI4]; b_8 65°[GI4]
d_4^{25} 0.799[AR4]
n_D^{25} 1.4330,[AR4] 1.4318[PO1]; n_D^{20} 1.4366[JO7]
pK_{a_1} 9.55, pK_{a_2} 6.18 at 25°[GE3]

Prepn.:

1. Reduction of *N,N,N',N'*-tetraethyloxamide with lithium aluminum hydride (87% yield).[AR4]
2. Diethylamine + 1,2-dibromoethane,[GE3,GI4] (71.4% yield)[TS2]; + unspecified 1,2-dihaloethane.[DA4]
3. Diethylamine + 1,2-bis(benzenesulfonoxy)ethane (79% yield),[RE16] (55% yield).[LA1]

4. Diethylamine + 2-chloroethylbenzenesulfonate (38% yield).[GI4]
5. By-product in the reaction of diethyl(2-chloroethyl)amine with sodium (12% yield).[PA15] The main products are ethylene, diethylamine, and triethylamine.
6. 1,2-Diaminoethane + ethylene and sodium under pressure (24.8% conversion). A mixture of ethylated ethylenediamines was also obtained.[HO23]
7. Diethylamine + β-chloroethyl-4-methylthiazole-5-carboxylate.[JO7]
8. As part of a mixture of three diamines obtained in the γ-ray irradiation of methyldiethylamine. This mixture of bases represented a yield of about 1%.[SM11]

Derivs.:

Bis-hydrochloride: m. 190–191°,[JO7] 187°[GI4]
Bis-picrate: m. 265°,[PA15] 243° (dec.),[JO7] 240–243°,[AR4] 242°[SM11]
Bis-perchlorate: m. 167°[SM11]
Bis-chloroaurate: m. 198°[GI4]
Chloroplatinate: m. 234°[GI4]
Bis-oxide: m. 105–107°[JE1]
Bis-picrate of dioxide: m. 155° (dec.)[JE1]
Bis-ethobromide: m. 245–246°[LU1]
Bis-ethiodide: m. 198°[TS2]
Bis-ethochloroplatinate: m. 211° (dec.)[LU1]
Monoethiodide: m. 91°[TS2]

$C_{11}H_{22}N_2$

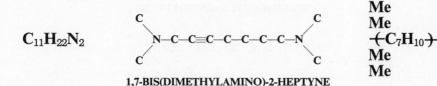

1,7-BIS(DIMETHYLAMINO)-2-HEPTYNE

Phys. Props.:

b_8 101°[EP2,OL6]
n_D^{20} 1.4520[EP2,OL6]

Prepn.:

6-Dimethylamino-1-hexyne + dimethylamine + formaldehyde (92% yield).[EP2,OL6]

Derivs.:

Bis-methiodide: m. 191–192°[OL6]

$C_{11}H_{24}N_2$

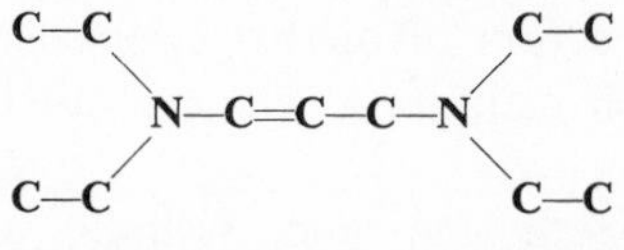

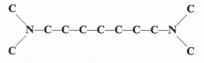

$$\begin{matrix} & & \text{C--C} & & & & & \text{C--C} & & & & \text{Et} \\ & & \diagdown & & & & & \diagup & & & & \text{Et} \\ & & \text{N--C==C--C--N} & & & & & & & \text{(}C_3H_4\text{)} \\ & & \diagup & & & & & \diagdown & & & & \text{Et} \\ & & \text{C--C} & & & & & \text{C--C} & & & & \text{Et} \end{matrix}$$

1,3-BIS(DIETHYLAMINO)PROPENE

Phys. Props.:

b_5 82° [F17]
d_4^{20} 0.8308 [F17]
n_D^{20} 1.4650 [F17]

Prepn.:

Dimethylamine + acrolein (65% yield). [F17]

Dervis.:

Bis-methopicrate: m. 234° (dec.) [IN7]
Methoetho-bis-picrate: m. 230° (dec.) [IN7]
Monopicrate monomethopicrate: m. 198° [IN7]
Monopicrate monoethopicrate: m. 167–188° [IN7]

$C_{11}H_{26}N_2$

$$\begin{matrix} \text{C} & & & & & & & & \text{C} & & & \text{Me} \\ \diagdown & & & & & & & & \diagup & & & \text{Me} \\ \text{N--C--C--C--C--C--C--C--N} & & & & & & & & & \text{(CH}_2\text{)}_7 \\ \diagup & & & & & & & & \diagdown & & & \text{Me} \\ \text{C} & & & & & & & & \text{C} & & & \text{Me} \end{matrix}$$

1,7-BIS(DIMETHYLAMINO)HEPTANE

Phys. Props.:

b. 225–230° (sl. dec.) [BR10]; b_{760} 228–230° (cor.) [CL2]; b_{10} 105–108°, [BA23]
        101–102° [BR10]
$d_4^{13.4}$ 0.8177 [CL2]
$n_\alpha^{13.4}$ 1.4407 [CL2]; $n_\gamma^{13.4}$ 1.4553 [CL2]

Prepn.:

1. 1,7-Diaminoheptane + formaldehyde + formic acid. [BA23]
2. Catalytic hydrogenation of 1,7-bis(dimethylamino)-2-heptyne. [EP2]
3. Thermal degradation of heptamethylene-1,7-bis-trimethylammonium hydroxide (56% yield) [BR10]; thermal degradation of the reaction product of the above hydroxide with hydrogen sulfide. [CL2]

Derivs.:

Bis-picrate: m. 136°, [BR10] 120° [CL2] (*sic*)
Bis-methiodide: m. 246°, [OL6] 242° [BR10]

Bis-methobromide: m. 245°[BR10]
Bis-ethobromide: m. 274–276° (dec.)[BA23]

$C_{11}H_{26}N_2$

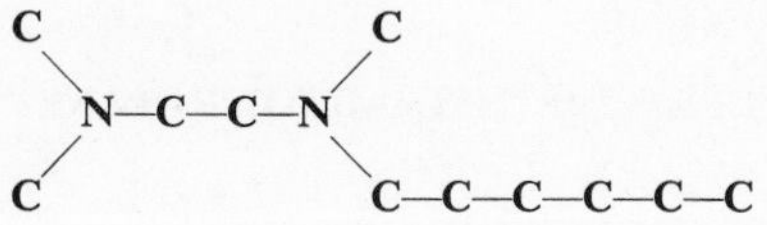

```
      C           C
       \         /
        N—C—C—N
       /         \
      C           C—C—C—C—C
```

Me
Me
—CH_2CH_2—
Me
n-C_6H_{13}

1-DIMETHYLAMINO-2-(METHYLHEXYLAMINO)ETHANE

Phys. Props.:

b_{20} 109–112°[GR4]

Prepn.:

1-Dimethylamino-2-chloroethane + methylhexylamine.[GR4]

$C_{11}H_{26}N_2$

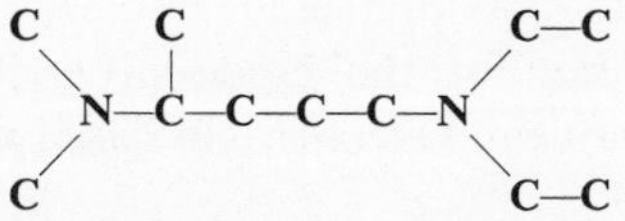

```
      C    C        C—C
       \   |       /
        N—C—C—C—C—N
       /            \
      C              C—C
```

Me
Me
$+C_5H_{10}+$
Et
Et

4-DIMETHYLAMINO-1-DIETHYLAMINOPENTANE

Phys. Props.:

b_5 87°[CU2]
n_D^{25} 1.4393[CU2]

Prepn.:

1-Diethylamino-4-aminopentane + formaldehyde + formic acid (59% yield).[AM2]

$C_{11}H_{26}N_2$

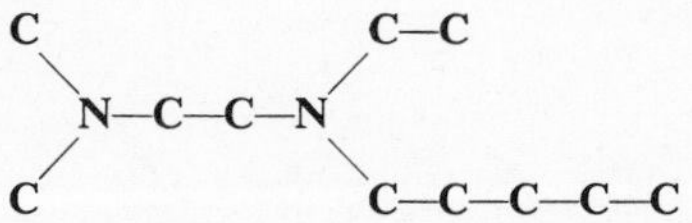

```
      C          C—C
       \        /
        N—C—C—N
       /        \
      C          C—C—C—C—C
```

Me
Me
—CH_2CH_2—
Et
n-Pent

1-DIMETHYLAMINO-2-(ETHYLPENTYLAMINO)ETHANE

Phys. Props.:

b_{18} 106–108°[GR4]

Prepn.:

1-Dimethylamino-2-chloroethane + ethylpentylamine.[GR4]

$C_{11}H_{26}N_2$

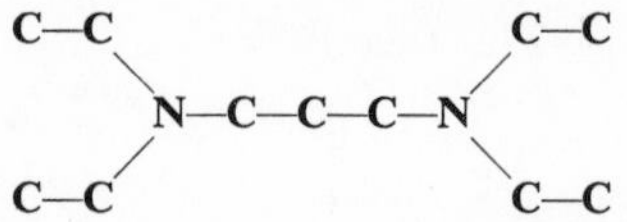

```
    C—C                C—C
       \              /
        N—C—C—C—N
       /              \
    C—C                C—C
```

Et
Et
$+CH_2+_3$
Et
Et

1,3-BIS(DIETHYLAMINO)PROPANE

Phys. Props.:

b. 214°,[GE3] 205–210°,[KH1] 205–209° [FL1]; b_{80} 133° [FI7]; b_{15} 95–100° [DA4]; b_9 81.9° [IN7]

d_4^{20} 0.8101[FI7]

n_D^{20} 1.4381[FI7]

pK_{a_1} 10.18, pK_{a_2} 8.20 at 25° [GE3]

Prepn.:

1. Diethylamine + 1,3-dibromopropane,[IN7,KH1] (44% yield),[TS2] (64% yield).[FL1]
2. 1,3-Diaminopropane + an ethyl halide.[KH1]
3. Catalytic hydrogenation of the crude product from the reaction of diethylamine with acrolein. Overall yield based on acrolein, 26%.[FI7]

Derivs.:

Bis-hydrochloride-bis-mercury(II) chloride: m. 124–125° [FL1]
Bis-methiodide: m. 234° [KH1]
Bis-methopicrate: m. 282° (dec.)[IN7,KH1]
Methoetho-bis-picrate: m. 263–264° (dec.)[IN7,KH1]
Bis-ethobromide: m. 245°,[LU1] 235° (dec.)[CA3]
Bis-ethiodide: m. 275° (dec.)[TS2]
Bis-ethochloroplatinate: m. 220° (dec.)[LU1]
Bis-propiodide: m. 178–179° [KH1]
Bis-butiodide: m. 161° [KH1]
Bis-isopentiodide: m. 119° [KH1]

$C_{12}H_{24}N_2$

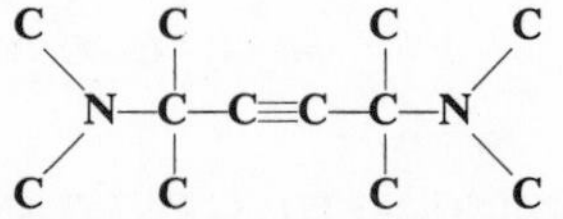

```
  C   C        C   C
   \  |        |  /
    N—C—C≡C—C—N
   /  |        |  \
  C   C        C   C
```

Me
Me
$+C_8H_{12}+$
Me
Me

2,5-BIS(DIMETHYLAMINO)-2,5-DIMETHYL-3-HEXYNE

Prepn.:

By-product in the preparation of 2-dimethylamino-2-methyl-3-butyne from dimethylamine, acetone, and acetylene in the presence of copper(I) chloride.[RE7]

$$C_{12}H_{24}N_2$$

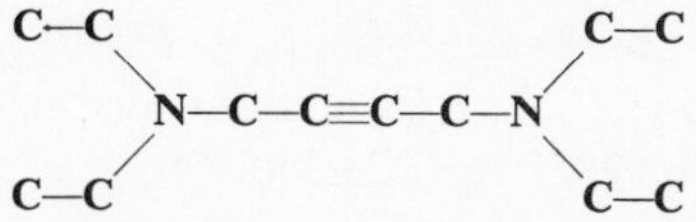

$$
\begin{array}{c}
\text{C—C} \qquad\qquad\qquad \text{C—C} \\
\quad\diagdown\qquad\qquad\qquad\qquad\diagup \\
\text{N—C—C}\!\equiv\!\text{C—C—N} \\
\quad\diagup\qquad\qquad\qquad\qquad\diagdown \\
\text{C—C} \qquad\qquad\qquad \text{C—C}
\end{array}
$$

Et
Et
$\left(C_4H_4\right)$
Et
Et

1,4-BIS(DIETHYLAMINO)-2-BUTYNE

Phys. Props.:

b_{14} 120°[NE4]; b_{10} 109–110°[RE7]; b_{10} 110°[WI8]; b_7 95°[FE2]; b_6 131–132°[MA7]; $b_{0.3-0.5}$ 73–79°[WA20]

n_D^{20} 1.4587[FE2]

Infrared absorption[WI8]

Prepn.:

1. Diethylamine + 1,4-diiodo-2-butyne (64% yield)[WI8]; + 1,4-diiodo-1,3-butadiene (62% yield)[WI8]; + 1,4-dichloro-2-butyne (54% yield),[MA7] (31% yield).[WA20]

2. Bis(diethylamino)methane + formaldehyde + acetylene in the presence of copper(I) chloride[FE2]; in the presence of copper(I) acetylide (9.6% yield).[RE7]

3. Sealed tube reaction of diethylamine, paraformaldehyde, and acetylene in dioxane with copper(II) acetate catalyst (58% yield).[NE4]

Derivs.:

Bis-hydrochloride: m. 205–206°,[NE4] 204–205° (dec.)[WA20]
Bis-picrate: m. 180–181°[WI8]
Bis-methiodide: m. 213.5–214° (dec.),[WA20] 203.5–205.5° (dec.)[NE4]
Bis-ethopicrate: m. 229–231° (dec.)[JO1]

$$C_{12}H_{24}N_2$$

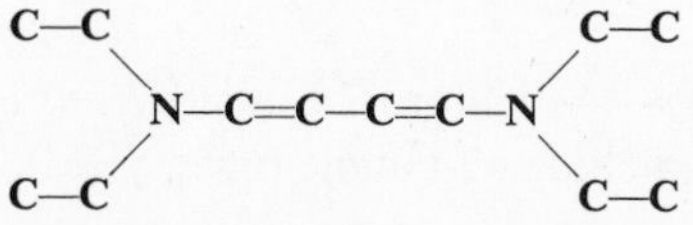

$$
\begin{array}{c}
\text{C—C} \qquad\qquad\qquad \text{C—C} \\
\quad\diagdown\qquad\qquad\qquad\qquad\diagup \\
\text{N—C}\!=\!\text{C—C}\!=\!\text{C—N} \\
\quad\diagup\qquad\qquad\qquad\qquad\diagdown \\
\text{C—C} \qquad\qquad\qquad \text{C—C}
\end{array}
$$

Et
Et
$\left(C_4H_4\right)$
Et
Et

1,4-BIS(DIETHYLAMINO)-1,3-BUTADIENE

Phys. Props.:

cis-trans isomer
b_1 77°[FE4]; $b_{0.25}$ 64°[FE2,FE5] *
n_D^{25} 1.5221[FE4]; n_D^{20} 1.5155[FE2,FE5] *
Ultraviolet absorption: 2925 A. (ϵ 19,400)[FE2,FE4]

---

* Although ref. FE5 does not identify the compound as the *cis-trans* isomer, subsequent ref. FE4 by the same workers clarifies the assignment.

trans-trans isomer

  $b_{1.6}$ 97–125°(*sic*)[FE6]*; b_1 90–93°[MC8]†; $b_{0.15}$ 77°[FE4]

  n_D^{25} 1.5403[FE4]; n_D^{20} 1.5423[FE6]*; n (conditions unspecified) 1.5330[MC8]†

  Ultraviolet absorption: 2877 A. (ϵ 23,350)[FE4]

Prepn.:

1. Transamination reaction between 1,4-bis(dimethylamino)-1,3-butadiene and diethylamine[FE6]*. (10% yield of the *trans-trans* isomer).[FE4]* The catalyst in this reaction is a mixture of acetic and hydrochloric acids.[FE4,FE6] A variety of acid catalysts can be used.[FE6]
2. Isomerization of 1,4-bis(diethylamino)-2-butyne with chromic oxide catalyst (30% yield)[MC8]; with sodium as catalyst[FE5]*; with sodium as catalyst to yield the *cis-trans* isomer.[FE2]
3. Diethylamine + 1-diethylamino-1-butyen-3-yne (no experimental details given).[SH4]

$C_{12}H_{26}N_2$

```
   C—C                    C—C              Et
      \                  /                 Et
       N—C—C=C—C—N                        +(C₄H₆)+
      /                  \                 Et
   C—C                    C—C              Et
```

1,4-BIS(DIETHYLAMINO)-2-BUTENE

Phys. Props.:

  b_{20} 115–116°[AM2]

trans isomer

  b_{36} 125°[RO1]; b_4 65–75°[RO1]

  n_D^{21} 1.4532[RO1]

Prepn.:

1. Diethylamine + *trans*-1,4-dichloro-2-butene (*trans* isomer, 45% yield).[RO1]
2. Diethylamine + 1,4-dichloro-2-butene (66% yield).[AM2]

Derivs.:

Bis-picrate: m. 154–155.5°[AM2]
trans-Bis-picrate: m. 154°[RO1]
Bis-allylobromide: n. 172–173°[BU16]

---

  * The preparative method used in ref. FE6 is reported by ref. FE4 to give the *trans-trans* isomer.

  † Although unspecified in ref. MC8, the configuration of this molecule, in analogy to the assignment made for the methyl analog in ref. FE2, should be *trans-trans*.

$C_{12}H_{26}N_2$

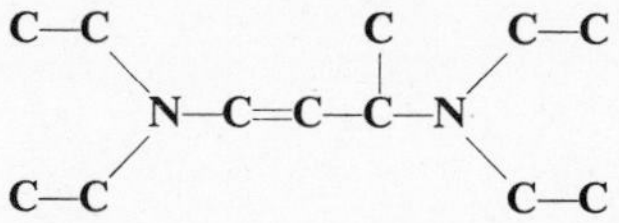

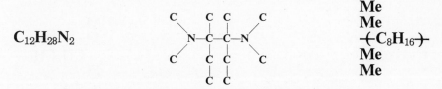

1,3-BIS(DIETHYLAMINO)-1-BUTENE

Et
Et
$+C_4H_6+$
Et
Et

Phys. Props.:

b_1 84–86° [LA12]; $b_{0.02}$ 72–73° [LA9]

Prepn.:

Diethylamine + 2-buten-1-al in the presence of potassium carbonate. [LA9]

$C_{12}H_{28}N_2$

3,4-BIS(DIMETHYLAMINO)-3,4-DIMETHYLHEXANE

Me
Me
$+C_8H_{16}+$
Me
Me

Phys. Props.:

b_{769} 171–175° [BR50]

Prepn.:

2-Cyano-2-dimethylaminobutane + ethylmagnesium bromide (very low yield). The main product of this reaction is 3-dimethylamino-3-methylpentane. [BR50]

$C_{12}H_{28}N_2$

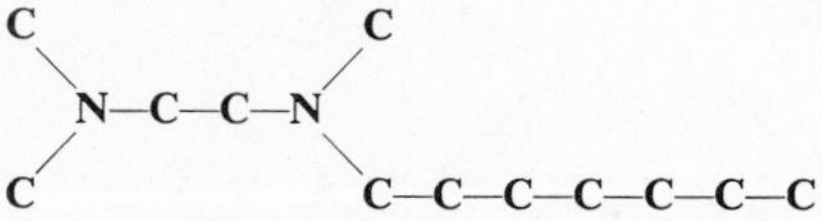

1-DIMETHYLAMINO-2-(METHYLHEPTYLAMINO)ETHANE

Me
Me
—CH₂CH₂—
Me
n-Hept

Phys. Props.:

b_{15} 113–116° [GR4]

Prepn.:

1-Dimethylamino-2-chloroethane + methylheptylamine. [GR4]

$C_{12}H_{28}N_2$

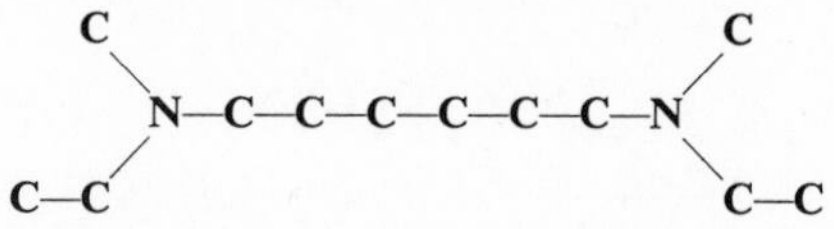

1,6-BIS(METHYLETHYLAMINO)HEXANE

Me
Et
$+CH_2+_6$
Me
Et

Prepn.:

Methylethylamine + 1,6-dibromohexane.[BA30]

Derivs.:

Bis-hydrobromide: m. 213–214°[BA30]

$C_{12}H_{28}N_2$

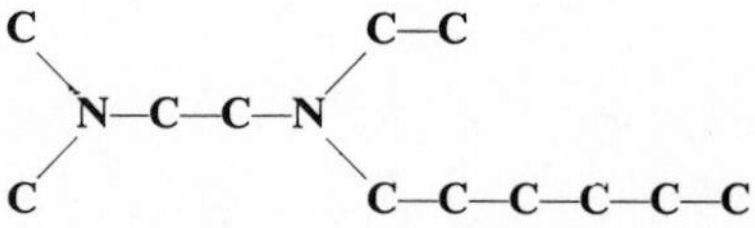

1-DIMETHYLAMINO-2-(ETHYLHEXYLAMINO)ETHANE

Me
Me
—CH_2CH_2—
Et
n-Hex

Phys. Props.:
b_{17} 110°[GR4]

Prepn.:

1-Dimethylamino-2-chloroethane + ethylhexylamine.[GR4]

$C_{12}H_{28}N_2$

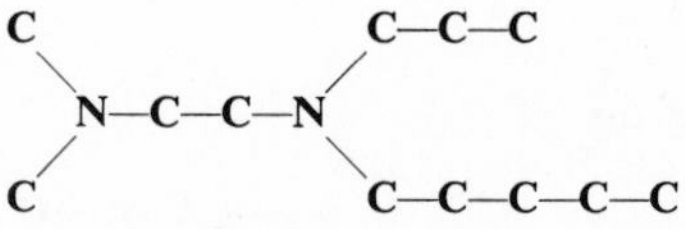

1-DIMETHYLAMINO-2-(PROPYLPENTYLAMINO)ETHANE

Me
Me
—CH_2CH_2—
n-Pr
n-Pent

Phys. Props.:
b_{22} 116–119°[GR4]

Prepn.:

1-Dimethylamino-2-chloroethane + propylpentylamine.[GR4]

$C_{12}H_{28}N_2$

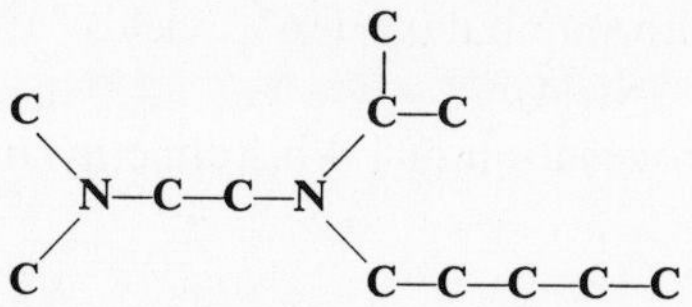

$$
\begin{array}{c}
\quad\quad\quad\quad\quad\quad C \\
C \quad\quad\quad\quad\quad C-C \\
\quad | \quad\quad\quad\quad\quad | \\
\quad N-C-C-N \\
\quad | \quad\quad\quad\quad\quad | \\
C \quad\quad\quad\quad\quad C-C-C-C
\end{array}
$$

Me
Me
—CH₂CH₂—
i-Pr
n-Pent

1-DIMETHYLAMINO-2-(ISOPROPYLPENTYLAMINO)ETHANE

Phys. Props.:

b_{20} 115–118°[GR4]

Prepn.:

1-Dimethylamino-2-chloroethane + isopropylpentylamine.[GR4]

$C_{12}H_{28}N_2$

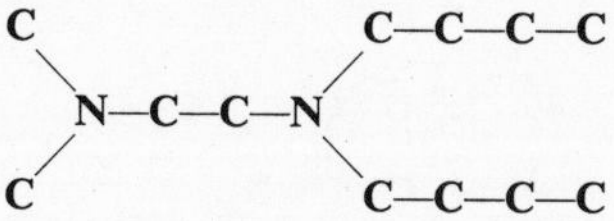

$$
\begin{array}{c}
C \quad\quad\quad\quad\quad C-C-C-C \\
\quad | \quad\quad\quad\quad\quad | \\
\quad N-C-C-N \\
\quad | \quad\quad\quad\quad\quad | \\
C \quad\quad\quad\quad\quad C-C-C-C
\end{array}
$$

Me
Me
—CH₂CH₂—
n-Bu
n-Bu

1-DIMETHYLAMINO-2-DIBUTYLAMINOETHANE

Phys. Props.:

b_{760} 201°[GR4]

Prepn.:

1-Dimethylamino-2-chloroethane + dibutylamine.[GR4]

$C_{12}H_{28}N_2$

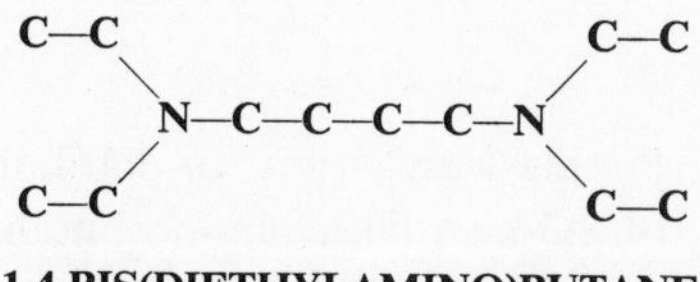

$$
\begin{array}{c}
C-C \quad\quad\quad\quad\quad C-C \\
\quad\backslash \quad\quad\quad\quad\quad\quad / \\
\quad N-C-C-C-C-N \\
\quad / \quad\quad\quad\quad\quad\quad \backslash \\
C-C \quad\quad\quad\quad\quad C-C
\end{array}
$$

Et
Et
―(CH₂)₄―
Et
Et

1,4-BIS(DIETHYLAMINO)BUTANE

Phys. Props.:

b_{25} 112–117°[BA24]; b_{22} 100°[PL2]; b_{13} 119°[JE1]; b_{3-4} 70–73.7°[AM2]
n_D^{20} 1.4421[AM2]

Prepn.:

1. Reduction of *N,N,N',N'*-tetraethylsuccinamide with lithium aluminum hydride (85% yield).[PL2]

2. Diethylamine + 1,4-dibromobutane (16% yield),[BA24] (10% yield)[JE1]; + 1,4-diiodobutane (12% yield).[PL2]
3. Nickel-catalyzed hydrogenation of 1,4-bis(dimethylamino)-2-butene (61% yield).[AM2]

Derivs.:

Bis-hydrochloride: m. 231–232° (dec.)[PL2]
Bis-hydrobromide: m. 80°[BU16]
Bis-picrate: m. 174–175°,[PL2] 172.0–173.9° (cor.)[AM2]
Bis-oxide dihydrate: m. 114°[JE1]
Bis-picrate of dioxide: m. 163° (dec.)[JE1]
Bis-methobromide: m. 284–287° (dec.)[BA23,BA24]
Bis-methiodide: m. 293–295°[FI7]
Bis-ethobromide: m. 278–280° (dec.)[BA23]
Bis-ethiodide: m. 259–260° (dec.)[PL2]

$C_{12}H_{28}N_2$

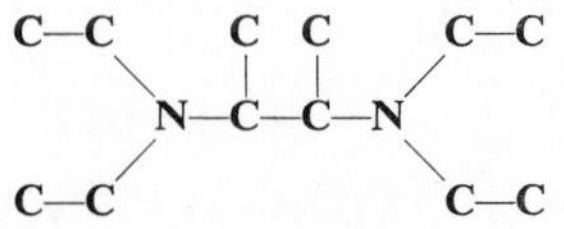

$$\begin{array}{c} \text{C—C} \qquad \text{C} \quad \text{C} \qquad \text{C—C} \\ \big\backslash \qquad \big| \quad \big| \qquad / \\ \text{N—C—C—N} \\ / \qquad \qquad \big\backslash \\ \text{C—C} \qquad \qquad \text{C—C} \end{array}$$

$$\begin{array}{c} \text{Et} \\ \text{Et} \\ \text{+}(\text{C}_4\text{H}_8)\text{+} \\ \text{Et} \\ \text{Et} \end{array}$$

2,3-BIS(DIETHYLAMINO)BUTANE

Phys. Props.:

meso isomer
  b. 208°[PF1]; b_{15} 110° (bath temp.)[SW3]
  n_D^{20} 1.4409[PF1]
racemic mixture
  b. 135° [*sic*][PF1]; b_{12} 110° (bath temp.)[SW3]
  n_D^{20} 1.4310[PF1]

Prepn.:

1. Irradiation of triethylamine with γ-rays for 300 hours (total dose 2.08 × 10^{23} e.v.) yields 1% of 2,3-bis-(diethylamino)butane as a mixture (about 50:50) of *meso* and racemic isomers.[SW3] Irradiation with ultraviolet light (24 hours) gives a similar mixture in about 3% yield.[PF1]
2. Reaction of *meso*-2,3-diaminobutane with ethyl iodide gives 29% yield of the corresponding *N,N,N',N'*-tetraethyl compound. The racemic compound was ethylated similarly (yield unspecified).[PF1]

Derivs.:

meso-Bis-hydrochloride: m. 238°[SW3]
meso-Bis-picrate: m. 178°[SW3]

dl-Bis-hydrochloride: m. 233°,[SW3] *ca.* 216° (dec.)[PF1]
dl-Bis-picrate: m. 177° (*sic*),[PF1] * 137°[SW3]

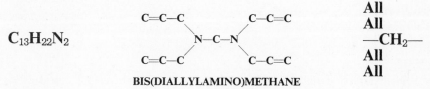

$C_{13}H_{22}N_2$

Me
Me
$+C_9H_{10}+$
Me
Me

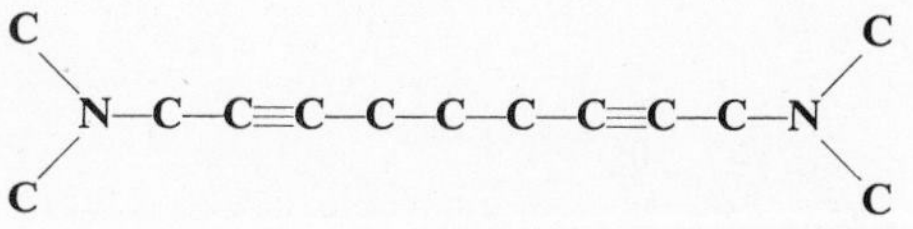

1,9-BIS(DIMETHYLAMINO)-2,7-NONADIYNE

Phys. Props.:
$b_{0.3}$ 98–99°[GU1]; $b_{0.05}$ 97°[GU2]
n_D^{23} 1.4720[GU1]; $n_D^{22.5}$ 1.4780[GU2]

Prepn.:
1,6-Heptadiyne + formaldehyde + dimethylamine,[FE2] (70–75% yield).[GU1]

Derivs.:
Bis-methiodide: m. 242–243°[GU1]

$C_{13}H_{22}N_2$

All
All
$-CH_2-$
All
All

BIS(DIALLYLAMINO)METHANE

Phys. Props.:
b_4 80°[BU10]
d_4^{25} 0.8410[BU10]
d_D^{25} 1.4668[BU10]

Prepn.:
Diallylamine + formaldehyde (83% yield).[BU10]

$C_{13}H_{26}N_2$

Et
Et
$+C_5H_6+$
Et
Et

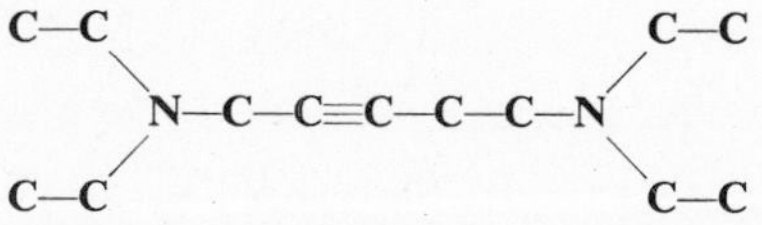

1,5-BIS(DIETHYLAMINO)-2-PENTYNE

Phys. Props.:
$b_{1.5}$ 85–90°[BI1,BI3]

---

* The values given by Pfordte and Leuschner[PF1] for the melting point of their racemic bis-picrate indicate that there probably is an error in their assignment of *meso* and racemic compounds. They say that their value for racemic bis-picrate at 177° agrees with that of Swan *et al.*[SW3] at 178°. This is not the case, however, because Swan *et al.* reported the value of 178° for the *meso*-bis-picrate.

Prepn.:

2-Chloroethyldiethylamine + the sodio derivative of 1-diethylamino-2-propyne,[BI1] (73% yield).[BI3]

Derivs.:

Bis-methobromide: m. 197–198°[BI3]

$C_{13}H_{26}N_2$

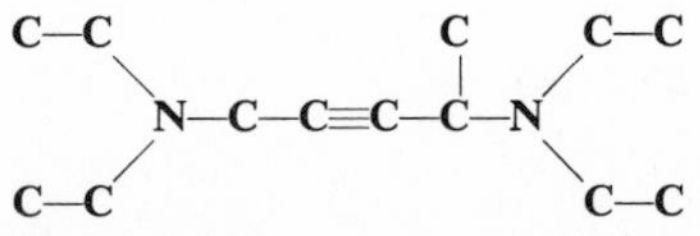

1,4-BIS(DIETHYLAMINO)-2-PENTYNE

Et
Et
$-(C_5H_6)-$
Et
Et

Phys. Props.:

b_8 104–106°[RO14]
n_D^{13} 1.4598 [RO14]
Ultraviolet absorption[RO14]

Prepn.:

3-Diethylamino-1-butyne + diethylamine + formaldehyde (73% yield).[RO14]

Derivs.:

Bis-hydrochloride: m. 205–206° [RO14]
Bis-picrate: m. 167–168.5°[RO14]
Bis-methiodide: m. 168°[RO14]

$C_{13}H_{28}N_2$

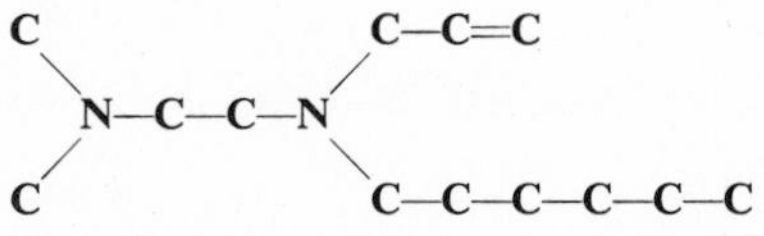

Me
Me
$-CH_2CH_2-$
All
n-Hex

1-DIMETHYLAMINO-2-(ALLYLHEXYLAMINO)ETHANE

Phys. Props.:

b_{20} 132–134°[GR4]

Prepn.:

1-Chloro-2-dimethylaminoethane + allylhexylamine.[GR4]

$C_{13}H_{28}N_2$

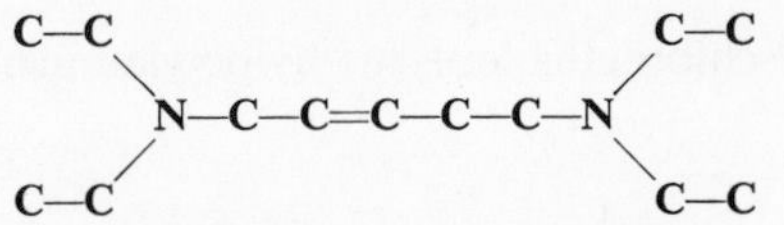

```
C—C                    C—C
   \                   /
    N—C—C=C—C—C—N
   /                   \
C—C                    C—C
```

Et
Et
$+C_5H_8+$
Et
Et

1,5-BIS(DIETHYLAMINO)-2-PENTENE

Phys. Props.:
cis isomer
  $b_{0.2}$ 67–71°[BI4]
trans isomer
  $b_{0.2}$ 70–72°[BI4]

Prepn.:
Catalytic hydrogenation of 1,5-bis(diethylamino)-2-pentyne in the presence of palladium yields the *cis* isomer[BI4]; reduction with sodium in liquid ammonia yields the *trans* isomer.[BI4]

Derivs.:
cis-Bis-methobromide: m. 225–227°[BI4]
trans-Bis-methobromide: m. 220–222°[BI4]

$C_{13}H_{30}N_2$

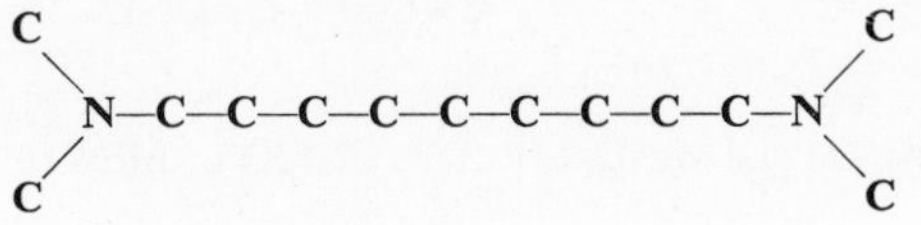

```
C                                     C
 \                                   /
  N—C—C—C—C—C—C—C—C—C—N
 /                                   \
C                                     C
```

Me
Me
$+CH_2+_9$
Me
Me

1,9-BIS(DIMETHYLAMINO)NONANE

Phys. Props.:
$b_{0.1}$ 83–84°[GU2]
n_D^{22} 1.4430[GU2]

Prepn.:
Catalytic hydrogenation of 1,9-dimethylamino-2,7-nonadiyne.[GU1,GU2]

Derivs.:
Bis-methiodide: m. 227°[GU2]

$C_{13}H_{30}N_2$

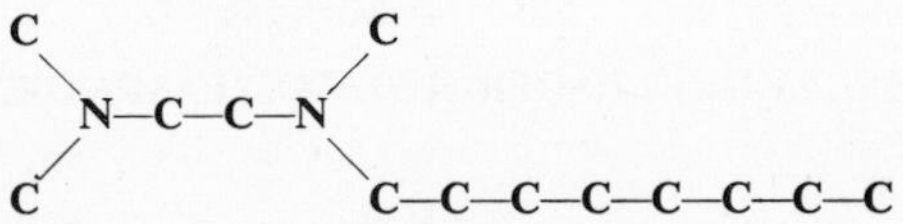

```
C           C
 \         /
  N—C—C—N
 /         \
C           C—C—C—C—C—C—C—C
```

Me
Me
—CH_2CH_2—
Me
n-C_8H_{17}

1-DIMETHYLAMINO-2-(METHYLOCTYLAMINO)ETHANE

Phys. Props.:
b_{23} 143–146°[GR4]

Prepn.:

1-Dimethylamino-2-chloroethane + methyloctylamine.[GR4]

$C_{13}H_{30}N_2$

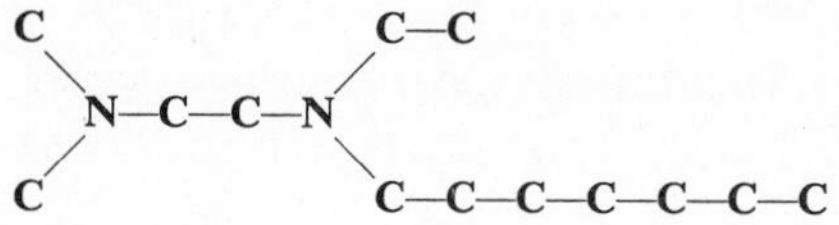

C		C—C	**Me**
\\		/	**Me**
N—C—C—N			**—CH₂CH₂—**
/		\\	**Et**
C		C—C—C—C—C—C—C	***n*-Hept**

1-DIMETHYLAMINO-2-(ETHYLHEPTYLAMINO)ETHANE

Phys. Props.:

b_{20} 136–139°[GR4]

Prepn.:

1-Dimethylamino-2-chloroethane + ethylheptylamine.[GR4]

$C_{13}H_{30}N_2$

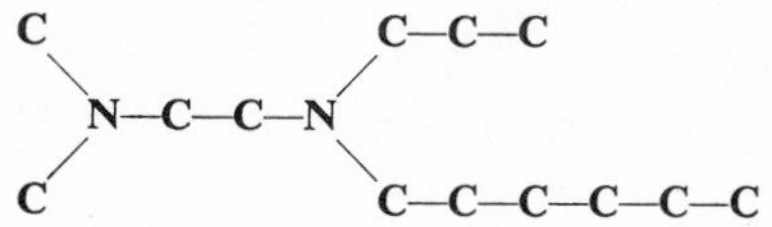

Me
Me
—CH₂CH₂—
***n*-Pr**
***n*-Hex**

1-DIMETHYLAMINO-2-(PROPYLHEXYLAMINO)ETHANE

Phys. Props.:

b_{22} 126–129°,[GR4] 126–134°[SC25]

Prepn.:

1-Dimethylamino-2-chloroethane + propylhexylamine.[GR4,SC25]

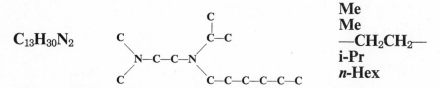

$C_{13}H_{30}N_2$

Me
Me
—CH₂CH₂—
i-Pr
***n*-Hex**

1-DIMETHYLAMINO-2-(ISOPROPYLHEXYLAMINO)ETHANE

Phys. Props.:

b_{33} 140–149°[SC25]; b_{32} 145–148°[GR4]

Prepn.:

1-Dimethylamino-2-chloroethane + isopropylhexylamine.[GR4,SC25]

$C_{13}H_{30}N_2$

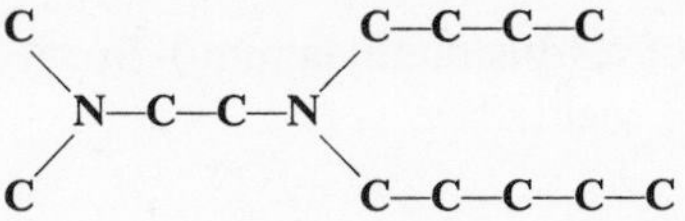

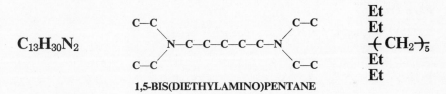

Me
Me
—CH$_2$CH$_2$—
n-Bu
n-Pent

1-DIMETHYLAMINO-2-(BUTYLPENTYLAMINO)ETHANE

Phys. Props.:

b_{18} 136–138°[RO3]

Prepn.:

1-Dimethylamino-2-chloroethane + butylpentylamine.[GR4]

$C_{13}H_{30}N_2$

Et
Et
$+CH_2+_5$
Et
Et

1,5-BIS(DIETHYLAMINO)PENTANE

Phys. Props.:

$b_{0.3}$ 95–100°[BI4]

Prepn.:

Catalytic hydrogenation of 1,5-bis(diethylamino)-2-pentyne in the presence of nickel (63% yield).[BI4]

Derivs.:

Bis-methobromide: m. 275–277° (dec.)[BA23]
Bis-ethobromide: m. 276–278° (dec.)[BA23]

$C_{13}H_{30}N_2$

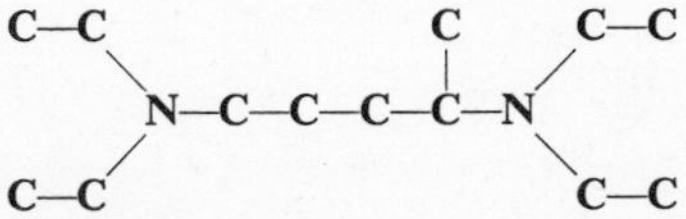

Et
Et
—C$_5$H$_{10}$—
Et
Et

1,4-BIS(DIETHYLAMINO)PENTANE

Phys. Props.:

b_{10} 105°[RO14]
n_D^{17} 1.4446[RO14]

Prepn.:

Catalytic hydrogenation of 1,4-bis(diethylamino)-2-pentyne in the presence of Raney nickel (50% yield).[RO14]

Derivs.:

Bis-picrate: m. 192–194°[RO14]

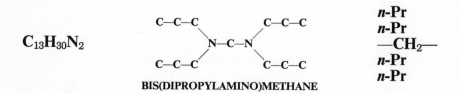

$C_{13}H_{30}N_2$

BIS(DIPROPYLAMINO)METHANE

n-Pr
n-Pr
—CH₂—
n-Pr
n-Pr

Phys. Props.:

b. 225–230° (dec.),[HE15] 215–225° (dec.)[EH1]; b_{15} 115°[BR23]
d_4^{18} 0.8014[HE15]

Prepn.:

Dipropylamine + formaldehyde in a sealed tube[EH1]; + aqueous formaldehyde at atmospheric pressure.[HE15]

Derivs.:

Bis-methiodide: m. 96°[BR23]*

$C_{14}H_{24}N_2$

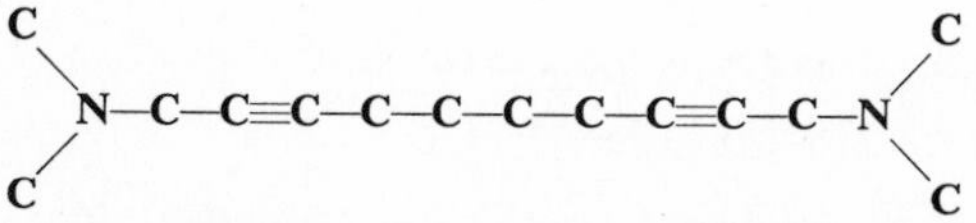

1,10-BIS(DIMETHYLAMINO)-2,8-DECADIYNE

Me
Me
—(C₁₀H₁₂)—
Me
Me

Phys. Props.:

$b_{0.4}$ 114°[GU1]; $b_{0.05}$ 108°[GU2]
n_D^{25} 1.4700[GU1]; $n_D^{17.5}$ 1.4810[GU2]

---

* Böhme and Lehners[BO10] claim that this material is a mixture of dipropylamine hydriodide and dimethyldipropylammonium iodide. These authors show also that, to prepare quaternary compounds of bis(dialkylamino)methanes, rigorously anhydrous conditions must be used. They thus prepared the monomethiodide and the monomethobromide (no melting point reported).

Prepn.:

1,7-Octadiyne + dimethylamine + formaldehyde in the presence of copper (II) acetate,[GU2] (70–75% yield).[GU1]

Derivs.:

Bis-methiodide: m. 263°[GU1,GU2]

$C_{14}H_{24}N_2$

Me
Me
$+C_{10}H_{12}+$
Me
Me

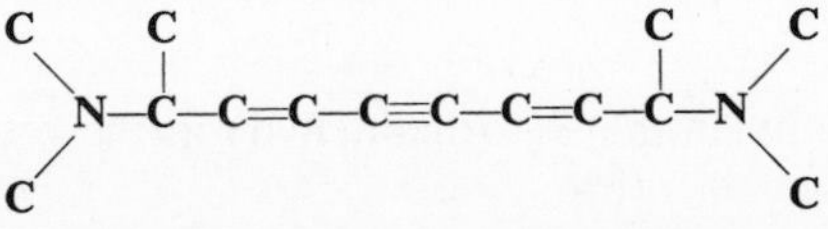

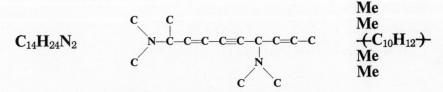

2,9-BIS(DIMETHYLAMINO)-3,7-DECADIEN-5-YNE

Phys. Props.:*

Ultraviolet absorption: 2670 A. (ϵ 8000)[JO5]

Prepn.:

Reaction of 2,9-dichloro-3,7-decadien-5-yne with dimethylamine.[JO5] Also obtained in this reaction *via* allylic shift is some 2,7-bis(dimethylamino) 3,8-decadien-5-yne.[JO5]

$C_{14}H_{24}N_2$

Me
Me
$+C_{10}H_{12}+$
Me
Me

2,7-BIS(DIMETHYLAMINO)-3,8-DECADIEN-5-YNE

Phys. Props.:*

Ultraviolet absorption: 2290 A. (ϵ 9,500)[JO5]

Prepn.:

Obtained (*via* allylic shift) as part of a mixture with 2,9-bis(dimethylamino)-3,7-decadien-5-yne upon reaction of dimethylamine with 2,9-dichloro-3,7-decadien-5-yne.[JO5]*

---

* Ref. JO5 gives the following physical properties for the mixture of isomers reported in the preparation: $b_{10^{-4}}$ 50° (bath temp.); n_D^{20} 1.5146. How the sample for the ultraviolet absorption data was obtained is not specified.

$C_{14}H_{24}N_2$

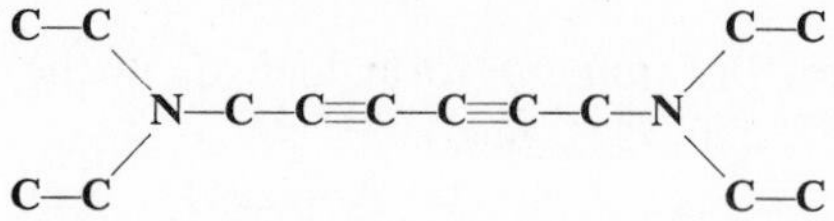

```
  C—C                    C—C
      \                  /
       N—C—C≡C—C≡C—C—N
      /                  \
  C—C                    C—C
```

Et
Et
$+(C_6H_4)+$
Et
Et

1,6-BIS(DIETHYLAMINO)-2,4-HEXADIYNE

Phys. Props.:

b_8 140–160° [FR5]

Prepn.:

1,3-Butadiyne + diethylamine + formaldehyde in the presence of copper(I) chloride (51% yield).[FR5]

$C_{14}H_{24}N_2$

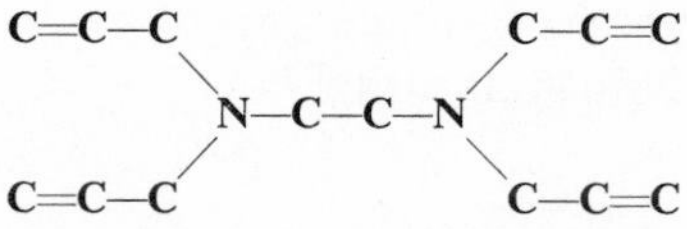

```
  C=C—C                C—C=C
       \              /
        N—C—C—N
       /              \
  C=C—C                C—C=C
```

All
All
—CH_2CH_2—
All
All

1,2-BIS(DIALLYLAMINO)ETHANE

Phys. Props.:

b_3 92° [BU15]
d_{25}^{25} 0.8517 [BU15]
n_D^{25} 1.4702 [BU15]

Prepn.:

1,2-Dibromoethane + diallylamine (41% yield).[BU15]

Derivs.:

Bis-methobromide: m. 191–192° (dec.)[BU12]
Bis-allylobromide: m. 142° [BU15]

$C_{14}H_{26}N_2$

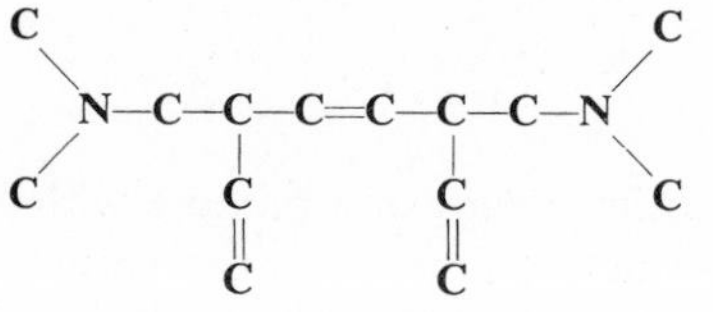

```
  C                          C
   \                        /
    N—C—C—C=C—C—C—N
   /      |     |      \
  C       C     C       C
          ‖     ‖
          C     C
```

Me
Me
$+(C_{12}H_{18})+$
Me
Me

3,6-BIS(DIMETHYLAMINOMETHYL)-1,4,7-OCTATRIENE

Phys. Props.:

b_{11} 130° [MA26]

Prepn.:

Dimerization of 2-dimethylaminomethyl-1,3-butadiene (*q.v.*) during its preparation *via* Hofmann degradation.[MA26]

Derivs.:

Bis-hydrochloride: m. 241–242°[MA26]
Bis-methiodide: m. 245°[MA26]

$C_{14}H_{28}N_2$

Me
Me
$+C_{10}H_{16}+$
Me
Me

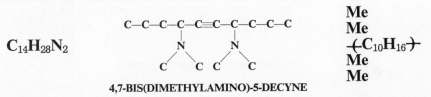

4,7-BIS(DIMETHYLAMINO)-5-DECYNE

Prepn.:

By-product in the preparation of 3-dimethylamino-1-hexyne by the reaction of butanal with dimethylamine and acetylene in formic acid in the presence of copper(I) chloride (low yield).[RE7]

$C_{14}H_{28}N_2$

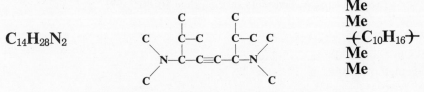

Me
Me
$+C_{10}H_{16}+$
Me
Me

3,6-BIS(DIMETHYLAMINO)-2,7-DIMETHYL-4-OCTYNE

Phys. Props.:

$b_{0.3}$ 67–70°[FE5]
n_D^{20} 1.4550[FE5]

Prepn.:

Isobutyraldehyde + diethylamine + acetylene in the presence of copper(I) chloride.[FE5]

$C_{14}H_{28}N_2$

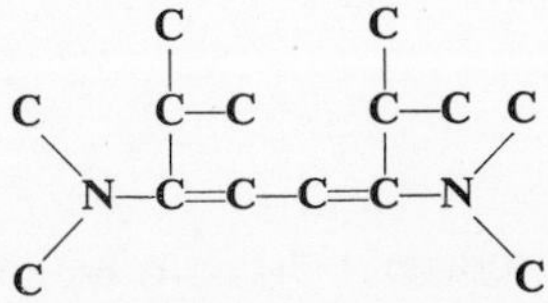

Me
Me
$+C_{10}H_{16}+$
Me
Me

3,6-BIS(DIMETHYLAMINO)-2,7-DIMETHYL-3,5-OCTADIENE

Phys. Props.:

$b_{0.2}$ 68–75°[FE5]
n 1.4948[FE5]

Prepn.:

Isomerization of 3,6-bis(dimethylamino)-2,7-dimethyl-4-octyne in the presence of sodium or benzyl sodium (65% conversion).[FE5]

$C_{14}H_{28}N_2$

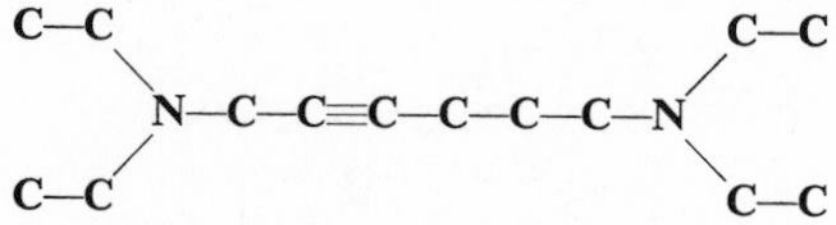

C—C   C—C
        N—C—C≡C—C—C—C—N
C—C   C—C

Et
Et
$\left(C_6H_8\right)$
Et
Et

1,6-BIS(DIETHYLAMINO)-2-HEXYNE

Phys. Props.:

$b_{0.5}$ 95–98°[BI1,BI3]

Prepn.:

Sodio derivative of 1-diethylamino-2-propyne + 1-diethylamino-3-chloro-propane (unspecified yield in the range 50–90%).[BI1]

Derivs.:

Bis-hydrochloride: m. 245–246°[BI3]
Bis-methobromide: m. 225–228°[BI3]

$C_{14}H_{28}N_2$

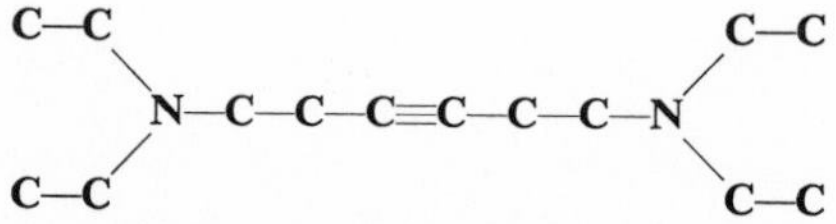

C—C   C—C
        N—C—C—C≡C—C—C—N
C—C   C—C

Et
Et
$\left(C_6H_8\right)$
Et
Et

1,6-BIS(DIETHYLAMINO)-3-HEXYNE

Phys. Props.:

$b_{0.5}$ 80–85°[BI2,BI3]
n_D^{20} 1.4591[BI2,BI3]

Prepn.:

Disodio derivative of acetylene + 1-diethylamino-2-chloroethane (88% yield).[BI2,BI3]

Derivs.:

Bis-hydrochloride: m. 235–237°[BI3]
Bis-methobromide: m. 234–236°[BI3]

$C_{14}H_{28}N_2$

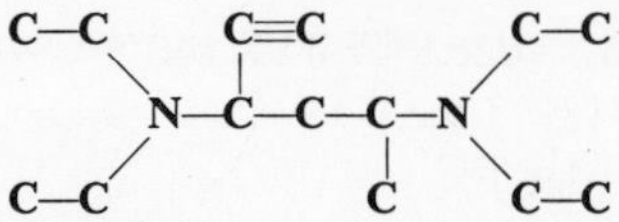

```
      C—C        C≡C            C—C        Et
         \       |            /           Et
          N—C—C—C—N                       (C6H8)
         /       |            \           Et
      C—C        C           C—C         Et
```

3,5-BIS(DIETHYLAMINO)-1-HEXYNE*

Phys. Props.:

$b_{0.1}$ 56°[GA3]
n_D^{21} 1.4729[GA3]

Prepn.:

Diethylamine + acetylene in the presence of copper(I) chloride.[GA3]

Derivs.:

Bis-hydrochloride: m. 260° (dec.)[GA3]
Bis-picrate: m. 213° (dec.)[GA3]
Bis-methiodide: m. 200–205°[GA3]

$C_{14}H_{32}N_2$

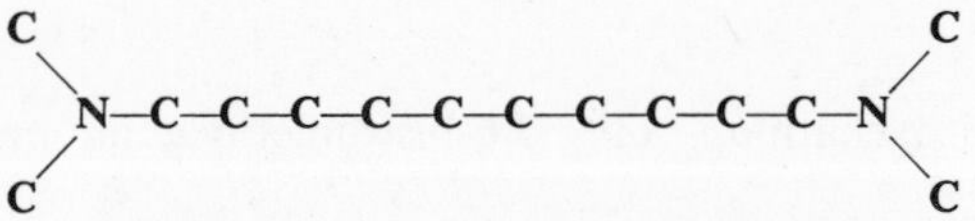

```
   C                                    C       Me
    \                                  /        Me
     N—C—C—C—C—C—C—C—C—C—C—N                   (CH2)10
    /                                  \        Me
   C                                    C       Me
```

1,10-BIS(DIMETHYLAMINO)DECANE

Phys. Props.:

b_{17} 157–158°[BO1,BO2,BR10]; b_5 115–120°[BA29]; $b_{0.5}$ 106–108°[CA19]; $b_{0.05}$ 95°[GU2]
n_D^{25} 1.4445[CO23]

Prepn.:

1. 1,10-Diaminodecane + formaldehyde + formic acid (75% yield),[BO2] (72% yield).[BO1]
2. 1,10-Dibromodecane + dimethylamine,[CA19] (60% yield).[BA29]
3. Catalytic hydrogenation of 1,10-bis(dimethylamino)-2,8-decadiyne.[BR10]
4. Thermal decomposition of decamethylene-1,10-bis(trimethylammonium)-hydroxide (50% yield from the corresponding diiodide).[BR10]
5. Reduction of amine oxide of 1,10-bis(dimethylamino)decane with zinc and hydrochloric acid.[BO1]

---

* The structure of this compound was not proved by ref. GA3 and was presented only as a likely structure from the limited evidence.

Derivs.:

Bis-picrate: m. 149.5–151° (dec.),[BO1] 139–140°[BR10]
Bis-chloroplatinate: m. 189° (dec.)[BR10]
Bis-oxide: m. 154–155° (dec.)[BO1]
Bis-picrolonate: m. 150–160° (dec.)[BO1]
Bis-methobromide: m. 268–270° (dec.),[BL4a] 250–251°[ON1]
Bis-methiodide: m. 249°,[GU2] 231–233°,[ON1] 231°[BR10]
Bis-ethiodide: m. 251–252°[BA29]
Bis-methosulfate: m. 157–158°[BO1]
Bis-benzochloride: m. 180–181° (dec.)[BO1]
Bis-benzobromide: m. 226°[SM10]

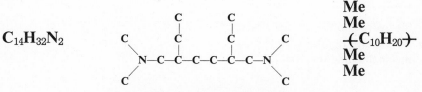

$C_{14}H_{32}N_2$

Me
Me
$-(C_{10}H_{20})-$
Me
Me

3,6-BIS(DIMETHYLAMINOMETHYL)OCTANE

Prepn.:

Catalytic hydrogenation of 3,6-bis(dimethylaminomethyl)-1,4,7-octatriene.[MA26]

Derivs.:

Chloroplatinate: m. 191°[MA26]

$C_{14}H_{32}N_2$

Me
Me
$-CH_2CH_2-$
Me
n-C_9H_{19}

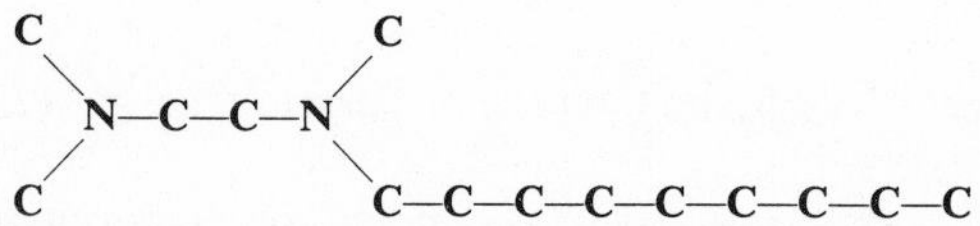

1-DIMETHYLAMINO-2-(METHYLNONYLAMINO)ETHANE

Phys. Props.:

b_{18} 152–155°[GR4]

Prepn.:

Methylnonylamine + 1-chloro-2-dimethylaminoethane.[GR4]

$C_{14}H_{32}N_2$

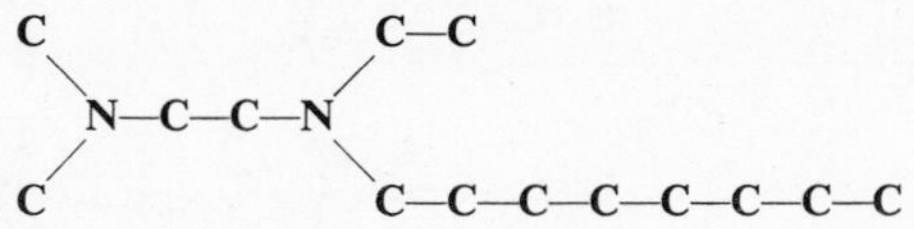

```
      C              C—C                    Me
       \            /                       Me
        N—C—C—N                            —CH₂CH₂—
       /            \                       Et
      C              C—C—C—C—C—C—C          n-C₈H₁₇
```

1-DIMETHYLAMINO-2-(ETHYLOCTYLAMINO)ETHANE

Phys. Props.:

b_{22} 146–149° [GR4]

Prepn.:

Ethyloctylamine + 1-chloro-2-dimethylaminoethane. [GR4]

$C_{14}H_{32}N_2$

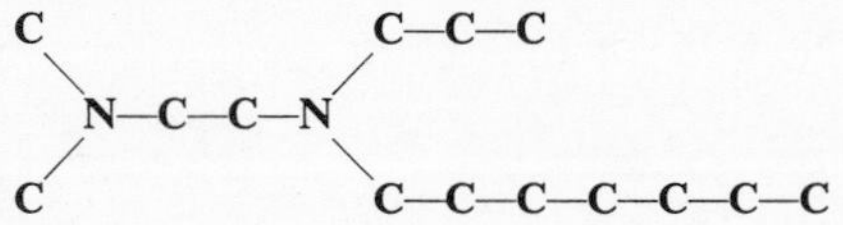

```
      C              C—C—C                  Me
       \            /                       Me
        N—C—C—N                            —CH₂CH₂—
       /            \                       n-Pr
      C              C—C—C—C—C—C—C          n-Hept
```

1-DIMETHYLAMINO-2-(PROPYLHEPTYLAMINO)ETHANE

Phys. Props.:

b_{20} 146–149° [GR4]

Prepn.:

Propylheptylamine + 1-chloro-2-dimethylaminoethane. [GR4]

$C_{14}H_{32}N_2$

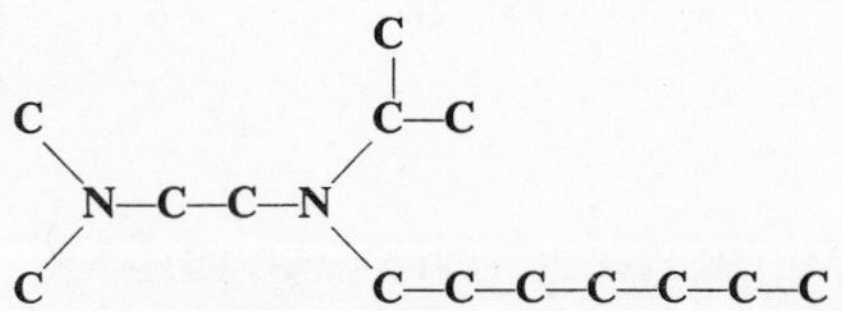

```
                     C
      C              C—C                    Me
       \            /                       Me
        N—C—C—N                            —CH₂CH₂—
       /            \                       i-Pr
      C              C—C—C—C—C—C—C          n-Hept
```

1-DIMETHYLAMINO-2-(ISOPROPYLHEPTYLAMINO)ETHANE

Phys. Props.:

b_{16} 136–139° [GR4]

Prepn.:

Isopropylheptylamine + 1-chloro-2-dimethylaminoethane. [GR4]

$C_{14}H_{32}N_2$

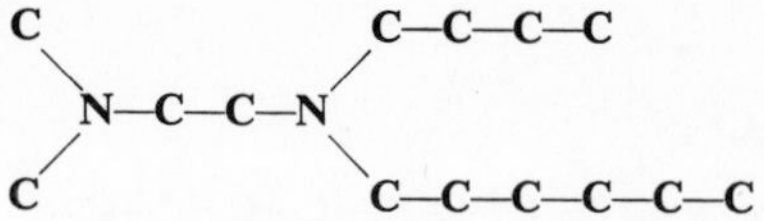

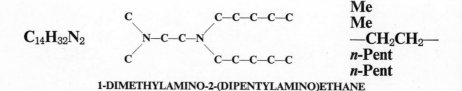

Me
Me
—CH₂CH₂—
n-**Bu**
n-**Hex**

1-DIMETHYLAMINO-2-(BUTYLHEXYLAMINO)ETHANE

Phys. Props.:

b_{20} 131–134° [GR4]

Prepn.:

Butylhexylamine + 1-chloro-2-dimethylaminoethane. [GR4]

$C_{14}H_{32}N_2$

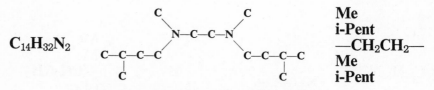

Me
Me
—CH₂CH₂—
n-**Pent**
n-**Pent**

1-DIMETHYLAMINO-2-(DIPENTYLAMINO)ETHANE

Phys. Props.:

b_{17} 136–138° [GR4]

Prepn.:

Dipentylamine + 1-chloro-2-dimethylaminoethane. [GR4]

$C_{14}H_{32}N_2$

Me
i-Pent
—CH₂CH₂—
Me
i-Pent

1,2-BIS(METHYLISOPENTYLAMINO)ETHANE

Phys. Props.:

b_{18} 130–131° [CL1a]
$d_4^{19.2}$ 0.8083 [CL1a]
$n_\alpha^{19.2}$ 1.43855 [CL1a]

Prepn.:

Methylisopentylamine + 1,2-dibromoethane. [CL1a]

$C_{14}H_{32}N_2$

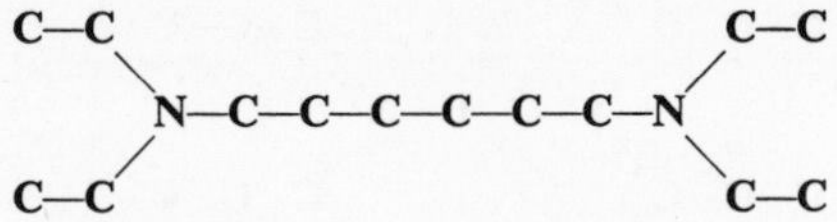

1,6-BIS(DIETHYLAMINO)HEXANE

Et
Et
$\text{+}CH_2\text{+}_6$
Et
Et

Phys. Props.:

b_{13} 135° [JE1]; b_1 90–92° [CA19]

Prepn.:

1,6-Dibromohexane + diethylamine,[BA30, CA19] (53% yield).[JE1]

Derivs.:

Bis-hydrobromide: m. 267° [BA30]
Bis-picrate of dioxide: m. 163–165° [JE1]
Bis-oxide: m. 98–102° [JE1]
Bis-methobromide: m. 269–270° (dec.)[BA22]
Bis-ethobromide: m. 267–269° (dec.)[BA22]

$C_{14}H_{32}N_2$

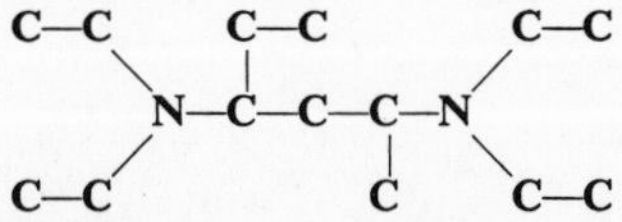

2,4-BIS(DIETHYLAMINO)HEXANE*

Et
Et
$\text{+}C_6H_{12}\text{+}$
Et
Et

Phys. Props.:

$b_{0.25}$ 64–65° [GA3]
n_D^{21} 1.4560[GA3]

Prepn.:

Catalytic hydrogenation over Raney nickel of a compound assumed to be 3,5-bis(diethylamino)-1-hexyne.[GA3]

Derivs.:

Bis-methiodide: m. 193–196° (dec.)[GA3]

---

* The assigned structure of this compound is not proved but is derived from its method of synthesis.

$C_{14}H_{32}N_2$

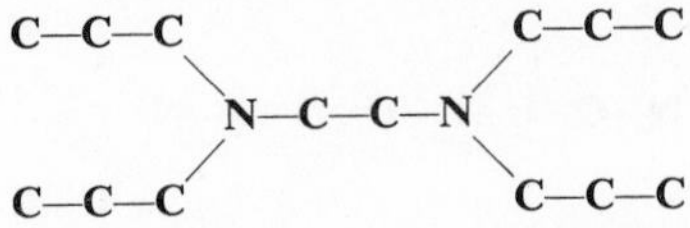

1,2-BIS(DIPROPYLAMINO)ETHANE

n-Pr
n-Pr
—CH₂CH₂—
n-Pr
n-Pr

Prepn.:

1,2-Dibromoethane + dipropylamine.[KH1]

Derivs.:

Bis-propiodide: m. 279–280° [KH1]

$C_{15}H_{24}N_2$

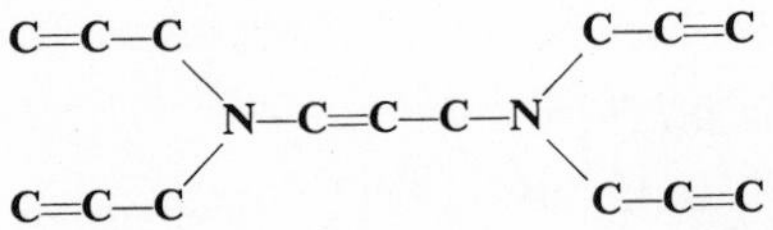

1,3-BIS(DIALLYLAMINO)-1-PROPENE

All
All
—(C₃H₄)—
All
All

Phys. Props.:

$b_{1.5}$ 93–105° [MA4]; $b_{0.08}$ 97–99° [SM5]
n_D^{20} 1.4953 [MA4]

Prepn.:

Diallylamine + acrolein.[SM5]

$C_{15}H_{26}N_2$

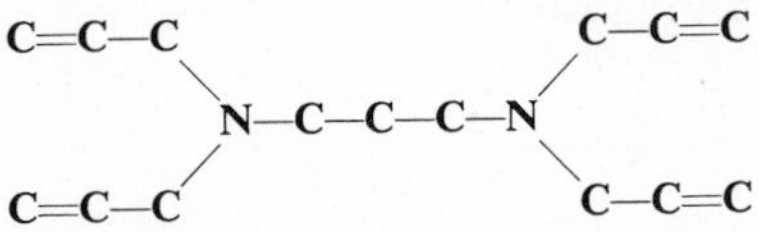

1,3-BIS(DIALLYLAMINO)PROPANE

All
All
—(CH₂)₃—
All
All

Phys. Props.:

$b_{0.5}$ 88–89° [BU12]
d_4^{25} 0.8415 [BU12]
n_D^{25} 1.4711 [BU12]

Prepn.:

1,3-Dibromopropane + diallylamine.[BU12]*

---

    * A yield of 80.5% is reported but it is not clear if it applies to this reaction or to another in the same paper.

Derivs.:

Bis-methobromide: m. 109–111°[BU12]
Bis-allylobromide: m. 185–187°[BU12]

$C_{15}H_{32}N_2$

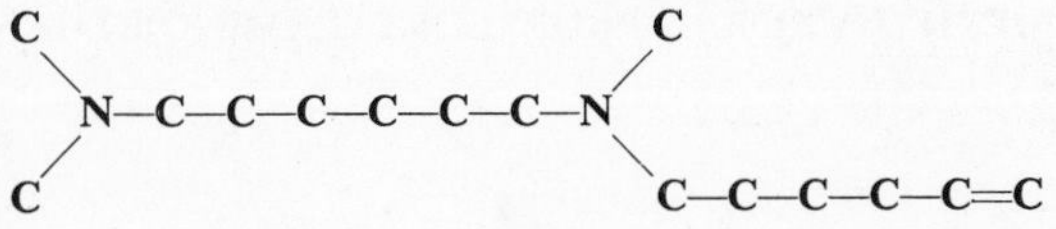

C
C
N—C—C—C—C—C—N
C—C—C—C—C=C

Me
Me
$-(CH_2)_6-$
Me
C_6H_{11}

1-DIMETHYLAMINO-6-(METHYL-5-HEXENYLAMINO)HEXANE

Derivs.:

Bis-methiodide: m. 223°[BR17] (this quaternary compound was prepared from
1-amino-6-(5-hexenylamino)hexane and methyl iodide)

$C_{15}H_{34}N_2$

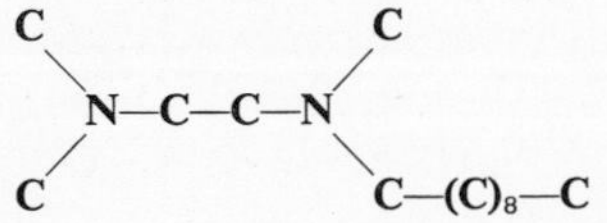

C
C
N—C—C—N
C—(C)₈—C

Me
Me
$-CH_2CH_2-$
Me
$n\text{-}C_{10}H_{21}$

1-DIMETHYLAMINO-2-(METHYLDECYLAMINO)ETHANE

Phys. Props.:

b_{20} 165–168°[GR4]

Prepn.:

Methyldecylamine + 1-chloro-2-dimethylaminoethane.[GR4]

$C_{15}H_{34}N_2$

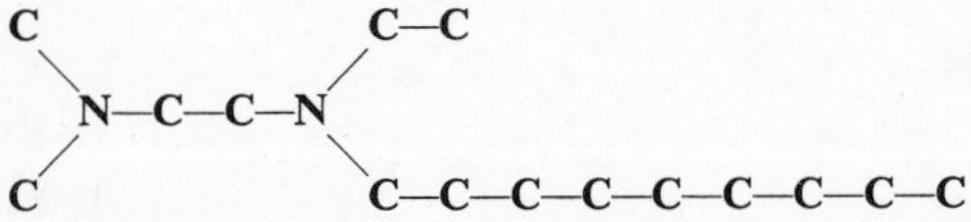

C
C—C
N—C—C—N
C—C—C—C—C—C—C—C—C

Me
Me
$-CH_2CH_2-$
Et
$n\text{-}C_9H_{19}$

1-DIMETHYLAMINO-2-(ETHYLNONYLAMINO)ETHANE

Phys. Props.:

b_{20} 164–168°[GR4]

Prepn.:

Ethylnonylamine + 1-chloro-2-dimethylaminoethane.[GR4]

$$C_{15}H_{34}N_2$$

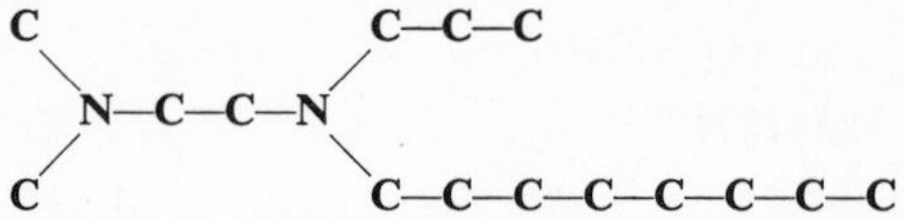

$$
\begin{array}{c}
\text{C} \\
\text{C} \\
\text{N—C—C—N} \\
\text{C}
\end{array}
\quad
\begin{array}{c}
\text{C—C—C} \\
\text{C—C—C—C—C—C—C—C}
\end{array}
$$

Me
Me
—CH₂CH₂—
***n*-Pr**
***n*-Oct**

1-DIMETHYLAMINO-2-(PROPYLOCTYLAMINO)ETHANE

Phys. Props.:
b_{22} 156–159°[GR4]

Prepn.:

Propyloctylamine + 1-chloro-2-dimethylaminoethane.[GR4]

$$C_{15}H_{34}N_2$$

$$
\begin{array}{c}
\text{C} \\
\text{C} \\
\text{N—C—C—N} \\
\text{C}
\end{array}
\quad
\begin{array}{c}
\text{C} \\
\text{C—C} \\
\text{C—C—C—C—C—C—C—C}
\end{array}
$$

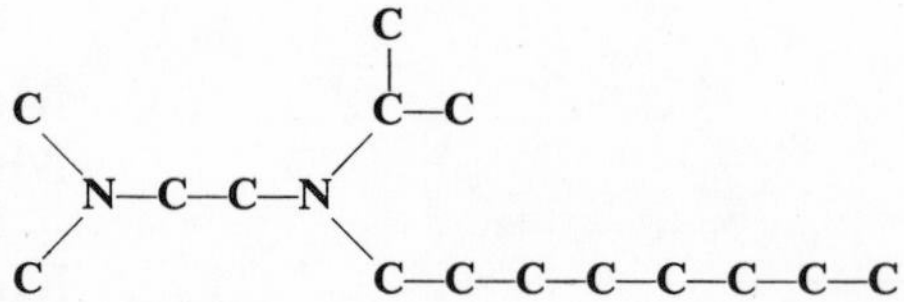

Me
Me
—CH₂CH₂—
i-Pr
***n*-Oct**

1-DIMETHYLAMINO-2-(ISOPROPYLOCTYLAMINO)ETHANE

Phys. Props.:
b_{20} 153–158°[GR4]

Prepn.:

Isopropyloctylamine + 1-chloro-2-dimethylaminoethane.[GR4]

$$C_{15}H_{34}N_2$$

$$
\begin{array}{c}
\text{C} \\
\text{C} \\
\text{N—C—C—N} \\
\text{C}
\end{array}
\quad
\begin{array}{c}
\text{C—C—C—C} \\
\text{C—C—C—C—C—C—C}
\end{array}
$$

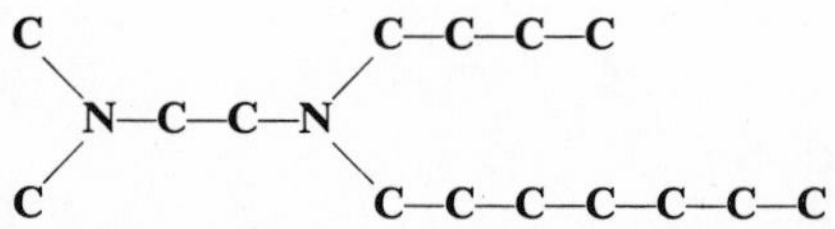

Me
Me
—CH₂CH₂—
***n*-Bu**
***n*-Hept**

1-DIMETHYLAMINO-2-(BUTYLHEPTYLAMINO)ETHANE

Phys. Props.:
b_{24} 160–163°[GR4]

Prepn.:

Butylheptylamine + 1-chloro-2-dimethylaminoethane.[GR4]

$C_{15}H_{34}N_2$

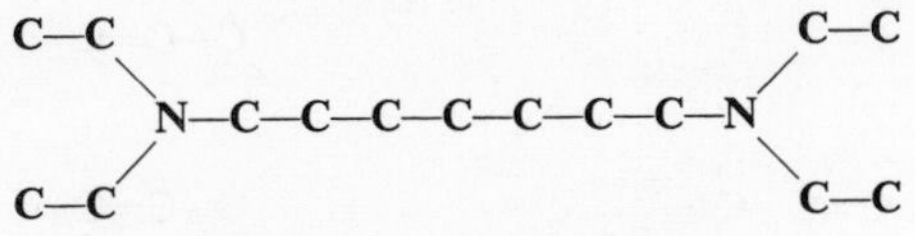

```
   C—C                        C—C        Et
         \                   /           Et
   C—C    N—C—C—C—C—C—C—C—N   C—C      +CH₂+₇
         /                   \           Et
   C—C                        C—C        Et
```

1,7-BIS(DIETHYLAMINO)HEPTANE

Phys. Props.:

b_{10} 118–120°[BA23]

Prepn.:

Thermal decomposition of heptamethylene-bis-1,7-triethylammonium sulfate.[BA23]

Derivs.:

Bis-methobromide: m. 281–284° (dec.)[BA23]
Bis-ethobromide: m. 267–269° (dec.)[BA23]

$C_{15}H_{34}N_2$

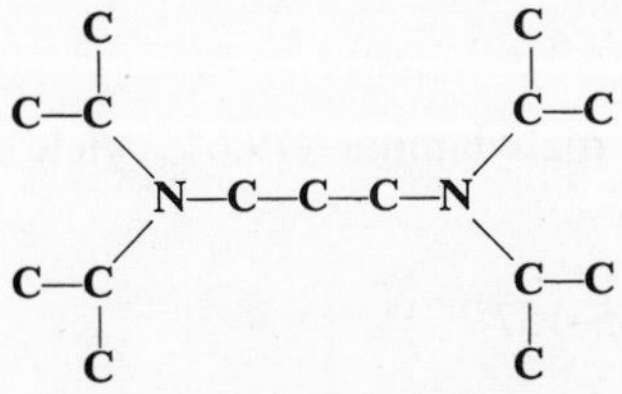

```
        C                 C
        |                 |
     C—C                 C—C          i-Pr
        \               /             i-Pr
     C—C  N—C—C—C—N    C—C          +CH₂+₃
        /               \             i-Pr
     C—C                 C—C          i-Pr
        |                 |
        C                 C
```

1,3-BIS(DIISOPROPYLAMINO)PROPANE

Phys. Props.:

$b_{10.25}$ 85.7°[LA1]*; $b_{0.25}$ 83°[RE16]*

Prepn.:

1,3-Di(*p*-toluenesulfonoxy)propane + diisopropylamine (85.7% yield).[LA1,RE16]

---

* These boiling points were reported by the same authors in different publications. The value $b_{0.25}$ 83° seems to be much more in line with the expected value for this type of compound than the other, $b_{10.25}$ 85.7°, which is probably a typographic error.

$C_{16}H_{24}N_2$

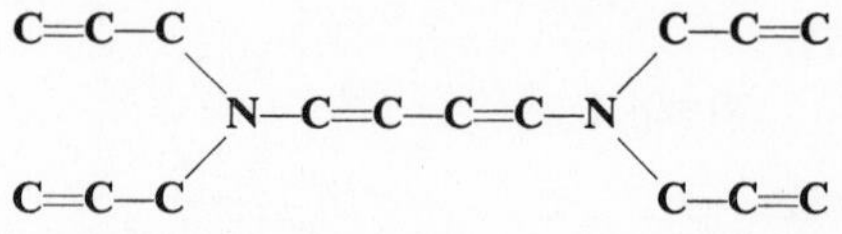

C=C—C   C—C=C
        N—C=C—C=C—N
C=C—C   C—C=C

All
All
$+C_4H_4+$
All
All

1,4-BIS(DIALLYLAMINO)-1,3-BUTADIENE*

Phys. Props.:
n_D^{20} 1.5501[FE6]

Prepn.:
Acid-catalyzed transamination reaction between diallylamine and 1,4-bis-(dimethylamino)-1,3-butadiene (31% yield).[FE6]

$C_{16}H_{26}N_2$

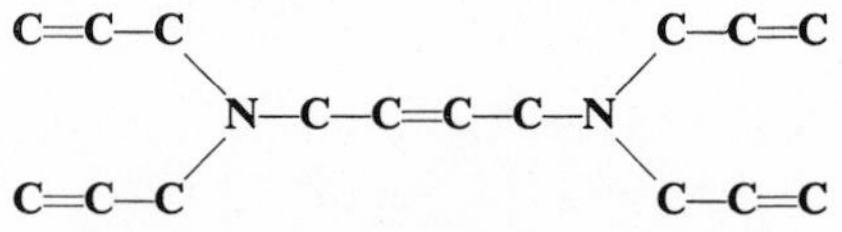

C=C—C   C—C=C
        N—C—C=C—C—N
C=C—C   C—C=C

All
All
$+C_4H_6+$
All
All

1,4-BIS(DIALLYLAMINO)-2-BUTENE

Phys. Props.:
$b_{0.8}$ 102° [BU16]
d_4^{25} 0.8647[BU16]
n_D^{25} 1.4820[BU16]

Prepn.:
1,4-Dichloro-2-butene + diallylamine (79.6% yield),[MO12] (68% yield).[BU16]

Derivs.:
Bis-allylobromide: m. 155–157° [BU16]

$C_{16}H_{28}N_2$

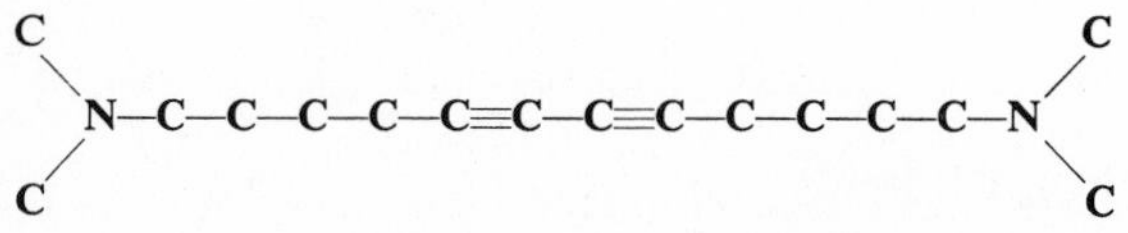

C   C
  N—C—C—C—C—C≡C—C≡C—C—C—C—C—N
C   C

Me
Me
$+C_{12}H_{16}+$
Me
Me

1,12-BIS(DIMETHYLAMINO)-5,7-DODECADIYNE

Phys. Props.:
$b_{0.2}$ 142° [OL6]
n_D^{27} 1.4960[OL6]

---

* Ref. FE6 (a patent) does not specify the configuration of this particular molecule. However, from another example in this patent and from some other work by the same authors (see ref. FE4) the configuration of this compound is most likely *trans,trans*.

Prepn.:

1-Dimethylamino-5-hexyne + oxygen in the presence of copper chloride and ammonium chloride (82% yield).[OL6]

$C_{16}H_{28}N_2$

```
C—C        C              C    C—C        Et
     \      |              |   /           Et
      N—C—C≡C—C≡C—C—N               {C8H8}
     /                    \          Et
C—C                        C—C       Et
```

2,7-BIS(DIETHYLAMINO)-3,5-OCTADIYNE

Phys. Props.:

$b_{0.2}$ 130–134° [RO13,RO14]
n_D^{18} 1.4958 [RO13,RO14]

Prepn.:

3-Diethylamino-1-butyne + air in the presence of copper(I) chloride and ammonium chloride,[RO13] (91% yield).[RO14]

Derivs.:

Bis-picrate: m. 230° (dec.)[RO14]

$C_{16}H_{28}N_2$

```
C=C—C              C—C=C        All
     \            /             All
      N—C—C—C—C—N               {CH2}4
     /            \             All
C=C—C              C—C=C        All
```

1,4-BIS(DIALLYLAMINO)BUTANE

Phys. Props.:

$b_{0.1}$ 96–98° [BU11]
n_D^{28} 1.4716 [BU11]

Prepn.:

1. Reduction of N,N,N',N'-tetraallylsuccinamide with lithium aluminum hydride (49.3% yield).[BU11]
2. Diallylamine + 1,4-di(p-toluensulfonoxy)butane (8% yield of impure product).[BU11]
3. 1,4-Dibromobutane + diallylamine.[BU16]*

---

* Ref. BU16 claims that the reaction of diallylamine with 1,4-dibromobutane followed by reaction with sodium hydroxide does not give 1,4-bis(diallylamino)butane. However, it is claimed that the dihydrobromide is obtained in 75% yield. It is not clear how this dihydrobromide was prepared, but the inference is that the foregoing reaction was used. In a later article by one of the same authors (ref. BU11), it is shown that reaction of 1,4-dibromobutane with diallylamine gives diallylpyrrolidinium bromide rather than 1,4-bis(diallylamino)butane.

Derivs.:

Bis-hydrobromide: m. 58°[BU16]
Bis-methiodide: m. 163–165°[BU11]

$C_{16}H_{34}N_2$

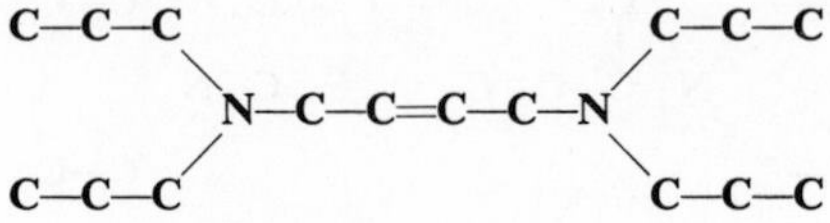

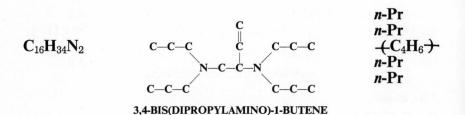

1,4-BIS(DIPROPYLAMINO)-2-BUTENE

n-Pr
n-Pr
+C₄H₆+
n-Pr
n-Pr

Phys. Props.:

b_{15} 150–154°[AM2]
n_D^{21} 1.4538 [AM2]

Prepn.:

Dipropylamine + 1,4-dichloro-2-butene (91.3% yield),[MO12] (51% yield).[AM2]

Derivs.:

Bis-picrate: m. 173–174°[AM2]

$C_{16}H_{34}N_2$

3,4-BIS(DIPROPYLAMINO)-1-BUTENE

n-Pr
n-Pr
+C₄H₆+
n-Pr
n-Pr

Prepn.:

Dipropylamine + 3,4-dichlorobutene (53.8% yield).[MO13]

$C_{16}H_{34}N_2$

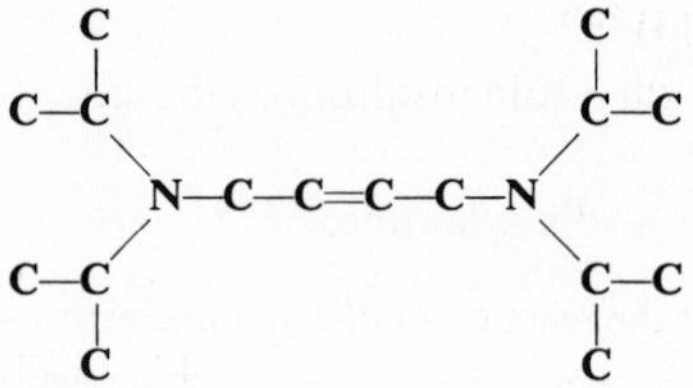

1,4-BIS(DIISOPROPYLAMINO)-2-BUTENE

i-Pr
i-Pr
+C₄H₆+
i-Pr
i-Pr

Prepn.:

1,4-Dichloro-2-butene + diisopropylamine,[MO11] (49.7% yield).[MO12]

$C_{16}H_{36}N_2$

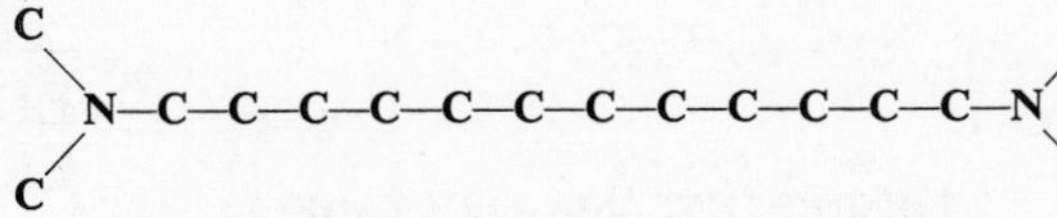

$$
\begin{array}{c}
C \\
| \\
N-C-C-C-C-C-C-C-C-C-C-C-N \\
| \\
C
\end{array}
\qquad
\begin{array}{l}
Me \\
Me \\
(CH_2)_{12} \\
Me \\
Me
\end{array}
$$

with the right-side C atoms bearing C substituents above and below each terminal N.

1,12-BIS(DIMETHYLAMINO)DODECANE

Derivs.:

Bis-methosulfate (from 1,12-diaminododecane and methyl sulfate): m. 186° [BR13]

$C_{16}H_{36}N_2$

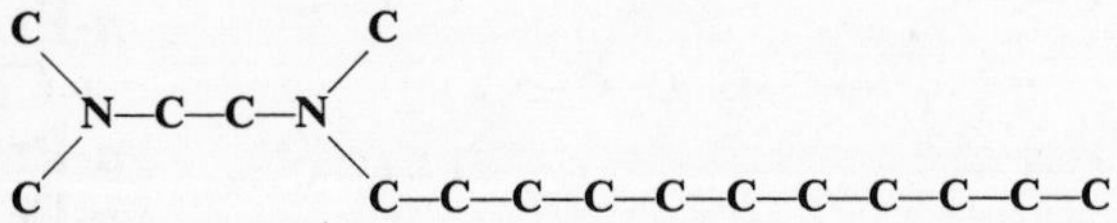

$$
\begin{array}{c}
C \qquad C \\
| \qquad | \\
N-C-C-N \\
| \qquad | \\
C \qquad C-C-C-C-C-C-C-C-C-C-C
\end{array}
\qquad
\begin{array}{l}
Me \\
Me \\
CH_2CH_2 \\
Me \\
n\text{-}C_{11}H_{23}
\end{array}
$$

1-DIMETHYLAMINO-2-(METHYLUNDECYLAMINO)ETHANE

Phys. Props.:

b_3 149–152° [GR4]

Prepn.:

Methylundecylamine + 1-chloro-2-dimethylaminoethane. [GR4]

$C_{16}H_{36}N_2$

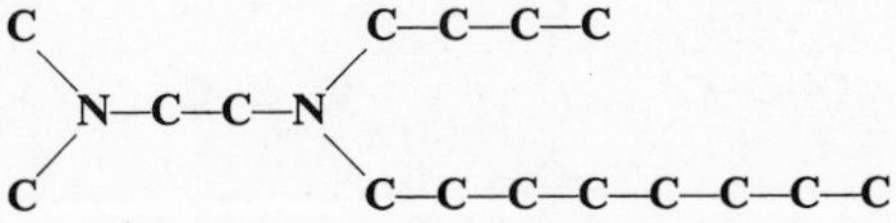

$$
\begin{array}{c}
C \qquad\qquad C-C-C-C \\
| \qquad\qquad | \\
N-C-C-N \\
| \qquad\qquad | \\
C \qquad\qquad C-C-C-C-C-C-C-C
\end{array}
\qquad
\begin{array}{l}
Me \\
Me \\
CH_2CH_2 \\
n\text{-}Bu \\
n\text{-}Oct
\end{array}
$$

1-DIMETHYLAMINO-2-(BUTYLOCTYLAMINO)ETHANE

Phys. Props.:

b_{13} 165–167° [GR4]

Prepn.:

Butyloctylamine + 1-chloro-2-dimethylaminoethane. [GR4]

$C_{16}H_{36}N_2$

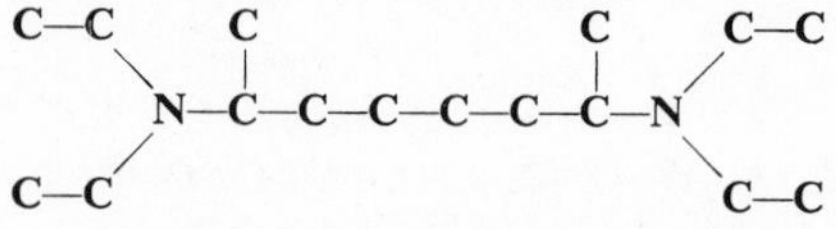

```
    C—C      C              C    C—C
      \      |              |    /
       N—C—C—C—C—C—C—C—N
      /                        \
    C—C                        C—C
```

Et
Et
$+C_8H_{16}+$
Et
Et

2,7-BIS(DIETHYLAMINO)OCTANE

Phys. Props.:
$b_{0.1}$ 83–87° [RO14]
n_D^{20} 1.4612 [RO14]

Prepn.:
Catalytic hydrogenation of 2,7-bis(diethylamino)-3,5-octadiyne.[RO14]

Derivs.:
Bis-picrate: m. 186–190° [RO14]

$C_{16}H_{36}N_2$

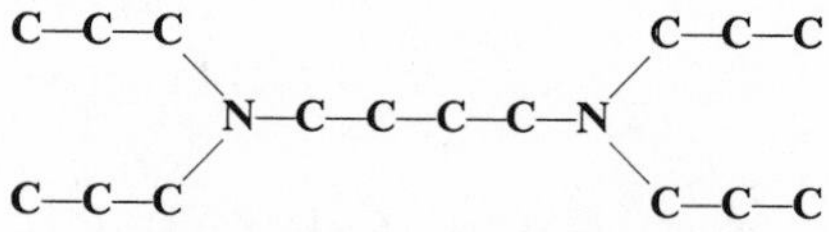

```
    C—C—C              C—C—C
        \             /
         N—C—C—C—C—N
        /             \
    C—C—C              C—C—C
```

***n*-Pr**
***n*-Pr**
$+CH_2+_4$
***n*-Pr**
***n*-Pr**

1,4-BIS(DIPROPYLAMINO)BUTANE

Phys. Props.:
b_4 129–130° [AM2]
n_D^{20} 1.4443 [AM2]

Prepn.:
Catalytic hydrogenation of 1,4-bis(dipropylamino)-2-butene in the presence of nickel (43% yield).[AM2]

Derivs.:
Bis-picrate: m. 194.0–195.5° [AM2]

$C_{16}H_{36}N_2$

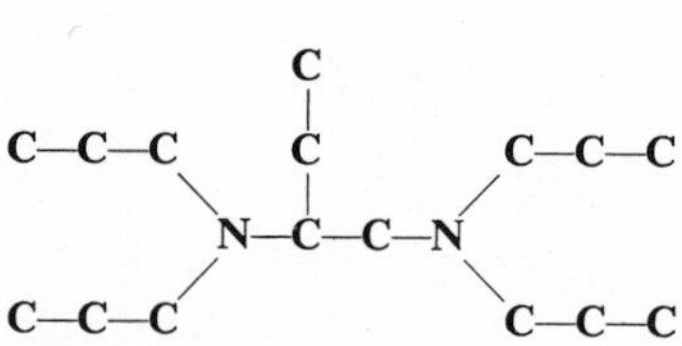

```
            C
            |
    C—C—C   C   C—C—C
        \   |   /
         N—C—C—N
        /       \
    C—C—C       C—C—C
```

***n*-Pr**
***n*-Pr**
$+C_4H_8+$
***n*-Pr**
***n*-Pr**

1,2-BIS(DIPROPYLAMINO)BUTANE

*Phys. Props.:**
b_{10} 109° [RE17]; b_3 108° [SP1]
d_4^{25} 0.8147 [SP1]
n_D^{25} 1.4430 [SP1]; n_D^{20} 1.4388 [RE17]

---

* These physical constants were obtained on samples prepared by ref. RE17, but the method of preparation was not specified.

$C_{16}H_{36}N_2$

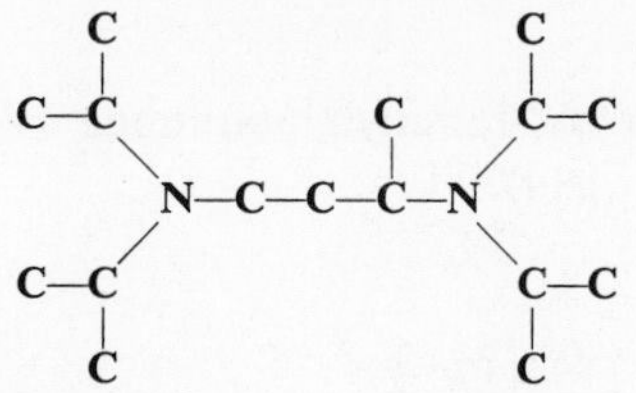

1,3-BIS(DIISOPROPYLAMINO)BUTANE

i-Pr
i-Pr
$+C_4H_8+$
i-Pr
i-Pr

Phys. Props.:

b_1 85–87° [LA1]

Prepn.:

Diisopropylamine + 1,3-bis(p-toluenesulfonoxy)butane (65% yield). [LA1]

$C_{17}H_{30}N_2$

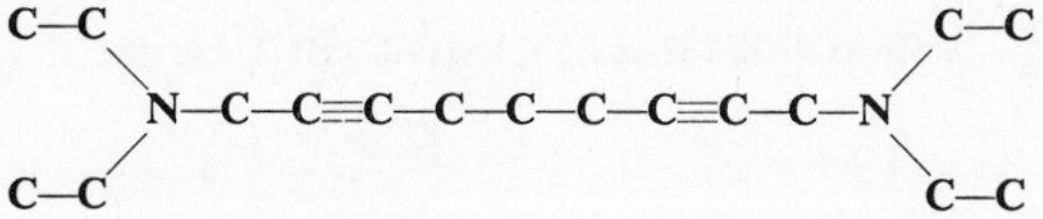

1,9-BIS(DIETHYLAMINO)-2,7-NONADIYNE

Et
Et
$+C_9H_{10}+$
Et
Et

Phys. Props.:

$b_{0.3}$ 119–120° [GU1]; $b_{0.05}$ 120° [GU2]
n_D^{21} 1.4700 [GU1]; n_D^{14} 1.4800 [GU2]

Prepn.:

1,6-Hexadiyne + formaldehyde + diethylamine in the presence of copper(II) acetate, [GU2] (70–75% yield). [GU1]

Derivs.:

Bis-ethiodide m. 147° [GU1,GU2]

$C_{17}H_{30}N_2$

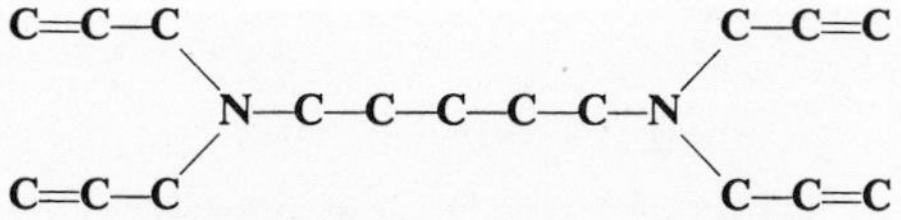

1,5-BIS(DIALLYLAMINO)PENTANE

All
All
$+CH_2+_5$
All
All

Phys. Props.:

$b_{0.02}$ 96–97° [BU11]
n_D^{22} 1.4743 [BU11]

Prepn.:

Reduction of *N,N,N',N'*-tetrallylglutaramide with lithium aluminum hydride (67.4% yield).[BU11]

Derivs.:

Bis-hydrobromide: m. 115–117°[BU11]
Bis-methobromide: m. 193–194° (dec.)[BU11]
Bis-allylobromide: m. 154–155°[BU11]

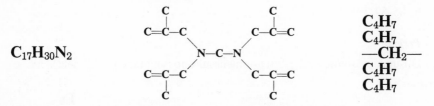

$C_{17}H_{30}N_2$ C_4H_7 C_4H_7 —CH_2— C_4H_7 C_4H_7

BIS(DIMETHALLYLAMINO)METHANE

Phys. Props.:

b_3 105°[BU10]
d_4^{23} 0.8556[BU10]
n_D^{23} 1.4758[BU10]

Prepn.:

Dimethallylamine + formaldehyde (79% yield).[BU10]

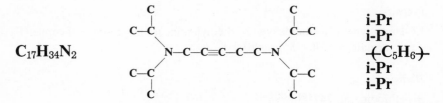

$C_{17}H_{34}N_2$ i-Pr i-Pr —(C_5H_6)— i-Pr i-Pr

1,5-BIS(DIISOPROPYLAMINO)-2-PENTYNE

Phys. Props.:

$b_{0.3}$ 100–105°[BI3]

Prepn.:

Sodio derivative of 1-diisopropylamino-2-propyne + 1-chloro-2-diisopropyl-aminoethane (unspecified yield in the range of 50–90%)[BI3]

Derivs.:

Bis-methobromide: m. 217–218°[BI3]

$C_{17}H_{38}N_2$

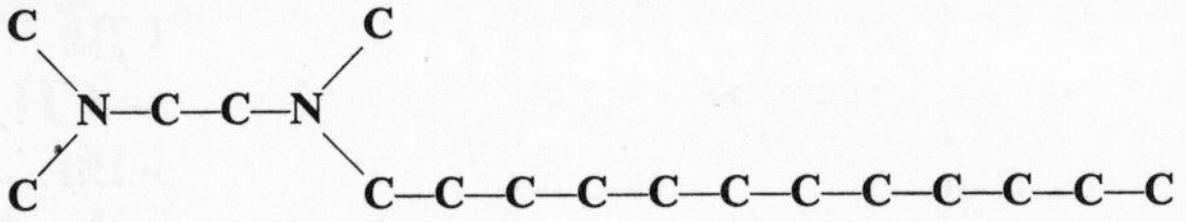

```
    C           C
     \         /
      N—C—C—N
     /         \
    C           C—C—C—C—C—C—C—C—C—C—C—C
```

Me
Me
—CH_2CH_2—
Me
n-$C_{12}H_{25}$

1-DIMETHYLAMINO-2-(METHYLDODECYLAMINO)ETHANE

Phys. Props.:

b_2 135–137,°[GR4] 135–142°[SC25]

Prepn.:

Methyldodecylamine + 1-chloro-2-dimethylaminoethane.[GR4,SC25]

$C_{17}H_{38}N_2$

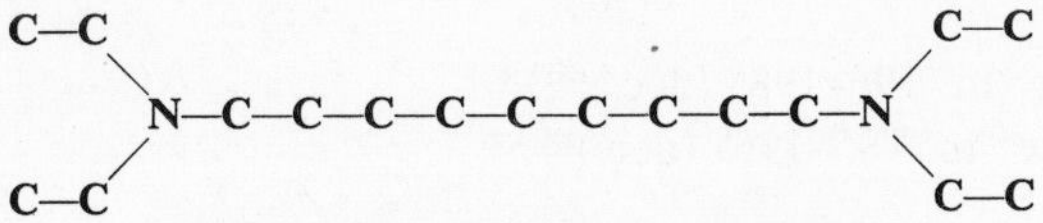

```
   C—C                           C—C
      \                         /
       N—C—C—C—C—C—C—C—C—C—N
      /                         \
   C—C                           C—C
```

Et
Et
$(CH_2)_9$
Et
Et

1,9-BIS(DIETHYLAMINO)NONANE

Phys. Props.:

b_4 142–144°[MA5]; $b_{0.05}$ 106–107°[GU2]
$n_D^{23.5}$ 1.4448[MA5]; $n_D^{21.5}$ 1.4495[GU2]

Prepn.:

1. Diethylamine + 1,9-dibromononane (67% yield).[MA5]
2. Catalytic hydrogenation of 1,9-bis(diethylamino)-2,7-nonadiyne.[GU1,GU2]

Derivs.:

Bis-ethiodide: m. 241°[GU2]

$C_{17}H_{38}N_2$

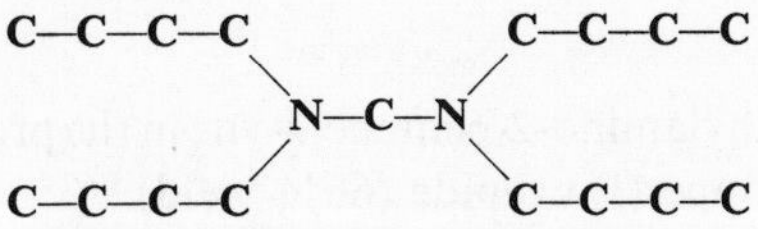

```
   C—C—C—C              C—C—C—C
          \            /
           N—C—N
          /            \
   C—C—C—C              C—C—C—C
```

n-Bu
n-Bu
—CH_2—
n-Bu
n-Bu

BIS(DIBUTYLAMINO)METHANE

Phys. Props.:

b_{760} 252–254°[BR32]; b_{21} 163°[BR32]

Prepn.:

1. Dibutylamine + formaldehyde.[BR32]
2. By-product in the reaction of dibutylamine, formaldehyde, and di-isopropyl ketone.[BR32]

$C_{17}H_{38}N_2$

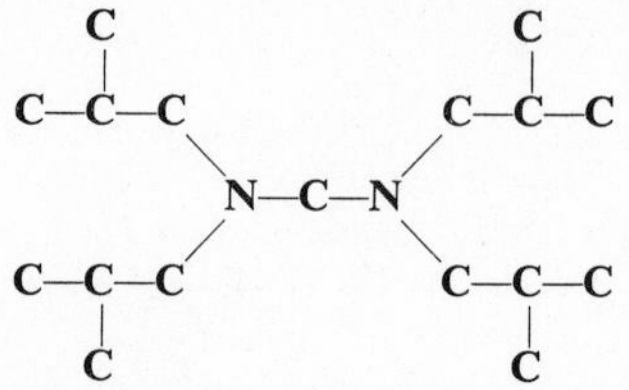

```
        C                      C
    C—C—C              C—C—C
        |                      |
        N—C—N
        |                      |
    C—C—C              C—C—C
        C                      C
```

i-Bu
i-Bu
—CH$_2$—
i-Bu
i-Bu

BIS(DIISOBUTYLAMINO)METHANE

Phys. Props.:

b. 245–255° (dec.)[EH1]; b$_1$ 93°[HU3]

Prepn.:

Sealed tube reaction of diisobutylamine and formaldehyde.[EH1,HU3]

Derivs.:

Chloroplatinate: m. 196–198° (dec.)[EH1]*
Bis-chloroaurate: m. 185–195° (dec.)[EH1]*
·CS$_2$: m. 54°[EH1]

$C_{18}H_{28}N_2$

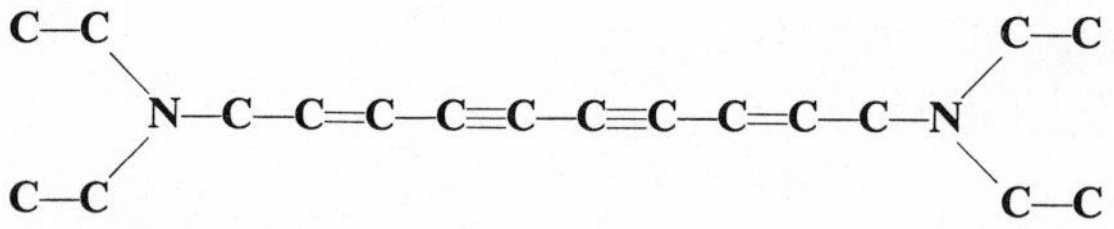

```
   C—C                                              C—C
       \                                           /
        N—C—C=C—C≡C—C≡C—C=C—C—N
       /                                           \
   C—C                                              C—C
```

Et
Et
$+C_{10}H_8+$
Et
Et

1,10-BIS(DIETHYLAMINO)-2,8-DECADIEN-4,6-DIYNE

Phys. Props.:

b$_{0.1}$ 155–160°[RO14]
n$_D^{25}$ 1.5630[RO14]
Ultraviolet absorption[RO14]

Prepn.:

Air oxidation of 1-diethylamino-2-pentene-4-yne in the presence of ammonium chloride and copper(I) cyanide (66% yield).[RO14]

Derivs.:

Bis-hydrochloride: m. 215° (dec.)[RO14]
Bis-picrate: m. 146–148° (dec.)[RO14]
Bis-methiodide: m. 211° (dec.)[RO14]

---

* A study by Hunt and Wagner[HU3] showed that most of the salts of methylene-bis-dialkylamines reported in the literature are in fact salts of the corresponding secondary dialkylamines. These secondary amines form extremely readily when the methylene-bis-dialkylamines are subjected to acid conditions.[HU3]

$C_{18}H_{32}N_2$

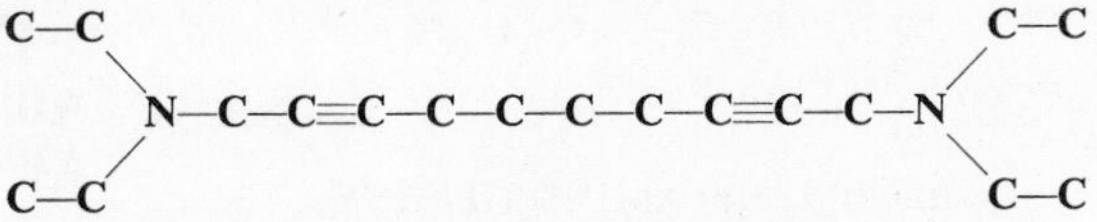

Et
Et
$-(C_{10}H_{12})-$
Et
Et

1,10-BIS(DIETHYLAMINO)-2,8-DECADIYNE

Phys. Props.:

$b_{0.4}$ 134–135° [GU1]; $b_{0.05}$ 123–124° [GU2]
n_D^{22} 1.4760 [GU2]; n_D^{21} 1.4700 [GU1]

Prepn.:

1,7-Octadiyne + diethylamine + formaldehyde in the presence of copper(II) acetate,[GU2] (70–75% yield).[GU1]

Derivs.:

Bis-ethiodide: m. 214° [GU1,GU2]

$C_{18}H_{32}N_2$

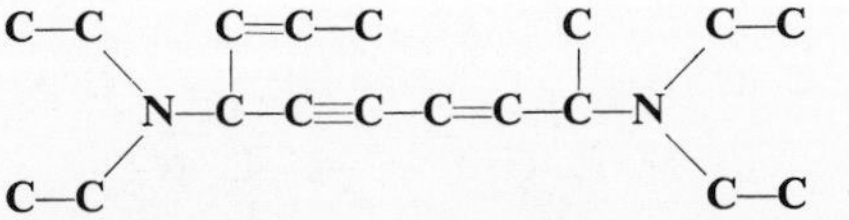

Et
Et
$-(C_{10}H_{12})-$
Et
Et

2,7-BIS(DIETHYLAMINO)-3,8-DECADIEN-5-YNE

See 4,7-bis(diethylamino)-2,8-decadiene-5-yne for preparation and physical properties of an unresolved mixture of two isomers which includes the subject amine.[JO5]

$C_{18}H_{32}N_2$

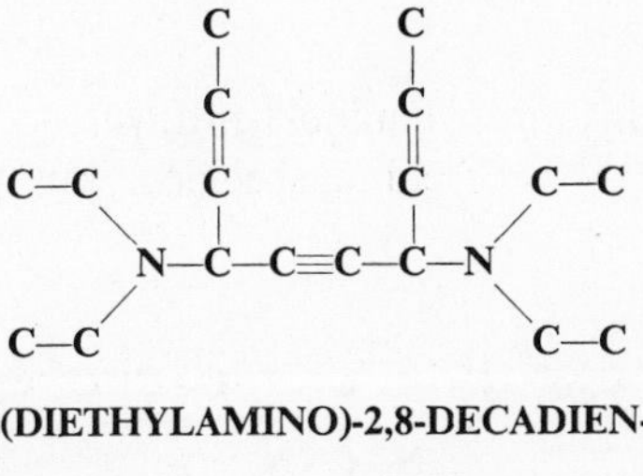

Et
Et
$-(C_{10}H_{12})-$
Et
Et

4,7-BIS(DIETHYLAMINO)-2,8-DECADIEN-5-YNE

The reaction of 2,9-dichloro-3,7-decadien-5-yne with diethylamine proceeds *via* allylic shift to give a 90% yield of an unresolved mixture of two isomers including the subject amine. The other isomer is 2,7-bis(diethylamino)-3,8-decadiene-5-yne (*q.v.*). The physical properties of the mixture are given as: $b_{0.001}$ 86–88°; $b_{0.1}$ 110°; n_D^{18} 1.4890; absorption maximum 2310 A (ϵ 7500). Redistillation of the mixtures gives the following physical properties: n_D^{17} 1.4815; absorption maximum 2200 Å, inflection 2420 A, (ϵ 4000).[JO5]

$C_{18}H_{32}N_2$

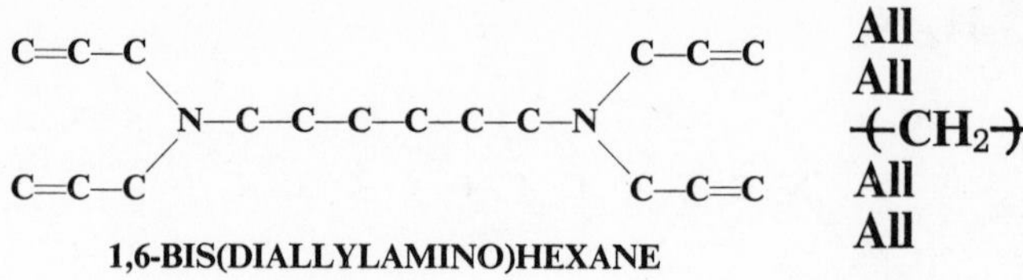

$$
\begin{array}{c}
\text{C=C—C} \qquad\qquad \text{C—C=C} \\
\text{N—C—C—C—C—C—C—N} \\
\text{C=C—C} \qquad\qquad \text{C—C=C}
\end{array}
$$

All
All
$(CH_2)_6$
All
All

1,6-BIS(DIALLYLAMINO)HEXANE

Phys. Props.:
$b_{0.8}$ 124° [BU12]
d_4^{25} 0.8465 [BU12]
n_D^{25} 1.4708 [BU12]

Prepn.:
1,6-Dibromohexane + diallylamine; allyl bromide + 1,6-diamino-hexane.[BU12] (One of these two reactions gives a 21.7% yield, but it is not clear which is meant.)

Derivs.:
Bis-methobromide: m. 202–203° (dec.)[BU12]
Bis-allylobromide: m. 179–180° [BU12]

$C_{18}H_{36}N_2$

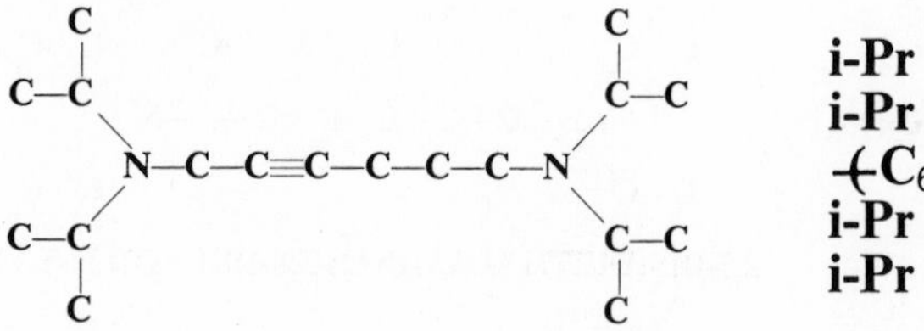

$$
\begin{array}{c}
\text{C} \qquad\qquad\qquad \text{C} \\
\text{C—C} \qquad\qquad\quad \text{C—C} \\
\text{N—C—C≡C—C—C—C—N} \\
\text{C—C} \qquad\qquad\quad \text{C—C} \\
\text{C} \qquad\qquad\qquad \text{C}
\end{array}
$$

i-Pr
i-Pr
(C_6H_8)
i-Pr
i-Pr

1,6-BIS(DIISOPROPYLAMINO)-2-HEXYNE

Phys. Props.:
$b_{0.2}$ 108–110° [BI1,BI3]

Prepn.:
Sodio derivative of 3-diisopropylamino-1-propyne + 1-diisopropylamino-3-chloropropane.[BI1,BI3] (Yield unspecified, but falls in the range of 50–90%.)

$C_{18}H_{38}N_2$

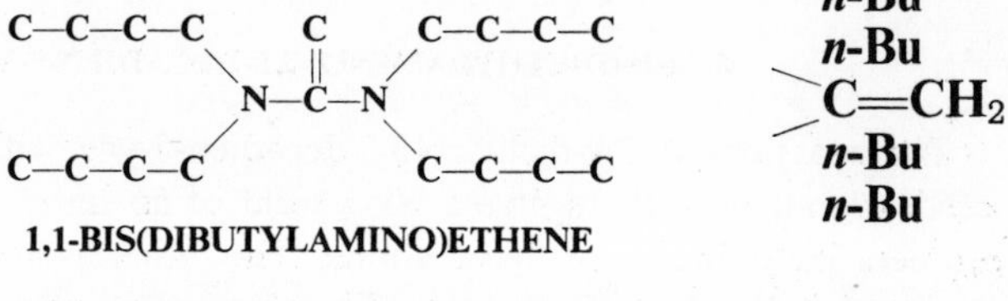

$$
\begin{array}{c}
\text{C—C—C—C} \quad \text{C} \quad \text{C—C—C—C} \\
\text{N—C—N} \\
\text{C—C—C—C} \qquad\quad \text{C—C—C—C}
\end{array}
$$

n-Bu
n-Bu
C=CH₂
n-Bu
n-Bu

1,1-BIS(DIBUTYLAMINO)ETHENE

Phys. Props.:
$b_{0.7}$ 105–109° [MC6]
d_4^{20} 0.8326 [MC6]
n_D^{20} 1.4582 [MC6]

Prepn.:

Dibutylamine + 1,1-diethoxyethene (34.5% yield).[MC6]

$C_{18}H_{40}N_2$

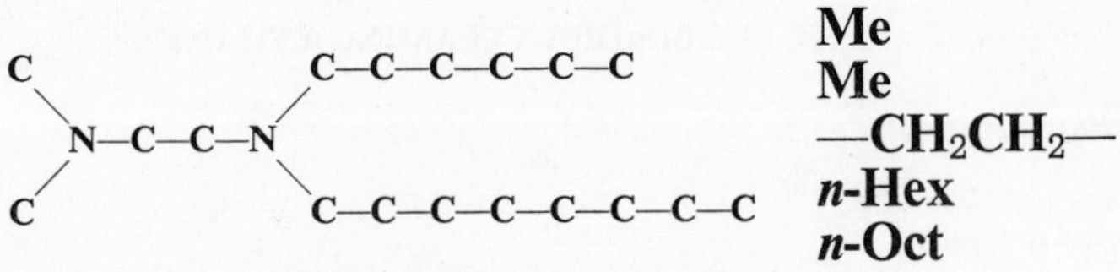

1-DIMETHYLAMINO-2-(HEXYLOCTYLAMINO)ETHANE

Phys. Props.:

b_3 136–139°[GR4]

Prepn.:

Hexyloctylamine + 1-chloro-2-dimethylaminoethane.[GR4]

$C_{18}H_{40}N_2$

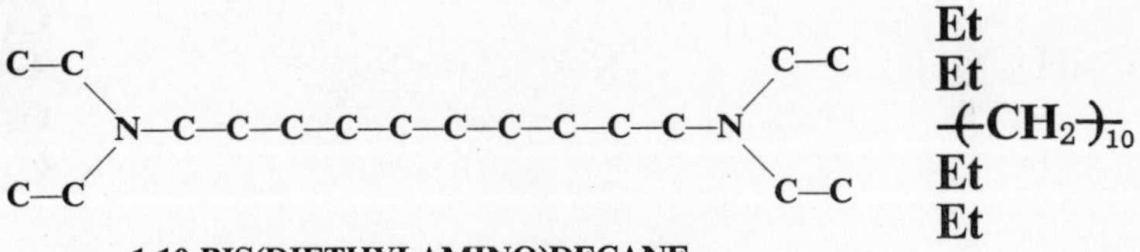

1,10-BIS(DIETHYLAMINO)DECANE

Phys. Props.:

b_{16} 186–188°[BA29]; b_{10} 173–176°[ON1]; $b_{3.3}$ 156°[SP1]; $b_{0.7}$ 130–135°[CA19]; $b_{0.3}$ 130–132°[RE17]; $b_{0.1}$ 121–122°[GU2]; $b_{0.01}$ 120–122°[JE1]
d_4^{25} 0.8191[SP1]
n_D^{25} 1.4491[SP1]; n_D^{21} 1.4508[GU2]; n_D^{20} 1.4520[RE17]; n_D^{16} 1.4537[BA29]

Prepn.:

1. Diethylamine + 1,10-dichlorodecane (93% yield)[ON1]; + 1,10-dibromo-decane,[CA19] (70% yield),[BA29] (64% yield).[JE1]
2. Catalytic hydrogenation of 1,10-bis(diethylamino)-2,8-decadiyne in the presence of nickel.[GU1,GU2]

Derivs.:

Bis-methiodide: m. 236–237°,[BA29] 228–230°[ON1]
Bis-ethiodide: m. 232–233°,[GU2] 217–218,°[ON1] 213–214°[BA29]

$$C_{18}H_{40}N_2$$

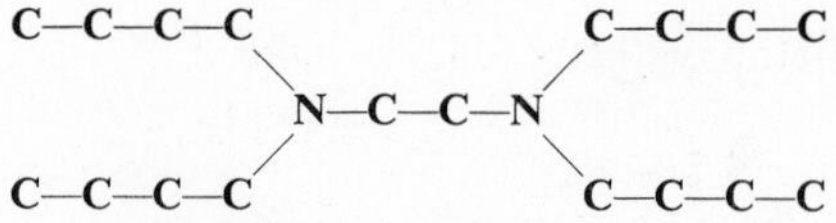

1,2-BIS(DIBUTYLAMINO)ETHANE

n-Bu
n-Bu
—CH₂CH₂—
n-Bu
n-Bu

Phys. Props.:

b_{11-13} 156–158° [AR4]
d_4^{25} 0.808 [AR4]
n_D^{25} 1.4438 [AR4]

Prepn.:

Reduction of *N,N,N',N'*-tetra-*n*-butyloxamide with lithium aluminum
hydride (74% yield). [AR4]

Derivs.:

Bis-picrate: m. 185–186° [AR4]

$$C_{19}H_{32}N_2$$

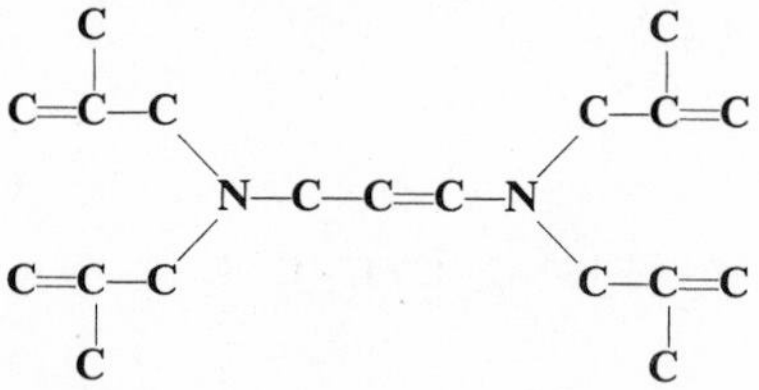

1,3-BIS[DI(2-METHYL-2-PROPENYL)AMINO]-1-PROPENE

C₄H₇
C₄H₇
(C₃H₄)
C₄H₇
C₄H₇

Prepn.:

Di(2-methyl-2-propenyl)amine + acrolein. [SM5]

$$C_{19}H_{34}N_2$$

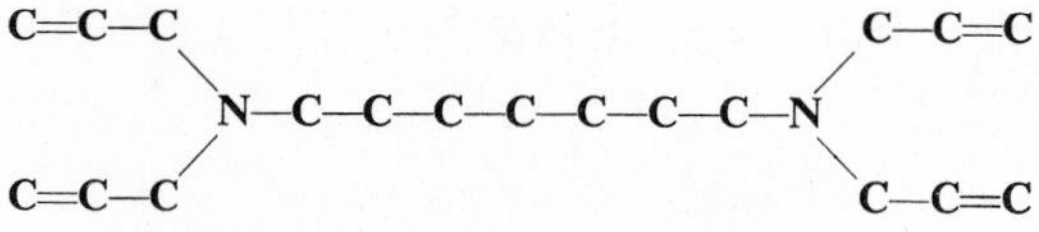

1,7-BIS(DIALLYLAMINO)HEPTANE

All
All
(CH₂)₇
All
All

Phys. Props.:

$b_{0.1}$ 124–126° [BU12]
n_D^{25} 1.4719 [BU12]

Prepn.:

1,7-Dibromoheptane + diallylamine (87.5% yield). [BU12]

Derivs.:

Bis-hydrobromide: m. 129–130°[BU12]
Bis-methobromide: m. 193–194° (dec.)[BU12]
Bis-allylobromide: m. 192–193° (dec.)[BU12]

$C_{19}H_{42}N_2$

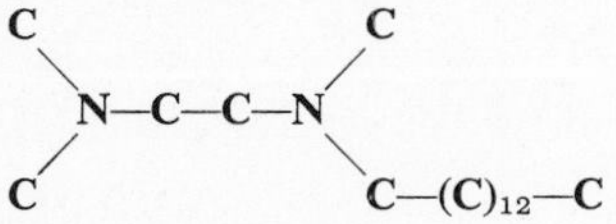

$$
\begin{array}{ccc}
C & & C \\
\backslash & & / \\
N-C-C-N & & \\
/ & & \backslash \\
C & & C-(C)_{12}-C
\end{array}
$$

Me
Me
—CH₂CH₂—
Me
***n*-C₁₄H₂₉**

1-DIMETHYLAMINO-2-(METHYLTETRADECYLAMINO)ETHANE

Phys. Props.:

b_6 185–187°[GR4]

Prepn.:

Methyltetradecylamine + 1-dimethylamino-2-chloroethane.[GR4]

$C_{19}H_{42}N_2$

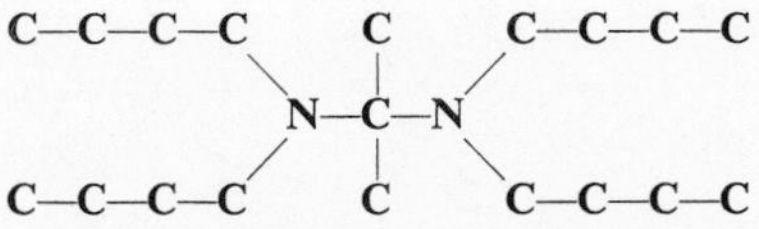

$$
\begin{array}{ccc}
C-C-C-C & C & C-C-C-C \\
\backslash & | & / \\
& N-C-N & \\
/ & | & \backslash \\
C-C-C-C & C & C-C-C-C
\end{array}
$$

***n*-Bu**
***n*-Bu**
⊢C₃H₆⊣
***n*-Bu**
***n*-Bu**

2,2-BIS(DIBUTYLAMINO)PROPANE

Phys. Props.:

m. 63°[IW1]

Prepn.:

N-(1-Methylethenyl)-*N'*-(*p*-ethoxyphenyl)urea + dibutylamine (20% yield).[IW1]

$C_{20}H_{34}N_2$

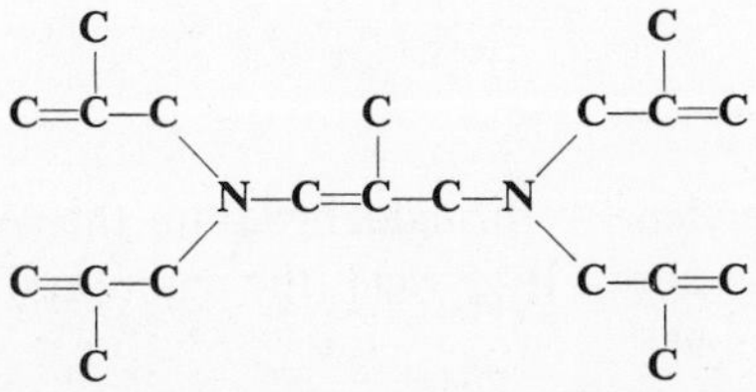

$$
\begin{array}{ccc}
C & & C \\
| & & | \\
C=C-C & C & C-C=C \\
\backslash & | & / \\
N-C=C-C-N & \\
/ & & \backslash \\
C=C-C & & C-C=C \\
| & & | \\
C & & C
\end{array}
$$

C₄H₇
C₄H₇
⊢C₄H₆⊣
C₄H₇
C₄H₇

1,3-BIS[DI(2-METHYL-2-PROPENYL)AMINO]-2-METHYL-1-PROPENE

Prepn.:

Dimethallylamine + methacrolein ("good yield").[SM5]

$C_{20}H_{36}N_2$

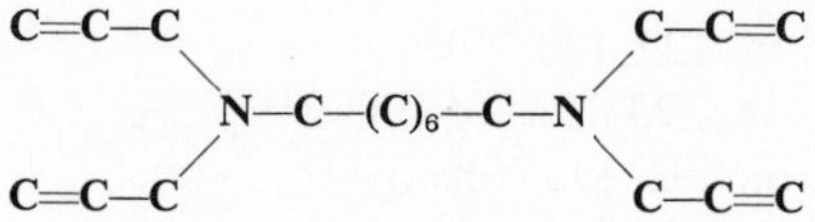

All
All
$+CH_2+_8$
All
All

1,8-BIS(DIALLYLAMINO)OCTANE

Phys. Props.:

$b_{0.1}$ 134–138°[BU12]
n_D^{23} 1.4651 [BU12]

Prepn.:

1,8-Dibromooctane + diallylamine.[BU12]

Derivs.:

Bis-hydrobromide: m. 137–139[BU12]
Bis-methobromide: m. 178–180° (dec.)[BU12]
Bis-allylobromide: m. 195–197° (dec.)[BU12]

$C_{20}H_{40}N_2$

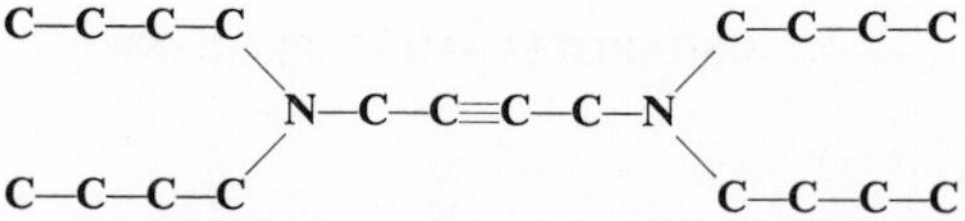

n-Bu
n-Bu
$+C_4H_4+$
n-Bu
n-Bu

1,4-BIS(DIBUTYLAMINO)-2-BUTYNE

Phys. Props.:

b_3 171–173°[RE7]*; b_1 133–135°[RE11]*; $b_{0.7}$ 136°[FE2]
n_D^{20} 1.4600[FE2]

Prepn.:

Dibutylamine + acetylene + formaldehyde in the presence of copper(I)
    chloride[FE2]; in about 10% yield (the main product is 3-dibutylamino-
    1-propyne).[RE7,RE11]

---

* These boiling points (b_1 133–135° and b_3 171–173°) were reported by the same
investigator in two different publications. The small difference in pressure should not
give such widely differing boiling points. The lower value seems to be the more nearly
correct one.

$C_{20}H_{40}N_2$

```
C—C—C—C                    C—C—C—C        n-Bu
         \                /                n-Bu
          N—C=C—C=C—N                      -(-C_4H_4-)-
         /                \                n-Bu
C—C—C—C                    C—C—C—C        n-Bu
```

1,4-BIS(DIBUTYLAMINO)-1,3-BUTADIENE

Phys. Props.:

cis,trans isomer

$b_{0.35}$ 142–146°* [FE2,FE4,FE5]

n_D^{20} 1.5020 [FE2,FE4,FE5]

Ultraviolet absorption:† 3000 A. (ϵ 20,4000) [FE4]

trans,trans isomer

$b_{0.03}$ 148–157°* [FE4,FE6]

n_D^{24} 1.5089 [FE4,FE6]

Ultraviolet absorption:† 2925 A. (ϵ 23,900) [FE4]

Prepn.:

1. Isomerization of 1,4-bis(dibutylamino)-2-butyne with sodium [FE2,FE5] gives the *cis,trans* isomer. [FE4]
2. Acid-catalyzed transamination reaction between 1,4-bis(dimethylamino)-1,3-butadiene and dibutylamine gives the *trans,trans* isomer (47% yield). [FE4,FE6]
3. Dibutylamine + 1-dibutylamino-1-buten-3-yne. [SH4]

$C_{20}H_{42}N_2$

```
C—C—C—C                    C—C—C—C        n-Bu
         \                /                n-Bu
          N—C—C=C—C—N                      -(-C_4H_6-)-
         /                \                n-Bu
C—C—C—C                    C—C—C—C        n-Bu
```

1,4-BIS(DIBUTYLAMINO)-2-BUTENE

Phys. Props.:

b_3 165–170° [AM2]

n_D^{21} 1.4572 [AM2]

Prepn.:

1,4-Dichloro-2-butene + dibutylamine, [MO11] (94% yield), [MO12] (57% yield). [AM2]

---

* The boiling points for the *cis,trans* and *trans,trans* isomers seem to differ more than expected.

† Ref. FE4 utilizes the increased extinction and lowered wavelength of the absorption maximum for the *trans,trans* isomer compared to the ultraviolet absorption of the *cis,trans* isomer to identify the respective isomer. This reference also considers the infrared spectral correlation for this purpose in ref. FE2 not to be generally applicable.

Derivs.:

Bis-picrate: m. 183–184°[AM2]

$C_{20}H_{42}N_2$

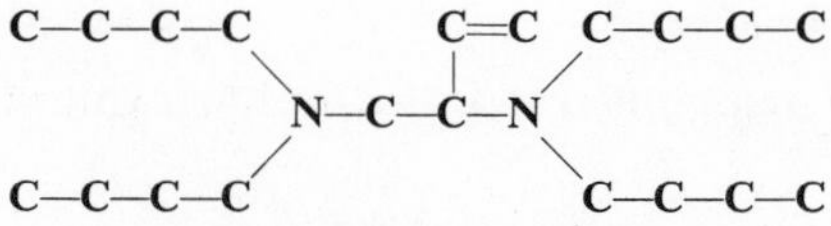

C—C—C—C   C=C   C—C—C—C

N—C—C—N

C—C—C—C   C—C—C—C

n-Bu
n-Bu
$+C_4H_6+$
n-Bu
n-Bu

3,4-BIS(DIBUTYLAMINO)-1-BUTENE

Prepn.:

3,4-Dichloro-1-butene + dibutylamine (53% yield).[MO13]

$C_{20}H_{42}N_2$

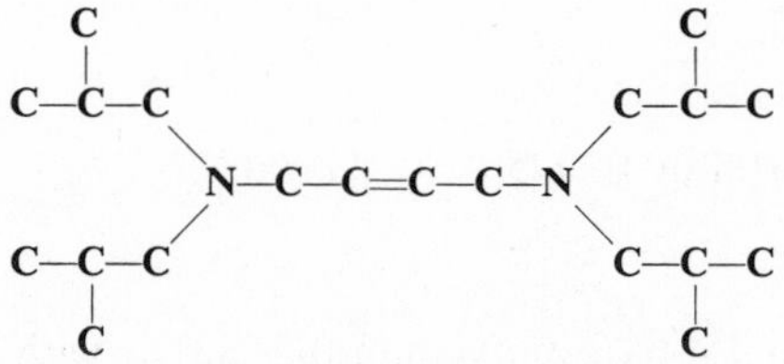

i-Bu
i-Bu
$+C_4H_6+$
i-Bu
i-Bu

1,4-BIS(DIISOBUTYLAMINO)-2-BUTENE

Prepn.:

1,4-Dichloro-1-butene + diisobutylamine (87.8% yield).[MO12]

$C_{20}H_{44}N_2$

C   C

N—C—(C)$_{14}$—C—N

C   C

Me
Me
$+CH_2+_{16}$
Me
Me

1,16-BIS(DIMETHYLAMINO)HEXADECANE

Prepn.:

1,16-Diaminohexane + formaldehyde + formic acid.[AM1]

Derivs.:

Bis-hydrochloride: m. 234°[AM1]

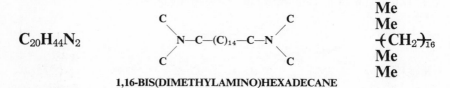

$C_{20}H_{44}N_2$

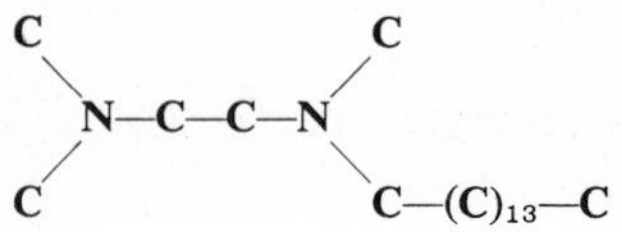

Me
Me
—CH$_2$CH$_2$—
Me
n-C$_{15}$H$_{31}$

1-DIMETHYLAMINO-2-(METHYLPENTADECYLAMINO)-ETHANE

Phys. Props.:

b$_8$ 175–178°[SC26]

Prepn.:

Methylpentadecylamine + 1-chloro-2-dimethylaminoethane.[SC26]

Derivs.:

Bis-hydrochloride: m. 253–255°[SC26]

$C_{20}H_{44}N_2$

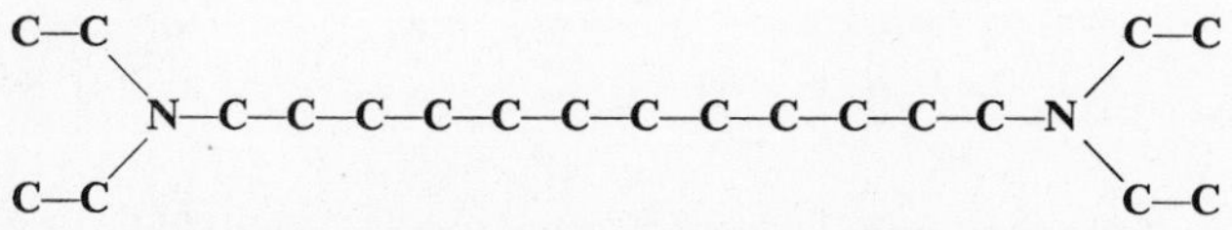

C—C   C—C   **Et**
    \   /   **Et**
     N—C—C—C—C—C—C—C—C—C—C—C—C—N $+CH_2)_{12}$
    /   \   **Et**
C—C   C—C   **Et**

1,12-BIS(DIETHYLAMINO)DODECANE

Phys. Props.:

$b_{0.01}$ 125–128°[JE1]

Prepn.:

1,12-Dibromododecane + diethylamine (35% yield).[JE1]

$C_{20}H_{44}N_2$

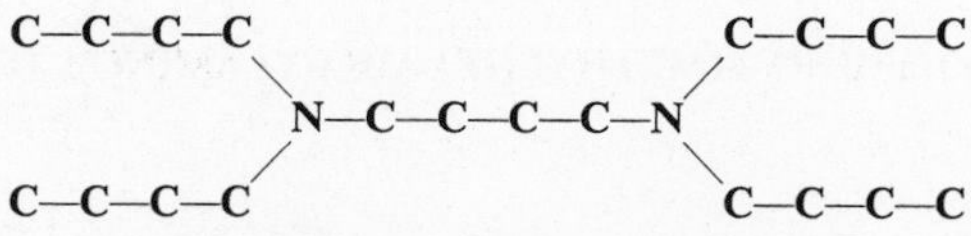

C—C—C—C   C—C—C—C   ***n*-Bu**
        \   /   ***n*-Bu**
         N—C—C—C—C—N $+CH_2)_4$
        /   \   ***n*-Bu**
C—C—C—C   C—C—C—C   ***n*-Bu**

1,4-BIS(DIBUTYLAMINO)BUTANE

Phys. Props.:

b_4 157.5–160°[AM2]; b_1 107–108°[LA1,RE16]
n_D^{20} 1.4505[AM2]

Prepn.:

1. 1,4-Bis(*p*-toluenesulfonoxy)butane + dibutylamine (77.5% yield).[LA1,RE16]
2. Catalytic hydrogenation of 1,4-bis(dibutylamino)-2-butene in the presence of nickel (38% yield).[AM2]

Derivs.:

Bis-picrate: m. 170.2–171.2°[AM2]

$C_{21}H_{38}N_2$

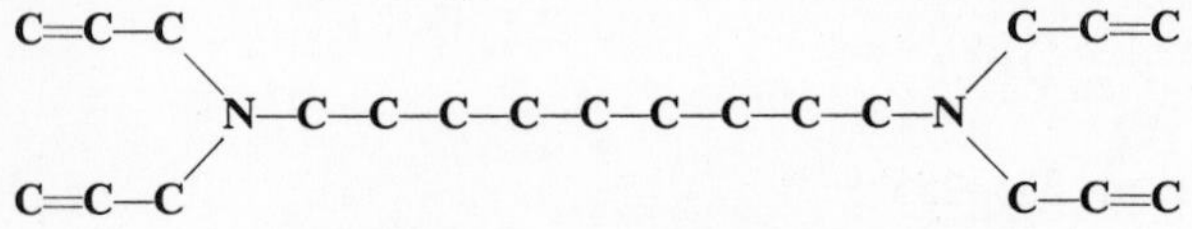

1,9-BIS(DIALLYLAMINO)NONANE

All
All
$+CH_2+_9$
All
All

Phys. Props.:

$b_{0.07}$ 146–148°[BU12]
n_D^{25} 1.4723[BU12]

Prepn.:

1,9-Bis(p-toluenesulfonoxy)nonane + diallylamine (94.5% yield).[BU12]

Derivs.:

Bis-methobromide: m. 187–189° (dec.)[BU12]
Bis-allylobromide: m. 201–202° (dec.)[BU12]

$C_{21}H_{46}N_2$

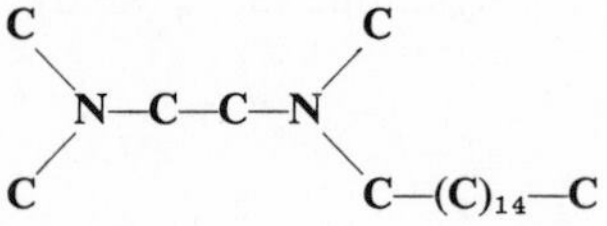

Me
Me
—CH₂CH₂—
Me
n-$C_{16}H_{33}$

1-DIMETHYLAMINO-2-(METHYLHEXADECYLAMINO)ETHANE

Phys. Props.:

b_4 195–199°[GR4]

Prepn.:

Methylhexadecylamine + 1-chloro-2-dimethylaminoethane.[GR4]

$C_{21}H_{46}N_2$

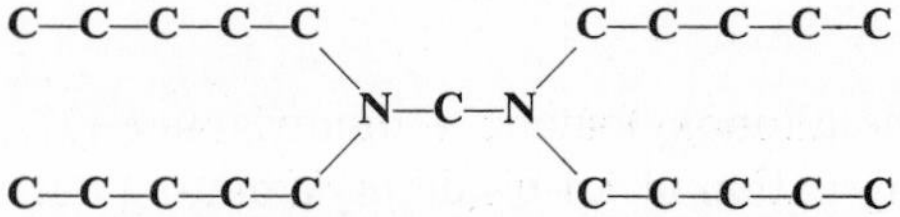

n-Pent
n-Pent
—CH₂—
n-Pent
n-Pent

BIS(DIPENTYLAMINO)METHANE

Phys. Props.:

b_4 163°[HU3]

Prepn.:

Dipentylamine + formaldehyde.[HU3]

Derivs.:

Attempted preparation of the hydriodide by reaction of the diamine with
hydriodic acid regenerates dipentylamine and the salt that is obtained
is dipentylamine hydriodide.[HU3]

$C_{21}H_{46}N_2$

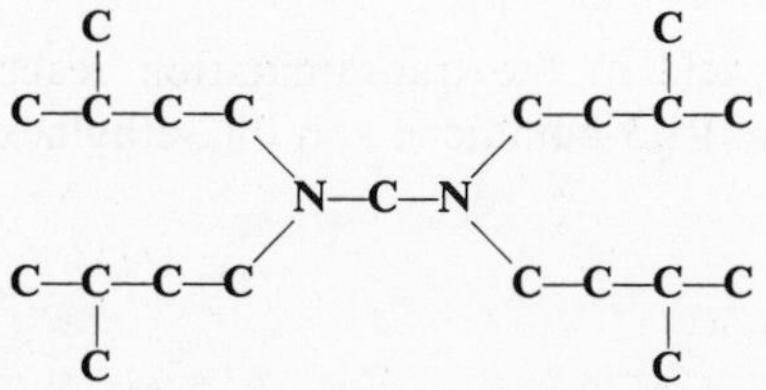

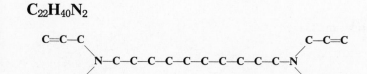

i-Pent
i-Pent
—CH$_2$—
i-Pent
i-Pent

BIS[DI(3-METHYLBUTYL)AMINO]METHANE

Phys. Props.:

b_{11} 165–169°[BR32]

Prepn.:

Diisopentylamine + formaldehyde.[BR32]

$C_{22}H_{40}N_2$

C=C—C⠀⠀⠀⠀⠀⠀⠀⠀⠀⠀⠀⠀⠀⠀⠀⠀C—C=C
⠀⠀⠀⠀N—C—C—C—C—C—C—C—C—C—C—N
C=C—C⠀⠀⠀⠀⠀⠀⠀⠀⠀⠀⠀⠀⠀⠀⠀⠀C—C=C

All
All
$\text{+CH}_2\text{+}_{10}$
All
All

1,10-BIS(DIALLYLAMINO)DECANE

Phys. Props.:

$b_{0.07}$ 152–158°[BU12]
n_D^{25} 1.4725[BU12]

Prepn.:

1,10-Bis(benzenesulfonoxy)decane + diallylamine (70.5% yield).[BU12]

Derivs.:

Bis-methobromide: m. 163–165° (dec.)[BU12]
Bis-allylobromide: m. 200° (dec.)[BU12]

$C_{22}H_{44}N_2$

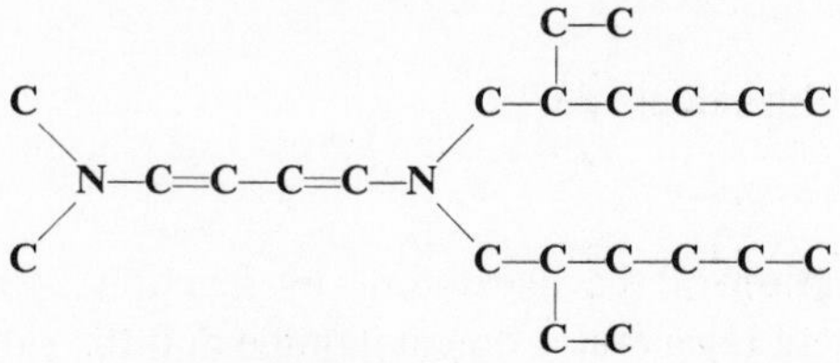

Me
Me
$\left(C_4H_4\right)$
C_8H_{17}
C_8H_{17}

1-DIMETHYLAMINO-4-[DI(2-ETHYLHEXYL)AMINO]-1,3-BUTADIENE

Prepn.:

Obtained in minor yield in the transamination reaction between 1,4-bis-(dimethylamino)-1,3-butadiene and di(2-ethylhexyl)amine.[FE6]

$C_{22}H_{48}N_2$

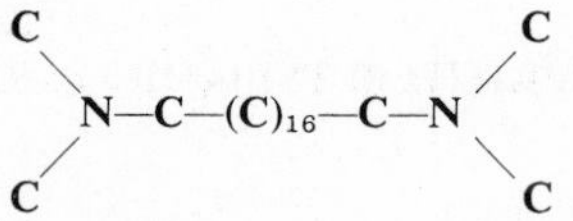

Me
Me
$\left(CH_2\right)_{18}$
Me
Me

1,18-BIS(DIMETHYLAMINO)OCTADECANE

Prepn.:

1,18-Diaminooctadecane + formaldehyde + formic acid.[AM1]

Derivs.:

Bis-hydrochloride: m. 234°[AM1]

$C_{22}H_{48}N_2$

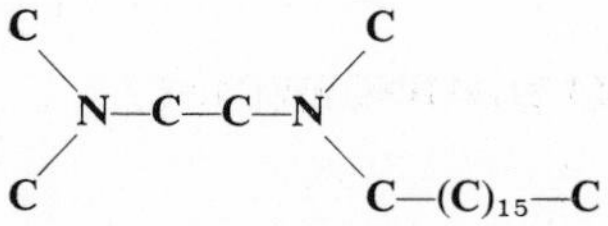

Me
Me
—CH_2CH_2—
Me
n-$C_{17}H_{35}$

1-DIMETHYLAMINO-2-(METHYLHEPTADECYLAMINO)ETHANE

Phys. Props.:

$b_{0.6}$ 160–169°[GR2]

Prepn.:

Methylheptadecylamine + 1-chloro-2-dimethylaminoethane.[GR2]

$C_{22}H_{48}N_2$

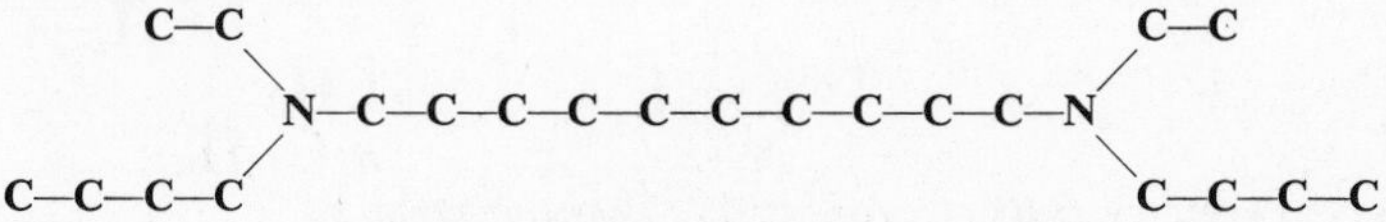

1,10-BIS(ETHYLBUTYLAMINO)DECANE

Et
n-Bu
$+CH_2+_{10}$
Et
n-Bu

Phys. Props.:

b_2 173–183° [PR4]

Prepn.:

Ethylbutylamine + 1,10-dibromodecane (55–80% yield). [PR4]

$C_{22}H_{48}N_2$

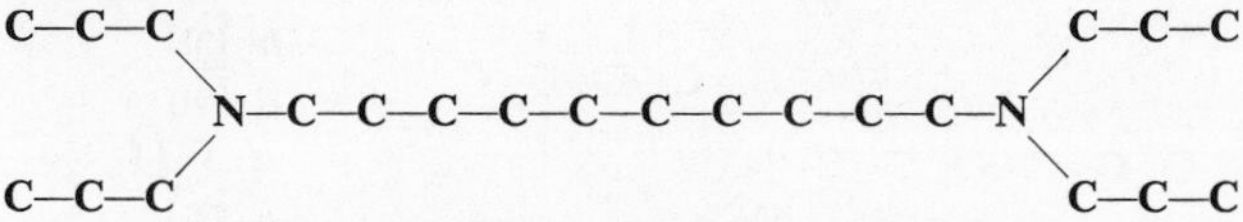

1,10-BIS(DIPROPYLAMINO)DECANE

n-Pr
n-Pr
$+CH_2+_{10}$
n-Pr
n-Pr

Phys. Props.:

b_{30} 230–235° [PY1]; b_8 200–205° [PR4]

Prepn.:

1,10-Dibromodecane + dipropylamine, [PY1] (55–80% yield). [PR4]

$C_{22}H_{48}N_2$

1,2-BIS(DIPENTYLAMINO)ETHANE

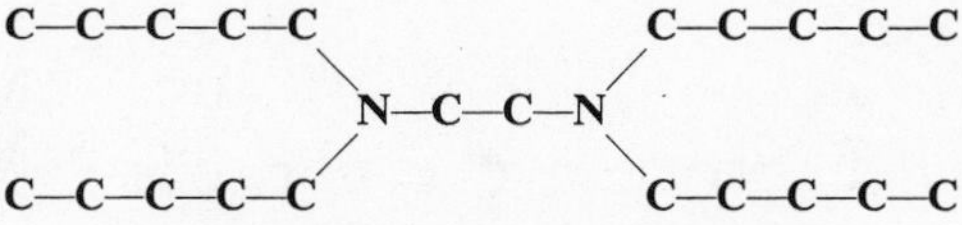

n-Pent
n-Pent
—CH_2CH_2—
n-Pent
n-Pent

Phys. Props.:

b_{10} 192–194° [AR4]
d_4^{25} 0.823 [AR4]
n_D^{25} 1.4472 [AR4]

Prepn.:

Reduction of *N,N,N',N'*-tetrapentyloxamide with lithium aluminum hydride. [AR4]

Derivs.:

Bis-picrate: m. 143–144° [AR4]

$C_{23}H_{50}N_2$

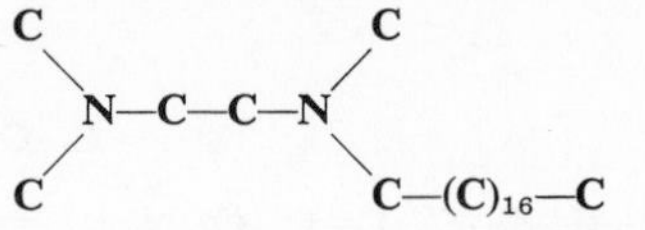

$$CH_3$$
$$CH_3$$
$$—CH_2CH_2—$$
$$CH_3$$
$$n\text{-}C_{18}H_{37}$$

1-METHYLOCTADECYLAMINO-2-DIMETHYLAMINOETHANE

Phys. Props.:

$b_{0.6}$ 177–178°[GR3]

Prepn.:

2-Dimethylaminoethyl chloride + methyloctadecylamine.[GR3]

$C_{23}H_{50}N_2$

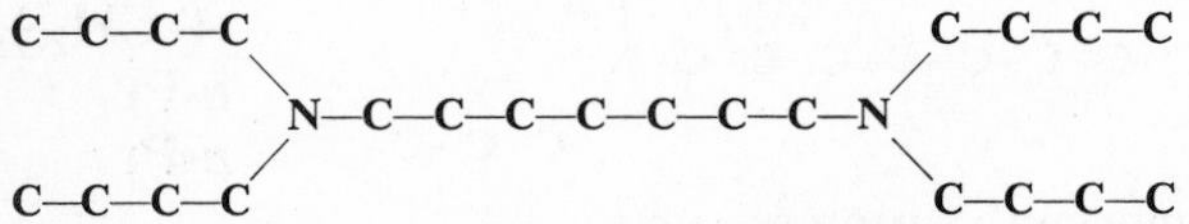

n-Bu
n-Bu
$(CH_2)_7$
n-Bu
n-Bu

1,7-BIS(DIBUTYLAMINO)HEPTANE

Phys. Props.:

b_{35} 255°[PY1]

Prepn.:

Dibutylamine + 1,7-dibromoheptane.[PY1]

$C_{24}H_{48}N_2$

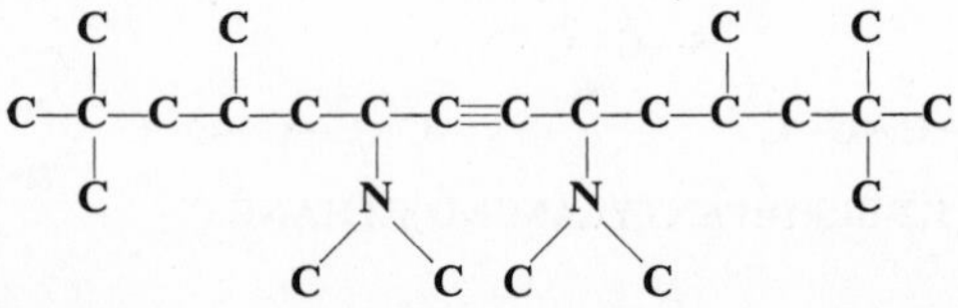

Me
Me
$(C_{20}H_{36})$
Me
Me

6,9-BIS(DIMETHYLAMINO)-2,2,4,11,13,13-HEXAMETHYL-7-TETRADECYNE

Phys. Props.:

b_1 128–133°[FE2]
n_D^{20} 1.4617[FE2]

Prepn.:

3,5,5-Trimethylhexanal + dimethylamine followed by reaction with 3-dimethylamino-5,7,7-trimethyl-1-octyne in the presence of copper(I) chloride (71% yield).[FE2]

$C_{24}H_{48}N_2$

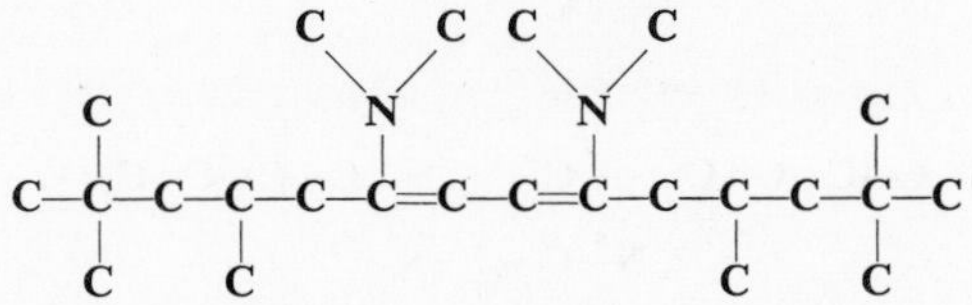

$$\begin{array}{c} \text{C} \quad \text{C C} \quad \text{C} \\ | \quad \text{N} \quad \text{N} \quad | \\ \text{C} \quad | \quad \quad \quad \text{C} \\ | \quad | \\ \text{C--C--C--C--C--C=C--C=C--C--C--C--C--C} \\ | \quad | \quad \quad \quad | \quad | \\ \text{C} \quad \text{C} \quad \quad \quad \text{C} \quad \text{C} \end{array}$$

Me
Me
$+C_{20}H_{36}+$
Me
Me

6,9-BIS(DIMETHYLAMINO)2,2,4,11,13,13-HEXAMETHYL-6,8-TETRADECADIENE

*Phys. Props.**

$b_{4.4-3.2}$ 187–192° [FE5]; $b_{4.0}$ 187–192° [FE2]; $b_{3.8}$ 187–192° [FE2]
n_D^{25} 1.4982 [FE2]; n_D^{20} 1.4986 [FE2,FE5]
Ultraviolet absorption: 2950 A. (ϵ 21,900) [FE2]

Prepn.:

Isomerization of 6,9-bis(dimethylamino)-2,2,4,11,13,13-hexamethyl-7-tetra-
decyne with sodium, [FE2] in 96% yield. [FE5]

$C_{24}H_{48}N_2$

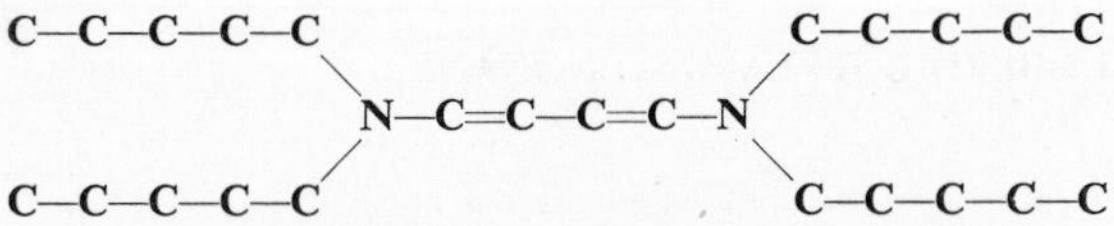

$$\begin{array}{c} \text{C--C--C--C--C} \quad \quad \quad \text{C--C--C--C--C} \\ \quad \quad \backslash \quad \quad \quad \quad \quad \quad \quad / \\ \text{N--C=C--C=C--N} \\ \quad \quad / \quad \quad \quad \quad \quad \quad \quad \backslash \\ \text{C--C--C--C--C} \quad \quad \quad \text{C--C--C--C--C} \end{array}$$

n-Pent
n-Pent
$+C_4H_4+$
n-Pent
n-Pent

1,4-BIS(DIPENTYLAMINO)-1,3-BUTADIENE

This compound was claimed by ref. SH4 as being prepared from dipentylamine and 1-dipentylamino-1-buten-3-yne. However, no experimental
details are given.

$C_{24}H_{52}N_2$

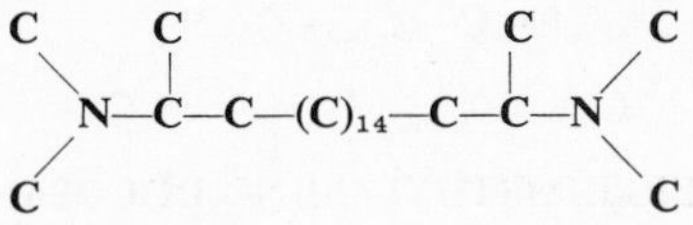

$$\begin{array}{c} \text{C} \quad \text{C} \quad \quad \quad \text{C} \quad \text{C} \\ \backslash \quad | \quad \quad \quad \quad \quad | \quad / \\ \text{N--C--C--(C)}_{14}\text{--C--C--N} \\ / \quad \quad \quad \quad \quad \quad \quad \quad \backslash \\ \text{C} \quad \quad \quad \quad \quad \quad \quad \quad \text{C} \end{array}$$

Me
Me
$+C_{20}H_{40}+$
Me
Me

2,19-BIS(DIMETHYLAMINO)EICOSANE

Prepn.:

Reductive alkylation of dimethylamine with 2,19-eicosanedione and hydrogen
in the presence of palladium on charcoal. [AM1]

Derivs.:

Bis-hydrochloride: m. 196° [AM1]

---

* These constants apply to what is probably the *cis-trans* isomer. [FE2]

$C_{24}H_{52}N_2$

n-Bu
n-Bu
$-(C_8H_{16})-$
n-Bu
n-Bu

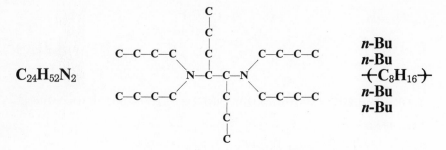

4,5-BIS(DIBUTYLAMINO)OCTANE*

Prepn.:

Tributylamine + di-*t*-butyl peroxide (25% yield).[RA2]

$C_{25}H_{54}N_2$

n-Bu
n-Bu
$-(CH_2)_9-$
n-Bu
n-Bu

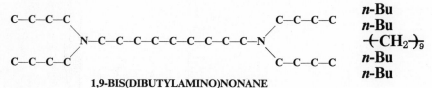

1,9-BIS(DIBUTYLAMINO)NONANE

Phys. Props.:

$b_{3.5}$ 192°[MA5]
n_D^{27} 1.4471[MA5]

Prepn.:

1,9-Dibromononane + dibutylamine (72% yield).[MA5]

$C_{26}H_{56}N_2$

Me
Me
$-(CH_2)_{22}-$
Me
Me

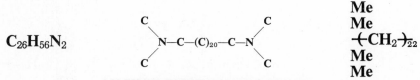

1,22-BIS(DIMETHYLAMINO)DOCOSANE

Prepn.:

1,22-Dibromodocosane + dimethylamine.[AM1]

Derivs.:

Bis-hydrochloride: m. 236°[AM1]

---

* The structure indicated is considered as the probable one by ref. RA2, on the basis of indirect evidence from other reactions and from the fact that molecular weight and nitrogen analysis are reasonably good. The possibility of other isomeric structures was not excluded.

$C_{26}H_{56}N_2$

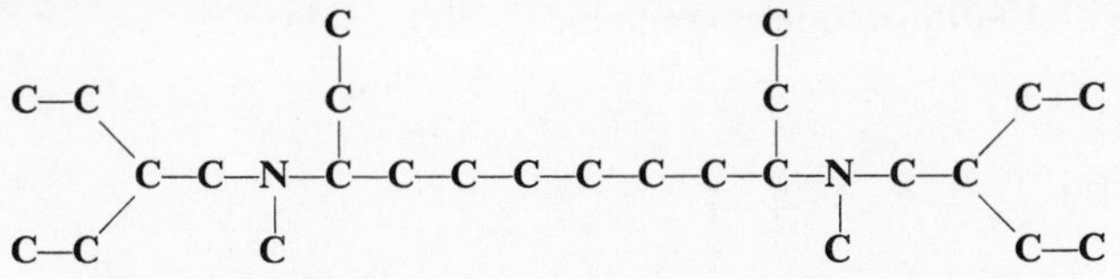

Me
C_6H_{13}
$\leftarrow C_{12}H_{24} \rightarrow$
C_6H_{13}
Me

3,10-BIS(METHYL-2-ETHYLBUTYLAMINO)DODECANE

Prepn.:

3,10-Bis-(2-ethylbutylamino)dodecane + formaldehyde + formic acid (70% yield).[FA1]

Derivs.:

Bis-hydrochloride: m. 169–172° [FA1]

$C_{26}H_{56}N_2$

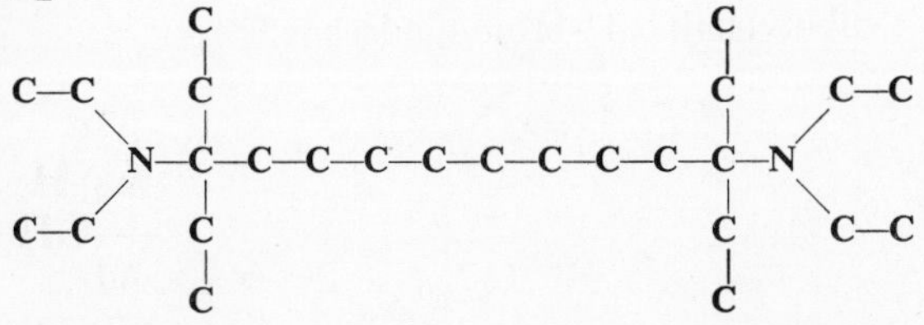

Et
Et
$\leftarrow C_{18}H_{36} \rightarrow$
Et
Et

3,12-BIS(DIETHYLAMINO)-3,12-DIETHYLTETRADECANE

Phys. Props.:

b_8 228–234° [PA4]*

Prepn.:

N,N,N′,N′-Tetraethyl-1,10-decanediamide + ethylmagnesium bromide (very low yield).[PA4]

$C_{26}H_{56}N_2$

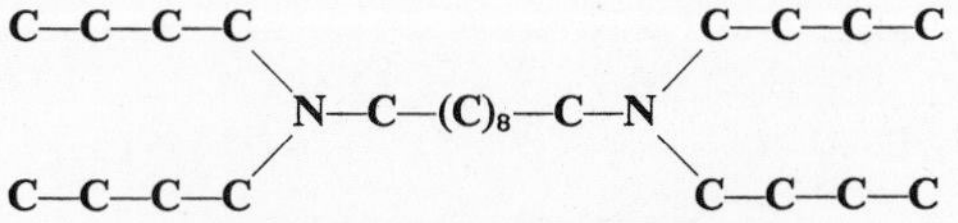

n-Bu
n-Bu
$\leftarrow CH_2 \rightarrow_{10}$
n-Bu
n-Bu

1,10-BIS(DIBUTYLAMINO)DECANE

Phys. Props.:

b_{30} 267° [PY1]; b_3 193–203° [PR4]

---

* Boiling point value is for a mixture containing $Et_2NC(Et)_2(CH_2)_8CONEt_2$ along with the subject amine.

Prepn.:

Dibutylamine + 1,10-dibromodecane,[PY1] (55%–80% yield).[PR4]

Derivs.:

Tartrate ("neutral"): m. 87° [PY1]

$C_{27}H_{58}N_2$

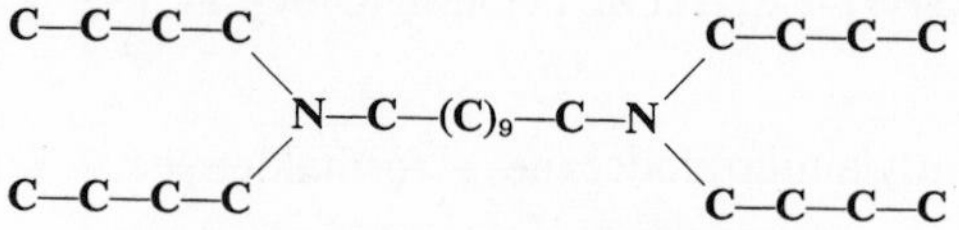

n-Bu
n-Bu
$+CH_2+_{11}$
n-Bu
n-Bu

1,11-BIS(DIBUTYLAMINO)UNDECANE

Phys. Props.:

b_3 219–222° [PY2]

Prepn.:

Dibutylamine + 1-dibutylamino-11-bromoundecane.[PY2]

$C_{28}H_{56}N_2$

Me
$C_{12}H_{23}$
—CH_2CH_2—
Me
$C_{12}H_{23}$

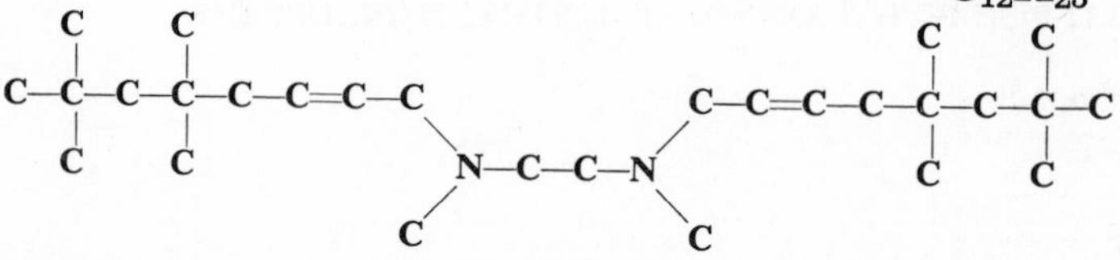

1,2-BIS[METHYL-(5,5,7,7-TETRAMETHYL-2-OCTENYL)AMINO]ETHANE

Derivs.:

Bis-methochloride: m. 194–196° [HW1] (this quaternary salt was prepared from
1,2-bis(dimethylamino)ethane and the appropriate dodecenyl chloride)

$C_{28}H_{60}N_2$

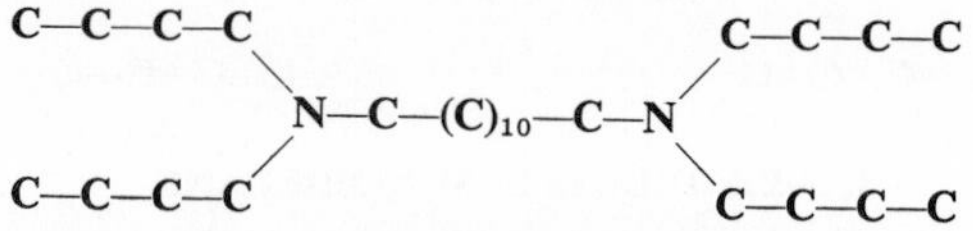

n-Bu
n-Bu
$+CH_2+_{12}$
n-Bu
n-Bu

1,12-BIS(DIBUTYLAMINO)DODECANE

Phys. Props.:

b_{11} 245° [PY1]

Prepn.:

Dibutylamine + 1,12-dibromododecane.[PY1]

$C_{28}H_{60}N_2$

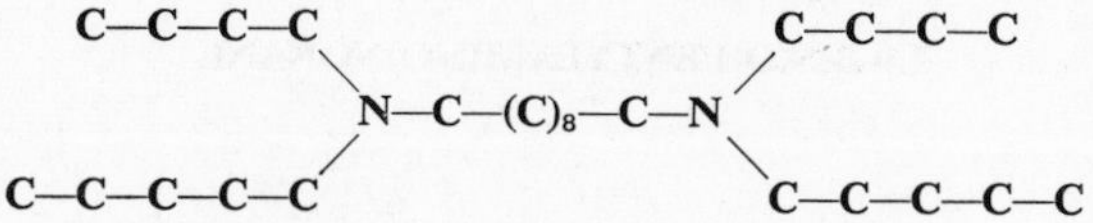

```
C—C—C—C              C—C—C—C     n-Bu
         N—C—(C)₈—C—N            n-Pent
C—C—C—C—C            C—C—C—C—C   +CH₂+₁₀
                                 n-Bu
                                 n-Pent
```

1,10-BIS(BUTYLPENTYLAMINO)DECANE

Phys. Props.:

b_{17} 257–262° [PY1]

Prepn.:

Butylpentylamine + 1,10-dibromodecane.[PY1]

$C_{28}H_{60}N_2$

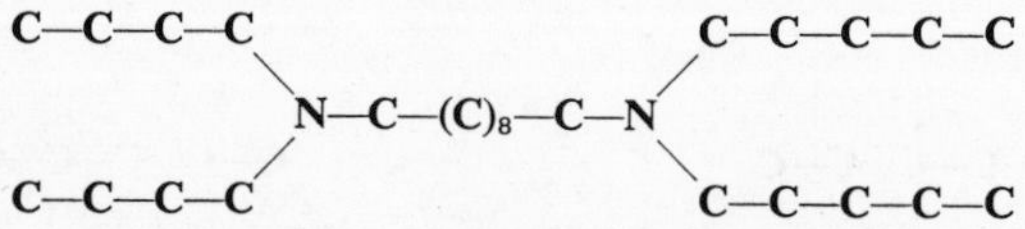

```
C—C—C—C              C—C—C—C—C   n-Bu
         N—C—(C)₈—C—N            n-Bu
C—C—C—C              C—C—C—C—C   +CH₂+₁₀
                                 n-Pent
                                 n-Pent
```

1-DIBUTYLAMINO-10-DIPENTYLAMINODECANE

Phys. Props.:

b_{28} 265–270° [PY2]

Prepn.:

Dibutylamine + 1-dipentylamino-10-chlorodecane.[PY2]

$C_{29}H_{62}N_2$

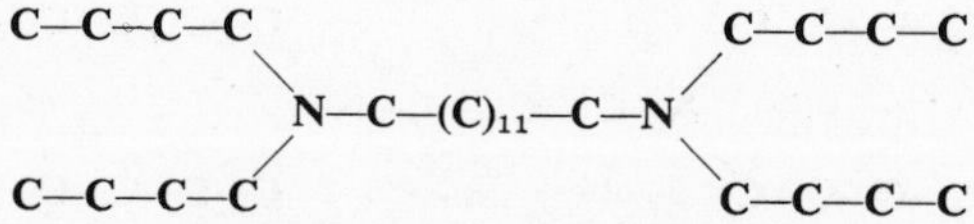

```
C—C—C—C              C—C—C—C     n-Bu
         N—C—(C)₁₁—C—N           n-Bu
C—C—C—C              C—C—C—C     +CH₂+₁₃
                                 n-Bu
                                 n-Bu
```

1,13-BIS(DIBUTYLAMINO)TRIDECANE

Phys. Props.:

b_{20} 260° [PY1]

Prepn.:

Dibutylamine + 1,13-dihalotridecane.[PY1]

$C_{29}H_{62}N_2$

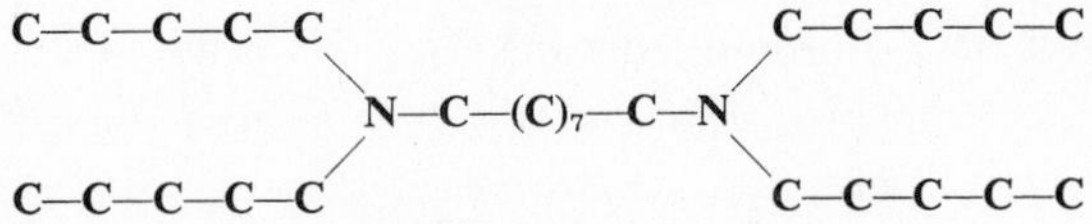

```
C—C—C—C—C                    C—C—C—C   n-Pent
           \                /           n-Pent
            N—C—(C)₇—C—N               +CH₂+₉
           /                \           n-Pent
C—C—C—C—C                    C—C—C—C   n-Pent
```

1,9-BIS(DIPENTYLAMINO)NONANE

Phys. Props.:

$b_{2.5}$ 225° [MA5]

n_D^{25} 1.4501 [MA5]

Prepn.:

Dipentylamine + 1,9-dibromononane (70% yield). [MA5]

$C_{30}H_{56}N_2$

Me
$C_{12}H_{23}$
+C_4H_4+
Me
$C_{12}H_{23}$

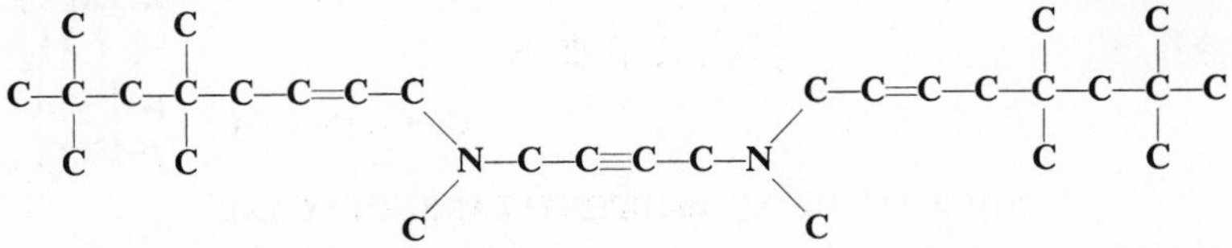

```
    C   C                              C   C
    |   |                              |   |
C—C—C—C—C—C=C—C              C—C=C—C—C—C—C—C
    |   |        \          /          |   |
    C   C         N—C—C≡C—C—N           C   C
                  |             |
                  C             C
```

1,4-BIS[METHYL-(5,5,7,7-TETRAMETHYL-2-OCTENYL)AMINO]-2-BUTYNE

Derivs.:

Bis-methochloride: m. 207–209° [HW1] (this quaternary salt was prepared from 1,4-bis(dimethylamino)-2-butyne and the appropriate dodecenyl chloride)

$C_{30}H_{64}N_2$

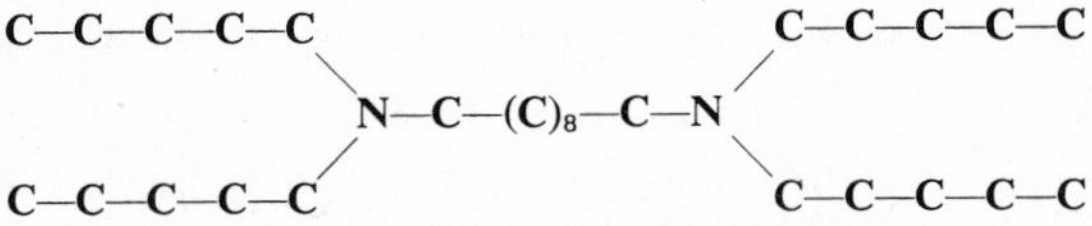

```
C—C—C—C—C                    C—C—C—C   n-Pent
           \                /           n-Pent
            N—C—(C)₈—C—N               +CH₂+₁₀
           /                \           n-Pent
C—C—C—C—C                    C—C—C—C   n-Pent
```

1,10-BIS(DIPENTYLAMINO)DECANE

Phys. Props.:

b_{20} 261–264° [PY1]

Prepn.:

Dipentylamine + 1,10-dichloro- or 1,10-dibromo-decane. [PY1]

Derivs.:

Bis-hydrochloride: m. 72° [PY1] (ref. PY1 does not indicate whether this is the mono- or di- salt, but does describe it as a "neutral crystalline salt")

$C_{30}H_{64}N_2$

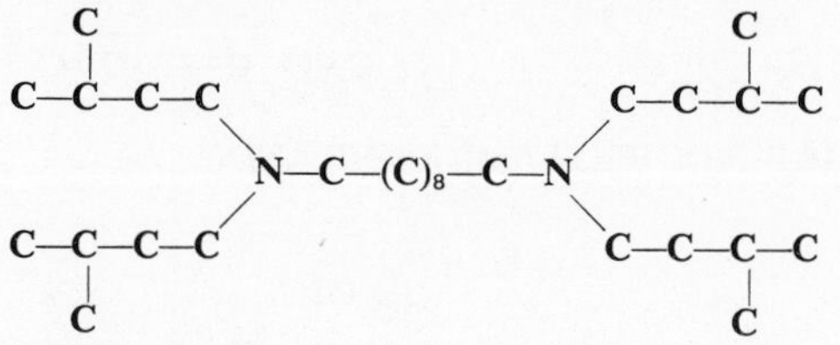

i-Pent
i-Pent
$\text{-(}CH_2\text{)}_{10}\text{-}$
i-Pent
i-Pent

1,10-BIS[DI(3-METHYLBUTYL)AMINO]DECANE

Phys. Props.:

b_6 235° [PY1]; b_3 205–213° [PR4]

Prepn.:

Diisopentylamine + 1,10-dibromodecane,[PY1] (55% yield).[PR4]

$C_{31}H_{66}N_2$

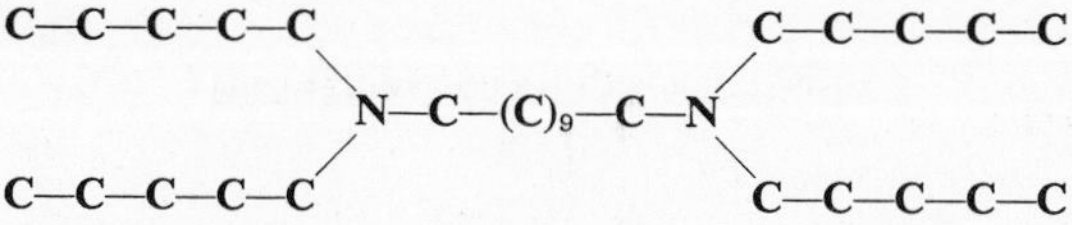

n-Pent
n-Pent
$\text{-(}CH_2\text{)}_{11}\text{-}$
n-Pent
n-Pent

1,11-BIS(DIPENTYLAMINO)UNDECANE

Phys. Props.:

b_{18} 272–275° [PY1]

Prepn.:

Dipentylamine + 1,11-dihaloundecane.[PY1]

$C_{31}H_{66}N_2$

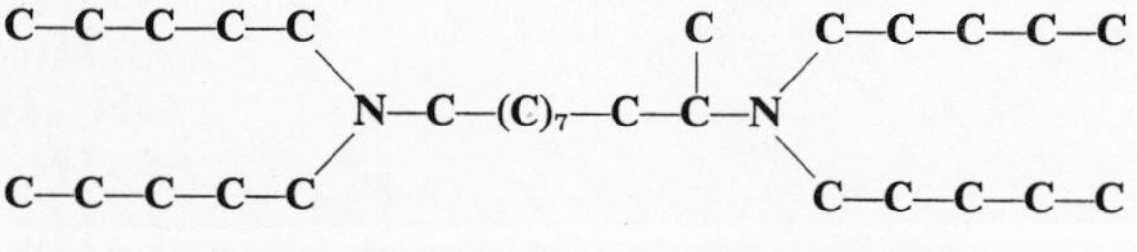

n-Pent
n-Pent
$\text{-(}C_{11}H_{22}\text{)}\text{-}$
n-Pent
n-Pent

1,10-BIS(DIPENTYLAMINO)UNDECANE

Phys. Props.:

b_{28} 272–275° [PY2]

Prepn.:

Dipentylamine + 1-dipentylamino-10-bromoundecane.[PY2]

Derivs.:

Bis-hydrochloride: m. 72° [PY2]

$C_{34}H_{72}N_2$

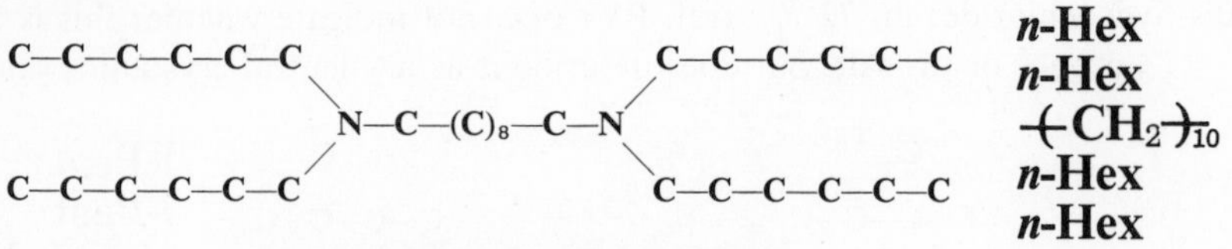

n-Hex
n-Hex
$+CH_2+_{10}$
n-Hex
n-Hex

1,10-BIS(DIHEXYLAMINO)DECANE

Phys. Props.:
b_5 288–292° [PY1]

Prepn.:
Dihexylamine + 1,10-dihalodecane.[PY1]

$C_{34}H_{72}N_2$

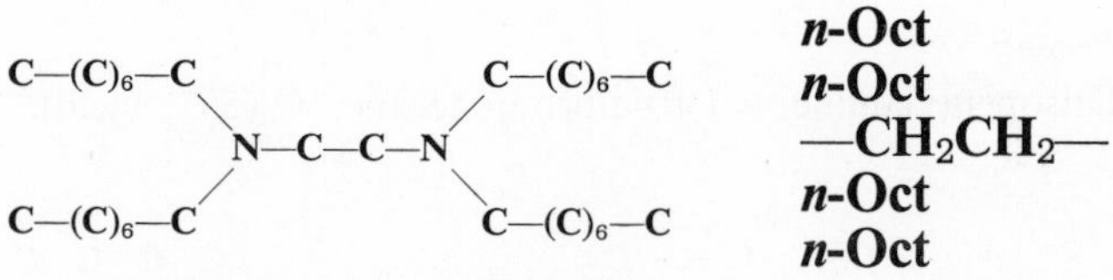

n-Oct
n-Oct
—CH_2CH_2—
n-Oct
n-Oct

1,2-BIS(DIOCTYLAMINO)ETHANE

Phys. Props.:
m. 130–133° [FR14]

Prepn.:
As a by-product* in the preparation of 1,2-bis(octylamino)ethane by the reaction of 1,2-dichloroethane with octylamine.[FR14]

$C_{36}H_{72}N_2$

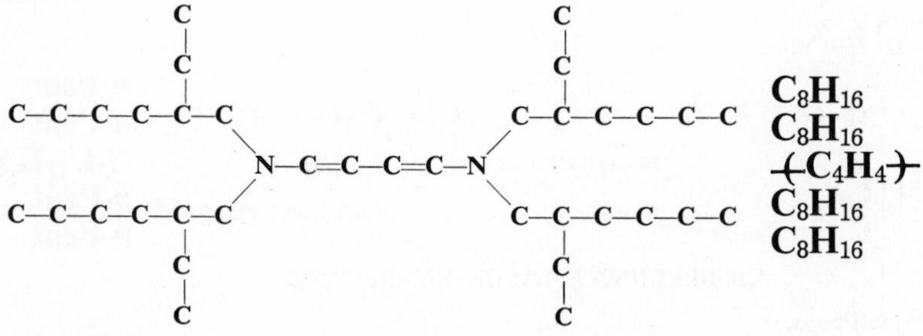

C_8H_{16}
C_8H_{16}
$+C_4H_4+$
C_8H_{16}
C_8H_{16}

1,4-BIS(DI-2-ETHYLHEXYLAMINO)-1,3-BUTADIENE†

---

* Ref. FR14 is a brief note with no other experimental details or explanation for formation of this compound.

† Ref. FE6 (a patent) does not specify the configuration of this particular molecule. However, from another example in the same patent and from some other work by the same authors (see ref. FE4), this compound most likely is the *trans,trans* isomer.

Phys. Props.:

b_3 171–180° [FE6]

n_D^{20} 1.4812 [FE6]

Prepn.:

Acid-catalyzed transamination reaction between 1,4-bis(dimethylamino)-1,3-butadiene and di(2-ethylhexyl)amine. [FE6]

$C_{37}H_{78}N_2$

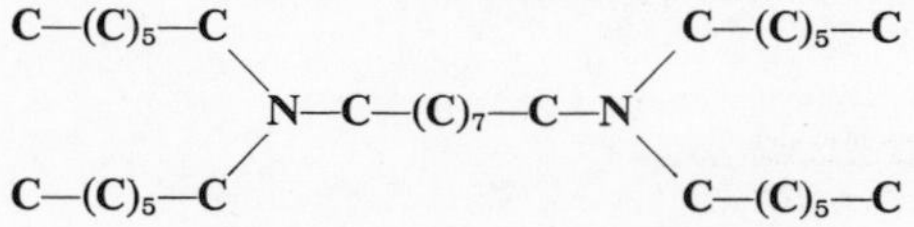

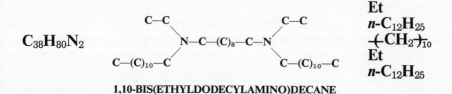

n-Hept
n-Hept
$+CH_2)_9$
n-Hept
n-Hept

1,9-BIS(DIHEPTYLAMINO)NONANE

Phys. Props.:

$b_{10^{-4}}$ 225–230° [MA5]

n_D^{26} 1.4540 [MA5]

Prepn.:

Diheptylamine + 1,9-dibromononane (63% yield). [MA5]

$C_{38}H_{80}N_2$

Et
n-$C_{12}H_{25}$
$+CH_2)_{10}$
Et
n-$C_{12}H_{25}$

1,10-BIS(ETHYLDODECYLAMINO)DECANE

Phys. Props.:

b_{24} 324–328° [PY1]

Prepn.:

Ethyldodecylamine + 1,10-dihalodecane. [PY1]

$C_{38}H_{80}N_2$

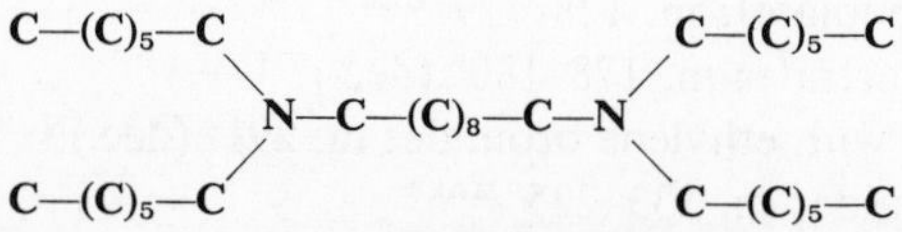

n-Hept
n-Hept
$+CH_2)_{10}$
n-Hept
n-Hept

1,10-BIS(DIHEPTYLAMINO)DECANE

Phys. Props.:

b_6 304–307° [PY1]

Prepn.:

Diheptylamine + 1,10-dihalodecane.[PY1]

$C_{42}H_{88}N_2$

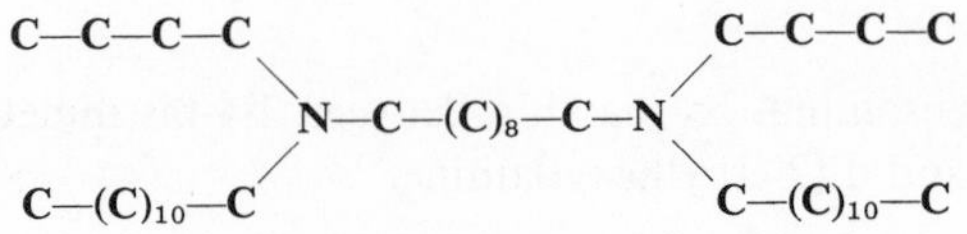

$$\begin{array}{ccc}
\text{C—C—C—C} & & \text{C—C—C—C} \\
& \text{N—C—(C)}_8\text{—C—N} & \\
\text{C—(C)}_{10}\text{—C} & & \text{C—(C)}_{10}\text{—C}
\end{array}$$

n-Bu
n-C₁₂H₂₅
$+CH_2+_{10}$
n-Bu
n-C₁₂H₂₅

1,10-BIS(BUTYLDODECYLAMINO)DECANE

Phys. Props.:

b_{17} 350–353° [PY1]

Prepn.:

Butyldodecylamine + 1,10-dibromodecane.[PY1]

$C_9H_{23}N_3$

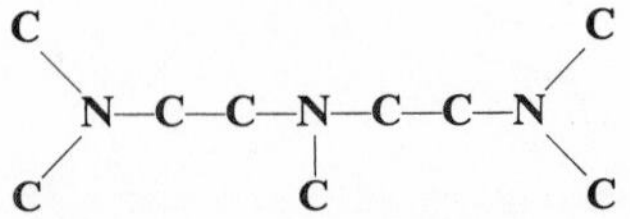

$$\begin{array}{ccccc}
\text{C} & & & & \text{C} \\
\diagdown & & & & \diagdown \\
\text{N—C—C—N—C—C—N} & & \\
\diagup & & \mid & & \diagup \\
\text{C} & & \text{C} & & \text{C}
\end{array}$$

METHYLBIS(2-DIMETHYLAMINOETHYL)AMINE

Phys. Props.:

b_{760} 198° [DA4]; b_{740} 139–140° [HR1]*; b_{12} 85–86° [MA38]
pK_a at 22°: pK_{a_1} 9.4, pK_{a_2} 8.4, pK_{a_3} 2.4[RO10]

Prepn.:

1. Diethylenetriamine + formaldehyde + formic acid. *Note:* Upon vacuum distillation of the product over KOH pellets, frothing was noticed. When the flask was opened an explosion occurred.[MA38]
2. Thermal degradation of *N*-methyl-*N'*,*N'*-dimethyl-1,4-diazinium hydroxide.[HR1]

Derivs.:

Tris-methiodide: m. 168–170° [MA38]
Tris-(2,4-dinitrophenolate): m. 128–129° [HR1]
Bis-ethohydrogen tartrate: m. 178–180° (dec.)[CI1]
Bis-quaternary salt with ethylene bromide: m. 291° (dec.)[MA38]
sym-Bis-methobromide: m. 233–235° [MA38]
sym-Bis-methiodide: m. 227–229° [MA38]
sym-Bis-methosulfate: m. 84–87° [MA38]

---

* This boiling point value is probably unreliable. It was obtained on a 0.36 g. cut from a complex distillation.

sym-Bis-ethochloride: m. 236–236.5°,[FR12] 236°[MA38]
sym-Bis-ethobromide: m. 212–215°[MA38]
sym-Bis-ethiodide: m. 207–210°[MA38]
sym-Bis-allylobromide: m. 176–179°[MA38]
sym-Bis-butobromide: m. 162–166°[MA38]

$C_{11}H_{27}N_3$

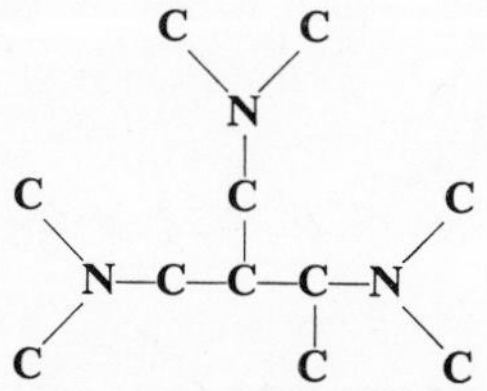

1,3-BIS(DIMETHYLAMINO)-2-DIMETHYLAMINOMETHYL-BUTANE

Phys. Props.:

b_{20} 100°[MA26]; b_{12} 91°[MA25]

Prepn.:

1. 3-Chloro-2-dimethylaminomethyl-1-dimethylaminobutane + dimethyl-amine ("almost quantitative yield").[MA26]
2. 3-Chloro-2-chloromethyl-1-dimethylaminobutane + dimethylamine. Same product was obtained with either the α or β stereoisomers of the halide ("almost quantitative yield").[MA25]

Derivs.:

Tris-nitrate: m. about 150° (violent decomposition)[MA26]
Bis-methiodide monohydriodide,

$\quad$ MeCH(NMe$_3$I)CH(CH$_2$NMe$_3$I)(CH$_2$NMe$_2$·HI): m. 211°[MA26]

$C_{11}H_{27}N_3$

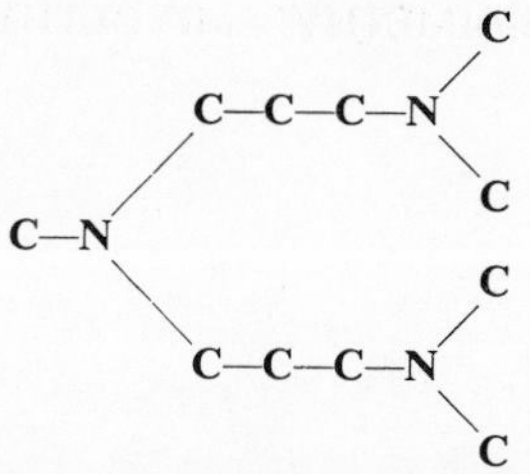

METHYLBIS(3-DIMETHYLAMINOPROPYL)AMINE

Phys. Props.:

b_{11} 100–102°[MA38]
pK_a at 22°: pK_{a_1} 10.0, pK_{a_2} 9.0, pK_{a_3} 6.4[RO10]

Prepn.:

Dipropylenetriamine + formaldehyde + formic acid.[MA38]

Derivs.:

Bis-methiodide: m. 262–264°[MA38]
Tris-methiodide: m. 279–281°[MA38]

$C_{13}H_{31}N_3$

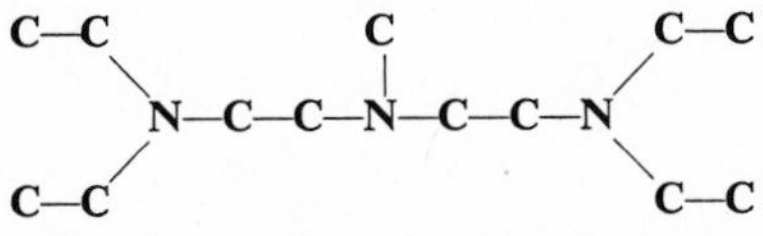

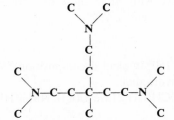

METHYLBIS(2-DIETHYLAMINOETHYL)AMINE

Phys. Props.:

b_{12} 120°[DA4]; b_{10} 116°[MA38]

Prepn.:

1. Bis(2-diethylaminoethyl)amine + formic acid + formaldehyde.[MA38]
2. 2-Diethylaminoethyl chloride + methylamine.[DA4]

$C_{14}H_{33}N_3$

1,1,1-TRIS(2-DIMETHYLAMINOETHYL)ETHANE

Phys. Props.:

b_4 112–113°[LU6]
d_4^{21} 0.8441[LU6]
n_D^{21} 1.4579[LU6]

Prepn.:

Reduction of $CH_3C[CH_2CON(CH_3)_2]_3$ with lithium aluminum hydride.[LU6]

Derivs.:

Picrate: m. 183–185°[LU6]
Tris-methiodide: m. 271–272°[LU6]

$C_{14}H_{33}N_3$

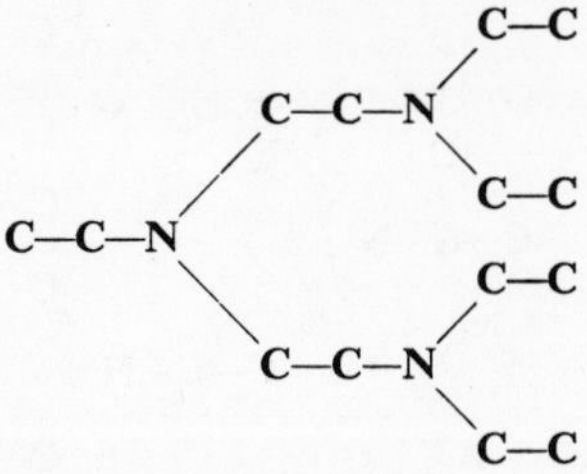

ETHYLBIS(2-DIETHYLAMINOETHYL)AMINE

Phys. Props.:
b_{11} 125°[DA4]

Prepn.:
2-Diethylaminoethyl chloride + ethylamine.[DA4]

$C_{15}H_{35}N_3$

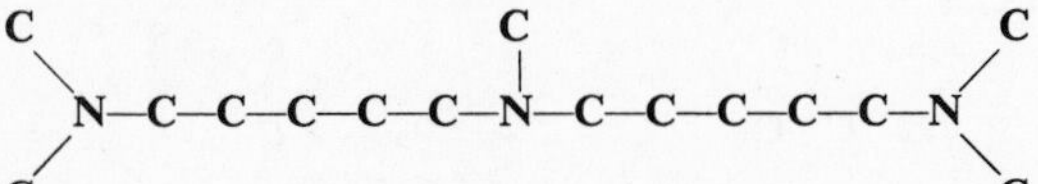

METHYLBIS(5-DIMETHYLAMINOPENTYL)AMINE

Derivs.:
Tris-methiodide:* does not melt below 300°[BR8]
Tris-methochloroplatinate: m. 260° (dec.)[BR8]

$C_{15}H_{35}N_3$

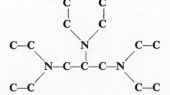

1,2,3-TRIS(DIETHYLAMINO)PROPANE

Phys. Props.:
b_{10} 110°[CE1]; b_4 103–106°[CE1]

Prepn.:
1. "Ethylation" of 1,2-bis(diethylamino)-3-aminopropane.[CE1]
2. Reductive alkylation of 1,3-bis(diethylamino)-2-nitropropane with acetaldehyde and hydrogen in the presence of platinum oxide (80% yield).[CE1]

Derivs.:
Chloroplatinate: m. 230° (dec.)[CE1]

---

* This compound was prepared from methyl iodide and dimethylbis(5-aminopentyl)ammonium iodide.

$C_{15}H_{35}N_3$

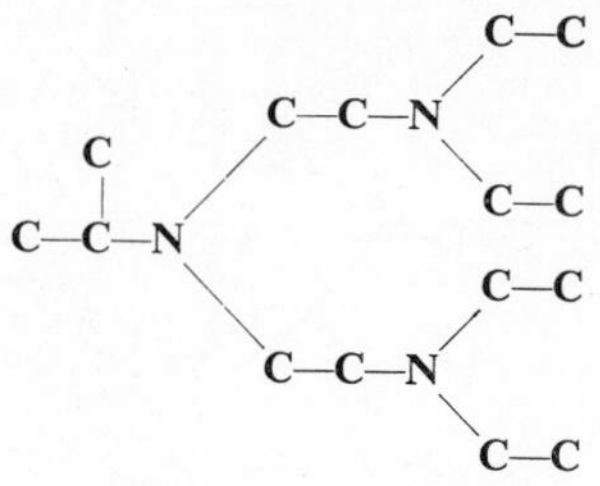

ISOPROPYLBIS(2-DIETHYLAMINOETHYL)AMINE

Phys. Props.:

b_{14} 141°[DA4]

Prepn.:

2-Diethylaminoethyl chloride + isopropylamine.[DA4]

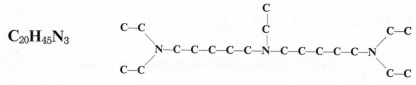

$C_{20}H_{45}N_3$

ETHYLBIS(5-DIETHYLAMINOPENTYL)AMINE

Phys. Props.:

$b_{0.25}$ 147–150° [ED2]
n_D^{23} 1.4585[ED2]

Prepn.:

5-Chloropentyldiethylamine + ethylamine (over 33% yield).[ED2]

Derivs.:

Tris-methiodide: m. 266° [ED2]
Tris-ethiodide: m. 273–274° [ED2]
Tris-propiodide: m. 221–222° [ED2]

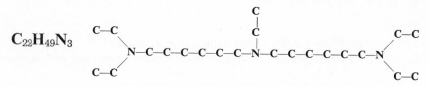

$C_{22}H_{49}N_3$

ETHYLBIS(6-DIETHYLAMINOHEXYL)AMINE

Phys. Props.:

$b_{0.75}$ 173–176° [CA9]; $b_{0.7}$ 165–168° [ED3]
n_D^{25} 1.4588[CA9]; n_D^{18} 1.4610[ED3]

Prepn.:

1. Reduction of *N*-(6-diethylaminohexyl)-*N*,*N'*,*N'*-triethyladipamide with lithium aluminum hydride (over 55.9% yield).[CA9]
2. 6-Ethylaminohexyldiethylamine + 6-bromohexyldiethylamine (19% yield).[ED3]

Derivs.:

Tris-methiodide: m. 227.5–228.5° [CA9]
Tris-ethiodide: m. 261–262° [ED3]
Tris-propiodide: m. 220° [CA9]
Tris-butiodide: m. 178° [CA9]

$C_{26}H_{57}N_3$

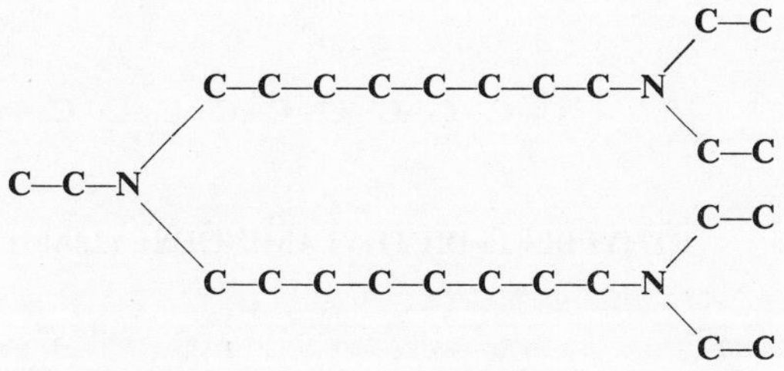

ETHYLBIS(8-DIETHYLAMINOOCTYL)AMINE

Phys. Props.:

$b_{0.8}$ 230–250° (bath temp.)[ED3]
n_D^{17} 1.4642[ED3]

Prepn.:

8-Chlorooctyldiethylamine + 8-ethylaminooctyldiethylamine (18% yield).[ED3]

Derivs.:

Tris-hydrochloride: m. 165–166° (dec.)[ED3]
Tris-methiodide: m. 251–252° (dec.)[ED3]

$C_{27}H_{59}N_3$

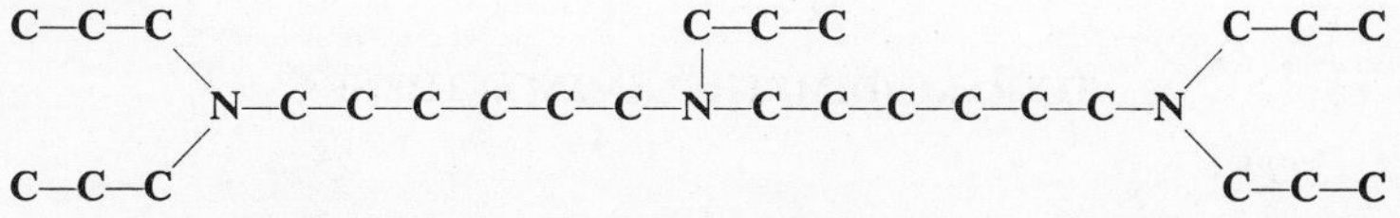

PROPYLBIS(6-DIPROPYLAMINOHEXYL)AMINE

Phys. Props.:

$b_{0.65}$ 211° [CA9]
n_D^{21} 1.4582[CA9]

Prepn.:

Reduction of *N*-(6-dipropylaminohexyl)-*N*,*N*′,*N*′-tripropyladipamide with lithium aluminum hydride (over 77.5% yield).[CA9]

Derivs.:

Tris-methiodide: m. 239° [CA9]
Tris-ethiodide: m. 221° [CA9]
Tris-propiodide: m. 206–207° [CA9]

$C_{30}H_{65}N_3$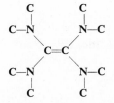

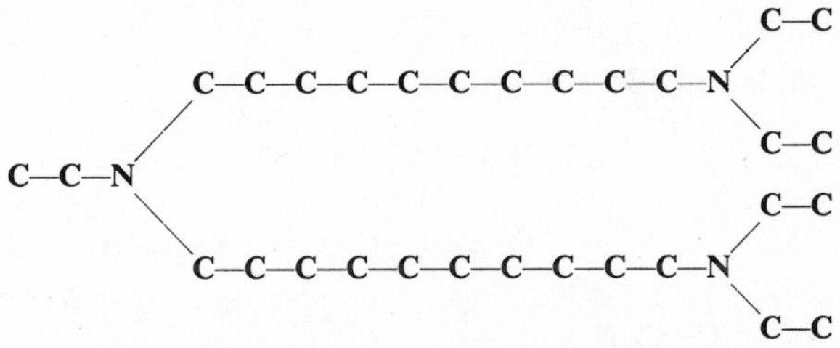

ETHYLBIS(10-DIETHYLAMINODECYL)AMINE

Phys. Props.:

$b_{0.25}$ 212–216° [ED3]
n_D^{14} 1.4660 [ED3]

Prepn.:

10-Bromodecyldiethylamine + 10-ethylaminodecyldiethylamine
    (26% yield).[ED3]

Derivs.:

Tris-hydrochloride: m. 118° [ED3]
Tris-ethiodide: m. 202.5–203.3° [ED3]

$C_{10}H_{24}N_4$

TETRAKIS(DIMETHYLAMINO)ETHENE*

Phys. Props.:

$b_{0.9}$ 59° [PR7]
d_4^{25} 0.8612 [PR7]
n_D^{25} 1.4785 [PR7]

---

* The only proof of structure is based on the correct elemental analysis of the dibromo addition derivative.

Prepn.:

1-Chloro-1,2,2-trifluoroethene + dimethylamine (54% yield).[PR7]

$C_{12}H_{30}N_4$

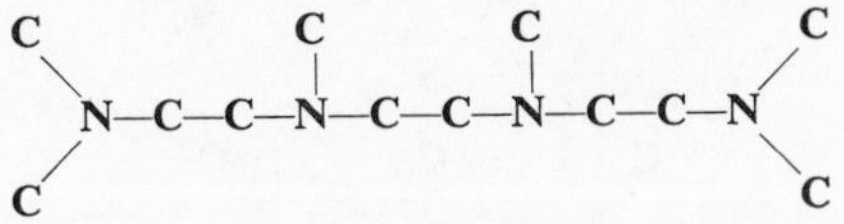

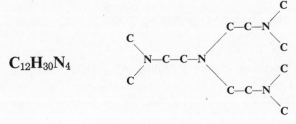

N,N'-DIMETHYL-N,N'-BIS(2-DIMETHYLAMINOETHYL)ETHYLENEDIAMINE

Phys. Props.:

b_{11} 130° [MA38]

pK_a at 22°: pK_{a_1} 9.4, pK_{a_2} 8.2, pK_{a_3} 4.8, pK_{a_4} < 2[RO10]

Prepn.:

Triethyleneaminetetramine + formic acid + formaldehyde.[MA38]

$C_{12}H_{30}N_4$

TRIS(2-DIMETHYLAMINOETHYL)AMINE

Phys. Props.:

"Above b_{14} 85°" [CI2]; $b_{0.2}$ 62–67° [MI5]

Prepn.:

1. Tris(2-chloroethyl)amine + dimethylamine.[CI2]
2. 2-Dimethylaminoethyl chloride + ammonia[CI2]; + 2-diethylaminoethyl-amine.[CI2]
3. Tris(2-aminoethyl)amine + formaldehyde + formic acid (43% yield).[MI5]

Derivs.:

Tris-hydrochloride monohydrate: m. 276–276.5° [MI5]
Tris-hydrochloride sinters above 190° and melts up to 235° (dec.)[LE16]
Tetrakis-hydrochloride: m. 278–278.5° (dec.)[CI2]
Tris-methochloride: m. 282–283° [LE16]
Tetrakis-methochloride: m. 285–286° (dec.)[LE16]
Tris-methopicrate: m. 230–232° (dec.)[LE16]

Tetrakis-methiodide: m. 295–296° (dec.)[LE16]

$(Me_3\overset{\oplus}{N}CH_2CH_2)_4\overset{\oplus}{N}Br_2\overset{\ominus}{Cl_3}\cdot H_2O$: m. 268–269° (dec.)[LE16]

$C_{13}H_{32}N_4$

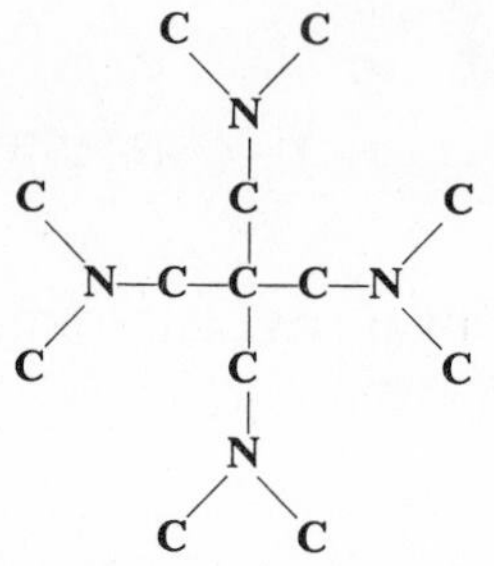

TETRAKIS(DIMETHYLAMINOMETHYL)METHANE

Phys. Props.:

b_{769} 248–249°[GI2]; b_{45} 157°[GI2]; b_{33} 137°[PA2]
d_4^{21} 0.881[PA2]
n_D^{25} 1.4610[PA2]
pK_a at 25°: pK_{a_1} 10.25, pK_{a_2} 7.37, pK_{a_3} 2.88, pK_{a_4} 2.36[SP1]

Prepn.:

1. Tetrakis(bromomethyl)methane + dimethylamine (67% yield),[PA2] (51% yield).[GI2]
2. Tetrakis(aminomethyl)methane + methyl iodide[MA18]; + dimethyl sulfate (52% yield).[LI13]

Derivs.:

Tetrakis-hydrochloride: m. 231°[LI13]
Tetrakis-hydrochloride trihydrate: m. 231°[LI13]
Bis-hydriodide dihydrate: m. 212–213°, 210.5–211.5°[GI3]
Tetrakis-methochloride: sub. above 330° without dec.[GO7]
Bis-methiodide: m. 149° (dec.),[LI13,GI3]
Tetrakis-methiodide: does not melt at 300°,[LI13] nor above 350°[GO7]
Tetrakis-methopicrate: m. 310° (dec.)[GO7]
Tetrakis-methoperchlorate: dec. explosively at 380°[GO7]
Bis-ethiodide: m. 128°[GI3]
Monoallyloiodide: m. 207°[GI3]
Monoallyloiodide monohydriodide: m. 157–158°[GI3]
Monomethiodide monoallyloiodide: m. 114–115° (dec.)[GI3]
Monobenzyloiodide: m. 190–196°[GI3]
Bis-benzyloiodide monohydrate: m. 128–129° (dec.)[GI3]
Monobenzyloiodide monohydroiodide: m. 170°[GI3]
Monobenzyloiodide monoallyloiodide: m. 145–146° (dec.)[GI3]

$C_{15}H_{36}N_4$

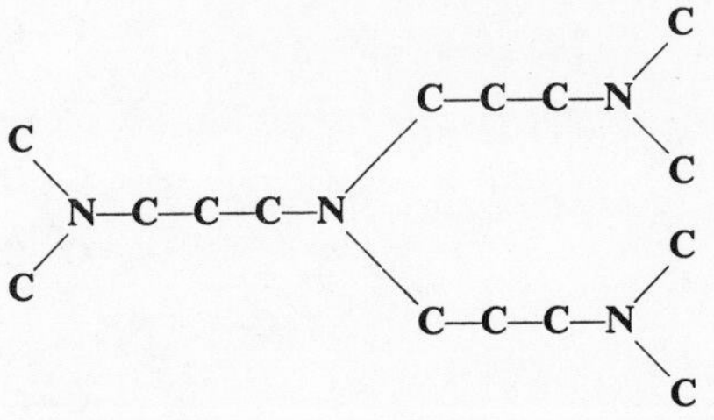

TRIS-(3-DIMETHYLAMINOPROPYL)AMINE

Prepn.:
Tris(3-aminopropyl)amine + formic acid + formaldehyde.[MI5]

Derivs.:
Tris-methiodide: m. 288–290°[MI5]

$C_{16}H_{38}N_4$

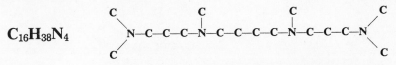

N,N'-DIMETHYL-*N,N'*BIS(3-DIMETHYLAMINOPROPYL)-
TETRAMETHYLENEDIAMINE

Prepn.:
Thermal decomposition of decamethylspermine sulfide.[DU3]

Derivs.:
Tetrakis-hydrochloride: m. 273–276° (dec.)[DU3]
Tetrakis-chloroaurate: m. 200–203° (dec.)[DU3]
Tetrakis-methochloraurate: m. 278–280° (dec.),[DU2] 278° (dec.)[WR1]
Tetrakis-methochloroplatinate: m. 286–288° (dec.),[DU2] dec. *ca.* 280°[WR1]
Tetrakis-methopicrate: m. 272–274° (dec.)[DU2]
Tetrakis-methochloride + $HgCl_2$ double salt: m. 268°[DU2]

$C_{17}H_{40}N_4$

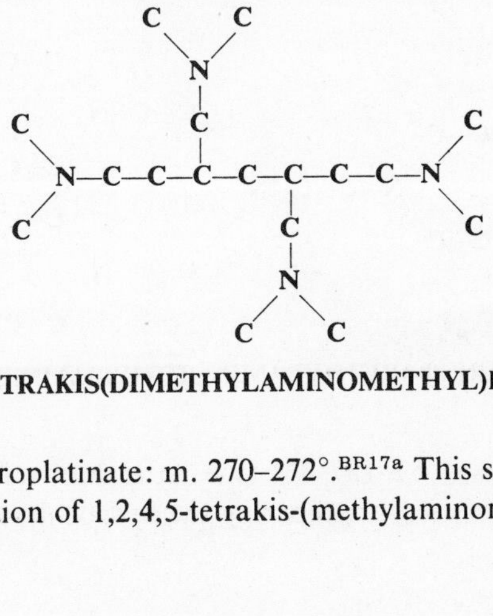

1,2,4,5-TETRAKIS(DIMETHYLAMINOMETHYL)PENTANE

Derivs.:
Tetrakis-methochloroplatinate: m. 270–272°.[BR17a] This salt was prepared *via*
exhaustive methylation of 1,2,4,5-tetrakis-(methylaminomethyl)pentane.

$C_{17}H_{40}N_4$

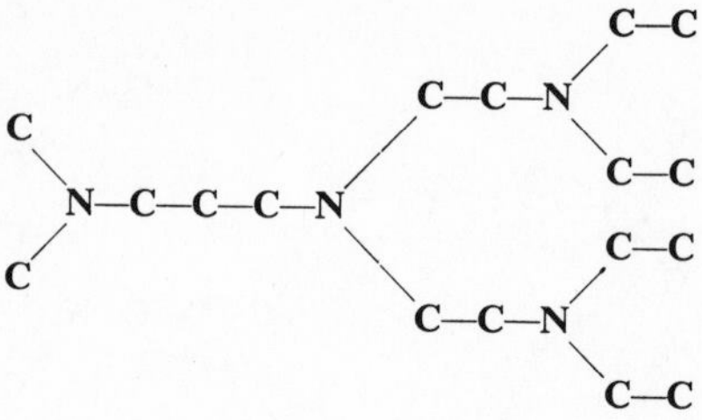

1-DIMETHYLAMINO-3-BIS(2-DIETHYLAMINOETHYL)AMINOPROPANE

Prepn.:

N,N-Dimethyl-1,3-propylenediamine + 2-diethylaminoethyl chloride.[MI5]

Derivs.:

Tris-hydrochloride: m. 201°[MI5]

$C_{18}H_{42}N_4$

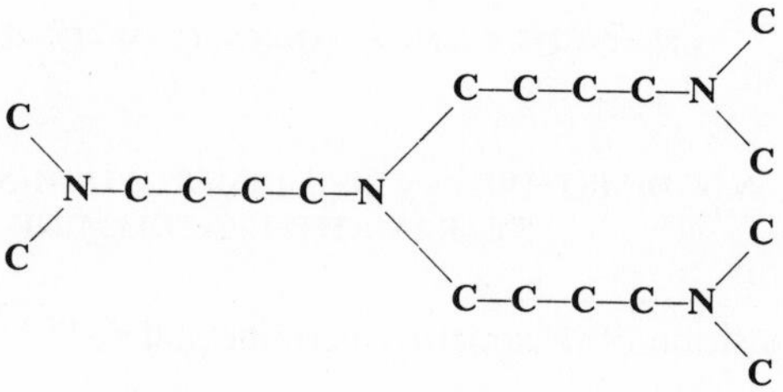

TRIS(4-DIMETHYLAMINOBUTYL)AMINE

Prepn.:

Tris(4-aminobutyl)amine + formic acid + formaldehyde.[MI5]

Derivs.:

Tetrakis-hydrochloride: m. 291–292°[MI5]
Tetrakis-methiodide: m. 269–271°[MI5]

$C_{18}H_{42}N_4$

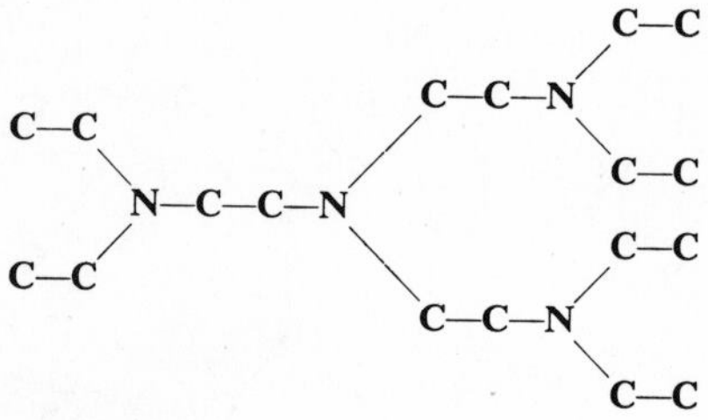

TRIS(2-DIETHYLAMINOETHYL)AMINE

Phys. Props.:

$b_{0.15}$ 105–110°[CI2]; $b_{0.05}$ 87–137°[MI5] (the latter b.p. refers to the range of
amine distillate used in preparing the hydrochlorides)

Prepn.:

N,N-Diethylethylenediamine + 2-diethylaminoethyl chloride,[C12] (55% yield).[M15]

Derivs.:

Tris-hydrochloride: m. 222.5–224.5°,[C12] 224.2–224.8°[M15]
Tetrakis-hydrochloride: m. 193.5–195°[M15]
Tris-citrate: m. 127–130°[C12]
Tris-methiodide: m. 275°[M15]

$C_{19}H_{44}N_4$

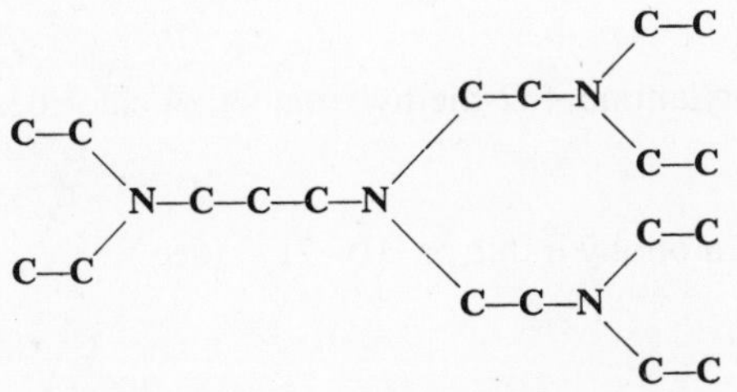

N,N-DIETHYL-N',N'-BIS(2-DIETHYLAMINOETHYL)TRIMETHYLENEDIAMINE

Prepn.:

3-Diethylaminopropylamine + 2-diethylaminoethyl chloride.[M15]

Derivs.:

Tris-hydrochloride: m. 230–231°[M15]
Tetrakis-hydrochloride: m. 218–220.2°[M15]

$C_{20}H_{46}N_4$

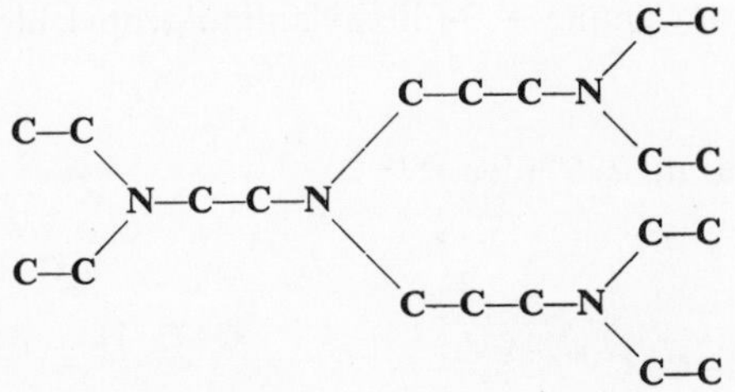

N,N-DIETHYL-N',N'-BIS(3-DIETHYLAMINOPROPYL)ETHYLENEDIAMINE

Prepn.:

3-Diethylaminopropyl chloride + 2-diethylaminoethylamine.[M15]*

Derivs.:

Tris-hydrochloride: m. 244–247°[M15]

---

* Ref. MI5, in what seems to be an obvious error, refers to the reaction as taking place between 3-diethylaminopropylamine and 2-diethylaminoethyl chloride.

$C_{21}H_{48}N_4$

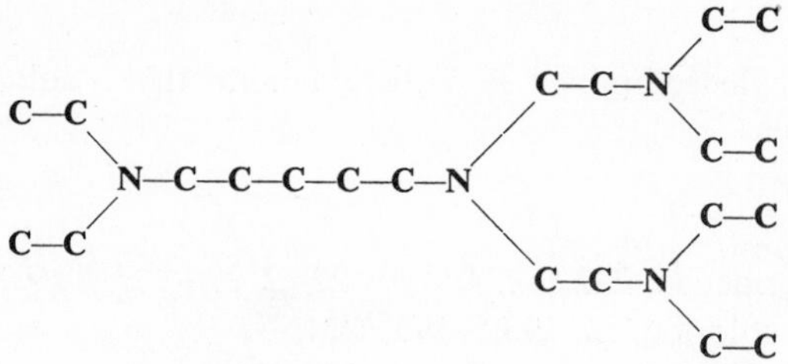

N,N-DIETHYL-N',N'-BIS-
(2-DIETHYLAMINOETHYL)PENTAMETHYLENEDIAMINE

Prepn.:

5-Diethylaminopentylamine + 2-diethylaminoethyl chloride.[MI5]

Derivs.:

Bis-chloroplatinate monohydrate: m. 216–217° (dec.)[MI5]

$C_{21}H_{48}N_4$

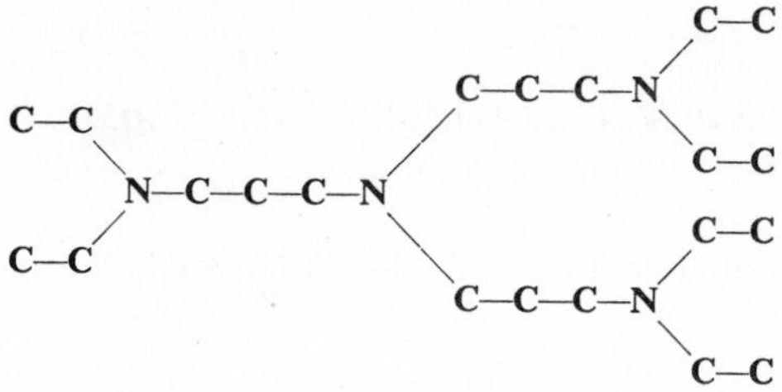

TRIS(3-DIETHYLAMINOPROPYL)AMINE

Prepn.:

3-Diethylaminopropylamine + 3-(diethylamino)propylchloride.[MI5]

Derivs.:

Tris-hydrochloride: m. 275° (dec.)[MI5]

$C_{21}H_{48}N_4$

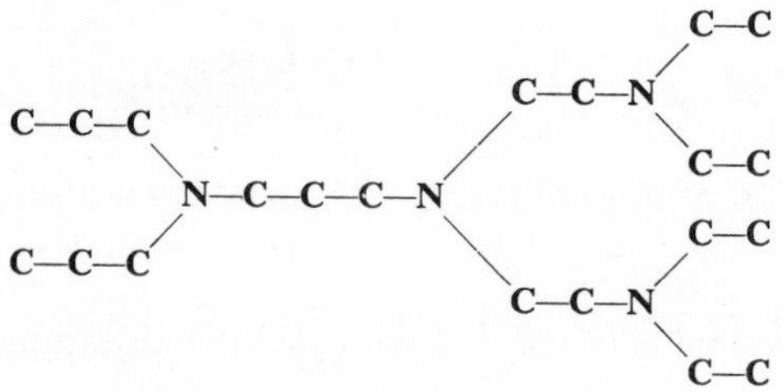

N,N-DIPROPYL-N',N'-BIS(2-DIETHYLAMINOETHYL)TRIMETHYLENEDIAMINE

Phys. Props.:

$b_{0.07}$ 135–158°[MI5]
n_D^{24} 1.4573[MI5]

Prepn.:

3-Dipropylaminopropyl chloride + bis(2-diethylaminoethyl)amine (56% yield).[MI5]

Derivs.:

Tris-hydrochloride dihydrate: m. 184–184.5° (*Note:* Initially the m.p. is 126.5° but on resolidification a m.p. of 184–184.5° is obtained. The latter is given in ref. MI5 as the m.p. of the dihydrate.)

$C_{23}H_{52}N_4$

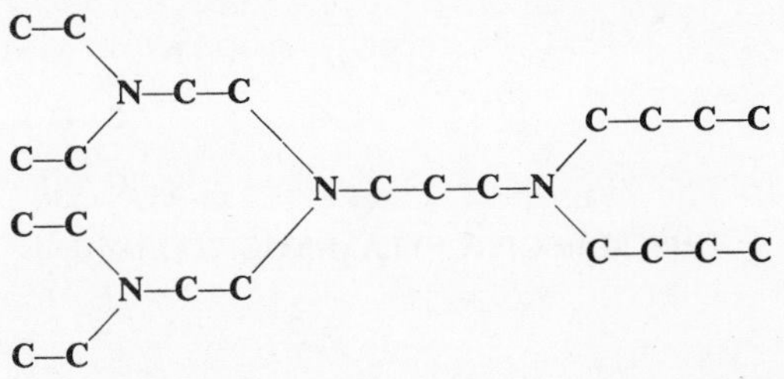

N,N-DIBUTYL-N′,N′-BIS(2-DIETHYLAMINOETHYL)TRIMETHYLENEDIAMINE

Prepn.:

3-Dibutylaminopropylamine + 2-diethylaminoethyl chloride.[MI5]

Derivs.:

Tetrakis-hydrochloride: m. 197–199°[MI5]

$C_{23}H_{52}N_4$

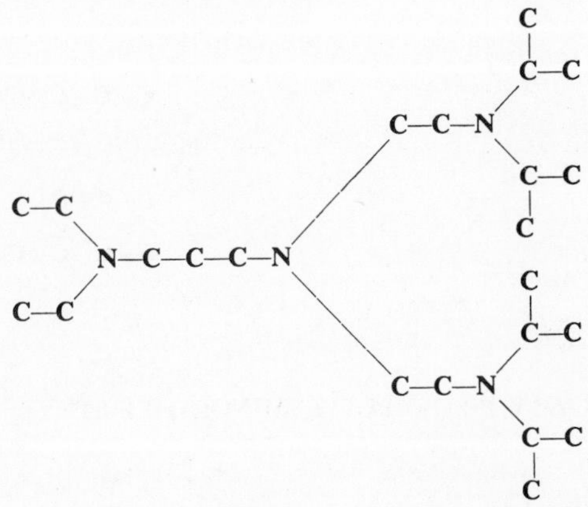

1-DIETHYLAMINO-3-BIS(2-DIISOPROPYLAMINOETHYL)AMINOPROPANE

Prepn.:

2-Diisopropylaminoethyl chloride + 3-diethylaminopropylamine.[MI5]

Derivs.:

Tris-hydrochloride: m. 193–195°[MI5]

$$C_{24}H_{54}N_4$$

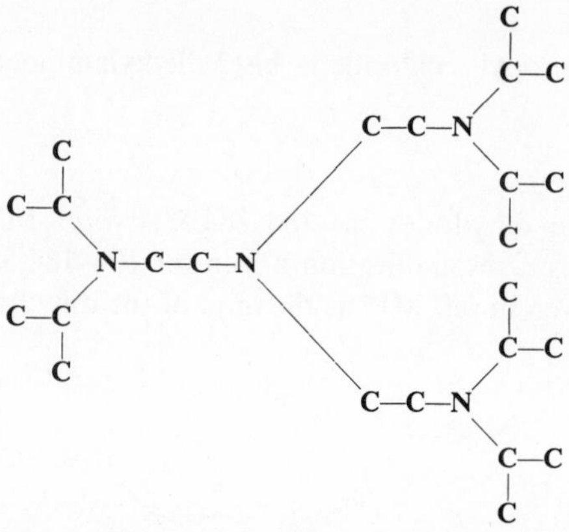

TRIS(2-DIISOPROPYLAMINOETHYL)AMINE

Phys. Props.:

$b_{0.1}$ 105–122° [CI2,MI5]

Prepn.:

Tris(2-chloroethyl)amine + diisopropylamine,[CI2] (14% yield).[MI5]

Derivs.:

Tetrakis-hydrochloride: m. 246.5–247.0° [CI2,MI5]

$$C_{26}H_{58}N_4$$

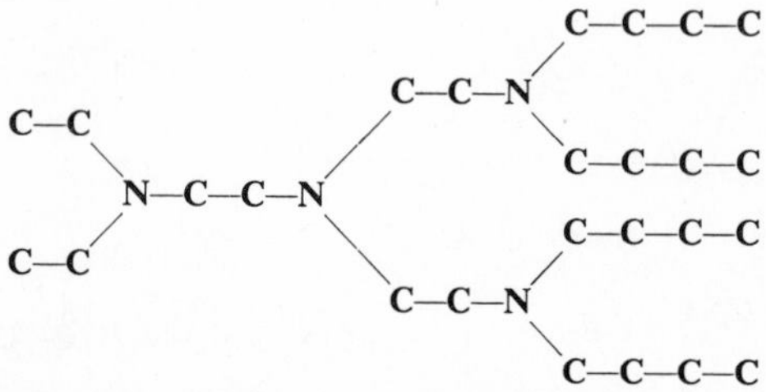

N,N-DIETHYL-*N'*,*N'*-BIS(2-DIBUTYLAMINOETHYL)ETHYLENEDIAMINE

Phys. Props.:

$b_{0.2}$ 110–160° [CI2]

Prepn.:

2-Dibutylaminoethyl chloride + 2-diethylaminoethylamine.[CI2,MI5]

Derivs.:

Tris-hydrochloride: m. 127.5–129.5° [CI2,MI5]

$C_{29}H_{64}N_4$

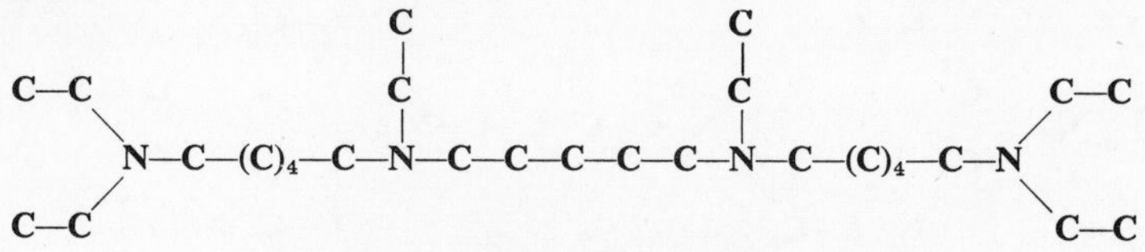

**N,N'-DIETHYL-N,N'-BIS(6-DIETHYLAMINOHEXYL)-
PENTAMETHYLENEDIAMINE**

Derivs.:

Tetrakis-methiodide: m. 236–237° [ED2]
Tetrakis-ethiodide: m. 264° [ED2]
Tetrakis-propiodide: m. 175–176° [ED2]

$C_{30}H_{66}N_4$

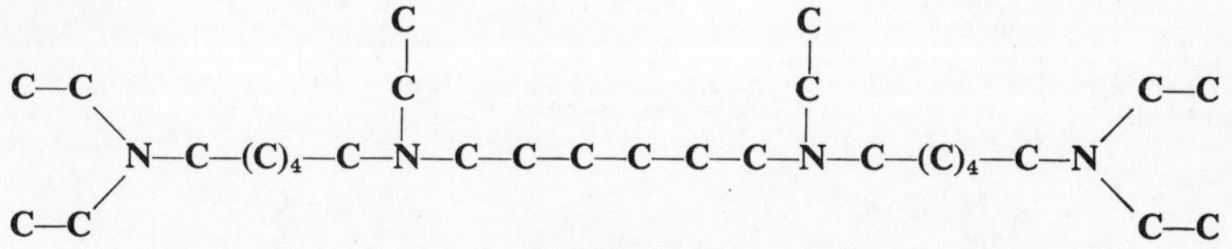

**N,N'-DIETHYL-N,N'-BIS(6-DIETHYLAMINOHEXYL)-
HEXAMETHYLENEDIAMINE**

Derivs.:

Tetrakis-ethiodide: m. 248–248.5° [ED3]

$C_{42}H_{90}N_4$

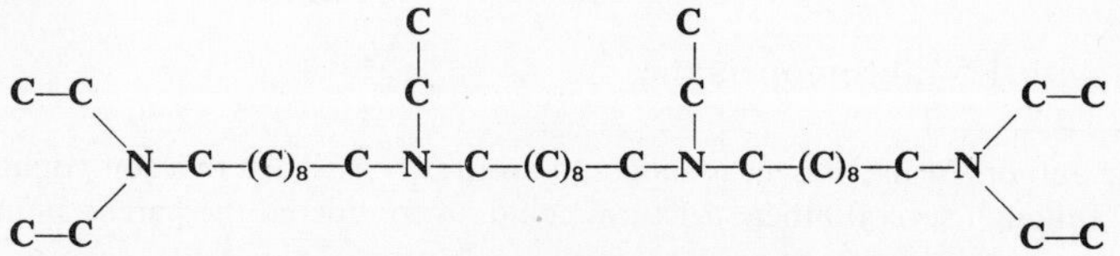

**N,N'-DIETHYL-N,N'-BIS(10-DIETHYLAMINODECYL)-
DECAMETHYLENEDIAMINE**

Derivs.:

Tetrakis-ethiodide: m. 186–187° [ED3]

$C_{20}H_{48}N_6$

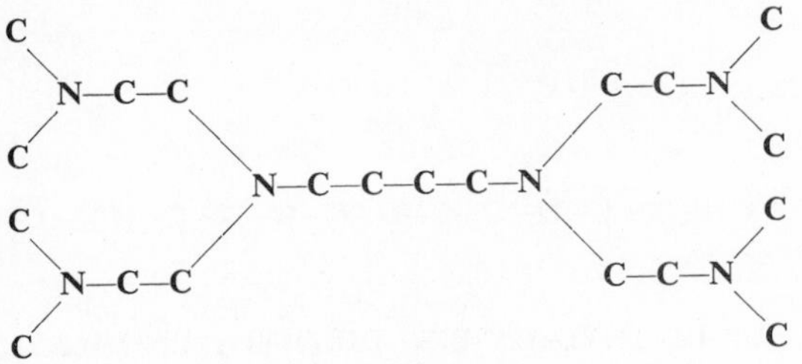

**N,N,N′,N′-TETRAKIS-
(2-DIMETHYLAMINOETHYL)TETRAMETHYLENEDIAMINE***

Derivs.:

A melting point of 280–281° (dec.) was reported for the following compound[LE16]:

$$[(CH_3)_3\overset{\oplus}{N}CH_2CH_2]_3\overset{\oplus}{N}(CH_2)_4\overset{\oplus}{N}[CH_2CH_2\overset{\oplus}{N}(CH_3)_3]_3 \cdot 6Cl^- \cdot 2Br^-$$

$C_{21}H_{50}N_6$

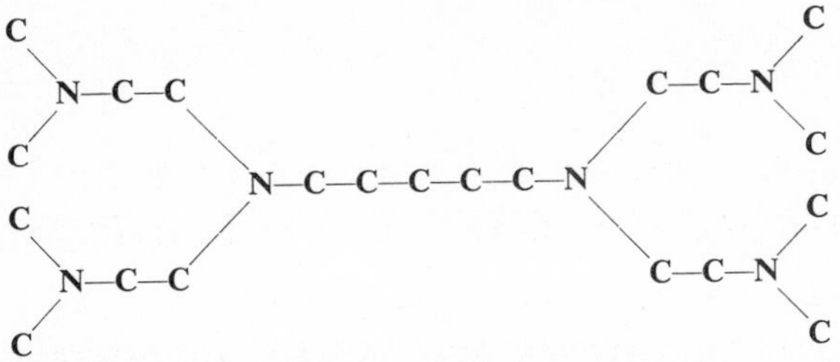

TETRAKIS(2-DIMETHYLAMINOETHYL)PENTAMETHYLENEDIAMINE*

A melting point of 287–288° (dec.) was reported for the following compound[LE16]:

$$[(CH_3)_3\overset{\oplus}{N}CH_2CH_2]_3\overset{\oplus}{N}(CH_2)_5\overset{\oplus}{N}[CH_2CH_2\overset{\oplus}{N}(CH_3)_3]_3 \cdot 6Cl^- \cdot 2Br^- \cdot H_2O$$

This quaternary salt was prepared from the reaction of

$$N[CH_2CH_2\overset{\oplus}{N}(CH_3)_2]_3 \cdot 3Cl^-$$

with 1,5-dibromopentane.

---

* The authors of the present monograph arbitrarily assigned this compound as parent amine, although several other structures could be considered the parent amine.

REFERENCES

A

AB1. ABLARD, J. E., McKINNEY, D. S., and WARNER, J. C., *J. Am. Chem. Soc.* **62**, 2181–2183 (1940).

AD1. ADAMS, R., and BROWN, B. K., *Org. Syntheses*, Coll. Vol. I, 528–531 (1941).

AD2. ADAMS, R., and MAHAN, J. E., *J. Am. Chem. Soc.* **64**, 2588–2593 (1942).

AI1. AINSWORTH, C., and EASTON, N. R., *J. Org. Chem.* **26**, 3776–3779 (1961).

AK1. AKAGI, K., OAE, S., and MURIKAMI, M., *J. Am. Chem. Soc.* **79**, 3118–3120 (1957).

AK2. AKERLÖF, G., *J. Am. Chem. Soc.* **50**, 733–744 (1938).

AL1. ALDER, B. J., and SMITH, E. B., *U.S. Atomic Energy Commission* **UCRL-5412-T** (1958).

AL2. ALLEN, P. W., and SUTTON, L. E., *Acta Cryst.* **3**, 46–72 (1950).

AL3. ALLENSTEIN, E., *Z. anorg. u. allgem. Chem.* **308**, 1–12 (1961).

AL4. ALLES, G. A., ELLIS, C. H., and REDEMANN, M. A., *J. Pharmacol. Exptl. Therap.* **107**, 332–343 (1953).

AM1. AMES, D. E., BOWMAN, R. E., BUTTLE, G. A. H., and SQUIRES, S., *J. Chem. Soc.* **1952**, 1057–1068.

AM1a. AMIARD, G., HEYMÈS, R., and VELLUZ, L., *Bull. soc. chim. France* **1956**, 698–700.

AM2. AMUNDSEN, L. H., MAYER, R. N., PITTS, L. S., and MALENTACCHI, L. A., *J. Am. Chem. Soc.* **73**, 2118–2121 (1951).

AN1. ANANTAKRISHNAN, S. N., *Proc. Indian Acad. Sci.* **21A**, 114–122 (1945).

AN2. ANDERSON, D. W., Jr., and FELLERS, C. R., *Food Technol.* **3**, 271–273 (1949).

AN3. ANDERSON, D. W., Jr., and FELLERS, C. R., *Food Research* **17**, 472–474 (1952).

AN4. ANDREWS, C. E., and Spence, L. U. (to Rohm and Haas Co.), U.S. Patent 2,153,405 (Apr. 4, 1939).

AN5. ANGYAL, S. J., PENMAN, D. R., and WARWICK, G. P., *J. Chem. Soc.* **1953**, 1737–1739.

AN6. ANTLER, M., and LAUBENGAYER, A. W., *J. Am. Chem. Soc.* **77**, 5250–5253 (1955).

AR1.   ARBUZOV, B. A., and GUZHAVINA, L. M., *Doklady Akad. Nauk S.S.S.R.* **61**, 63–66 (1948).

AR2.   ARENS, J. F., KOERTS, D. H., PLIEGER, P., *Rec. trav. chim.* **75**, 1454–1458 (1956).

AR3.   ARENS, J. F., and RIX, Th. R., *Koninkl. Ned. Akad. Wetenschap. Proc.* **57B**, 275–280 (1954).

AR4.   ARMBRECHT, B. H., RICE, L. M., GROGAN, C. H., and REID, E. E., *J. Am. Chem. Soc.* **75**, 4829–4830 (1953).

AR5.   ARMITAGE, J. B., and WHITING, M. C., *J. Chem. Soc.* **1952**, 2005–2010.

AR6.   ARNOLD, H. R. (to E. I. du Pont de Nemours & Co.), U.S. Patent 1,799,722 (Apr. 7, 1931).

AR7.   ARNOLD, H. R. (to E. I. du Pont de Nemours & Co.), U.S. Patent 2,078,922 (May 4, 1937).

AR8.   ARNOLD, Z., *Collection Czechoslov. Chem. Communs.* **25**, 1308–1312 (1960).

AR9.   ARNOLD, Z., *Chem. & Ind. (London)* **1960**, 1478.

AR10.   ARONEY, M., and LeFÈVRE, R. J. W., *J. Chem. Soc.* **1958**, 3002–3008.

AR11.   ARTHUR, J. C., and FELSING, W. A., *J. Am Chem. Soc.* **68**, 1883–1885 (1946).

AR12.   ARTOM, C., and LOFLAND, H. B. *Congr. intern. biochim., Résumés communs., 3ᵉ Congr., Brussels* **1955**, 40.

AS1.   ASHBY, E. C., *J. Am. Chem. Soc.* **81**, 4791–4795 (1959).

AS2.   ASHLEY-MONTAGU, M. F., *Nature* **142**, 1121–1122 (1938).

AS3.   ASTON, G. J., SAGENKAHN, M. L., SZASZ, G. J., MOESSEN, G. W., and ZUHR, H. F., *J. Am. Chem. Soc.* **66**, 1171–1177 (1944).

AS4.   ASTON, J. G., SILLER, C. W., and MESSERLY, G. H., *J. Am. Chem. Soc.* **59**, 1743 (1937).

AT1.   ATKINS, W. R. G., and WERNER, E. A., *J. Chem. Soc.* **101**, 1990 (1912).

AT2.   ATTWOOD, C. W., FORD, I. A. M., HOYLE, E. R., and PARKES, D. W., *J. Soc. Chem. Ind.* **69**, 181–186 (1950).

AU1.   AUWERS, K. von, and MAUSS, W., *Ber.* **61**, 2411–2420 (1928).

AU2.   AUDOINOT, R., and KAHANE, E., *Compt. rend.* **247**, 2051–2054 (1958).

AY1.   AYCOCK, B. F., EISENBRAUN, E. J., and SCHRADER, R. W., *J. Am. Chem. Soc.* **73**, 1351–1352 (1951).

B

BA1.   BABAYAN, A. T., *Izvest. Vysshikh Ucheb. Zavedenii, Khim. i Khim. Tekhnol.* **2**, 594–600 (1959).

BA2.   BABAYAN, A. T., GEGELYAN, Z. G., and INDZHIKYAN, M. G., *J. Gen. Chem. (U.S.S.R.)* **31**, 611–616 (1961).

BA3.   BABAYAN, A. T., GRIGORYAN, A. A., and GRIGORYAN, A. N., *Zhur. Obshcheĭ Khim.* **27**, 1827–1832 (1957).

BA4.   BABAYAN, A. T., GRIGORYAN, A. A., and MARTIROSYAN, G. T., *Doklady Akad. Nauk Armyan. S.S.R.* **26**, 153–162 (1958).

BA5.   BABAYAN, A. T., GRIGORYAN, A. A., and MARTIROSYAN, G. T., *Zhur. Obshcheĭ Khim.* **29**, 386–389 (1959); *J. Gen. Chem. (U.S.S.R.)* **29**, 390–400 (1959) (Eng. Trans.).

BA6.   BABAYAN, A. T., INDZHIKYAN, M. G., and BAGDASARYAN, G. B., *Doklady Akad. Nauk S.S.S.R.* **133**, 1334–1336 (1960).

BA7.   BABAYAN, A. T., and MARTIROSYAN, G. T., *Doklady Akad. Nauk Armyan. S.S.R.* **30**, 271–277 (1960).

BA8.   BABAYAN, A. T., and MARTIROSYAN, G. T., *Zhur. Obshcheĭ Khim.* **31**, 819–825 (1961).

BA9.   BABAYAN, A. T., and MARTIROSYAN, G. T., *Zhur. Obshcheĭ Khim.* **31**, 825–829 (1961).

BA10.   BABAYAN, A. T., MKRYAN, G. M., and GYULI-KEVKHYAN, R. S., *Zhur. Obshcheĭ Khim.* **28**, 1259–1263 (1958); *J. Gen. Chem. (U.S.S.R.)* **28**, 1314–1317 (1958) (Eng. Trans.).

BA11.   BABAYAN, A. T., MKRYAN, G. M., and MNDZHOYAN, Sh. L., *Zhur. Obshcheĭ Khim.* **27**, 604–606 (1957).

BA12.   BABAYAN, A. T., MKRYAN, G. M., and VARTANYAN, N. G., *Doklady Akad. Nauk Armyan. S.S.R.* **19**, No. 3, 83–84 (1954).

BA13.   BABAYAN, A. T., MKRYAN, G. M., and ZURABOV, I. Ya., *Izvest. Akad. Nauk Armyan. S.S.R., Ser. Fiz.-Mat., Estestven. i Tekh. Nauki* **9**, No. 8, 25–29 (1956).

BA14.   BABAYAN, A. T., and VARTANYAN, N. G., *Zhur. Obshcheĭ Khim.* **26**, 2789–2792 (1956).

BA15.   BABAYAN, A. T., VARTANYAN, N. G., and ZURABOV, I. Ya., *Zhur. Obshcheĭ Khim.* **25**, 1610–1613 (1955); *J. Gen. Chem. (U.S.S.R.)* **25**, 1567–1569 (1955) (Eng. Trans.).

BA16.   BABAYAN, A. T., and ZURABOV, I. Ya., *Zhur. Obshcheĭ Khim.* **25**, 2445–2448 (1955); *J. Gen. Chem. U.S.S.R.* **25**, 2331–2333 (1955) (Eng. Trans.).

BA17.   BABAYAN, V. O. *Doklady Akad. Nauk Armyan. S.S.R.* **19**, 41–45 (1954).

BA18.   BABCOCK, D. F. (to E. I. du Pont de Nemours & Co.), U.S. Patent 2,461,191 (Feb. 8, 1949).

BA19.   BAILEY, A. S., POLGAR, N., TATE, F. E. G., and WILKINSON, A., *J. Chem. Soc.* **1955**, 1547–1551.

BA20.   BAILEY, W. J., and NICHOLAS, L., *J. Org. Chem.* **21**, 648–650 (1956).

BA20a. BAKER, W., FLOYD, A. J., McOMIE, J. F. W., POPE, G., WEAVING, A. S., and WILD, J. H., *J. Chem. Soc.* **1956**, 2010–2017.

BA21.   BALDWIN, W. C. G., *Proc. Roy. Soc. (London)* **A162**, 204–214 (1937).

BA21a. BANUS, M. S., GIBB, T. R. P., Jr., and BRAGDON, R. W. (to U.S. Atomic Energy Commission), U.S. Patent 2,678,949 (May 18, 1954).

BA22.   BARBER, H. J., and Gaimster, K., *J. Pharm. & Pharmacol.* **3**, 663–669 (1951).

BA23.   BARBER, H. J., and GAIMSTER, K., *J. Appl. Chem.* **2**, 565–575 (1952).

BA23a. BARBER, D. W., PHILLIPS, C. S. G., TUSA, G. F., and VERDIN, A., *J. Chem. Soc.* **1959**, 18–24.

BA24.   BARBER, H. J., WEIN, R., GAIMSTER, K., and MASON, D. F. J., British Patent 714,867 (Sept. 1, 1954).

BA25.   BARCELÓ-MATUTANO, J. R., and BELLANATO, J., *Spectrochim. Acta* **8**, 27–40 (1956).

BA25a. BARCLAY, G. A., LeFèvre, R. J. W., and SMYTHE, B. M., *Trans. Faraday Soc.* **46**, 812–820 (1950).

BA26. BARKER, T. V., and PORTER, M. W., *J. Chem. Soc.* **117**, 1303–1321 (1920).

BA27. BARKLEY, F. A., MAST, G. W., GRAIL, G. F., TENENBAUM, L. E., ANDERSON, F. E., LEONARD, F., and GREEN, D. M., *Antibiot. Chemotherapy* **6**, 554–560 (1956).

BA28. BARLOW, R. B., and ING, H. R., *Brit. J. Pharmacol.* **3**, 298–304 (1948).

BA29. BARLOW, R. B., ROBERTS, T. D. M., and REID, D. V., *J. Pharm. & Pharmacol.* **5**, 35–38 (1953).

BA30. BARLOW, R. B., and VANE, J. R., *Brit. J. Pharmacol.* **11**, 198–201 (1956).

BA30a. BARRER, R. M., and BROOK, D. W., *Trans. Faraday Soc.* **49**, 940–948 (1953).

BA31. BARROW, G. M., and YERGER, E. A., *J. Am. Chem. Soc.* **76**, 5211–5216 (1954).

BA32. BARTLETT, P. D., and NOZAKI, K., *J. Am. Chem. Soc.* **69**, 2299–2306 (1947).

BA32a. BARTOCHA, B., GRAHAM, W. A. G., and STONE, F. G. A., *J. Inorg. & Nuclear Chem.* **6**, 119–129 (1958).

BA33. BARTOS, J., *Ann. pharm. franç.* **19**, 610–611 (1961).

BA34. BATEMAN, L. C., HUGHES, E. D., and INGOLD, C. K., *J. Chem. Soc.* **1944**, 243–247.

BA35. BATTAGLIA, A., BRUIN, F., and GOZZINI, A., *Nuovo cimento* **7**, 87–94 (1958).

BA36. BATTAGLIA, A., GOZZINI, A., and BRUIN, F., *Arch. sci. (Geneva)* **9**, Spec. No. 68 (1956).

BA36a. BAUER, S. H., and BLANDER, M., *J. Mol. Spectroscopy* **3**, 132–137 (1959).

BA37. BAUER, S. H., and McCOY, R. E., *J. Phys. Chem.* **60**, 1529–1532 (1956).

BA38. BAUM, L., *Über die katalytische Alkylierung von Ammoniak. Zurich*, (1945).

BA39. BAUMGARTEN, H. E., and SETTERQUIST, R. A., *J. Am. Chem. Soc.* **81**, 2132–2136 (1959).

BA40. BAX, C. M., KATRITZKY, A. R., and SUTTON, L. E., *J. Chem. Soc.* **1959**, 1258–1263.

BA41. BAYER and Co., German Patent 247,144 (Jan. 21, 1911).

BA42. BAYER and Co., German Patent 254,529 (Jan. 13, 1912).

BA43. BAYLE, J. W., and CHETWYN, A., *J. Chem. Soc.* **1958**, 2328–2335.

BE1. BEATTY, S. A., and Collins, V. K., *J. Fisheries Research Board Can.* **5**, 32–35 (1940).

BE1a. BEATTY, S. A., *J. Fisheries Research Board Can.* **4**, 63–68 (1938).

BE1b. BEATTY, S. A., and GIBBONS, M. E., *J. Biol. Board Can.* **3**, 77–91 (1936).

BE2. BEL'CHEV, F. V., *Trudy Beloruss. Sel'skokhoz. Akad.* **27**, No. 2, 87–92 (1958).

BE3. BELL, F. K., *J. Am. Chem. Soc.* **49**, 1837–1845 (1927).

BE4. BELL, I., MADRONERO, R., WHITING, M. C., *J. Chem. Soc.* **1958**, 3195–3202.

BE5. BELL, R. P., and BAYLES, J. W., *J. Chem. Soc.* **1952**, 1518–1524.

BE6. BELLANATO, J., TERESA-SARDINA, M. A., and BARCELÓ-MATUTANO, J. R., *Anales real soc. españ. fís. y quím. (Madrid)* **51B**, 271–275 (1955).

BE6a.   BENDER, M. L., and HOEG, I. F., *J. Am. Chem. Soc.* **79**, 5649–5654 (1957); *Chem. & Ind.* (*London*) **1957**, 463–464.

BE7.   BENDER, M. L., and TURNQUEST, B. W., *J. Am. Chem. Soc.* **79**, 1656–1663 (1957).

BE7a.   BENKO, J., *Acta Chim. Acad. Sci. Hung.* **21**, 351–361 (1959).

BE8.   BENNETT, H., *Concise Chemical and Technical Dictionary.* Chemical Publishing Co., Brooklyn, N.Y. (1947).

BE9.   BERG, A., *Ann. chim.* **3**, 289–308 (1894).

BE9a.   BERTETTI, J., *Ann. chim.* (*Rome*) **43**, 351–360 (1953).

BE9b.   BERTETTI, J., *Ann. chim.* (*Rome*) **43**, 361–364 (1953).

BE10.   BERTHELOT, M., *Ann. chim.* **23**, 243–252 (1881).

BE11.   BERTHOLD, R., *Chem. Ber.* **90**, 2743–2747 (1957).

BE12.   BERTRAND, D., *Bull. soc. chim.* (*France*) **12**, 1017–1019 (1945).

BE13.   BEWAD, J., *Zhur. Russ. Fiz.-Khim. Obshchestva* **1889**, 43–47.

BI1.   BIEL, J. H. (to Lakeside Laboratories, Inc.), U.S. Patent 2,830,048 (Apr. 8, 1958).

BI2.   BIEL, J. H. (to Lakeside Laboratories, Inc.), British Patent 843,194 (Aug. 4, 1960).

BI3.   BIEL, J. H., and DiPIERRO, F., *J. Am. Chem. Soc.* **80**, 4609–4614 (1958).

BI4.   BIEL, J. H., and DiPIERRO, F., *J. Am. Chem. Soc.* **80**, 4614–4618 (1958).

BI5.   BIELECKI, J., and HENRI, V., *Compt. rend.* **156**, 1860–1863 (1913).

BI5a.   BIILMANN, E., JENSEN, K. A., and BEHRNTS-JENSEN, H., *Bull. soc. chim.* [5], **3**, 2295–2305 (1936).

BI6.   BINGHAM, E. C., and SPOONER, L. W., *J. Rheology* **3**, 221–244 (1932).

BI6a.   BIRNBAUM, G., *J. Chem. Phys.* **27**, 360–368 (1957).

BI7.   BISHOP, R., and DENTON, W. I. (to Socony-Vacuum Co.), U.S. Patent 2,487,299 (Nov. 8, 1949).

BL1.   BLICKE, F. F., and LU, C. L., *J. Am. Chem. Soc.* **74**, 3933–3934 (1953).

BL2.   BLICKE, F. F., *Org. Reactions* **1**, 303 (1942).

BL3.   BLICKE, F. F., and ZIENTY, F. B., *J. Am. Chem. Soc.* **61**, 91–93 (1939).

BL4.   BLICKE, F. F., and ZIENTY, F. B., *J. Am. Chem. Soc.* **61**, 771–773 (1939).

BL4a.   BLOMQUIST, A. T., HALLAM, B. F., and JOSEY, A. D., *J. Am. Chem. Soc.* **81**, 678–680 (1959).

BL5.   BLUNDELL, R., and GRAYMORE, J., *J. Chem. Soc.* **1939**, 1787–1789.

BO1.   BOBRÁNSKI, B., JAKÓBIEC, T., and PRELICZ, D., *Acta Polon. Pharm.* **12**, 129–134 (1955).

BO2.   BOBRÁNSKI, B., JAKÓBIEC, T., and PRELICZ, D., *Roczniki Chem.* **30**, 623–625 (1956).

BO3.   BODE, J., *Ann.* **267**, 268–299 (1891).

BO4.   BODFORSS, S., and EHRLEN, I., *Kgl. Fysiograf. Sällskap. Lund, Förh.* **15**, 3–12 (1945).

BO7.   BOEHRINGER, C. F., German Patent 175,071 (Sept. 19, 1906).

BO8.   BÖHME, H., and BOLL, E., *Z. anorg. u. allgem. Chem.* **292**, 61–64 (1957).

BO8a.   BÖHME, H., and BOLL, E., *Z. anorg. u. allgem. Chem.* **291**, 160–163 (1957).

BO9.   BÖHME, H., *Chem. Ber.*, **89**, 2873–2876 (1956).

BO9a.   BÖHME, H., and KRAUSE, W., *Chem. Ber.* **84**, 170–181 (1951).

BO10.   BÖHME, H., and LEHNERS, W., *Ann.* **595**, 169–178 (1955).

BO11.   BOLLE, J., and BOURGEOIS, L., *Mém. serv. chim. état (Paris)* **38**, 159–163 (1953).

BO12.   BOLLE, J., MOUSSERON, M., and BOURGEOIS, L., *Mém. serv. chim. état (Paris)* **38**, 147–157 (1953).

BO12a.   BOLTO, B. A., and MILLER, J., *J. Org. Chem.* **20**, 558–562 (1955).

BO12b.   BOOTH, J. C., *The Encyclopedia of Chemistry*. Henry Carey Baird and Co., Philadelphia, Pa. (1883), 8th ed., p. 146.

BO13.   BORROWS, E. T., HARGREAVES, B. M. C., Page, J. E., RESUGGAN, J. C. L., and ROBINSON, F. A., *J. Chem. Soc.* **1947**, 197–202.

BO14.   BORTNIK, N. M., LUSKIN, L. S., HURWITZ, M. D., CRAIG, W. E., EXNER, L. J., and MIRZA, J., *J. Am. Chem. Soc.* **78**, 4039–4042 (1956).

BO14a.   BÖTTCHER, K. (to I. G. Farbenindustrie A.-G.), German Patent 473,215 (Mar. 14, 1929).

BO14b.   BÖTTCHER, K. (to I. G. Farbenindustrie A.-G.), German Patent 487,787 (Dec. 16, 1929).

BO14c.   BOUD, A. H., and SMITH, J. W., *J. Chem. Soc.* **1956**, 4507–4513.

BO15.   BOUVEAULT, L., *Bull. soc. chim. France* **31**, 1322–1327 (1904).

BO16.   BOWDEN, K., BRAUDE, E. A., JONES, E. R. H., and WEEDON, B. C. L., *J. Chem. Soc.* **1946**, 45–52.

BR1.   BRAND, J. C. D., EGLINTON, G., and MORMAN, J. F., *J. Chem. Soc.* **1960**, 2526–2533.

BR2.   BRANSON, H., and GARNER, L. B., *Phys. Rev.* **99**, 341 (1955).

BR3.   BRAUCHLI, E., and CLOETTA, M., *Arch. exptl. Pathol. Pharmakol.* **129**, 72–84 (1928).

BR4.   BRAUDE, E. A., and WAIGHT, E. S., *J. Chem. Soc.* **1952**, 1116–1122.

BR5.   BRAUN, J. VON, *Ber.* **33**, 1438–1452 (1900).

BR6.   BRAUN, J. VON, *Ber.* **42**, 2532–2538 (1909).

BR7.   BRAUN, J. VON, *Ber.* **43**, 2853–2864 (1910).

BR8.   BRAUN, J. VON, *Ber.* **43**, 2864–2879 (1910).

BR9.   BRAUN, J. VON, *Ann.* **382**, 2–50 (1911).

BR10.   BRAUN, J. VON, *Ann.* **386**, 273–304 (1912).

BR11.   BRAUN, J. VON, *Ber.* **70B**, 979–993 (1937).

BR12.   BRAUN, J. VON, and ANTON, E., *Ber.* **62**, 1489–1491 (1929).

BR13.   BRAUN, J. VON, and ANTON, E., *Ber.* **64B**, 2865–2869 (1931).

BR14.   BRAUN, J. VON, and BUCHMAN, E. R., *Ber.* **64B**, 2610–2617 (1931).

BR15.   BRAUN, J. VON, and CAHN, R. S., *Ann.* **436**, 263–273 (1924).

BR16.   BRAUN, J. VON, and DEUTSCH, H., *Ber.* **44**, 3062–3065 (1911).

BR17.   BRAUN, J. VON, and GOLL, O., *Ber.* **60**, 1533–1534 (1927).

BR17a.   BRAUN, J. VON, and IRMISCH, G., *Ber.* **64**, 2621–2629 (1931).

BR18.   BRAUN, J. VON, and KLAR, R., *Ber.* **73B**, 1417–1419 (1940).

BR19.   BRAUN, J. VON, and KRÖPER, H., *Ber.* **62B**, 2880–2885 (1929).

BR20.   BRAUN, J. VON, and LEMKE, G., *Ber.* **55**, 3536–3559, (1922).

BR21.   BRAUN, J. VON, and MANZ, G., *Ber.* **67B**, 1696–1712 (1934).

BR22.   BRAUN, J. VON, and MURJAHN, R., *Ber.* **59B**, 1202–1209 (1926).

BR23.   BRAUN, J. VON, and RÖVER, E., *Ber.* **36**, 1196–1199 (1903).

BR24.   BRAUN, J. VON, and SCHIRMACHER, W., *Ber.* **56**, 538–548 (1923).

BR25.   BRAUN, J. VON, and TEUFFERT, W., *Ber.* **61**, 1092–1099 (1928).

BR26. BRAUN, J. VON, and TEUFFERT, W., *Ber.* **62**, 235–241 (1929).

BR27. BRAUN, J. VON, TEUFFERT, W., and WEISSBACH, K., *Ann.* **472**, 121–142 (1929).

BR28. BRAUN, J. VON, and WEISSBACH, K., *Ber.* **63B**, 489–497 (1930).

BR28a. BREDERECK, H., and BÄDER, E., *Chem. Ber.* **87**, 129–139 (1954).

BR29. BREDIG, G., *Z. physik. Chem.* **13**, 191–326 (1894).

BR30. BRIEGLEB, G., *Z. Elektrochem.* **53**, 350–361 (1949).

BR30a. BRIGHT, J. R., and FERNELIUS, W. C., *J. Am. Chem. Soc.* **65**, 735–736 (1943).

BR31. BRINER, E., and GANDILLON, J., *Helv. Chim. Acta* **14**, 1283–1307 (1931).

BR32. BRINTZINGER, H., and HESSE, B., *Kolloid-Z.* **111**, 156–166 (1948).

BR32a. BRISSETTE, C., and SANDORFY, C., *Can. J. Chem.* **38**, 34–44 (1960).

BR33. BRITTON, H. T. S., and WILLIAMS, W. G., *J. Chem. Soc.* **1935**, 796–801.

BR34. BROCHET, A., and CAMBIER, R., *Bull. soc. chim. France* **13**, 533–537 (1895).

BR35. BROCKWAY, L. O., and JENKINS, H. O., *J. Am. Chem. Soc.* **58**, 2036–2044 (1936).

BR36. BROWN, A. B., and REID, E., *J. Phys. Chem.* **28**, 1067–1076 (1924).

BR37. BROWN, C. A., and OSTHOFF, R. C., *J. Am. Chem. Soc.* **74**, 2340–2345 (1952).

BR38. BROWN, H. C., *J. Am. Chem. Soc.* **67**, 378–380 (1945).

BR39. BROWN, H. C. (to Ethyl Corp.), U.S. Patent 2,860,167 (Nov. 11, 1958).

BR40. BROWN, H. C., and BARTHOLOMAY, H., Jr., *J. Chem. Phys.* **11**, 43 (1943).

BR41. BROWN, H. C., and BONNER, W. H., *J. Am. Chem. Soc.* **75**, 14–16 (1953).

BR42. BROWN, H. C., and GERSTEIN, M., *J. Am. Chem. Soc.* **72**, 2926–2933 (1950).

BR43. BROWN, H. C., and JOHANNESEN, R. B., *J. Am. Chem. Soc.* **75**, 16–20 (1953).

BR44. BROWN, H.C., and MORITANI, I., *J. Am. Chem. Soc.* **78**, 2203–2210 (1956).

BR45. BROWN, H. C., TAYLOR, M. D., and BARTHOLOMAY, H., Jr., *J. Am. Chem. Soc.* **66**, 435–442 (1944).

BR46. BROWN, H. C., TAYLOR, M. D., and GERSTEIN, M., *J. Am. Chem. Soc.* **66**, 431–435 (1944).

BR47. BROWN, H. C., SCHLESINGER, H. I., and CARDON, S. Z., *J. Am. Chem. Soc.* **64**, 325–329 (1942).

BR48. BRÜHL, J. W., *Z. physik. Chem.* **16**, 193–226 (1895).

BR48a. BRÜHL, J. W., *Ann.* **200**, 182 (1879).

BR49. BRUYLANTS, P., *Bull. soc. chim. Belg.* **33**, 467–478 (1924).

BR50. BRUYLANTS, P., *Bull. sci. acad. roy. Belg.* **11**, 261–280 (1925).

BU1. BUCKINGHAM, A. D., *Proc. Roy. Soc.* (*London*) **A238**, 235–244 (1956).

BU2. BUCKLEY, D., DUNSTAN, S., and HENBEST, H. B., *J. Chem. Soc.* **1957**, 4880–4891.

BU2a. BUCKLEY, D., DUNSTAN, S., and HENBEST, H. B., *J. Chem. Soc.* **1957**, 4901–4905.

BU3. BUCKLEY, J., and MARYOTT, A. A., *J. Research Natl. Bur. Standards* **53**, 229–244 (1954).

BU4.   BULL, H. B., *Biochemistry of the Lipids*. John Wiley and Sons, Inc., New York, N.Y. (1937).

BU5.   BURG, A. B., *J. Am. Chem. Soc.* **65**, 1629–1635 (1943).

BU5a.   BURG, A. B., and GREEN, A. A., *J. Am. Chem. Soc.* **65**, 1838–1841 (1943).

BU6.   BURG, A. B., and RANDOLPH, C. L., Jr., *J. Am. Chem. Soc.* **71**, 3451–3455 (1949).

BU7.   BURG, A. B., and SCHLESINGER, H. I., *J. Am. Chem. Soc.* **59**, 780–787 (1937).

BU7a.   BURG, A. B., and WAGNER, R. I., *J. Am. Chem. Soc.* **76**, 3307–3310 (1954).

BU8.   BURNETT, W. B., JENKINS, R. L., PEET, C. H., DREGER, E. E., and ADAMS, R., *J. Am. Chem. Soc.* **59**, 2248–2252 (1937).

BU9.   BUSCH, M., and FLEISCHMANN, M., *Ber.* **43**, 2553–2556 (1910).

BU10.   BUTLER, G. B., *J. Am. Chem. Soc.* **78**, 482–484 (1956).

BU11.   BUTLER, G. B., and ANGELO, R. J., *J. Am. Chem. Soc.* **77**, 1767–1769 (1955).

BU12.   BUTLER, G. B., and ANGELO, R. J., *J. Am. Chem. Soc.* **78**, 4797–4800 (1956).

BU13.   BUTLER, G. B., and BENJAMIN, B. M., *J. Chem. Educ.* **28**, 191 (1951).

BU14.   BUTLER, G. B., and BUNCH, R. L., *J. Am. Chem. Soc.* **71**, 3120–3122 (1949).

BU15.   BUTLER, G. B., and BUNCH, R. L., *J. Am. Chem. Soc.* **74**, 3453 (1952).

BU16.   BUTLER, G. B., and GOETTE, R. L., *J. Am. Chem. Soc.* **76**, 2418–2421 (1954).

BU17.   BUTLER, G. B., and JOHNSON, R. A., *J. Am. Chem. Soc.* **76**, 713–714 (1954).

C

CA1.   CADOGAN, J. I. G., *J. Chem. Soc.* **1957**, 1079–1082.

CA2.   CADOGAN, J. I. G., *J. Chem. Soc.* **1957**, 4154–4155.

CA3.   CAHOURS, A., and HOFMANN, A. W., *Ann.* **102**, 285–311 (1857).

CA4.   CALDERBANK, A., and GHOSH, R., *J. Chem. Soc.* **1960**, 637–642.

CA5.   CALDWELL, A. G., and JONES, E. R. H., *J. Chem. Soc.* **1946**, 597–599.

CA6.   CAMPBELL, B. K., and CAMPBELL, K. C., *J. Am. Chem. Soc.* **60**, 1372–1376 (1938).

CA7.   CAMPBELL, K. N., FATORA, F. C., Jr., and CAMPBELL, B. K., *J. Org. Chem.* **17**, 1141–1148 (1952).

CA8.   CAPPELAERE, M., JEANNIN, S., and MONTEL, G., *Ann. Univ. Ferrara, Sez. 5*, Suppl. No. 3, 359–389 (1960).

CA9.   CAREY, F. A., EDWARDS, D., LEWIS, J. J., and STENLAKE, J. B., *J. Pharm. & Pharmacol.* **11**, Suppl. 70T–86T (1959).

CA10.   CARIGNAN, C. J., and KRAUS, C. A., *J. Am. Chem. Soc.* **71**, 2983–2987 (1949).

CA10a. CARNELL, P. J. H., and FOWLES, G. W. A., *J. Chem. Soc.* **1959**, 4113–4118 (1959).

CA11.   CAROTHERS, W. H. (to E. I. du Pont de Nemours & Co.), U.S. Patent 2,110,199 (Mar. 8, 1938).

CA11a. CAROTHERS, W. H., and BERCHET, G. J. (to E. I. du Pont de Nemours & Co.), U.S. Patent 2,073,363 (Mar. 9, 1932), 2,136,177 (Nov. 8, 1937).

CA12. CASPE, S. *J. Am. Chem. Soc.* **54,** 4457 (1932).

CA13. CASPE, S., U.S. Patent 1,993,542 (Mar. 5, 1935).

CA14. CASPE, S., *Am. J. Pharm.* **114,** 56–57 (1942).

CA15. CASTELL, C. H., *J. Fisheries Research Board Can.* **7,** 421–429 (1949).

CA16. CASTELL, C. H., *Food in Canada* **9,** No. 4, 44–45 (1949).

CA17. CASTELL, C. H., and MACCALLUM, W. A., *Fisheries Research Board Can. Progr. Repts. Atlantic Coast Stas.* **No. 55,** 17–23 (1953).

CA18. CASTELL, C. H., and SNOW, J. M., *J. Fisheries Research Board Can.* **8,** 195–206 (1951).

CA19. CAVALLITO, C. J., GRAY, A. P., and SPINNER, E. E., *J. Am. Chem. Soc.* **76,** 1862–1866 (1954).

CE1. CERF DE MAUNY, H., *Compt. rend.* **195,** 1084–1086 (1932); *Bull. soc. chim.* [5] **4,** 1451–1460 (1937).

CE1a. CELANESE CORP. OF AMERICA, British Patent 811,177 (Apr. 2, 1959).

CH1. CHAUVELIER, J., and GAUDEMAR, M., *Compt. rend.* **232,** 167–169 (1951).

CH1a. CHATT, J., and GAMLEN, G. A., *J. Chem. Soc.* **1956,** 2371–2378.

CH2. CHEM. FABR. WEILER-TER MEER, and FROELICH, E., German Patent 376,013 (Aug. 22, 1920).

CH3. CHEMICAL SOCIETY (London), *Tables of Interatomic Distances and Configuration in Molecules and Ions*, (Special Publication **No. 11,** 1958), p. M156.

CH4. CHEMODANOVA, L. S., *Gasovaya Khromatografiya, Trudy 1-oi (Pervoi) Vsesoyuz. Konf., Akad. Nauk S.S.S.R., Moscow 1959*, 299–301.

CH5. CHIANCONE, F. M., *Boll. soc. ital. biol. sper.* **14,** 560–561 (1939).

CH6. CHIANCONE, F. M., *Boll. soc. ital. biol. sper.* **15,** 579–580 (1940).

CH6a. CHITWOOD, H. C., and FREURE, B. T. (to Union Carbide & Carbon Corp.), U.S. Patent 2,795,600 (June 11, 1957).

CH6b. CHODKIEWICZ, W., *Ann chim.* (Paris) [13] **2,** 819–869 (1957).

CH7. CHOPEY, N. P., *Chem. Eng.* **68,** No. 17, 100–102 (1961).

CH8. CHREITZBERG, A. M., and VOSBURGH, W. C., *J. Electrochem. Soc.* **104,** 1–5 (1957).

CH9. CHRIST, B. (to I.G. Farbenindustrie A.-G.), German Patent 673,017 (Mar. 14, 1939); British Patent 491,036 (Aug. 25, 1938).

CH10. CHRIST, B. (to I.G. Farbenindustrie A.-G.), German Patent 671,839 (Feb. 14, 1939).

CI1. CIBA LTD., British Patent 717,476 (Oct. 27, 1954).

CI2. CIBA LTD., British Patent 711,654 (July 7, 1954).

CL1. CLARKE, H. T., *J. Chem. Soc.* **101,** 1788–1809 (1912).

CL1a. CLARKE, H. T., *J. Chem. Soc.* **99,** 1927–1937 (1911).

CL2. CLARKE, H. T., *J. Chem. Soc.* **103,** 1689–1704 (1913).

CL3. CLARKE, H. T., GILLESPIE, H. B., and WEISSHAUS, S. Z., *J. Am. Chem. Soc.* **55,** 4571–4587 (1933).

CL4. CLARKE, L., *Am. Chem. J.* **33,** 496–500 (1905).

CL5. CLASS, J. E. (to Hercules Powder Co.), U.S. Patent 2,944,082 (July 5, 1960).

CL6. CLASS, J. B., ASTON, J. G., and OAKWOOD, T. S., *J. Am. Chem. Soc.* **75,** 2937–2939 (1953).

CL7. CLEMO, G. R., and ROPER, N., *J. Chem. Soc.* **1946,** 891–892.

CL7a. CLINTON, R. O., and LASKOWSKI, S. C., *J. Am. Chem. Soc.* **74,** 2226–2237 (1952).

CL8. CLOSSON, R. D., KOLKA, A. J., and LIGETT, W. B. (to Ethyl Corp.), U.S. Patent 2,750,417 (June 12, 1956).

CO1. COAN, S. B., and PAPA, D., *J. Am. Chem. Soc.* **77,** 2402–2404 (1955).

CO1a. COATES, G. E., and GLOCKLING, F., *J. Chem. Soc.* **1954,** 2526–2529.

CO1b. COATES, G. E., and HAYTER, R. G., *J. Chem. Soc.* **1953,** 2519–2524.

CO1c. COATES, G. E., and HUCK, N. D., *J. Chem. Soc.* **1952,** 4501–4511.

CO1d. COATES, G. E., and WHITCOMBE, R. A., *J. Chem. Soc.* **1956,** 3351–3354.

CO2. COFFMAN, D., *J. Am. Chem. Soc.* **57,** 1978–1980 (1935).

CO3. COHEN, G. N., NISMAN, B., and RAYMOND, M., *Compt. rend.* **225,** 647–650 (1947).

CO4. COLEMAN, G. H., *J. Am. Chem. Soc.* **55,** 3001–3005 (1933).

CO5. COLLANDER, R., *Acta. Chem. Scand.* **4,** 1085–1098 (1950).

CO6. COLLANDER, R., *Acta. Chem. Scand.* **3,** 717–747 (1949).

CO7. COLLENGBERG, O., *Z. anorg. Chem.* **102,** 275 (1918).

CO8. COLLIE, N., and SCHRYVER, S. B., *J. Chem. Soc.* **57,** 767–782 (1890).

CO9. COLLIN, J., *Bull. soc. roy. sci. Liège* **21,** 446–456 (1952).

CO9a. COLLIN, J., *Bull. soc. chim. Belges* **62,** 411–427 (1953).

CO9b. COLLIN, J., *Bull. soc. chim. Belges* **63,** 500–524 (1954).

CO10. COLLIN, J., *Can. J. Chem.* **37,** 1053–1055 (1959).

CO11. COLLOCOTT, T. C., and THORNE, J. O., Eds., *The Macmillan World Gazetteer and Geographical Dictionary.* The Macmillan Co., New York, N.Y. (1955), p. 622.

CO12. COLUCCI, G., *Ginecologia* **12,** 323–331 (1946).

CO13. COMANDUCCI, E., and ARENA, M., *Giorn. farm. chim.* **56,** 385–388 (1907).

CO13a. COMYNS, A. E., *J. Chem. Soc.* **1955,** 1557–1562.

CO14. CONSORTIUM DE PRODUITS CHIMIQUES ET DE SYNTHÈSE, French Patent 1,085,934 (Feb., 1955).

CO15. CONWAY, E. J., and BYRNE, A., *Biochem. J.* **27,** 419–429, 430–434 (1933).

CO16. COOK, A. S., *Can. Chem. Met.* **15,** 22–23 (1931).

CO16a. COPE, A.C., *Org. Reactions* **11,** 317–493 (1960).

CO17. COPE, A. C., and LEE, R. H., *J. Am. Chem. Soc.* **79,** 964–965 (1957).

CO18. COPE, A. C., and BUMGARDNER, C. L., *J. Am. Chem. Soc.* **79,** 960–964 (1957).

CO19. COPE, A., and CIGANEK, E., *Org. Syntheses* **39,** 20 (1959).

CO20. COPE, A. C., ENGELBERT, C., FLECKENSTEIN, L. J., and MEISINGER, M. A. P., *J. Am. Chem. Soc.* **82,** 4651–4655 (1960).

CO21. COPE, A. C., FOSTER, T., and TOWLE, P. H., *J. Am. Chem. Soc.* **71,** 3929–3935 (1949).

CO22. COPE, A. C., and LEBEL, N. A., *J. Am. Chem. Soc.* **82,** 4656–4662 (1960).

CO23. COPE, A. C., LEBEL, N. A., LEE, H. H., and MOORE, W. R., *J. Am. Chem. Soc.* **79,** 4720–4729 (1957).

CO24. COPE, A. C., and ROSS, D. L., *J. Am. Chem. Soc.* **83**, 3854–3858 (1961).

CO25. COPE, A. C., and TOWLE, P. H., *J. Am. Chem. Soc.* **71**, 3423–3428 (1949).

CO26. COPENHAVER, J. W., and BIGELOW, M. H., *Acetylene and Carbon Monoxide Chemistry*. Reinhold Publishing Co., New York, N.Y. (1949), pp. 116–117.

CO27. COPP, J. L., *Trans. Faraday Soc.* **51**, 1056–1061 (1955).

CO27a. COPP, J. L., and EVERETT, D. H., *Discussions Faraday Soc.* **1953**, No. 15, 174–188.

CO27b. COPP, J. L., and FINDLAY, T. J. V., *Trans. Faraday Soc.* **56**, 13–22 (1960).

CO28. COSTELLO, J. M., and BOWDEN, S. T., *Rec. trav. chim.* **78**, 391–403 (1959).

CO29. COTTE, J., and KAHANE, E., *Bull. soc. chim. France* **1950**, 639–648.

CO30. COTTE, J., and KAHANE, E., *Bull. soc. chim. France* **1953**, 151–157.

CO31. COUNSELL, J. F., EVERETT, D. H., and MUNN, R. J., *Pure Appl. Chem.* **2**, 335–338 (1961).

CO31a. COVERT, L. W. (to Rohm and Haas Co.) U.S. Patent 2,160,058 (May 30, 1938).

CO32. COWLEY, E. G., *J. Chem. Soc.* **1952**, 3557–3570.

CR1. CRANE, R. E., Jr., *Anal. Chem.* **26**, 1794–1797 (1956).

CR1a. CROMWELL, B. T., *Biochem. J.* **46**, 578–581 (1950).

CR2. CROMWELL, N. H., and HASSNER, A., *J. Am. Chem. Soc.* **77**, 1568–1572 (1955).

CR3. CROXALL, W. J., HOOK, J. O. VAN, SCHNEIDER, H. J., *J. Am. Chem. Soc.* **73**, 2713–2716 (1951).

CU0. CULLIS, C. F., and WADDINGTON, D. J., *Symposium on Combustion, Fifth Symposium, Pittsburgh*, **1954**, 545–553 (1955).

CU1. CUNDIFF, R. H., and RIDDICK, J. A., *Anal. Chem.* **24**, 910–911 (1952).

CU2. CUTLER, R. A., and SURREY, A., *J. Am. Chem. Soc.* **72**, 3394–3395 (1950).

D

DA1. DADIEU, A., and KOHLRAUSCH, K. W. F., *Sitzber. Akad. Wiss. Wien, Abt. IIa* **139**, 459–472 (1930); *Monatsh.* **57**, 225–240 (1931).

DA2. DAEN, J., and MARCUS, R. A., *J. Chem. Phys.* **26**, 162–168 (1957).

DA3. DAFERT, *Monatsh.* **1883**, 496

DA4. DAMIENS, R., *Ann. chim.* **6**, 835–879 (1951).

DA5. DAMSGAARD-SORENSEN, P., and UNMACK, A., *Z. physik. Chem.*, **A172**, 389 (1935).

DA6. DANFORTH, J. D. (to Universal Oil Products), U.S. Patent 2,518,528 (Aug. 15, 1950).

DA7. DANNLEY, R. L., LUKIN, M., and SHAPIRO, J., *J. Org. Chem.* **20**, 92–94 (1955).

DA7a. DARWENT, B. DeB., and PHIBBS, M. K., *J. Chem. Phys.* **22**, 110–113 (1955).

DA8. DASHKEVICH, B. N., *J. Gen. Chem.* (*U.S.S.R.*) **18**, 205–208 (1938).

DA9. DATA, J. B., *Ph.D. Thesis*, Univ. of Michigan, 1941.

DA10. DATTA, R. L., and CHATTERJEE, N. R., *J. Chem. Soc.* **115**, 1006–1010 (1919).

DA11. DATTA, R. L., and CHOUDHURY, J. K., *J. Am. Chem. Soc.* **38**, 1079–1086 (1916).

DA12. DATTA, R. L., and SEN, J. N., *J. Am. Chem. Soc.* **39**, 750–759 (1917).

DA12a. DAVIDSON, N., and BROWN, H. C., *J. Am. Chem. Soc.* **64**, 316–324 (1942).

DA13. DAVIS, P., REYNOLDS, P. W., COATS, R. R., and TAYLOR, A. W. C., U.S. Patent 2,609,394 (Sept. 2, 1952); British Patent 679,713 (Sept. 24, 1952).

DA14. DAVIS, T. L., and ELDERFIELD, R. C., *J. Am. Chem. Soc.* **54**, 1499–1503 (1932).

DA14a. DAVIS, M. M., and HETZER, H. B., *J. Research Natl. Bur. Standards* **48**, 381–391 (1952); Research Paper #2326.

DA15. DAVIS, M. M., and HETZER, H. B., *J. Research Natl. Bur. Standards* **54**, 309–320 (1955).

DA16. DAVIS, M. M., and HETZER, H. B., *J. Am. Chem. Soc.* **76**, 4247–4260 (1954).

DA17. DAY, H. O., and FELSING, W. A., *J. Am. Chem. Soc.* **72**, 1698–1699 (1950).

DE1. DeBENNEVILLE, P. L. (to Rohm and Haas Co.) U.S. Patent 2,578,787 (Dec. 18, 1951).

DE2. DeBENNEVILLE, P. L., and MACARTNEY, J. H., *J. Am. Chem. Soc.* **72**, 3073–3075 (1950).

DE3. DeCARLI, F., and GALLIMBERTI, L., *Boll. sci. fac. chim. ind. Univ. Bologna* **1940**, 62–70.

DE3a. DECARVALHO, H. G., *Anais assoc. quím. Brasil* **3**, 88–94 (1944).

DE4. DE FILIPPI, Z. *physiol. Chem.* **49**, 433–444 (1906).

DE5. DEHN, W. M., *J. Am. Chem. Soc.* **34**, 288 (1912).

DE6. DEHN, W. M., *J. Am. Chem. Soc.* **34**, 1407 (1912).

DE6a. DEĬCHMEĬSTER, M. V., and LEVKOEV, I. I., *Zhur. Obshcheĭ Khim.* **23**, 1529–1535 (1953).

DE6b. DEĬCHMEĬSTER, M. V., SYTNIK, Z. P., and LIFSHITS, E. B., *Zhur. Obshcheĭ Khim.* **22**, 166–175 (1952).

DE7. DE LA HUERGA, J., and POPPER, H., *J. Clin. Invest.* **31**, 598–603 (1952).

DE8. DELÈPINE, M., *Ann. chim.* **8**, 439–465 (1896).

DE9. DEL RE, G., *J. Chem. Soc.* **1958**, 4031–4040.

DE9a. DENHAM, W. S., and KNAPP, L. F., *J. Chem. Soc.* **117**, 236–247 (1920).

DE10. DEPTULA, C., *Chem. Anal.* (*Warsaw*) **6**, 91–94 (1961).

DE11. DER HORST, H. D. V., German (East) Patent 13,031 (Apr. 8, 1957); German (East) Patent 12,438 (Dec. 6, 1956).

DE12. DER HORST, H. D. V., *Chem. Tech.* (*Berlin*) **9**, 478–479 (1957).

DE13. DeWIJN, H. W., *Physica* **25**, 1222–1224 (1959).

DI1. DIHLMANN, W., *Wiss. Z. Friedrich-Schiller-Univ. Jena, Math.-Naturwiss. Reihe* **1953/1954**, 369–373.

DI2. DiPORTO, A., *Policlinico* (*Rome*), *Sez. med.* **57**, 359–368 (1950).

DI3. DiPORTO, A., and MAYMORE, S., *Policlinico* (*Rome*), *Sez. med.* **60**, 59–68 (1953).

DO1.   DOBBIN, L., and MASSON, O., *J. Chem. Soc.* **49**, 846–857 (1886).

DO1a.   DOERING, W. E., and HOFFMANN, A. K., *J. Am. Chem. Soc.* **77**, 521–526 (1955).

DO2.   DOERNER, M. P. (to Dow Chemical Co.), U.S. Patent 2,901,886 (Sept., 1959).

DO3.   DOEUVRE, J., and POIZAT, J., *Compt. rend.* **224**, 286–288 (1947).

DO3a.   DONFOR, A., KENDRICK, W., and BRANSON, H., *Phys. Rev.* **79**, 129.

DO3b.   DORNOW, A., GHERT, H. H., *Z. anorg. u. allgem. Chem.* **294**, 81–91 (1958).

DO4.   DORREL, G. W., *J. Chem. Soc.* **127**, 2399–2407 (1925).

DO5.   DOSS, R. C., and BOST, H. W. (to Phillips Petroleum Co.), U.S. Patent 2,881,217 (Apr. 7, 1959).

DO6.   DOSS, R. C., and SCHNITZER, A. M., (to Phillips Petroleum Co.), U.S. Patent 2,800,509 (July 23, 1957).

DR1.   DREISBACH, R. R., *Physical Properties of Chemical Compounds-II* (Advances in Chemistry Series No. 22). American Chemical Society, Washington, D. C. (1959).

DR2.   DREYFUS, H., British Patents 398,502-3-4 (Sept. 11, 1933).

DU1.   DUBOIS, J. E., and LACAZE, P. C., *Compt. rend.* **252**, 748–750 (1961).

DU2.   DUDLEY, H. W., and ROSENHEIM, O., *Biochem. J.* **19**, 1032–1033 (1925).

DU3.   DUDLEY, H. W., ROSENHEIM, O., and STARLING, W. W., *Biochem. J.* **20**, 1082–1094 (1926).

DU4.   DULOU, R., ELKIK, E., and VEILLARD, A., *Bull. soc. chim. France* **1960**, 967–971.

DU5.   DUNSTAN, W. R., and GOULDING, E., *J. Chem. Soc.* **75**, 792–807 (1899).

DU6.   DUNSTAN, W. R., and GOULDING, E., *J. Chem. Soc.* **75**, 1004–1011 (1899).

DU7.   DURAND, A., *Bull. soc. chim. France* **17**, 405–408 (1897).

DU8.   DUVILLIER, E., and BUISINE, A., *Ann. chim.* **23**, 289–356 (1881).

DY1.   DYER, W. J., *Fisheries Research Board Can. Progr. Repts. Atlantic Coast Stas.* No. 34, 4–5 (1943).

DY2.   DYER, W. J., *J. Assoc. Offic. Agr. Chemists* **42**, 292–294 (1959); *J. Fisheries Research Board Can.* **6**, 351–358 (1945).

DY3.   DYER, W. J., *J. Fisheries Research Board Can.* **7**, 461–470 (1949).

DY4.   DYER, W. J., *J. Fisheries Research Board Can.* **7**, 576–579 (1950).

DY5.   DYER, W. J., DYER, F. E., and SNOW, J. M., *J. Fisheries Research Board Can.* **8**, 309–313 (1952).

DY6.   DYER, W. J., *J. Fisheries Research Board Can.* **8**, 314–324 (1952).

DY7.   DYER, W. J., DYER, F. E., and SNOW, M., *J. Fisheries Research Board Can.* **6**, 403–413 (1946).

DY8.   DYER, F. E., and WOOD, A. J., *J. Fisheries Research Board Can.* **7**, 17–21.

DZ1.   DZBANOVSKIĬ, N. A., MAROCHKO, S. V., and KOST, A. N., *Sbornik Stateĭ Obshcheĭ Khim. Akad. Nauk S.S.S.R.* **1**, 607–609 (1953).

E

EA1.   EASTMAN ORGANIC CHEMICALS, CATALOG, (Distillation Products Industries, Rochester 3, N.Y.) 43rd ed., 1962.

EB1. EBSWORTH, E. A. V., and SHEPPARD, N., *J. Inorg. & Nuclear Chem.* **9**, 95–96 (1959).

EC1. ECKSTEIN, M., and KOCWA, A., *Dissertationes Pharm.* **8**, 1–8 (1956).

ED1. EDDY, B. P., *Nature* **171**, 573–574 (1953).

ED2. EDWARDS, D., LEWIS, J. J., MCPHAIL, D. E., MUIR, T. C., and STENLAKE, J. B., *J. Pharm. & Pharmacol.* **12**, Suppl. 137T–152T (1960).

ED3. EDWARDS, D., LEWIS, J. J., STENLAKE, J. B., and ZOHA, M. S., *J. Pharm. & Pharmacol.* **10**, Suppl. 106T–121T (1958).

EG1. EGLY, R. S., and SMITH, E. F., *Chem. Eng. Progress* **44**, No. 5, *Trans. Am. Inst. Chem. Engrs.*, 387–398 (1948).

EH1. EHRENBERG, A., *J. prakt. Chem.* **36**, 117–131 (1887).

EK1. EKWALL, P., *Acta Acad. Aboensis, Mathes. Phys.* **8**, No. 2, 133 pp. (1933).

EL1. ELDERFIELD, R. C., KREYSA, F. J., and DUNN, J. H., *J. Am. Chem. Soc.* **70**, 40–44 (1948).

EL2. ELDERFIELD, R. C., KREYSA, F. J., DUNN, J., and HUMPHREYS, D. D., *J. Am. Chem. Soc.* **69**, 186–187 (1947).

EL3. ELEY, D. D., and WATTS, H., *J. Chem. Soc.* **1952**, 1914–1918.

EL3a. ELEY, D. D., and WATTS, H., *J. Chem. Soc.* **1954**, 1319–1324.

EL4. ELLIOTT, M. A., and FUOSS, R. M., *J. Am. Chem. Soc.* **61**, 294–299 (1939).

EL5. ELLIS, J. W., *J. Am. Chem. Soc.* **50**, 685–695 (1928).

EL6. ELSEY, H. M., *J. Am. Chem. Soc.* **42**, 2454–2476 (1920).

EM1. EMDE, H., *Arch. Pharm.* **244**, 289 (1906).

EM2. EMDE, H., *Arch. Pharm.* **247**, 376–378 (1909).

EM3. EMDE, H., *Ber.* **42**, 2590–2594 (1909).

EM4. EMDE, H., *Helv. Chim. Acta* **15**, 1330–1336 (1932).

EM5. EMDE, H., and KULL, H., *Arch. Pharm.* **272**, 469–481 (1934).

EM6. EMDE, H., and SCHELLBACH, H., *Arch. Pharm.* **249**, 111–117, (1911).

EM7. EMDE, H., and SCHELLBACH, H., *Arch. Pharm.* **249**, 118–122 (1911).

EM8. EMERSON, W. S., U.S. Patents 2,388,606-7-8 (Nov. 6, 1945).

EM8a. EMERSON, W. S., U.S. Patent 2,380,420 (July 31, 1945).

EM9. EMERSON, W. S., U.S. Patent 2,414,031 (Jan. 4, 1947).

EM10. EMERSON, W. S., *Org. Reactions* **4**, 174–255 (1948).

EM11. EMERSON, W. S., and URANECK, C. A., *J. Am. Chem. Soc.* **63**, 749–751 (1941).

EM12. EMMERT, B., *Ber.* **42**, 1509 (1909).

EM13. EMMONS, W. D., MCCALLUM, K. S., and FREEMAN, J. P., *J. Org. Chem.* **19**, 1472–1476 (1954).

EN1. ENGELHARDT, V. A. (to E. I. du Pont de Nemours & Co.), U.S. Patent 2,647,147 (July 28, 1953).

EN2. ENGELHARDT, V. A., *J. Am. Chem. Soc.* **78**, 107–109 (1956).

EP1. EPSZTEIN, R., and MARSZAK, I., *Mém. serv. chim. état (Paris)* **38**, 165–170 (1953).

EP2. EPSZTEIN, R., OLOMUCKI, M., and MARSZAK, I., *Bull. soc. chim. France* **1953**, 952–957.

ER1. ERDMANN, C. C., *J. Biol. Chem.* **8**, 57–60 (1910).

ER2. ERICKSON, J. G. (to General Mills Inc.), U.S. Patent 2,776,314 (Jan. 1, 1957).

ER3.   ERIKSEN, S. P., TUCK, L. D., and ONETO, J. F., *J. Org. Chem.* **25,** 849–850 (1960).

ES1.   ESCHWEILER, W., German Patent 80,520 (Dec. 17, 1893).

ES2.   ESCHWEILER, W., *Ber.* **38,** 880–882 (1905).

EU1.   EULER, W., *J. prakt. Chem.* **57,** 131–159 (1898). *Über eine Synthese und die Konstitution des Isoprens,* Habilitationsschrift, University of Leipzig, Oct. 14, 1897.

EV1.   EVANS, R. F., *Chem. & Ind. (London)* **1959,** 729–730.

EV2.   EVERETT, D. H., and WYNNE-JONES, W. F. K., *Proc. Roy. Soc. (London)* **A177,** 499–516 (1941).

EY1.   EYKMAN, J. F., *Ber.* **25,** 3069–3079 (1892).

F

FA1.   FANCHER, O. E. (to Miles Laboratories, Inc.), British Patent 791,745 (Mar. 12, 1958).

FA1a. FAIRFULL, A. E. S., and PEAK, D. A., *J. Chem. Soc.* **1955,** 796–802.

FA2.   FARBENFABRIKEN, BAYER A.-G., British Patent 686,500 (Jan. 28, 1953).

FA2a. FARBENFABRIKEN BAYER A.-G., British Patent 822,229 (Oct. 21, 1959).

FA3.   I.G. FARBENINDUSTRIE A.-G., British. Patent 334,579 (1928).

FA4.   I.G. FARBENINDUSTRIE, A.-G., French Patent 780,028 (April 17, 1935).

FA5.   I.G. FARBENINDUSTRIE, A.-G., French Patent 802,105 (August 28, 1936).

FA6.   I.G. FARBENINDUSTRIE, A.-G., French Patent 815,312 (July 9, 1937); British Patent 487,337 (June 20, 1938).

FA7.   I.G. FARBENINDUSTRIE, A.-G., British Patent 339,962 (Jan. 15, 1931).

FA8.   I.G. FARBENINDUSTRIE, A.-G., British Patent 371,822 (May 26, 1932).

FA9.   I.G. FARBENINDUSTRIE, A.-G., British Patent 435,404 (Sept. 19, 1935).

FA10. I.G. FARBENINDUSTRIE, A.-G., French Patent 774,853 (Dec. 15, 1934).

FA11. I.G. FARBENINDUSTRIE, A.-G., British Patent 437,530 (Oct. 31, 1935).

FA12. I.G. FARBENINDUSTRIE, A.-G., German Patent 681,850 (1933).

FE1.   FEDOSEEV, V. M., KOVALENKO, S. P., SILAEV, A. B., and NESMEYANOV, A. N., *Zhur. Obshcheĭ Khim.* **29,** 1703–1707 (1959); *J. Gen. Chem. (U.S.S.R.)* **29,** 1680–1684 (1959) (Eng. Trans.).

FE2.   FEGLEY, M. F., BORTNICK, N. M., and McKEEVER, C. H., *J. Am. Chem. Soc.* **79,** 4140–4144 (1957).

FE3.   FEGLEY, M. F., BORTNICK, N. M., and McKEEVER, C. H., *J. Am. Chem. Soc.* **79,** 4144–4146 (1957).

FE4.   FEGLEY, M. F., BORTNICK, N. M., McKEEVER, C. H., and FARNUM, F. B., *J. Am. Chem. Soc.* **79,** 4734–4735 (1957).

FE5.   FEGLEY, M. F., CLARE, M., and BORTNICK, N. M. (to Rohm and Haas Co.) U.S. Patent 2,752,343 (June 26, 1956); British Patent 742,342 (Dec. 21, 1955).

FE6.   FEGLEY, M. F., CLARE, M., and BORTNICK, N. M. (to Rohm and Haas Co.) U.S. Patent 2,827,488 (Mar. 18, 1958).

FE7.   FELSING, W. A., and BALL, E., *J. Am. Chem. Soc.* **63,** 2525 (1941).

FE7a. FELSING, W. A., and PHILLIPS, B. A., *J. Am. Chem. Soc.* **58,** 1973–1975 (1936).

FE8.   FELSING, W. A., and JESSEN, F. W., *J. Am. Chem. Soc.* **55,** 4418–4422 (1933).

FE8a. FERGUSSON, J. E., GRANT, D. K., HICKFORD, R. H., and WILKINS, C. J., *J. Chem. Soc.* **1959**, 99–103.

FE9. FERNANDEZ DEL RIEGO, A., and RODRIQUEZ DE LAS HERAS, A., *Bol. inst. español. oceanog.* **65**, 1–9 (1954).

FI1. FICHTER, F., and SPENGEL, A., *Z. anorg. Chem.* **82**, 201 (1913).

FI2. FICINI, J., and NORMANT, H., *Bull. soc. chim. France* **1957**, 1454–1458.

FI3. FICINI, J., and NORMANT, H., *Compt. rend.* **247**, 1627–1628 (1958).

FI4. FIEGER, E. A., and FRILOUX, J. J., *Food Technol.* **8**, 35–37 (1954).

FI5. FIESER, L. F., and FIESER, M., *Organic Chemistry*. D. C. Heath and Co., Boston, Mass. (1950), 2nd ed., p. 233.

FI6. FIESER, L., and FIESER, M., *Organic Chemistry*, D. C. Heath and Co., Boston, Mass. (1956), 3rd ed., p. 499.

FI7. FINCH, H. D., PETERSON, E. A., and BALLARD, S. A., *J. Am. Chem. Soc.* **74**, 2016–2018 (1952).

FI7a. FINDLAY, T. J. V., *Australian J. Chem.* **14**, 520–526 (1961).

FI7b. FISCHBACK, B. C., and Harris, G. H. (to Dow Chemical Co.), U.S. Patent 2,789,114 (Apr. 16, 1957).

FI7c. FISCHBACK, B. C., and HARRIS, G. H. (to Dow Chemical Co.), U.S. Patent 2,827,483 (Mar. 18, 1958).

FI8. FISCHER, E., *Ber.* Sonderheft, 197–288 (1902).

FI9. FISHER, L. B., *Uspekhi Khim.* **27**, 589–621 (1958).

FL1. FLÜRSCHEIM, B., *J. prakt. Chem.* **68**, 345–356 (1903).

FO1. FOGELBERG, J. M., and WILLIAMS, J. W., *Physik. Z.* **32**, 27–31 (1931).

FO1a. FOLDI, Z., *Acta Chim. Acad. Sci. Hung.* **3**, 501–510 (1953).

FO1b. FOLIN, Z. *physiol. Chem.* **32**, 515 (1901).

FO2. FORMAN, E. A., and HUME, D. M., *J. Phys. Chem.* **63**, 1949–1952 (1959).

FO2a. FOSTER, R., *Chem. & Ind.* (*London*) **1959**, 1492.

FO2b. FOSTER, R., *Chem. & Ind.* (*London*) **1960**, 1354–1355.

FO3. FOURNEAU, E., and BILLETER, J. R., *Bull. soc. chim. France* **6**, 1616–1625 (1939).

FO3a. FOWLES, G. W. A., and PLEASS, C. M., *J. Chem. Soc.* **1957**, 1674–1681.

FO4. FOX, H. H., and WENNER, W., *J. Org. Chem.* **16**, 225–231 (1951).

FR1. FRANCHIMONT, P. M., *Rec. trav. chim.* **2**, 336–339 (1883).

FR1a. FRANC, J., and WURST, M., *Collection Czechoslov. Chem. Communs.* **25**, 2290–2294 (1960).

FR2. FRANÇOIS, H., and HOARAU, J., *Compt. rend.* **240**, 1220–1221 (1955).

FR3. FRANÇOIS, M., *Compt. rend.* **144**, 567–569 (1907).

FR4. FRANKE, W., and THIELE, W. (to Badische Anilin und Soda-Fabrik, from I.G. Farbenindustrie A.-G., "In Auflösung"), German Patent 844,155 (July 17, 1952).

FR5. FRANKE, W., and THIELE, W. (to Chemische Werke Hüls A.-G.), German Patent 879,990 (June 18, 1953).

FR6. FRÄNKEL, S., and NUSSBAUM, K., *Biochem. Z.* **182**, 424–434 (1927).

FR6a. FRANKLIN, J. L., *J. Chem. Phys.* **22**, 1304–1311 (1954).

FR7. FRANZEN, V., *Chemiker-Ztg.* **82**, 832–834 (1958).

FR7a. FRENCH, F. A., and RASMUSSEN, R. S., *J. Chem. Phys.* **14**, 389–394 (1946).

FR8. FREUND, M., and MICHAELS, H., *Ber.* **30**, 1374–1386 (1897).

FR9. FREUNDLER, P., and JUILLARD, *Compt. rend.* **148**, 289–290 (1909).

FR10.   FRIDAU, F., *Ann.* **83**, 1–39 (1852).

FR10a. FRIEND, J. N., and HARGREAVES, W. D., *Phil. Mag.* **35**, 619–631 (1944)

FR11.   FRITZCHE, J., *Ann.* **36**, 84–88 (1840).

FR12.   FRÖMMEL, H., German (East) Patent 12,734 (Feb. 18, 1957).

FR13.   FRÖMMEL, H., German (East) Patent 12,883 (Mar. 8, 1957).

FR14.   FROST, A. E., Jr., CHABEREK, S., Jr., and MARTELL, A. E., *J. Am. Chem. Soc.* **71**, 3842–3843 (1949).

FU1.   FUKS, N. A., and RAPPOPORT, M. A., *Doklady Akad. Nauk S.S.S.R.* **60**, 1219–1221 (1948).

FU2.   FUNK, H., and KOCH, H. J., *Wiss. Z. Martin-Luther-Univ.* **8**, 1025–1032 (1959).

FU3.   FURTH, R., *Compt. rend. réunion ann. avec comm. thermodynam., Union intern. phys. (Paris) 1952*, Changements de phases 59–65.

FY1.   FYFE, W. S., *J. Chem. Soc.* **1955**, 1347–1350.

GA1.   GABEL, Y. C., and KIPRIYANOV, G. I., *Ukrain. Khem. Zhur.* **4**, Tech. Pt., 45–63 (1929).

GA1a.   GALLAIS, F., and VOIGT, D., *Bull. soc. chim. France* **1960**, No. 1, 70–83.

GA2.   GALLAIS, F., and WOLF, R., *Compt. rend.* **242**, 494–496 (1956).

GA3.   GARDNER, C., KERRIGAN, V., ROSE, J. D., and WEEDON, B. C. L., *J. Chem. Soc.* **1949**, 780–782.

GA4.   GARDNER, C., KERRIGAN, V., ROSE, J. D., and WEEDON, B. C. L., *J. Chem. Soc.* **1949**, 789–792.

GA5.   GARNER, W. E., and TYRER, D., *J. Chem. Soc.* **109**, 174–175 (1916).

GA5a.   GARVIN, D., and KISTIAKOWSKY, G. B., *J. Chem. Phys.* **20**, 105–113 (1952).

GA6.   GASSON, E. J., GRAHAM, A. R., MILLIDGE, A. F., ROBSON, I. K. M., WEBSTER, W., WILD, A. M., and YOUNG, D. P., *J. Chem. Soc.* **21**, 70–79 (1954).

GA6a.   GAUDEMAR, M., *Ann. chim. (Paris)* (13) **1**, 161–213 (1956).

GA7.   GAUDION, G., *Ann. chim.* **25**, 125–136 (1912).

GA8.   GAUTIER, J. A., RENAULT, J., and LEROI, E., *Bull. soc. chim. France* **1955**, 634–636.

GA9.   GAUTIER, J. A., RENAULT, J., and RABIANT, J., *Bull. soc. chim. France* **1957**, 1014–1019.

GE1.   GEIGY, J. R., A.-G., British Patent 832,078 (Apr. 6, 1960).

GE2.   GERICHTEN, E. VON, and SCHRÖTTER, R., *Ber.* **15**, 1484–1488 (1882).

GE3.   GERO, A., *J. Am. Chem. Soc.* **76**, 5158–5159 (1954).

GE4.   GESSNER, O., *Med. Monatsschr.* **3**, 825–828 (1949).

GE5.   GEUTHER, A., *Ann.* **240**, 66–85 (1887).

GH1.   GHOSH, P. N., and CHATTERJEE, T. P., *Phys. Rev.* **37**, 427–429 (1931).

GH2.   GHOSH, P. N., and CHATTERJEE, T. P., *Phys. Rev.* **37**, 427–429 (1931).

GI0.   GIBBS, J. H., *J. Phys. Chem.* **59**, 644–649 (1955).

GI1.   GIBSON, D. T., and MACBETH, A. K., *J. Chem. Soc.* **119**, 438–442 (1921).

GI2.   GIBSON, G. M., HARLEY-MASON, J., LITHERLAND, A., and MANN, F. G., *J. Chem. Soc.* **1942**, 163–175.

GI3.   GIBSON, G. M., and MANN, F. G., *J. Chem. Soc.* **1942**, 175–181.

GI4.   GILMAN, H., and PICKENS, R. M., *J. Am. Chem. Soc.* **47**, 251 (1925).

GI5.   GIRARD, A., and FOURNEAU, E., *Bull. soc. chim. France* **37**, 1669–1673 (1925); *Compt. rend.* **181**, 610–611 (1925).

GI6.   GIVAUDON, O., *Compt. rend.* **248**, 1494–1497 (1959).

GL1.   GLACET, C., and GAUMETON, A., *Bull. soc. chim. France* **1956**, 1425–1429; *Compt. rend. congr. sci. savantes Paris et dépts., Sect. sci., 80ᵉ Congr. Toulouse,* **1955**, 89–93.

GL2.   GLADSTONE, J. H., *J. Chem. Soc.* **1884**, 241–259.

GL3.   GLADSTONE, J. H., *J. Chem. Soc.* **1891**, 290–301.

GO1.   GOL'DFARB, YA. L., and IBRAGIMOVA, M. B., *Doklady Akad. Nauk S.S.S.R.* **106**, 469–472 (1956).

GO2.   GOODSON, L. H., and CHRISTOPHER, H., *J. Am. Chem. Soc.* **72**, 358–363 (1950).

GO3.   GORDON, K. F., *Ind. Eng. Chem.* **45**, 1813–1815 (1953).

GO4.   GORDY, W., *J. Chem. Phys.* **7**, 93–99 (1939).

GO5.   GOULD, C. W., and GROSS, S. T., *Anal. Chem.* **25**, 749–751 (1953).

GO6.   GOUY, *Ann. chim.* **9**, 93–112 (1906).

GO7.   GOVAERT, F., CAZIER, J., *Natuurw. Tijdschr. (Ghent)* **23**, 149 (1942).

GO8.   GOVE, J. L., BAUM, H., and STANLEY, E. L., *Anal. Chem.* **23**, 721–724 (1951).

GO9.   GOWENLOCK, B. G., JONES, P. P., and MAJER, J. R., *Trans. Faraday Soc.* **57**, 23–27 (1961).

GR1.   GRAEBE, C., *Geschichte der organischen Chemie.* J. Springer, Berlin (1920), p. 142.

GR2.   GRAIL, G. F. (to Nepera Chemical Co., Inc.), U.S. Patent 2,742,504 (Apr. 17; 1956).

GR3.   GRAIL, G. F., and ANDERSON, F. E. (to Nepera Chemical Co., Inc.), German Patent 1,024,977 (Feb. 27, 1958).

GR4.   GRAIL, G. F., TENENBAUM, L. E., DUCA, C. J., TOLSTOOUHOV, A. V., REINHARD, J. F., ANDERSON, F. E., and SCUDI, J. V., *J. Am. Chem. Soc.* **74**, 1313–1315 (1952).

GR4a. GRAMSTAD, T., and HASZELDINE, R. N., *J. Chem. Soc.* **1957**, 4069–4079.

GR5.   GRANT, J., Ed., *Hackh's Chemical Dictionary.* The Blakiston Co., Philadelphia, Pa. (1944), p. 863.

GR6.   GRAY, A. P., and O'DELL, T. B., *Nature* **181**, 634–635 (1958).

GR7.   GRAYBILL, B. M., RUFF, J. K., and HAWTHORNE, M. F., *J. Am. Chem. Soc.* **83**, 2669–2670 (1961).

GR8.   GRAYMORE, J., *J. Chem. Soc.* **1938**, 1311–1313.

GR9.   GRIGOROVSKII, A. M., and MARGOLINA, R. S., *J. Appl. Chem. (U.S.S.R.)* **18**, 644–666 (1945).

GR10. GROENEWOUD, P., and ROBINSON, R., *J. Chem. Soc.* **127**, 1692–1697 (1934).

GR10a. GROGGINS, P. H., and STIRTON, A. J., *Ind. Eng. Chem.* **29**, 1353–1361 (1937).

GR11. GROSHEINTZ, H., *Bull. soc. chim. France* **31**, 391–393 (1897).

GR11a. GROSSE, A. V., WACKHER, R. C., and LINN, C. B., *J. Phys. Chem.* **44**, 275–296 (1940).

GR12. GROVES, L. G., and SUGDEN, S., *J. Chem. Soc.* **1937**, 1779–1782.

GR13. GROVENSTEIN, E., Jr., GORDON, D. A., and STEVENSON, R. W., *J. Am. Chem. Soc.* **81**, 4842–4850 (1959).

GR14.   GROVENSTEIN, E., Jr., and STEVENSON, R. W., *J. Am. Chem. Soc.* **81**, 4850–4857 (1959).

GR14a.   GROVES, L., and SUGDEN, S., *J. Chem. Soc.* **1937**, 1779–1782.

GR15.   GRUNWALD, E., LOEWENSTEIN, A., and MEIBOOM, S., *J. Chem. Phys.* **27**, 641–642 (1957).

GU1.   GUERMONT, J. P., *Compt. rend.* **237**, 1098–1100 (1953).

GU2.   GUERMONT, J. P., *Mém. serv. chim. état (Paris)* **40**, 147–166 (1955).

GU3.   GUINOT, H., and BELLIER, *Bull. soc. chim. France* **1954**, 727–732.

GU4.   GULEWITSCH, W., and BROUDE, L., *Ber.* **57**, 1645–1653 (1924).

GU5.   GUTBEZAHL, B., and GRUNWALD, E., *J. Am. Chem. Soc.* **75**, 559–565 (1953).

GU6.   GUTBIER, A., and WISSMÜLLER, M., *J. prakt. Chem.* **90**, 491–508 (1914).

GU7.   GUTHRIE, F., *Philosophical Mag.* **18**, 30, 504 (1884).

H

HA1.   HAASE, R., and REHAGE, G., *Z. Elektrochem.* **59**, 994–997 (1955).

HA1a.   HABADA, M., and ŠEHA, Z., *Chem. Zvesti* **10**, 23–30 (1956).

HA2.   HACKETT, N., and LeFÈVRE, R. J. W., *J. Chem. Soc.* **1961**, 2612–2615.

HA2a.   HADNI, A., *J. phys. radium* **15**, 375–376 (1954).

HA3.   HAGER, F. D., and MARVEL, C. S., *J. Am. Chem. Soc.* **48**, 2689–2698 (1926).

HA3a.   HAINEY, R. M., *Science* **119**, 609–610 (1954).

HA4.   HALBAN, H. V., *Z. physik. Chem.* **84**, 129 (1913).

HA5.   HALL, H. K., Jr., *J. Phys. Chem.* **60**, 63–70 (1956).

HA6.   HALL, H. K., Jr., *J. Am. Chem. Soc.* **79**, 5441–5444, 5444–5447 (1957).

HA7.   HALL, N. F., *J. Am. Chem. Soc.*, **52**, 5115–5128 (1930).

HA8.   HALL, N. F., and SPRINKLE, M. R., *J. Am. Chem. Soc.* **54**, 3469–3485 (1932).

HA8a   HALVERSTADT, I. F., HARDIE, W. R., and WILLIAMS, A. R., *J. Am. Chem. Soc.* **81**, 3618–3628 (1959).

HA9.   HAMANN, S. D., and LIM, S. C., *Australian J. Chem.* **7**, 329–334 (1954).

HA9a.   HAMANN, S. D., and STRAUSS, W., *Trans. Faraday Soc.* **51**, 1684–1690 (1955).

HA10.   HANCOCK, E. M., and COPE, A. C., *Org. Syntheses*, Coll. Vol. III, 219 (1955).

HA11.   HANHART, W., and INGOLD, C. K., *J. Chem. Soc.* **1927**, 997–1020.

HA11a.   HANSLEY, V. L. (to E. I. du Pont de Nemours & Co.), U.S. Patent 2,452,460 (Oct. 22, 1948).

HA12.   HANSSON, J., *Svensk Kem. Tidskr.* **60**, 183–189 (1948).

HA13.   HANSSON, J., *Acta Chem. Scand.* **8**, 365–366 (1951).

HA14.   HANSSON, J., *Svensk Kem. Tidskr.* **66**, 351–358 (1954).

HA15.   HANSSON, J., *Svensk Kem. Tidskr.* **67**, 256–262 (1955).

HA16.   HANSSON, J., *Svensk Kem. Tidskr.* **67**, 263–268 (1955).

HA17.   HANTZSCH, A., and HILLAND, W., *Ber.* **31**, 2064, (1898).

HA18.   HANTZSCH, A., and SEBALDT, H., *Z. physik. Chem.* **30**, 258–299 (1899).

HA19.   HANTZSCH, A., and VAGT, A., *Z. physik. Chem.* **38**, 705–742 (1901).

HA20.   HARLEY-MASON, J., *J. Chem. Soc.* **1949**, 518–519.

HA21.   HARNED, H. S., and OWEN, B. B., *J. Am. Chem. Soc.* **52**, 5079–5091 (1930).

HA22.   HARNED, H. S., and OWEN, B. B., *J. Am. Chem. Soc.* **52**, 5079–5091 (1930).

HA23.   HARNED, H. S., and ROBINSON, R. A., *J. Am. Chem. Soc.* **50**, 3157–3178 (1928).

HA24.   HARRIES, C., and DÜVEL, F., *Ann.* **410**, 54–70 (1915).

HA24a. HARRIS, G. H., and FISCHBACK, B. C. (to Dow Chemical Co.), U.S. Patent 2,764,593 (Sept. 25, 1956).

HA25.   HARTLEY and HUNTINGTON, *Phil. Trans. Roy. Soc. London* **A170**, 257 (1879).

HA26.   HATTON, J. V., and RICHARDS, R. E., *Trans. Faraday Soc.* **56**, 315–317 (1960).

HA26a. HAUPTSCHEIN, M., and BRAUN, R. A., *J. Am. Chem. Soc.* **77**, 4930–4931 (1955).

HA27.   HAWTHORNE, M. F., *J. Am. Chem. Soc.* **83**, 2671–2673 (1961).

HA28.   HAWTHORNE, M. F., *J. Am. Chem. Soc.* **83**, 831–833 (1961).

HA28a. HAWTHORNE, M. F., *J. Am. Chem. Soc.* **80**, 4291–4292 (1958).

HA28b. HAWTHORNE, M. F., and PITOCHELLI, A. R., *J. Am. Chem. Soc.* **81**, 5519 (1959).

HA28c. HAWTHORNE, M. F., PITOCHELLI, A. R., STRAHM, R. D., and MILLER J. J., *J. Am. Chem. Soc.* **82**, 1825–1829 (1960).

HA29.   HAZLEHURST, D. A., HOLLIDAY, A. K., and PASS, G., *J. Chem. Soc.* **1956**, 4653–4658.

HE1.   HEIN, F., and SEGITZ, F. A., *Z. anal. Chem.* **72**, 120 (1927).

HE2.   HEINEMANN, H., WERT, R. W., McCARTER, W. S. W., *Ind. Eng. Chem.* **41**, 2928–2931 (1949).

HE2a.   HEININGER, S. A., *J. Org. Chem.* **22**, 704–706 (1957).

HE3.   HELFERICH, B., and DOMMER, W., *Ber.* **53**, 2004–2017 (1920).

HE4.   HELLIN, M., and COUSSEMANT, F. (to Institut Français du pétrole des carburants et lubrifiants), French Patent 1,216,263 (Apr. 25, 1960).

HE4a.   HELLIN, M., and COUSSEMANT, F., *Bull. soc. chim. France* **1958**, 1145–1155.

HE5.   HELLMAN, H., and SCHUMACHER, O., *Chem. Ber.* **89**, 95–106 (1956).

HE6.   HENBEST, H. B., and SLADE, P., *J. Chem. Soc.* **1960**, 1558–1560.

HE7.   HENNION, G. F., and CAMPBELL, J. M., *J. Org. Chem.* **21**, 791–794 (1956).

HE8.   HENNION, G. F., and HANZEL, R. S., *J. Am. Chem. Soc.* **82**, 4908–4912 (1960).

HE9.   HENNION, G. F., and NELSON, K. W., *J. Am. Chem. Soc.* **79**, 2142–2145 (1957).

HE10.   HENNION, G. F., PRICE, C. C., and WOLFF, V. C., Jr., *J. Am. Chem. Soc.* **77**, 4633–4636 (1955).

HE11.   HENNION, J. F., and TEACH, E. G., *J. Am. Chem. Soc.* **75**, 4297–4300 (1953).

HE12.   HENRY, A. J., *Brit. J. Pharmacol.* **3**, 187–188 (1948).

HE13.   HENRY, A. J., GRINDLEY, D. N., *J. Soc. Chem. Ind.* (*London*) **68**, 9–12 (1949).

HE14. HENRY, L., *Ber.* **7**, 753–765 (1947).

HE15. HENRY, L., *Acad. roy. Belg., Classe sci., Mém.* **26**, 200–208 (1892).

HE16. HENRY, L., *Acad. roy. Belg., Classe sci., Mém.* **29**, 355–378 (1895).

HE17. HENRY, L., *Bull. classe sci., Acad. roy. Belg,* **1902**, 537–582.

HE18. HERZ, W., and FISCHER, H., *Ber.* **37**, 4746–4753 (1904).

HE19. HERZ, W., and FISCHER, H., *Ber.* **37**, 4746–4753 (1904).

HE20. HERZ, W., and FISCHER, H., *Ber.* **38**, 1138–1144 (1905).

HE21. HERZ, W., and NEUKIRCH, E., *Z. physik. Chem.* **104**, 433–450 (1923).

HE22. HERZBERG, G., and KÖLSCH, N., *Z. Elektrochem.* **39**, 572–573 (1933).

HE23. HESS, E., *Fisheries Research Board Can. Progr. Repts. Atlantic Stas.* No. **30**, 10–12 (1941).

HE23a HEWITT, F., and HOLLIDAY, A. K., *J. Chem. Soc.* **1953**, 530–534.

HI1. HIGASI, K., *Sci. Papers Inst. Phys. Chem. Research (Tokyo)* **31**, 311–316 (1937).

HI2. HIERS, G. S., and ADAMS, R., *Ber.* **59**, 170 (1926).

HI3. HINSBERG, K., and GANGL-REUSS, E., *Z. Krebsforsch.* **52**, 227–233 (1942).

HJ1. HJORTH-HANSON, S., *Anal. Chim. Acta* **6**, 438–441 (1952).

HO1. HOFFMAN, E. G., *Z. anal. Chem.* **170**, 176–205 (1959).

HO1a. HOFMANN, A. W., *Ann.* **47**, 37–87 (1843).

HO2. HOFMANN, A. W., *Ann.* **73**, 91–92 (1850); *Jahresbericht über die Fortschritte der Chemie* **1861**, 494; *Ber.* **3**, 109–112 (1870).

HO3. HOFMANN, A. W., *Ann.* **74**, 117–177 (1850).

HO4. HOFMANN, A. W., *Ann.* **78**, 253–286 (1851).

HO5. HOFMANN, A. W., *Ann.* **79**, 11–39 (1851).

HO6. HOFMANN, A. W., *Ber.* **14**, 494–496 (1881).

HO7. HOFMANN, A. W., *Ber.* **14**, 659–669 (1881).

HO8. HOFMANN, A. W., *Ber.* **22**, 699–705 (1889).

HO9. HOFMANN, A. W., and REIMER, H., *Ber.* **3**, 756–757 (1869).

HO10. HOFMANN, K. A., HÖBOLD, K., and QUOOS, F., *Ann.* **386**, 304–317 (1912).

HO11. HOFMANN, K. A., ROTH, R., HÖBOLD, K., and METZLER, A., *Ber.* **43**, 2624–2630 (1910).

HO12. HOLLÓ, J., LENGYEL, T., and UZONYI, H. M., *Periodica Polytech.* **4**, 173–182 (1960).

HO13. HOLMBERG, K. E., *Acta Chem. Scand.* **13**, 717–727 (1959).

HO14. HOLMBERT, K. E. O. (to Quartz and Silica S.A.), U.S. Patent 3,004,064 (Oct. 10, 1961).

HO14a. HOLMES, R. R., *J. Phys. Chem.* **64**, 1295–1299 (1960).

HO14b. HOLMES, R. R., BERTAUT, E. F., *J. Am. Chem. Soc.* **80**, 2980–2983 (1958).

HO15. HOLMOV, V., *Rybnoe Khoz.* **1939**, No. 3, 38–39; *Khim. Referat. Zhur.* **1939**, No. 7, 132.

HO16. HOLMSTEDT, B., LARSSON, L., and SUNDWALL, A., *Biochem. Pharmacol.* **3**, 155–162 (1960).

HO17. HÖLZL, F., *Monatsh.* **47**, 760 (1926).

HO18. HÖLZL, F., *Monatsh.* **50**, 294 (1928).

HO19. HORN, H., and GOULD, E. S., *J. Am. Chem. Soc.* **78**, 5772–5773 (1956).

HO20. HORNER, L., and NICKEL, H., *Ann.* **597**, 20–47 (1955).

HO20a. HORNER, L., and NICKEL, H., *Chem. Ber.* **89**, 1681–1690 (1956).

HO21. HORNER, L., SCHEFER, H., and LUDWIG, W., *Chem. Ber.* **91**, 75–81 (1958).

HO22. HORNING, C. H., and BERGSTROM, F. W., *J. Am. Chem. Soc.* **67**, 2110–2111 (1945).

HO22a. HOROWITZ, R. M., and GEISSMAN, T. A., *J. Am. Chem. Soc.* **72**, 1518–1522 (1950).

HO23. HOWK, B. W., LITTLE, E. L., SCOTT, S. L., and WHITMAN, G. M., *J. Am. Chem. Soc.* **76**, 1899–1902 (1934).

HO24. HOWTON, D. R., *J. Am. Chem. Soc.* **69**, 2555–2557 (1947).

HO25. HOWTON, D. R., *J. Org. Chem.* **14**, 1–9 (1949).

HO26. HOYT, F. W., *Iowa State Coll. J. Sci.* **15**, 75–77 (1940).

HR1. HROMATKA, O., and SKOPALIK, C., *Monatsh.* **83**, 38–53 (1952).

HU1. HÜNIG, S., and BARON, W., *Chem. Ber.* **90**, 395–402 (1957).

HU2. HÜNIG, S., and KAHANEK, H., *Chem. Ber.* **90**, 238–245 (1957).

HU2a. HUGHES, E. D., *J. Chem. Soc.* **1933**, 75–77.

HU2b. HUGHES, E. D., and INGOLD, C. K., *J. Chem. Soc.* **1933**, 69–75.

HU2c. HUISGEN, R., BAYERLEIN, F., and HEYDKAMP, W., *Chem. Ber.* **92**, 3223–3241 (1959).

HU3. HUNT, W. C., and WAGNER, E. C., *J. Org. Chem.* **16**, 1792–1804 (1951).

HU3a. HUNT, C. K., *Ind. Eng. Chem.* **35**, 1048–1052 (1942).

HU3b. HURD, D. T., and OSTHOFF, R. C., *Inorganic Syntheses*. McGraw-Hill Book Co., Inc., New York, N.Y. (1957), Vol. 5, pp. 26–29.

HU4. HUTIN, A., *Monit. sci. Docteur Quesneville* **9**, II, 194–195 (1917); *Chem. Zentr.* **1920**, II, 494.

HW1. HWA, J. C. H. (to Rohm and Haas Co.), U.S. Patent 2,933,529 (Apr. 19, 1960).

I

IC1. ICKE, R. N., and WISEGARVER, B. B., *Org. Syntheses*, Coll. Vol. III, p. 724 (1955).

IL1. ILIAS, D., and BOUDOURIS, G., *Compt. rend.* **250**, 1833–1835 (1960).

IN1. INDZHIKYAN, M. G., SURMANYAN, S. A., and BABAYAN, A. T., *Izvest. Akad. Nauk Armyan. S.S.R., Khim. Nauk* **10**, 213–221 (1957).

IN2. INGOLD, C. K., *Structure and Mechanism in Organic Chemistry*. Cornell University Press, Ithaca, N.Y. (1953).

IN3. INGOLD, C. K., *Structure and Mechanism in Organic Chemistry*. Cornell University Press, Ithaca, N.Y. (1953), pp. 346–347.

IN4. INGOLD, C. K., and JESSOP, J. A., *J. Chem. Soc.* **1929**, 2357–2361.

IN5. INGOLD, C. K., and JESSOP, J. A., *J. Chem. Soc.* **132**, 2357–2361 (1929).

IN6. INGOLD, C. K., and PATEL, C. S., *J. Chem. Soc.* **1933**, 66–67.

IN6a. INGOLD, C. K., and PATEL, C. S., *J. Chem. Soc.* **1933**, 68–69.

IN7. INGOLD, C. K., and ROTHSTEIN, E., *J. Chem. Soc.* **1931**, 1666–1683.

IN8. INGOLD, C. K., and VASS, C. C. N., *J. Chem. Soc.* **1928**, 3125–3127.

IS1. ISHAM, R. M. (to Southern Production Co., Inc.), U.S. Patent 2,657,237 (Oct. 27, 1953).

IS2. ISHIDATE, M., NISHIZAWA, H., SANO, H., and HORIKOSHI, I., *Yakugaku Zasshi* **81**, 1303–1307, 1307–1309 (1961).

IS3. ISHIGURO, T., YAGYU, M., IKUSHIMA, M., and NAKAZAWA, T., *J. Pharm. Soc. (Japan)* **75**, 434–438 (1955).

IS4. ISHIKURO, T., Japanese Patent 162,908 (Mar. 15, 1944).

IS5. ISSOIRE, J., *Mém. poudres* **42**, 409–424 (1960).

IS6. ISSOIRE, J., and CHAPUT, L., *Chim. anal.* **43**, 313–320 (1961).

IW1. IWAKURA, Y., SATO, M., and IKEGAMI, A., *Nippon Kagaku Zasshi* **80**, 632–635 (1959).

J

JA1. JACOB, J., MARSZAK, I., EPSZTEIN, R., and GUERMONT, J. P., *Compt. rend.* **234**, 1230–1232 (1952).

JA2. JACOBI, W., and MERLING, G., *Ann.* **278**, 1–20 (1894).

JA3. JAEGER, F. M., *Z. anorg. Chem.* **101**, 1–214 (1917).

JA4. JAEGER, F. M., *Z. anorg. Chem.* **101**, 214 pp. (1917); (with Kahn, J.) *Proc. Koninkl. Akad. Wetenschap. Amsterdam* **18**, 75–91 (1915).

JA5. JAKOBSEN, F., *Tidsskr. Kjemi Bergvesen Met.* **4**, 14 (1944).

JA6. JAMES, A. T., and MARTIN, A. J. P., *Analyst* **77**, 915–932 (1952).

JA7. JANDER, G., and WICKERT, K., *Z. physik. Chem.* **A178**, 57–73 (1936).

JA8. JATKAR, S. K. K., and KULKARNI, S. B., *J. Univ. Poona* **1**, Chem. Sect. 1–2 (1952).

JE1. JERCHEL, D., and JUNG, G., *Ber.* **85**, 1130–1138 (1952).

JE2. JERUSALEM, G., *J. Chem. Soc.* **95**, 1275–1291 (1909).

JO1. JOHNSON, A. W., *J. Chem. Soc.* **1946**, 1009–1014.

JO2. JOHNSON, A. W. (to Imperial Chemical Industries Ltd.), British Patent 595,540 (Dec. 8, 1947).

JO3. JOHNSON, F., *VI Nord. Veterinärmötet* **1951**, 197–202.

JO4. JOLLY, W. J., *J. Am. Chem. Soc.* **77**, 4958–4960 (1955).

JO5. JONES, E. R. H., LACEY, R. N., and SMITH, P., *J. Chem. Soc.* **1946**, 940–944.

JO6. JONES. E. R. R., MARSZAK, I., and BADER, H., *J. Chem. Soc.* **1947**, 1578–1579.

JO7. JONES, E. R. H., ROBINSON, F. A., and STRACHAN, M. N., *J. Chem. Soc.* **1946**, 87–91.

JO8. JONES, L. W., and WHALEN, H. F., *J. Am. Chem. Soc.* **47**, 1343–1353 (1925).

JO9. JOSHI, K. K., and WYATT, P. A. H., *J. Chem. Soc.* **1959**, 3825–3829.

JO10. JOUKOVSKY, N. I., *Bull. soc. chim. Belges* **43**, 397–446 (1934).

JU1. JULG, A., and BONNET, M., *Compt. rend.* **252**, 1144–1145 (1961).

K

KA1. KABIL, A., and PREY, V., *Monatsh.* **89**, 497–504 (1958).

KA1a. KAGAN, Y. B., BASHKIROV, A. N., KLIGER, G. A., and ERMAKOV, Y. N., *Izvest. Akad. Nauk S.S.S.R., Otdel. Khim. Nauk* **1959**, 1345–1346.

KA2. KAHANE, E., and LÉVY, J., *Colamine, Trimethylamine, Betaine, Carnitine Muscarine, Betainaldehyde, Sinapine.* (Actualite scientifiques et industrielles No. 753). Hermann & Cie., Paris, (1939), 90 pp.

KA3. KAHANE, E., and SIMENAUER, A., *Bull. soc. chim. France* **1954**, 514–520.

KA4. KAHN, W., *Doctoral Dissertation*, Univ. of Munich, 1904.

KA5. KAHOVEC, L., *Acta Phys. Austriaca* **1**, 307–310 (1948).

KA6. KANITZ, A., *Z. physik. Chem.* **22**, 336 (1897).

KA7. KÄSTNER, D. (to Badische Anilin und Soda-Fabrik A.-G.), German Patent 870,845 (Mar. 16, 1953).

KA8. KÄSTNER, D. (to Badische Anilin und Soda-Fabrik A.-G.), German Patent 871,004 (Mar. 19, 1953).

KA9. KAO, G. N., TILAK, B. D., and VENKATARAMAN, K., *J. Sci. Ind. Research (India)* **14B**, 624–631 (1955).

KA10. KARRER, P., *Organic Chemistry*. Elsevier Publishing Co., New York, N.Y. (1950), 4th English ed. p. 133.

KA11. KARRER, P., *Organic Chemistry*. Elsevier Publishing Co., New York, N.Y. (1950), 4th English ed., p. 218.

KA12. KARRER, P., CANAL, F., ZOHNER, K., and WIDMER, R., *Helv. Chim. Acta* **11**, 1062–1084 (1928).

KA13. KATO, T., MORIKAWA, T., and SUZUKI, Y., *J. Pharm. Soc. Japan* **72**, 1177–1182 (1952).

KA14. KATRITZKY, A. R., *J. Chem. Soc.* **1959**, 2049–2051.

KA15. KATZ, J. R., and SELMAN, J., *Z. Physik* **46**, 392–405 (1928).

KA16. KAUFFMANN, M., and VORLÄNDER, D., *Ber.* **43**, 2738 (1910).

KA17. KAUFLER, F., and KUNZ, E., *Ber.* **42**, 2484 (1909).

KA18. KAZAKOVA, V. M., and FEL'DSHTEIN, L. S., *Zhur. Fiz. Khim.* **35**, 488–591 (1961).

KE1. KEIL, W., *Z. physiol. Chem.* **171**, 249 (1927).

KE2. KEIL, W., *Z. physiol. Chem.* **196**, 81–86 (1931).

KE3. KENNER, G. W., and MURRAY, M. A., *J. Chem. Soc.* **1950**, 406.

KE3a. KENNER, G. W., TODD, A. R., WEBB, R. F., and WEYMOUTH, F. J., *J. Chem. Soc.* **1954**, 2288–2293.

KH1. KHANNA, M. M., and DHAR, M. L., *J. Sci. India* **12B**, 532–536 (1953).

KH1a. KHARASCH, M. S., *J. Research Natl. Bur. Standards* **2**, 359–430 (1929).

KH2. KHARASCH, M. S., and FIELDS, E. K., *J. Am. Chem. Soc.* **63**, 2316–2320 (1943).

KH3. KHARASCH. M. S., and FUCHS, F., *J. Org. Chem.* **9**, 359–372 (1944).

KH4. KHARASCH, M. S., and FUCHS, F., *J. Org. Chem.* **10**, 159–169 (1945).

KH5. KHARASCH, M. S., and FUCHS, F., U.S. Patent 2,409,287 (Oct. 15, (1946).

KH6. KHARASCH, M. S., WILLIAMS, G. N., and NUDENBERG, W., *J. Org. Chem.* **20**, 937–952 (1955).

KI1. KIJNER, *J. Russ. Phys.-Chem. Soc.* **31**, 877, 1033 (1899); **32**, 381 (1900).

KI2. KINCAID, F., and HENRIQUES, F. C., Jr., *J. Am. Chem. Soc.* **62**, 1474–1477 (1940).

KI3. KING, H., and WORK, T. S., *J. Chem. Soc.* **1942**, 401–404.

KI4. KING, T. J., *J. Chem. Soc.* **1951**, 898–900.

KI5. KIRBY, E. (to E. I. du Pont de Nemours & Co.), U.S. Patent 2,366,534 (Jan. 2, 1945).

KI5a. KIRCHHOF, W., STUMPF, W., and FRANKE, W. (to Chemische Werke Huls A.-G.), German Patent 1,019,313 (Nov. 14, 1957).

KI6. KIRILYUK, S. S., and MISKIDZH'YAN, S. P., *Izvest. Vysshikh Ucheb. Zavadenii, Khim. i Khim. Tekhnol.* **3**, 1002–1007 (1960).

KI7.　KIRK, R. E., and OTHMER, D. F., Eds., *Encyclopedia of Chemical Technology*. Interscience Publishers Inc., New York, N.Y., (1947), Vol. 1, p. 771.

KI8.　KIRMSE, E. M., *Z. Chem.* 1, 334–337 (1961).

KL1.　KLAGES, F., NOBER, G., and FRANK, R., *Ann.* 547, 39–64 (1941).

KL2.　KLAGES, F., NOBER, G., KIRCHER, F., and BOCK, M., *Ann.* 547, 1–38 (1941).

KL2a.　KLAGES, F., and ZANGE, E., *Ann.* 607, 35–45 (1957).

KL3.　KLAVEHN, W., (to Knoll A.-G. Chemische Fabriken), German Patent 617,596 (Aug. 26, 1935); Austrian Patent 135,705 (Dec. 11, 1933).

KL4.　KLEBANSKIĬ, A. L., and VILESOVA, M. S., *Zhur. Obshcheĭ Khim.* 28, 1524–1528 (1958); *J. Gen. Chem. (U.S.S.R.)* 28, 1574–1576 (1958) (Engl. Trans.).

KL4a.　KLINE, R. J., and IHDE, A. J., *J. Colloid Sci.* 13, 163–169 (1958).

KN1.　KNAPP, E. F., and DENHAM, W. S., *J. Chem. Soc.* 117, 236–247 (1920).

KN2.　KNORR, L., *Ber.* 37, 3494–3498 (1904).

KN3.　KNORR, L., *Ber.* 37, 3499–3504 (1904).

KN4.　KNORR, L., *Ber.* 37, 3504–3519 (1904).

KN5.　KNORR, L., and PSCHORR, R., *Ber.* 38, 3172–2181 (1905).

KN6.　KNORR, L., and ROTH, P., *Ber.* 39, 1427–1428 (1906).

KN6a.　KNOTT, E. B., *J. Chem. Soc.* 1956, 1644–1649.

KN7.　KNUDSEN, P., *Ber.* 42, 3994–4003 (1909).

KO1.　KOBE, K. A., and HARRISON, R. H., *Petroleum Refiner*, 33, No. 11, 161–164 (1954).

KO1a.　KOCH, F. W., *J. Biol. Chem.* 15, 43–62 (1913).

KO2.　KODAMA, S., MURATA, Y., TAKASE, S., and TANA, I., *J. Chem. Soc. Japan, Ind. Chem. Sect.* 52, 112–113 (1949).

KO3.　KOEPPEN, A., *Ber.* 38, 882–884 (1905).

KO3a.　KOHLER, F., *Montash.* 88, 388–402 (1957).

KO4.　KOHLER, F., ARNOLD, H., and MUNN, R. J., *Monatsh.* 92, 876–906 (1961).

KO4a.　KOHLER, F., and NECKEL, A., *Monatsh.* 87, 199–211 (1956).

KO5.　KOHLER, F., and RICE, O. K., *J. Chem. Phys.* 26, 1614–1618 (1957).

KO5a.　KOHLRAUSCH, K. W. F., *Monatsh.* 68, 349–358 (1936).

KO5b.　KOHLRAUSCH, K. W. F., *Ramanspektren*. Becker und Erler, Leipzig (1943), p. 185 ff.

KO6.　KOHLRAUSCH, K. W. F., and WAGNER, J., *Z. physik. Chem.* 1352, 185–201 (1942).

KO7.　KOHN, M., *Ann.* 351, 134–150 (1907).

KO8.　KOHN, M., and MORGENSTERN, O., *Monatsh.* 28, 479–508 (1907).

KO9.　KOHN, M., and MORGENSTERN, O., *Monatsh.* 28, 529–536 (1907).

KO10.　KOHN, M., and SCHLEGL, K., *Monatsh.* 28, 509–528 (1907).

KO11.　KOHNSTAMM, P. H., and TIMMERMANS, J., *Proc. Koninkl. Akad. Wetenschap Amsterdam* 1913, 1021.

KO12.　KOLLER, G., and KANDLER, E., *Monatsh.* 58, 213–237 (1931).

KO13.　KOLOSOVSKIĬ, N. A., and ANDRYUSHCHENKO, S. V., *Zhur. Obshcheĭ Khim.* 4, 1070–1072 (1934).

KO14.　KOLOSOVSKIĬ, N. A., and ANDRYUSHCHENKO, S. V., *Zhur. Obshcheĭ Khim.* 4, 1070–1072 (1934).

KO15. KOLOTOW, S., *Zhur. Russ. Fiz.-Khim. Obshchestva* **1**, 229–250 (1885).

KO16. KONOWALOWA, R. A., and MAGIDSON, O. J., *Arch. Pharm.* **1928**, 449–452.

KO17. KORMER, V. A., and PETROV, A. A., *Zhur. Obshchei Khim.* 918–927 (1960).

KO18. KÖSTER, E., *Angew. Chem.* **69**, 94 (1957).

KO18a. KOTELLNIKOV, V. V., and SKRIPOV, V. P., *Nauch. Doklady. Vysshei Shkoly, Khim. i. Khim. Tekhnol.* **1959**, No. 2, 248–249.

KO19. KOZLOV, N. S., and PANOVA, N. I., *Zhur. Obshchei Khim.* **25**, 183–187 (1955); *J. Gen. Chem. (U.S.S.R.)* **25**, 167–170 (1955) (Eng. Trans.).

KO20. KOZLOV, N. S., and PANOVA, N. I., *Zhur. Obshchei Khim.* **26**, 2602–2604 (1956); *J. Gen. Chem. (U.S.S.R.)* **26**, 2901–2907 (1955) (Eng. Trans.).

KO21. KOZLOV, N. S., and PANOVA, N. I., *Zhur. Obshchei Khim.* **27**, 3208–3210 (1957); *J. Gen. Chem. (U.S.S.R.)* **27**, 3244–3246 (1957) (Eng. Trans.).

KO22. KOZLOV, N. S., and PANOVA, N. I., *Zhur. Obshchei Khim.* **28**, 2421–2422 (1958) (Eng. Trans.).

KR1. KRAFFT, F., and MOYE, A., *Ber.* **22**, 814 (1889).

KR2. KRAMIS, C. J. (to E. I. du Pont de Nemours & Co.), U.S. Patent 2,848,386 (Aug. 19, 1958); U.S. Patent 2,999,053 (Sept. 5, 1961).

KR3. KRASOUSKII, K., and KIPRIANOV, A., *J. chim. Ukraine* **1**, 68–74 (1925).

KR3a. KRAUS, C. A., and BROWN, E. H., *J. Am. Chem. Soc.* **51**, 2690–2696 (1929).

KR4. KRAUS, W., *Textil-Rundschau* **5**, 395–399 (1950).

KR5. KRAUS, W., *Ciba Rev. (Am. Ed.)* **No. 99**, 3573–3575 (1953).

KR5a. KRAUSE, E., *Ber.* **57B**, 813–818 (1924).

KR5b. KRESHKOV, A. P., BYKOVA, L. N., and SHEMET, N. S., *Doklady Akad. Nauk S.S.S.R.* **134**, 96–99 (1960).

KR6. KRESHKOV, A. P., BYKOVA, L. N., and SHEMET, N. S., *Zhur. Anal. Khim.* **16**, 331–336 (1961).

KR7. KRICHEVSKIĬ, I. R., KHAZANOVA, N. E., and LINSHITS, L. R., *Doklady Akad. Nauk S.S.S.R.* **100**, 737–740 (1955).

KR8. KRICHEVSKIĬ, I. R., KHAZANOVA, N. E., and LINSHITS, L. R., *Kriticheskie Yavleniya i Flyuktuatsii v Rastvorakh, Trudy Soveshchaniya* (Moskov. Gosudarst. Univ.) Moscow **1960**, pp. 61–72.

KR8a. KRICHEVSKIĬ, I. R., KHAZANOVA, N. E., and LINSHITS, L. R., *Zhur. Fiz. Khim.* **29**, 547–557 (1955).

KR9. KRISHNAMURTHY, V. A., and RAO, M. R. A., *J. Indian Inst. Sci.* **39A**, 138–160 (1957).

KR10. KRÖLLER, E., *Deut. Lebensm. Rundschau* **46**, 6 (1950).

KR10a. KRUPATKIN, I. L., *Zhur. Obshchei Khim.* **25**, 2023–2028 (1955).

KR11. KRUSE, C. W., and KLEINSCHMIDT, R. F., *J. Am. Chem. Soc.* **83**, 216–220 (1961).

KU1. KUFFNER, F., and POLKE, E., *Monatsh.* **82**, 330–335 (1951).

KU2. KUFFNER, F., and SEIFRIED, W., *Monatsh.* **83**, 748–752 (1952).

KU3. KUL'BAKH, V. O., ZVEREVA, N. A., and POROSHINA, A. N., *Med. Prom. S.S.S.R.* **13**, No. 7, 46–9 (1959).

KU4.   KUL'BAKH, V. O., ZVEREVA, N. A., and POROSHINA, A. N., U.S.S.R.
        Patent 116,767 (Jan. 19, 1959).
KU5.   KUM-TATT, L., *Anal. Chim. Acta* **24**, 397–409 (1961).
KU6.   KUSS, E., *Z. angew. Phys.* **7**, 372–378 (1955).
KY1.   KYI, Z. Y., and WILSON, W., *Brit. J. Pharmacol.* **12**, 38 (1957).
KY2.   KYNASTON, W., LARCOMBE, B. E., and TURNER, H. S., *J. Chem. Soc.*
        1960, 1772–1778.
KY3.   KYRIDES, L. P. (to Monsanto Chemical Co.), U.S. Patent 2,548,898
        (Apr. 17, 1951).

                                    L

LA1.   LAAKSO, T., and REYNOLDS, D. D., *J. Am. Chem. Soc.* **73**, 3518–3520
        (1951).
LA2.   LADENBURG, A., *Ber.* **12**, 948–950 (1879).
LA3.   LADENBURG, A., *Ber.* **15**, 1143–1149 (1882).
LA4.   LADENBURG, A., *Ann.* **247**, 1–98 (1888).
LA5.   LADENBURG, A., MUGDAN, M., and BRZOSTOVICZ, O., *Ann.* **279**,
        344–366 (1894).
LA5a.   LAMB, J., *Colloq. intern. centre natl. recherche sci.* (*Paris*) No. 77,
        475–488 (1959).
LA6.   LAMBERT, A., and ROSE, J. D., *J. Chem. Soc.* **1947**, 1511–1513.
LA7.   LANGELI, T., *Gazz. chim. ital.* **16**, 385–390 (1886).
LA8.   LANGENBECK, W., *Ber.* **81**, 356–369 (1948).
LA9.   LANGENBECK, W., GÖDDE, O., WESCHKY, L., and SCHALLER, R., *Ber.*
        75, 232–236 (1942).
LA10.   LANGENBECK, W., HÖLSHER, K., and WESCHKY, L. (to W. Langenbeck),
        German Patent 713,747 (Nov. 25, 1941).
LA11.   LANGENBECK, W., SCHALLER, R., and ARNEBERG, K., *Ber.* **75B**, 1483–1488
        (1942).
LA12.   LANGENBECK, W., and WESCHKY, L. (to W. Langenbeck), German
        Patent 715,544 (Dec. 23, 1941).
LA12a. LASSLO, A., PFEIFFER, C. C., and WALLER, P. D., *J. Am. Pharm. Assoc.*
        48, 345–347 (1959).
LA13.   LATTEY, R. T., *J. Chem. Soc.* **91**, 1959–1971 (1907).
LA13a. LAUBENGAYER, A. W., and SMITH, W. C., *J. Am. Chem. Soc.* **76**,
        5985–5989 (1954).
LA14.   LAUN, W., *Ber.* **17**, 675–679 (1884).
LA14a. LAUTSCH, W. F., ERZBERGER, P., and TRÖBER, A., *Wiss. Z. tech. Hochsch.*
        Chem. Leuna-Merseburg, **1**, 31–33 (1958–1959).
LA15.   LAWSON, A. T., and COLLIE, N., *J. Chem. Soc.* **53**, 624–636 (1888).
LE1.   LEA, *Jahresbericht über die Fortschritte der Chemie* **1861**, 493; **1862**, 331.
LE2.   LEBEAU, P., and PICON, M., *Compt. rend.* **156**, 1077–1079 (1913).
LE3.   LE BEL, J. A., *Compt. rend.* **129**, 548–550 (1899).
LE4.   LEDUC, A., *Compt. rend.* **148**, 1173–1176 (1909).
LE5.   LEDUC, A., *Ann. chim.* **19**, 441–475 (1910).
LE5a.   LEE, J. (to Hoffmann-La Roche, Inc.), U.S. Patent 2,367,878 (Jan. 23,
        1945).

LE6. LeFèvre, R. J. W., and Russell, P., *Trans. Faraday Soc.* **43**, 374–393 (1947).

LE7. Leithe, W., *Ber.* **63B**, 800–805 (1930).

LE8. Lemmon, R. M., *Nucleonics* **11**, 44 (1953).

LE9. Lemmon, R. M., Parsons, M. A., and Chin, D. M., *J. Am. Chem. Soc.* **77**, 4139–4142 (1955).

LE10. Lemon, R. C., and Myerly, R. C., (to Union Carbide Corp.), U.S. Patent 3,022,349 (Feb. 20, 1962).

LE11. Lemoult, P., *Compt. rend.* **143**, 746–749 (1906).

LE12. Lemoult, P., *Ann. chim. phys.* **10**, 395–432 (1907).

LE13. Leonard, N. J., and Gelfand, S., *J. Am. Chem. Soc.* **77**, 3272–3278 (1955).

LE14. Leonard, N. J., Kraft, F. M., and Wolfman, V., *J. Am. Chem. Soc.* **70**, 867–868 (1948).

LE14a. Leonard, N. J., and Locke, D. M., *J. Am. Chem. Soc.* **77**, 437–439 (1955).

LE15. Leonard, N. J., and Musker, W. K., *J. Am. Chem. Soc.* **81**, 5631–5633 (1959).

LE16. Lettré, H., and Riemenschneider, W., *Ann.* **575**, 18–31 (1951).

LE17. Leuckart, R., *Ber.* **18**, 2341 (1885).

LE18. Leuckart, R., and Back, E., *Ber.* **19**, 2128 (1886).

LI0. Lide, D. R., Jr., and Mann, D. E., *J. Chem. Phys.* **28**, 572–576 (1958).

LI1. Lieben, A., and Rossi, A., *Ann.* **158**, 137–180 (1871).

LI2. Lieben, A., and Rossi, A., *Ann.* **165**, 109–126 (1873).

LI3. Liebermann, C., and Hagen, A., *Ber.* **16**, 1641–1642 (1883).

LI4. Liebermann, C., and Paal, C., *Ber.* **16**, 523–534 (1883).

LI5. Liebig, J. von, *Ann.* **36**, 88–89 (1840).

LI6. Liebig, J. von, Wöhler, A., and Poggendorff, J. C., *Handworterbuch der Chemie* (1837), Vol. I, pp. 698–699.

LI7. Linckh, E. (to I.G. Farbenindustrie A.-G.), German Patent 619,754 (Oct. 5, 1935).

LI7a. Linton, E. P., *J. Am. Chem. Soc.* **62**, 1945–1948 (1940).

LI8. Lintzel, W., *Biochem. Z.* **273**, 243–261 (1934).

LI9. Lintzel, W., and Herring, E., *Vorratspflege u. Lebensmittelforsch.* **2**, 263–269 (1939).

LI10. Lippmann, E. O. von, *Chemiker-Ztg.* **33**, 117–118 (1909).

LI11. Lippmann, E. O. von, *Chemiker-Ztg.* **33**, 186 (1909).

LI12. Lister, M. W., and Sutton, L. E., *Trans. Faraday Soc.* **35**, 495–505 (1939).

LI13. Litherland, A., and Mann, F., *J. Chem. Soc.* **1938**, 1588–1595.

LI14. Litvinov, N. D., *Nauch. Doklady Vysshei Shkoly, Khim. i Khim. Tekhnol.* **1959**, No. 1, 13–15.

LO1. Lo, C. P., *J. Am. Chem. Soc.* **80**, 3466–3468 (1958).

LO1a. Lo, C. P. and Croxall, W. J., *J. Am. Chem. Soc.* **76**, 4166–4169 (1954).

LO1b. Lorentzen, H. L., and Hansen, B. B., *Acta Chem. Scand.* **12**, 139–141 (1958).

LO1c. Lorenzelli, V., Möller, K. D., and Hadni, A., *Compt. rend.* **249**, 239–240 (1959).

LO2. LOSSEN, W., *Ann.* **181**, 364–383 (1876).

LO3. LOTT, W. A., and KRAPCHO, J. (to Olin Mathieson Chemical Corp.), U.S. Patent 2,813,904 (Nov. 19, 1957).

LO4. LOVELAND, J. W., and DIMELER, G. R., *Anal. Chem.* **33**, 1196–1201 (1961).

LU1. LUCIUS, R., *Arch. Pharm.* **245**, 251–254 (1907).

LU2. LUDECKE, O., *Ann.* **240**, 85–92 (1887).

LU3. LUDER, W. F., KRAUS, P., KRAUS, C. A., and FUOSS, R. M., *J. Am. Chem. Soc.* **58**, 255–258 (1936).

LU3a. LUDER, W. F., and KRAUS, C. A., *J. Am. Chem. Soc.* **59**, 2481–2483 (1947).

LU4. LUDOWIEG, J., *Bol. soc. quím. Peru* **14**, 77–86 (1948).

LU4a. LUKEŠ, R., *Collection Czechoslov. Chem. Communs.* **12**, 71–80 (1947).

LU5. LUKEŠ, R., and FERLES, M., *Collection Czechoslov. Chem. Communs.* **16**, 252–257 (1951).

LU6. LUKEŠ, R., and FERLES, M., *Collection Czechoslov. Chem. Communs.* **16**, 420–422 (1951); *Chem. Listy* **45**, 421 (1951).

LU7. LUKEŠ, R., and HOFMAN, J., *Chem. Ber.* **93**, 2556–2561 (1960).

LU8. LUKEŠ, R., and JIZBA, J., *Collection Czechoslov. Chem. Communs.* **19**, 930–940 (1954); *Chem. Listy* **46** 622–628 (1952).

LU9. LUKEŠ, R., and JIZBA, J., *Collection Czechoslov. Chem. Communs.* **19**, 941–948 (1954).

LU10. LUKEŠ, R., and LANGTHALER, J., *Collection Czechoslov. Chem. Communs.* **24**, 110–115 (1959); *Chem. Listy* **51**, 1869–1874 (1957).

LU11. LUKEŠ, R., LANGTHALER, J., and CERVENA, I., *Collection Czechoslov. Chem. Communs.* **25**, 461–464 (1960).

LU12. LUKEŠ, R., and PLIML, J., *Collection Czechoslov. Chem. Communs.* **15**, 463–471 (1950); *Chem. Listy* **44**, 297–300 (1950).

LU13. LUKEŠ, R., and PLIML, J., *Collection Czechoslov. Chem. Communs.* **15**, 512–519 (1950); *Chem. Zvesti* **4**, 336–343 (1950).

LU14. LUKEŠ, R., and PLIML, J., *Collection Czechoslov. Chem. Communs.* **21**, 625–631 (1956); *Chem. Listy* **49**, 1815–1820 (1955).

LU15. LUKEŠ, R., and PLIML, J., *Collection Czechoslov. Chem. Communs.* **24**, 2560–2564 (1959); *Chem. Listy* **52**, 663–667 (1958).

LU16. LUKEŠ, R., and PLIML, J., *Collection Czechoslov. Chem. Communs.* **24**, 2826–2828 (1959).

LU17. LUKEŠ, R., PLIML, J., and TROJANEK, J., *Collection Czechoslov. Chem. Communs.* **24**, 3109–3114 (1959); *Chem. Listy* **52**, 1603–1607 (1958).

LU18. LUKEŠ, R., and PREUCIL, J., *Collection Czechoslov. Chem. Communs.* **10**, 384–398 (1938).

LU18a. LUKEŠ, R., and SMOLEK, K., *Collection Czechoslov. Chem. Communs.* **11**, 506–516 (1939).

LU19. LUKEŠ, R., and TROJANEK, J., *Collection Czechoslov. Chem. Communs.* **14**, 688–692 (1949).

LU20. LUKEŠ, R., and TROJANEK, J., *Collection Czechoslov. Chem. Communs.* **16**, 603–610 (1951); *Chem. Listy* **45**, 389–392 (1951).

LU21. LUKEŠ, R., and TROJANEK, J., *Collection Czechoslov, Chem. Communs.* **16**, 603–610 (1951); *Chem. Listy* **45**, 389–392 (1951).

LU22. LUKEŠ, R., and TROJANEK, J., *Collection Czechoslov. Chem. Communs.* **23**, 321–325 (1958); *Chem. Listy* **51**, 1149–1152 (1957).

LU23. LUKEŠ, R., TROJANEK, J., and LUKEŠ, V., *Collection Czechoslov. Chem. Communs.* **23**, 321–325 (1958); *Chem. Listy* **51**, 1149–1152 (1957).

LU24. LUNSFORD, C. D., MURPHEY, R. S., and ROSE, E. K., *J. Org. Chem.* **22**, 1225–1228 (1957).

M

MA1. MACALLUM, A. D., and WHITBY, G. S., *Trans. Roy. Soc. Can.* **22**, 33–38 (1928).

MA1a. MACLEAN, H., and MACLEAN, I. S., *Lecithin and Allied Substances: The Lipins.* Longmans, Green & Co., Ltd., London, 2nd Ed., 1927.

MA2. MACOVSKI, E., *Bull. soc. chim. France* **3**, 498–500 (1936).

MA3. MAGGIOLO, A., and NIEGOWSKI, S. J., *Advances in Chem. Ser.* **No. 21**, 202–204 (1959).

MA4. MAHAN, J. E., (to Phillips Petroleum Co.), U. S. Patent 2,941,005 (June 14, 1960).

MA5. MAHBOOB, S., and DHAR, M. L., *J. Sci. Ind. Research (India)* **14B**, 1–6 (1955).

MA6. MAHLMAN, H. A., LEDDICOTTE, G. W., and MOORE, F. L., *Anal. Chem.* **26**, 1939–1941 (1954).

MA7. MAIER, K., (to Badische-Anilin und Soda-Fabrik A.-G.), German Patent 896,810 (Nov. 16, 1953).

MA8. MAILHE, A., *Bull. soc. chim. France* **33**, 962–966 (1905).

MA9. MAILHE, A., *Compt. rend.* **140**, 1691–1693 (1905).

MA10. MAILHE, A., and BELLEGARDE, M. L., *Bull. soc. chim. France* **25**, 589 (1919).

MA11. MAILHE, A., and DEGODON, F., *Ann. chim.* **13**, 191 (1917); *Bull. soc. chim. France* **21**, 289 (1917); *Compt. rend.* **165**, 558 (1917).

MA12. MAILHE, A., and DEGODON, F., *J. pharm. chim.* **16**, 225–229 (1917).

MA13. MAILHE, A., *Bull. soc. chim. France* **27**, 541–547 (1920); *Compt. rend.* **170**, 1120–1123 (1920).

MA14. MALBOT, H., *Ann. chim.* **13**, 474–515 (1888); *Compt. rend.* **104**, 63–71 (1887).

MA15. MALBOT, H., *Bull. soc. chim. France* **50**, 89–90 (1888).

MA16. MALLETTE, M. F., ALTHOUSE, P. M., and CLAGETT, C. O., *Biochemistry of Plants and Animals.* John Wiley and Sons, Inc., New York, N. Y. (1960), pp. 88, 349.

MA17. MAMLOCK, L., and WOLFFENSTEIN, R., *Ber.* **34**, 2499–2505 (1901).

MA18. MANN. F. G., and LITHERLAND, A., *Nature* **141**, 789–790 (1938).

MA19. MANN, F. G., and WATSON, H. R., *J. Chem. Soc.* **1958**, 2772–2780.

MA20. MANNICH, C., and CHANG, F. T., *Ber.* **66**, 418–420 (1933).

MA21. MANNICH, C., and DAVIDSEN, H., *Ber.* **69B**, 2106–2112 (1936).

MA22. MANNICH, C., HANDKE, L. E., and ROTH, K., *Ber.* **69B**, 2112–2123 (1936).

MA23. MANNICH, C., and MARGOTTE, E., *Ber.* **68B**, 273–278 (1935).

MA24. MANNICH, C., and RITSERT, K., *Ber.* **57**, 1116–1118 (1924).

MA25. MANNICH, C., and SALZMANN, O., *Ber.* **72B**, 499–505 (1939).

MA26. MANNICH, C., and SALZMANN, O., *Ber.* **72B**, 506–510 (1939).

MA27. MARCKWALD, W., and DROSTE-HUELSHOFF, A. F. von, *Ber.* **32,** 560–564 (1899).

MA28. MARKUZIN, N. P., *Zhur. Priklad, Khim.* **34,** 1175–1176 (1961).

MA28a. MARKUZIN, N. P., and STORONKIN, A. V., *Vestnik Leningrad. Univ.* **12,** No. 10, *Ser. Fiz. i Khim.* No. 2, 123–147 (1957).

MA29. MARSHALL, H. P., and GRUNWALD, E., *J. Am. Chem. Soc.* **76,** 2000–2004 (1954).

MA30. MARSZAK, I. and EPSZTEIN, R., *Bull. soc. chim. France* **1952,** 441–442.

MA31. MARSZAK, I., EPSZTEIN, R., and OLOMUCKI, M., *Compt. rend.* **235,** 1409–1410 (1952).

MA32. MARSZAK, I., GUERMONT, J. P., and EPSZTEIN, R., *Mém. serv. chim. état (Paris)* **36,** 301–308 (1951).

MA33. MARSZAK, I., GUERMONT, J. P., EPSZTEIN, R., and JACOB, J., *Compt. rend.* **233,** 530–532 (1951).

MA34. MARSZAK, I., and MARSZAK-FLEURY, A., *Compt. rend.* **226,** 1289–1290 (1948).

MA35. MARSZAK, I., and MARSZAK-FLEURY, A., *Mém. serv. chim. état (Paris)* **34,** 419–422 (1948).

MA36. MARUTA, S., *J. Chem. Soc. Japan, Pure Chem. Sect.* **74,** 805–808 (1953).

MA37. MARVEL, C. S., SCOTT, E. W., and AMSTUTZ, K. L., *J. Am. Chem. Soc.* **51,** 3638–3641 (1929).

MA38. MARXER, A., and MIESCHER, K., *Helv. Chim. Acta* **34,** 924–931 (1951).

MA38a. MARYOTT, A. A., and BUCKLEY, F., *Natl. Bur. Standards (U.S.) Circ.* No. **537** (1953).

MA39. MASON, E. A., and KREEVOY, M. M., *J. Am. Chem. Soc.* **77,** 5808–5814 (1955).

MA40. MASSIE, S. P., *Iowa State Coll. J. Sci.* **21,** 41–45 (1946).

MA41. MATIZEN, E. V., and KUSKOVA, N. V., *Zhur. Fiz. Khim.* **34,** 2223–2229 (1960).

MA41a. MATTER, O., German Patent 301,450 (Oct. 22, 1917).

MA42. MAUGE, R., MALEN, C., and BOISSIER, J. R., *Bull. soc. chim. France* **1956,** 425–428.

MA42a. MAVEL, G., and MARTIN, G., *Compt. rend.* **252,** 110–112 (1961).

MA43. MAXIM, N., *Bull. soc. chim. France* **41,** 809–813 (1927).

MA44. MAXIM, N., and MAVRODINEANU, R., *Bull. soc. chim. France* **2,** 591–600 (1935).

MA45. MAXIM, N., and MAVRODINEANU, R., *Bull. soc. chim. France* **3,** 1084–1093 (1936).

MC1. MCCORKLE, M. R., *Iowa State Coll. J. Sci.* **14,** 64–66 (1939).

MC2. MCCOY, R. E., and BAUER, S. H., *J. Am. Chem. Soc.* **78,** 2061–2065 (1956).

MC3. MCCROSKY, C. R., BERGSTROM, F. W., and WAITKINS, G., *J. Am. Chem. Soc.* **62,** 2031–2034 (1940).

MC4. MCDANIEL, D. H., *Science* **125,** 545–546 (1957).

MC5. MCDOWELL, M. J., and KRAUS, C. A., *J. Am. Chem. Soc.* **73,** 2170–2173 (1951).

MC6. MCELVAIN, S. M., and TATE, B. E., *J. Am. Chem. Soc.* **67,** 202–204 (1945).

MC7. McIntosh, R. L., Mead, D. J., and Fuoss, R. M., *J. Am. Chem. Soc.* **62**, 506–508 (1940).

MC7a. McIvor, R. A., Hubley, C. E., Grant, G. A., and Grey, A. A., *Can. J. Chem.* **36**, 820–834 (1958).

MC8. McKeever, C. H., and Nemec, J. W. (to Rohm and Haas Co.), U.S. Patent 2,617,827 (Nov. 11, 1952).

ME1. Meerburg, P. A., *Z. physik. Chem.* **40**, 647 (1902).

ME1a. Meerwein, H., Battenberg, E., Gold, H., Pfeil, E., and Willfang, G., *J. prakt. Chem.* **154**, 83–156 (1939).

ME2. Meiners, A. F., Bolze, C., Scherer, A., and Morriss, F. V., *J. Org. Chem.* **23**, 1122–1125 (1958).

ME3. Meisenheimer, J., and Bernhard, H., *Ann.* **428**, 254–268 (1922).

ME4. Meisenheimer, J., and Bratring, K., *Ann.* **397**, 273–300 (1913).

ME5. Meisenheimer, J., Greeske, H., and Willmersdorf, A., *Ber.* **55**, 513–522 (1922).

ME6. Meisenheimer, J., and Link, J., *Ann.* **479**, 211–277 (1930).

ME7. Meisenheimer, J., and Lohsner, A., *Ann.* **428**, 269–278 (1922).

ME8. Mellor, J. W., *A Comprehensive Treatise on Inorganic and Theoretical Chemistry.* Longmans, Green & Co., New York, N. Y. (1928), Vol. VIII, p. 144.

ME8a. Mel'nikov, N. N., Shvetsova-Shilovskaya, K. D., and Millshtein, I. M., *Zhur. Obshcheĭ Khim.* **30**, 197–199 (1960).

ME9. Menschutkin, N., *Z. physik. Chem.* **5**, 598 (1890).

ME10. Menschutkin, N., *Z. physik. Chem.* **6**, 41 (1890).

ME11. Menschutkin, N., *Ber.* **28**, 1398–1407 (1895).

ME12. Menschutkin, N., *Zhur. Russ. Fiz.-Khim. Obshchestva* **31**, 43 (1899).

ME13. Men'shikov, G. P., *Izvest. Akad. Nauk S.S.S.R., Otdel. Khim. Nauk* **1937**, 1035–1048.

ME13a. Mercier, P. L., and Kraus, C. A., *Proc. Natl. Acad. Sci. U.S.* **42**, 65–67 (1956).

ME14. Merling, G., *Ann.* **264**, 310–351 (1891).

ME15. Merz, V., and Gasiorowski, K., *Ber.* **17**, 623–640 (1884).

ME16. Meyer, H., and Hopff, H., *Ber.* **54**, 2274–2282 (1921).

ME17. Meyer, V., and Lecco, J., *Ann.* **180**, 173–191 (1876).

MI1. Middleton, W. J. (to E. I. du Pont de Nemours & Co.), U.S. Patents 2,766,243 (Oct. 9. 1956); 2,766,246–7 (Oct. 9, 1956).

MI1a. Middleton, W. J., Little, E. L., Coffman, D. D., and Englehardt, V. A., *J. Am. Chem. Soc.* **80**, 2795–2806 (1958).

MI1b. Mikhaĭlov, B. M., Blokhina, A. N., and Kostroma, T. V., *Zhur. Obshcheĭ Khim.* **29**, 1483–1486 (1959).

MI1c. Mikhaĭlov, B. M., and Fedotov, N. S., *Izvest. Akad. Nauk S.S.S.R., Otdel. Khim. Nauk* **1960**, 1590–1594.

MI1d. Mikhailov, G. I., *Zhur. Priklad. Khim.* **27**, 217–219 (1954).

MI2. Missan, S. P., Becker, L. I., and Meites, L., *J. Am. Chem. Soc.* **83**, 58–61 (1961).

MI3. Miyahara, S., *Nippon Kagaku Zasshi* **81**, 1158–1163 (1960).

MI4. Mizutani, M., *Z. Phys. Chem.* **116**, 350–358 (1925); **118**, 337 (1925).

MI5.   MIZZON, R. H., HENNESSEY, M. A., and SCHOLZ, C. R., *J. Am. Chem. Soc.* **76**, 2414–2417 (1954).

MO1.   MOEDE, J. A., and CURRAN, C., *J. Am. Chem. Soc.* **71**, 852–858 (1949).

MO1a.   MOGILEVSKIĬ, M. Y. U., TSEL'M, N. K., ALEKSEEV, N. F., TAVOBILOV, M. F., KISELEV, V. M., and BUKHRYAKOVA, V. I., U.S.S.R. Patent 127,662 (Apr. 12, 1960).

MO2.   MOHR, W., and ARBET, A., *Fette u. Seifen* **46**, 678–682 (1939).

MO3.   MONSOUR, V., and COLMER, A. R., *J. Bact.* **63**, 597–603 (1952).

MO4.   MONTAGNE, M., *Ann. chim.* **13**, 40–135 (1930).

MO5.   MONTAGNE, M., and GUILMART, T., *Bull. soc. chim. France* **12**, 836–839 (1945).

MO6.   MONVAL, P. M., *Compt. rend.* **205**, 1154–1156 (1937).

MO7.   MOORE, M. L., *Org. Reactions* **5**, 301–330 (1949).

MO8.   MOORE, T. S., and WINMILL, T. F., *J. Chem. Soc.* **101**, 1635 (1912).

MO9.   MOORE, T. S., and WINMILL, T. F., *J. Chem. Soc.* **101**, 1651–1662 (1912).

MO10.   MOORE, T. S., and WINMILL, T. F., *J. Chem. Soc.* **101**, 1635–1676 (1912).

MO11.   MOREY, G. H., U.S. Patent 2,415,020 (Jan. 28, 1947).

MO12.   MOREY, G. H. (to Commercial Solvents Corp.), U.S. Patent 2,440,724 (May 4, 1948).

MO13.   MOREY, G. H. (to Commercial Solvents Corp.), U.S. Patent 2,441,669 (May 18, 1948).

MO14.   MORIN, H., *Therapie* **7**, No. 1, 57–62 (1952).

MO14a.   MORTON, A. A., and WARD, F. K., *J. Org. Chem.* **25**, 120–124 (1960).

MO15.   MOSHER, H. S., and LaCOMBE, E., *J. Am. Chem. Soc.* **72**, 3994, 4991 (1950).

MO16.   MOSHIER, R. W., and SPIALTER, L., *J. Org. Chem.* **21**, 1050–1051 (1956).

MO17.   MOUSSERON, M., JACQUIER, R., and ZAGDOUN, R., *Bull. soc. chim. France* **1953**, 974–981.

MO18.   MOZGOV, I. E., and BABAYAN, A. T., *Farmakol. i Toksikol.* **20**, 36–42 (1957).

MU1.   MUELLER, E., and HUBER-EMDEN, H., *Ann.* **649**, 70–87 (1961).

MU1a.   MUELLER, E., HUBER-EMDEN, H., and RUNDEL, W., *Ann.* **623**, 34–46 (1959).

MU1.   MUTTERTIES, E. J., *J. Inorg. & Nuclear Chem.* **15**, 182–183 (1960).

MU2.   MULLER, A., *Bull. soc. chim. France* **43**, 213–217 (1885).

MU2a.   MÜLLER, E., RUNDEL, W., and HUBER-EMDEN, H., *Angew. Chem.* **69**, 614 (1957).

MU3.   MULLER, J. A., *Ann. chim.* **20**, 116–130 (1910).

MU4.   MULLER, M. A., *Bull. soc. chim. France* **44**, 608–611 (1885).

MU4a.   MULLER, N., and PRITCHARD, D. E., *J. Chem. Phys.* **31**, 1471–1476 (1959).

MU5.   MULLER, R., *Ann.* **108**, 1–7 (1856).

MU6.   MUMFORD, S. A., and PHILLIPS, J. W. C., *J. Chem. Soc.* **1929**, 2128.

N

NA1.   NADEAU, A., *J. Fisheries Research Board Can.* **4**, 355–362 (1939); **5**, 121–130 (1940).

NA1a.   NADOR, K., and L., GYERMEK, *Acta Chim. Acad. Sci. Hung.* **2**, 95–101 (1952).

NA2. NAGASAWA, T., and SOGA, O., *Shimane Diagaku Ronshû, Shizen Kagaku* No. 10, 32–39 (1961).

NA2a. NAKANISHI, K., GOTO, T., and OHASI, M., *Bull. Chem. Soc. Japan* **30**, 403–408 (1957).

NA2b. NAKANISHI, K., *Infrared Absorption Spectroscopy.* Holden-Day, Inc., San Francisco, Calif. (1962), pp. 38, 156.

NA3. NAZAROV, I. N., and MISTRYUKOV, E. A., *Izvest. Akad. Nauk S.S.S.R., Otdel. Khim. Nauk* **1958**, 335–338.

NA4. NAZAROV, I. N., RAKCHEEVA, V. N., and SHMONINA, L. I., *Zhur. Obshcheǐ Khim.* **22**, 611–617 (1952).

NA5. NADEAU, A., *J. Fisheries Research Board Can.* **4**, 412–423 (1939).

NE1. NECKEL, A., and KOHLER, F., *Monatsh.* **87**, 176–198 (1956).

NE1a. NEILANDS, J. B., *J. Fisheries Research Board Can.* **6**, 368–379 (1945).

NE2. NEKRASOVA, V. A., and SHUǏKIN, N. I., *Izvest. Akad. Nauk S.S.S.R., Otdel. Khim. Nauk* **1952**, 495–497.

NE3. NEKRASOVA, V. A., and SHUǏKIN, N. I., *Izvest. Akad. Nauk S.S.S.R., Otdel. Khim. Nauk* **1952**, 646–648.

NE3a. NESMEYANOV, A. N., FREǏDLINA, R. KH., and BELYAVSKIǏ, A. B., *Doklady Akad. Nauk S.S.S.R.* **122**, 821–824 (1958).

NE4. NEUMEYER, J. L., CANNON, J. G., and BUCKLEY, J. P., *J. Med. Pharm. Chem.* **5**, 784–792 (1962).

NI1. NICKERSON, J. T. R., GOLDBLITH, S. A., and PROCTOR, B. E., *Food Technol.* **4**, 84–88 (1950).

NI2. NICODEMUS, O., and SCHMIDT, W. (to I.G. Farbenindustrie A.-G.), U.S. Patent 1,857,655 (May 10, 1929); French Patent 685,345 (Nov. 21, 1929).

NI3. NIEUWLAND, J. A., and VOGT, R. R., *The Chemistry of Acetylene.* Reinhold Publishing Corp., New York, N.Y. (1945), pp. 74–75.

NI4. Nippon Chemical Industries Co., Japanese Patent 157,986 (July 28, 1943).

NO1. NOMURA, M., YAMAMOTO, K., and ODA, R., *J. Chem. Soc. Japan, Ind. Chem. Soc.* **57**, 219–220 (1954).

NO1a. NORRIS, J. F., and FRANKLIN, A. I., *Am. Chem. J.* **21**, 499–509 (1899).

NO2. NOTEVARP, O., *Tidsskr. Kjemi Bergvesen Met.* **3**, 2–6 (1943).

NO3. NÖTH, H., and BEYER, H., *Chem. Ber.* **93**, 928–938 (1960).

O

OB1. OBATA, Y., *J. Arg. Chem. Soc. Japan* **18**, 1008–1009 (1942).

OB2. OBATA, Y., *J. Arg. Chem. Soc. Japan* **18**, 1010–1012 (1942).

OB3. OBATA, Y., and MATANO, K., *J. Oil Chemists' Soc.* (*Japan*) **2**, 112–114 (1953).

OB4. OBATA, Y., and YAMANISHI, T., *Bull. Japan Soc. Sci. Fisheries* **16**, 361–362 (1951).

OD1. ODDO, G., and SCANDOLA, E., *Z. physik. Chem.* **66**, 138–152 (1909); *Gazz. chim. ital.* **39**, I, 572 (1909).

OF1. Office national d'études et de recherches aeronautiques (O.N.E.R.A.), Brit. Patent 736,505 (Sept. 7, 1955).

OG1. OGATA, A., and KOMODA, T., *J. Pharm. Soc. Japan* **63**, 653–658 (1943).

OG2.   Ogg, R. A., Jr., and Ray, J. D., *J. Chem. Phys.* **26,** 1339–1340 (1957).

OK1.   O'Konski, C. T., and Flautt, T. J., *J. Chem. Phys.* **27,** 815–816 (1957).

OL1.   Olin, J. F. (to Sharples Chem., Inc.), U.S. Patent 2,411,802 (Nov. 26, 1946).

OL2.   Olin, J. F. (to Sharples Chem., Inc.), U.S. Patent 2,388,218 (Oct. 30, 1945).

OL3.   Olin, J. F., and McKenna, J. F. (to Sharples Chem., Inc.), U.S. Patent 2,365,721 (Dec. 26, 1944).

OL4.   Olin, J. F., and Schwoegler, E. J. (to Sharples Chem., Inc.), U.S. Patent 2,373,705 (April 17, 1945).

OL5.   Olomucki, M., *Compt. rend.* **237,** 192–194 (1953).

OL6.   Olomucki, M., *Ann. chim.* **5,** 846–904 (1960).

OM1.   Omura, I., Higasi, K., and Baba, H., *Bull. Chem. Soc. Japan* **29,** 504–507 (1956).

ON1.   Onda, M., *J. Pharm. Soc. Japan* **74,** 911–914 (1954).

OP1.   Opitz, G., Hellmann, H., and Schubert, H. W., *Ann.* **623,** 112–117 (1959).

OS1.   Ostwald, W., *J. prakt. Chem.* **33,** 364 (1886).

OS1a.   Osthoff, R. C., and Brown, C. A., *J. Am. Chem. Soc.* **74,** 2378–2380 (1952).

OS2.   Osugi, K., *J. Pharm. Soc. Japan* **75,** 1281–1286 (1955).

OT1.   Ota, Y., Otani, G., and Enomoto, R., *Yakugaku Zasshi* **80,** 1153–1155 (1960).

OT2.   Ott, E., and Dittus, G., *Ber.* **76B,** 80–84 (1943).

OV1.   Ovakimian, G., Christman, C., Kuna, M., and Levene, P. B., *J. Biol. Chem.* **134,** 151–161 (1940).

OX1.   Oxley, H. F., Thomas, E. B., and Hindley, F. (to British Celanese Ltd.), British Patent 656,154 (Aug. 15, 1951).

P

PA1.   Palazzo, G., Rogers, E. F., and Marini-Bettolo, G. B., *Gazz. chim. ital.* **84,** 915–920 (1954).

PA1a.   Palmer, R. R., Ed., *Rand McNally Atlas of World History.* Rand McNally and Co., New York, N. Y. (1957), p. 30.

PA2.   Pappalardo, J. A., and Dolle, R., private communication. See Senior Thesis of R. Dolle, Univ. of Dayton, 1957.

PA3.   Pappalardo, J. A., and Larimore, R., private communication. See Senior Thesis of R. Larimore, Univ. of Dayton, 1961.

PA3a.   Pappalardo, J. A., and O'Brien, P., private communication. See M.S. Thesis of P. O'Brien, Univ. of Dayton, 1963.

PA4.   Paraskova, V., *Compt. rend.* **198,** 1701–1703 (1934).

PA5.   Parcell, R. F., and Pollard, C. B., *J. Am. Chem. Soc.* **72,** 2385–2386 (1950).

PA6.   Parcell, R. F., and Pollard, C. B., *J. Am. Chem. Soc.,* **72,** 3312–3313 (1950).

PA6a.   Parry, R. W., Kodama, G., and Schultz, D. R., *J. Am. Chem. Soc.* **80,** 24–27 (1958).

PA7.   PARTHEIL, A., *Ann.* **268,** 152–197 (1892).

PA8.   PARTHEIL, A., and BROICH, H. VON, *Ber.* **30,** 618–621 (1897).

PA9.   PARTMANN, W., *Z. Lebensm.-Untersuch. u.-Forsch.* **93,** 341–356 (1951).

PA10.   PASCAL, P., *Ann. chim.* **19,** 5–69 (1910).

PA11.   PASSINO, H. J., (to The M. W. Kellogg Co.), U.S. Patent 2,768,878 (Oct. 30, 1956).

PA12.   PASSON, M., *Ber.* **24,** 1681–1686 (1891).

PA13.   PATHAK, K. D., and SUBBA-RAO, B. C., *J. Sci. Ind. Research (India)* **20D,** 142–145 (1961).

PA14.   PATTERSON, A., Jr., and FELSING, W. A., *J. Am. Chem. Soc.* **60,** 2693–2695 (1938).

PA15.   PAUL, R., and TCHELITCHEFF, S., *Compt. rend.* **238,** 2089–2091 (1954).

PE1.   PEAK, D. A., and WATKINS, T. I., *J. Chem. Soc.* **1951,** 3292–3296.

PE1a.   PEARSON, R. G., and VOGELSONG, D. C., *J. Am. Chem. Soc.* **80,** 1038–1043 (1958).

PE2.   PEARSON, R. G., and WILLIAMS, F. V., *J. Am. Chem. Soc.* **76,** 258–260 (1954).

PE2a.   Pennsalt Chemicals Corp., *Amines Properties and Applications.* Bulletin S-129B, Pennsalt Chemicals Corp., Three Penn Center, Philadelphia 2, Pa. (1961), 48 pp.

PE3.   PERKIN, W. D., *J. Chem. Soc.* **155,** 680–749 (1889).

PE4.   PERRINE, T. D., *J. Org. Chem.* **16,** 1303–1307 (1951).

PE5.   PERRINE, T. D., *J. Org. Chem.* **18,** 1356–1367 (1953).

PE6.   PETERS, W., *Ber.* **40,** 1478–1482 (1907).

PE7.   PETERSON, T., *Ann.* **102,** 312–317 (1857).

PE8.   PETERSON, T., *Ann.* **102,** 317–324 (1875).

PE9.   PETERSON, T., and GÖSSMANN, A., *Ann.* **101,** 310–313 (1857).

PE9a.   PETRACHKOV, F. A., *Zhur. Fiz. Khim.* **28,** 1408–1416 (1954).

PE9b.   PETRACHKOV, F. A., and GOL'TSCHMIDT, V. A., *Zhur. Fiz. Khim.* **28,** 1213–1218 (1954).

PE10.   PETROV, A. A., and KORMER, V. A., *Doklady Akad. Nauk S.S.S.R.* **126,** 1278–1281 (1959).

PE11.   PETROV, A. A., and MARETINA, I. A., *Zhur. Obshcheĭ Khim.* **29,** 2458 (1959); *J. Gen. Chem. (U.S.S.R.)* **29,** 2423 (1959) (Eng. Trans.).

PE12.   PETROV, A. A., and MARETINA, I. A., *Zhur. Obshcheĭ Khim.* **30,** 696 (1960); *J. Gen. Chem. (U.S.S.R.)* **30,** 718 (1960) (Eng. Trans.).

PE12a. PETROV, A. A., MINGALEVA, K. S., MARETINA, I. A., and NEMIROVSKIĬ, V. D., *Zhur. Obshcheĭ Khim.* **30,** 2238–2243 (1960).

PE13.   PETROV, A. A., RAZUMOVA, N. A., GENUSOV, M. L., and YAKOVLEVA, T. V., *Zhur. Obshcheĭ Khim.* **30,** 1160–1165 (1960).

PF1.   PFORDTE, K., and LEUSCHNER, G., *Ann.* **646,** 25–30 (1961).

PH1.   PHILLIPS, A. P., *J. Am. Chem. Soc.* **77,** 1693–1695 (1955).

PH2.   PHILLIPS, G. M., HUNTER, J. S., and SUTTON, L. E., *J. Chem. Soc.,* **1945,** 146–162.

PI0.   PIAUX, L., and GAUDEMAR, M., *Bull. soc. chim. France* **1957,** 786–789.

PI1.   PICKERING, S. U., *J. Chem. Soc.* **63,** 178 (1893).

PI2.   PICKERING, S. U., *J. Chem. Soc.* **63,** 141–198 (1893).

PI3.   PICON, M., *Bull. soc. chim. France* **33,** 89 (1923).

PI4.   PIERSON, R. H., FLETCHER, A. N., and GANTZ, E. S., *Anal. Chem.* **28**, 1218–1239 (1956).

PI5.   PINNER, A., *Ber.* **12**, 2053–2058 (1879).

PL1.   PLATE, A. F., VOLPIN, M. E., REFORMATSKAYA, E. A., and ZOTOVA, S. V., *Zhur. Obshcheĭ Khim.* **26**, 684–689 (1956); *J. Gen. Chem.* (*U.S.S.R.*) **26**, 785–790 (1956) (Eng. Trans.).

PL2.   PLIML, J., BOROVIČKA, M., and PROTIVA, M., *Chem. Listy* **50**, 1630–1635 (1956).

PL3.   PLIMPTON, R. T., *J. Chem. Soc.* **39**, 332 (1881).

PL4.   PLIMPTON, R. T., *J. Chem. Soc.* **39**, 335 (1881).

PL5.   PLÖCHL, J., *Ber.* **21**, 2117 (1888).

PO0.   POHLAND, E., and MEHL, W., *Z. physik. Chem.* A164, 48–54 (1933).

PO1.   POLITO, A., private communication from The Ames Laboratories, Inc., 132 Water Street, South Norwalk, Conn.

PO2.   POLONI, A., *Giorn. psichiat. e neuropatol.* **78**, 457–464 (1950).

PO3.   POPE, W. J., and READ, J., *J. Chem. Soc.* **101**, 519–529 (1912).

PO4.   POPOV, M. A., *J. Gen. Chem.* (*U.S.S.R.*) **18**, 438–442 (1948).

PO5.   POPOV, M. A., *Zhur. Obshcheĭ Khim.* **18**, 1109–1112 (1948).

PO6.   POPOV, M. A., and SHUIKĬN, N. I., *Izvest. Akad. Nauk S.S.S.R., Otdel. Khim. Nauk* **1955**, 308–313; *Bull. Acad. Sci. U.S.S.R. Div. Chem. Sci.* **1955**, 275–279 (Engl. Trans.).

PO7.   POZZO-BALBI, T., *Ann. chim.* (*Rome*) **45**, 1178–1184 (1955).

PR1.   PRATT, H. R. C., and NORRIS, G. O. (to Imperial Chemical Industries Ltd.), U.S. Patent 2,349,461 (May 23, 1944).

PR1a.   PRASAD, S., and CHATTERJEE, K. N., *J. Indian Chem. Soc.* **35**, 901–903 (1958).

PR1b.   PRASAD, S., and KRISHNAMURTY, D. R., *J. Indian Chem. Soc.* **34**, 563–567 (1957).

PR1c.   PRASAD, S., and KRISHNAN, V., *J. Indian Chem. Soc.* **35**, 352–354 (1958).

PR1d.   PRASAD, S., and TRIPATHI, J. B., *J. Indian Chem. Soc.* **34**, 749–752 (1957).

PR1e.   PRASAD, S., and TRIPATHI, J. B., *J. Indian Chem. Soc.* **35**, 415–418 (1958).

PR2.   PRELOG, V., *Collection Czechoslov. Chem. Communs.* **2**, 712–722 (1930).

PR3.   PRÉVOST, C., and DEMAUNY, H. C., *Compt. rend.* **216**, 771–772 (1943).

PR4.   PRICE, C. C., GUTHRIE, D. B., PEEL, E. W., and HERBRANDSON, H. F., *J. Org. Chem.* **11**, 281–285 (1946).

PR5.   PRICE, W. C., *Chem. Revs.* **41**, 257–272 (1947).

PR6.   PROCTOR, B. E., NICKERSON, J. T. R., and GOLDBLITH, S. A., *Refrig. Eng.* **58**, 375–379 (1950).

PR7.   PRUETT, R. L., BARR, J. T., RAPP, K. E., BAHNER, C. T., GIBSON, J. P., and LAFFERTY, R. N., Jr., *J. Am. Chem. Soc.* **72**, 3646–3650 (1950).

PU1.   PULLMANN, B. J., and WEST, B. O., *J. Inorg. & Nuclear Chem.* **19**, 262–271 (1961).

PU2.   PUTERBAUGH, W. H., and HAUSER, C. R., *J. Org. Chem.* **24**, 416–418 (1959).

PY1.   PYMAN, F. L., and LEVENE, H. H. L., (to Boot's Pure Drug Company, Ltd.), British Patent 433,086 (Aug. 8, 1935); U.S. Patent 2,056,867 (Oct. 6, 1936).

PY2.   PYMAN, F. L., and LEVENE, H. H. L. (to Boot's Pure Drug Company, Ltd.), U.S. Patent 2,121,509 (June 21, 1936); British Patent 456,916 (Nov. 18, 1936).

R

RA1.   RAKSHIT, J. N., *J. Am. Chem. Soc.* **35**, 1781–1783 (1913).

RA2.   RALEY, J. H., and SEUBOLD, F. H., Jr. (to Shell Development Co.), U.S. Patent 2,537,857 (Jan. 9, 1951).

RA3.   RALSTON, A. W., HOERR, C. W., and DUBROW, P. L., *J. Org. Chem.* **9**, 259–266 (1944).

RA4.   RALSTON, A. W., RECK, R. A., HARWOOD, H. J., and DUBROW, P. L., *J. Org. Chem.* **13**, 186–190 (1948).

RA5.   RASSOW, H., *Z. anorg. Chem.* **114**, 131 (1920).

RA6.   RATAJCZAK, S., *Bull. soc. chim. France* **1960**, 487–488.

RE1.   RECK, R. A., HARWOOD, H. J., and RALSTON, A. W., *J. Org. Chem.* **12**, 517–521 (1947).

RE2.   REED, T. M., III, *J. Phys. Chem.* **59**, 428–432 (1955).

RE2a.   REESE, C. B., *J. Chem. Soc.* **1958**, 899–901.

RE3.   REIBER, H. G., and STEWART, T. D., *J. Am. Chem. Soc.* **62**, 3026–3030 (1940).

RE4.   REMICK, A. E., *Electronic Interpretations of Organic Chemistry.* John Wiley and Sons, Inc., New York, N.Y. (1949), 2nd ed., p. 282.

RE5.   RENSHAW, R. R., *J. Am. Chem. Soc.* **34**, 1615–1619 (1912).

RE6.   REPPE, W. (to Badische Anilin- und Soda-Fabrik A.-G.), German Patent 839,800 (May 26, 1952).

RE7.   REPPE, W., *et al.*, *Ann.* **596**, 1–25 (1955).

RE8.   REPPE, W., *et al.*, *Ann.* **596**, 80–158 (1955).

RE9.   REPPE, W., FRIEDERICH, H., and SCHWECKENDIEK, W., German Patent 878,352 (June 1, 1953).

RE10.   REPPE, W., HEINTZELER, M., and KUTEPOW, N. VON, German Patent 931,948 (Aug. 22, 1955).

RE11.   REPPE, W., KEYSSNER, E., and HECHT, O. (to I. G. Farbenindustrie A.-G.), U.S. Patent 2,273,141 (Feb. 17, 1942); German Patent 724,759 (July 23, 1942); British Patent 510,904 (Aug. 10, 1939).

RE12.   REPPE, W., KUTEPOW, N. VON, and HEINTZELER, M. (to I. G. Farbenindustrie A.-G.), German Patent 909,937 (Apr. 29, 1954).

RE13.   REPPE, W., and SCHOLZ, H. (to I. G. Farbenindustrie A.-G.), U.S. Patent 2,268,129 (Dec. 30, 1941); British Patent 510,457 (Aug. 2, 1939); German Patent 730,850 (Dec. 24, 1942).

RE14.   REPPE, W., and VETTER, H., *Ann.* **582**, 133–161 (1953).

RE15.   REYCHLER, A., *Bull. soc. chim. Belges* **27**, 217–225, 300–303 (1913).

RE16.   REYNOLDS, D. D., and LAAKSO, T. M. (to Eastman Kodak Co.), U.S. Patent 2,716,134 (Aug. 23, 1955).

RE17.   REYNOLDS, W. B., Phillips Petroleum Company, Bartlesville, Okla., private communication.

RI1.   RICE, R. C., and KOHN, E. J., *J. Am. Chem. Soc.* **77**, 4052–4054 (1955),

RI1a.   RICHARZ, W., LUTZ, M., and GUYER, A., *Helv. Chim. Acta* **42**, 2212–2218 (1959).

RI2.   RICHTER, H., *Physik. Z.* **36**, 85–91 (1935).

RI3.   RIEGEL, B., STANGER, D. W., WIKHOLM, D. M., MOLD, J. D., and SOMMER, H., *J. Biol. Chem.* **177**, 7–11 (1949).

RI4.   RIES, A., *Z. Kryst.* **36**, 354 (1902).

RI5.   RIES, A., *Z. Kryst.* **49**, 513–617 (1911).

RI6.   RIES, A., *Z. Kryst.* **55**, 454–522 (1920).

RI7.   RIMBACH, E., and VOLK, H., *Z. physik. Chem.* **77**, 385–410 (1911).

RI8.   RINNE, A., *Ann.* **168**, 261–266 (1873).

RO1.   ROBERTS, J. J., and ROSS, W. C. J., *J. Chem. Soc.* **1952**, 4288–4295.

RO2.   ROBERTS, L. D., and MAYER, J. E., *J. Chem. Phys.* **9**, 852–858 (1941).

RO2a. ROBINSON, D. W., and MCQUARRIE, D. A., *J. Chem. Phys.* **32**, 556–559
       (1960).

RO3.   ROBINSON, G. M., and ROBINSON, R., *J. Chem. Soc.* **123**, 532–543 (1923).

RO4.   ROBINSON, R. A., *J. Org. Chem.* **16**, 1911–1920 (1951).

RO5.   ROBINSON, R. H. M., INGRAM, G. C., and EDDY, B. P., *J. Sci. Food Agr.*
       3, 175–179 (1952).

RO6.   ROEMER, H., *Ber.* **6**, 1101–1103 (1873).

RO7.   ROGERS, M. T., and PANISH, M. B., *J. Am. Chem. Soc.* **77**, 3684–3686
       (1955).

RO8.   Rohm and Hass Co., *The Methylamines*. Philadelphia, Pa. (1954).

RO9.   ROINE, P., ANTILA, M., and SUHONEN, I., *J. Animal Sci.* **12**, 117–123
       (1953).

RO9a. ROMERS, C., and KEULEMANS, E. W. M., *Koninkl. Ned. Akad. Wetenschap.
       Proc., Ser. B*, **61**, 345–348 (1958).

RO10. ROMETSCH, R., MARXER, A., and MEISCHER, K., *Helv. Chim. Acta* **34**,
       1611–1618 (1951).

RO11. RONOLD, O. A., and JAKOBSEN, F., *J. Soc. Chem. Ind.* **66**, 160–166 (1947).

RO12. ROSE, J. D., *B.I.O.S. Final Report No. 359*, Item No. 22 H.M.S.O.,
       1946.

RO13. ROSE, J. D., and WEEDON, B. C. L. (to Imperial Chemical Industries
       Ltd.), British Patent 619,206 (Mar. 4, 1949).

RO14. ROSE, J. D., and WEEDON, B. C. L., *J. Chem. Soc.* **1949**, 782–785.

RO15. ROSENBAUM, E. J., RUBIN, D. J., and SANDBURG, C. R., *J. Chem. Phys.*
       8, 366–368 (1940).

RO16. ROTHMUND, V., *Z. physik. Chem.* **26**, 433–492 (1898).

RO17. ROTHROCK, D. A., Jr., and KRAUS, C. A., *J. Am. Chem. Soc.* **59**,
       1699–1703 (1937).

RO18. ROTHSTEIN, E., *J. Chem. Soc.* **1940**, 1558–1560.

RO19. ROTHSTEIN, E., *J. Chem. Soc.* **1940**, 1560–1565.

RU1.   RUFF, J. K., *J. Am. Chem. Soc.* **83**, 1798–1800 (1961).

RU2.   RUFF, J. K., and HAWTHORNE, M. F., *J. Am. Chem. Soc.* **82**, 2141–2144
       (1960).

RU3.   RUNGE, F., ENGELBRECHT, H. J., and FRANKE, H., *Chem. Ber.* **88**,
       533–541 (1955).

RU4.   RUNGE, F., and PFEIFFER, F., *Chem. Ber.* **90**, 1757–1760 (1957).

RU5.   RUPPERT, W. (to Badische Anilin- und Soda-Fabrik A.-G.), German
       Patent 1,080,112 (Apr. 21, 1960).

S

SA1.   SABATIER, P., and FERNANDEZ, A., *Compt. rend.* **185**, 241–244 (1927).

SA2.   SABATIER, P., and MAILHE, A., *Ann. chim.* **16**, 70–107 (1909).

SA3.   SABATIER, P., and MAILHE, A., *Compt. rend.* **148**, 898–901 (1909).

SA4. SABATIER, P., and REID, E. E., *Catalysis in Organic Chemistry*. D. Van Nostrand Company, New York, N.Y. (1923).

SA5. SABATIER, P., and SENDERENS, J. B., *Compt. rend.* **140**, 482–486 (1905).

SA6. SACHTLEBEN, R., *Ber.* **11**, 734 (1878).

SA6a. SAHASRABUDHEY, R. H., PRASAD-RAO, M. A., and BOKIL, I., *J. Indian Chem. Soc.* **30**, 652–664 (1953).

SA7. SAHASRABUDHEY, R. H., and RAMACHANDRAN, P. K., *J. Indian Chem. Soc.* **29**, 489–492 (1952).

SA7a. SAKHAROVA, M., and ZEMSKOV, S. V., *Doklady Akad. Nauk S.S.S.R.* **120**, 539–540 (1958).

SA8. SALANT, E. O., *Proc. Natl. Acad. Sci. U.S.* **12**, 74–80 (1926).

SA9. SANDELL, K. B., *Naturwiss.* **42**, 605–606 (1955).

SA9a. SÄNGER, R., STEIGER, O., and GÄCHTER, K., *Helv. Phys. Acta* **5**, 200–210 (1932).

SA9b. SANDERSON, R. T., *J. Am. Chem. Soc.* **77**, 4531–4532 (1955).

SA10. SANNO, Y., KURITA, A., and IMAI, K., *J. Pharm. Soc. Japan* **75**, 1461–1466 (1955).

SA11. SANO, H., *Yakugaku Zasshi* **81**, 1310–1313, 1313–1317 (1961).

SA12. SASAKI, R., and FUJIMAKI, M., *J. Agr. Chem. Soc. Japan* **27**, 420–424 (1953).

SA13. SASAKI, S., WATANABE, T., and TASAKA, Y., *J. Sericult. Sci. Japan* **19**, 375–381 (1950).

SA14. SAUER, J. C., HOWK, B. W., and STIEHL, R. T., *J. Am. Chem. Soc.* **81**, 693–696 (1959).

SA15. SAWA, Y., *J. Pharm. Soc. Japan* **66**, 40–41 (1946).

SC1. SCHAEFFER, G. W., and ANDERSON, E. R., *J. Am. Chem. Soc.* **71**, 2143–2145 (1949).

SC2. SCHIFF, R., *Ber.* **19**, 566 (1886).

SC3. SCHLEGEL, F., *Ber.* **64B**, 1739–1743 (1931).

SC3a. SCHLESINGER, H. I., FLODIN, N. W., and BURG, A. B., *J. Am. Chem. Soc.* **61**, 1078–1083 (1939).

SC4. SCHLÖGL, K., and ORGLER, K., *Monatsh.* **90**, 306–320 (1959).

SC5. SCHLUBACH, H. H., and BALLAUF, F., *Ber.* **54B**, 2811–2834 (1921).

SC6. SCHLUNDT, H., *J. Phys. Chem.* **5**, 503–526 (1901).

SC7. SCHMIDLE, C. J. (to Rohm and Haas Co.), U.S. Patent 2,778,826 (Jan. 22, 1957).

SC8. SCHMIDLE, C. J., and MANSFIELD, R. C., *J. Am. Chem. Soc.* **77**, 4636–4638 (1955).

SC9. SCHMIDT, B. M., BROWN, L. C., and WILLIAMS, D., *J. Mol. Spectroscopy* **2**, 539–550 (1958).

SC10. SCHMIDT, E., *Ann.* **267**, 254–268 (1891).

SC11. SCHMIDT, E., and KLEINE, G., *Ann.* **337**, 81–102 (1904).

SC12. SCHMIDT, W., and ALBRECHT, H., German Patent 611,283 (Mar. 25, 1935).

SC13. SCHMITZ, K. H., German Patent 270,260 (June 3, 1913).

SC14. SCHNEIDER, H. J., ADKINS, H., and McELVAIN, S. M., *J. Am. Chem. Soc.* **74**, 4287–4290 (1952).

SC15. SCHOLL, R., *Ber.* **74B**, 1171–1181 (1941).

SC16. SCHOLTZ, M., *Arch. Pharm.* **247**, 538 (1909).

SC17. SCHÖNE, A., *Chemiker-Ztg.* **33**, 77 (1909).

SC18. SCHOTTEN, C., *Ber.* **15**, 421–427 (1882).

SC19. SCHRIEBER, R. S., and SCHRINER, R. L., *J. Am. Chem. Soc.* **57**, 1445–1447 (1935).

SC19a. SCHLUBACH, H. H., and BALLAUF, F., *Ber.* **54B**, 2811–2834 (1921).

SC19b. SCHLUBACH, H. H., *Ber.* **53B**, 1689–1693 (1920).

SC20. SCHULTE, K. E., and GOES, M., *Arch. Pharm.* **290**, 118–130 (1957).

SC21. SCHWARZENBACH, G., EPPRECHT, A., and ERLENMEYER, H., *Helv. Chim. Acta* **19**, 1292–1304 (1936).

SC22. SCHWOEGLER, E. J., and ADKINS, H., *J. Am. Chem. Soc.* **61**, 3499–3502 (1939).

SC23. SCHWYZER, R., *Acta Chem. Scand.* **6**, 219–222 (1952).

SC24. SCOTT, F. L., OESTERLING, R. E., TYCZKOWSKI, E. A., and INMAN, C. E., *Chem & Ind. (London)* **1960**, 528–529.

SC25. SCUDI, J. V., and TENENBAUM, L. E. (to Nepera Chemical Co., Inc.), U.S. Patent 2,788,371 (Apr. 9, 1957).

SC26. SCUDI, J. V., TENENBAUM, L. E., ARDSLEY, and GRAIL, G. F. (to Nepera Chemical Co., Inc.), U.S. Patent 2,739,986 (Mar. 27, 1956).

SE1. SEHA, Z., Czechoslovakian Patent 88,639 (Feb. 15, 1959).

SE1a. SEHA, Z., *Collection Czechoslov. Chem. Communs.* **26**, 2435–2438 (1961).

SE2. SEIFERT, H., and QUAEDVLIEG, M., German Patent 837,696 (May 2, 1952).

SE3. SEKERA, V. C., and MARVEL, C. S., *J. Am. Chem. Soc.* **55**, 345–349 (1933).

SE4. SELTZER, L. E., Ed., *The Columbia Lippincott Gazetteer of the World.* Columbia Univ. Press, New York, N.Y. (1952), pp. 62, 1778.

SE5. SEMENCHENKO, V. K., and SKRIPOV, V. P., *Zhur. Fiz. Khim.* **25**, 362–368 (1951).

SE5a. SEMENCHENKO, V. K., and ZORINA, E. L., *Doklady Akad. Nauk S.S.S.R.* **84**, 1191–1193 (1952); *Zhur. Fiz. Khim.* **26**, 520–529 (1952).

SE6. SEMENCHENKO, V. K., and ZORINA, E. L., *Zhur. Fiz. Khim.* **33**, 1176–1183 (1959).

SE6a. SERCHI, G., BICH, G., and MUNTONI, A., *Chimica (Milan)* **34**, 60–61 (1958).

SE7. SEWARD, R. P., *J. Am. Chem. Soc.*, **73**, 515–517 (1951).

SE8. SEWARD, R. P., *J. Phys. Chem.* **62**, 758–759 (1958).

SH1. SHEWAN, J. M., *Biochem. Soc. Symp. (Cambridge, Engl.)* No. 6 ("Biochemistry of Fish") 28–48 (1951).

SH1a. SHEWAN, J. M., *Nature* **143**, 284 (1939).

SH2. SHIMUZU, K., *J. Chem. Soc. Japan, Pure Chem. Sect.* **77**, 1103–1105 (1956).

SH3. SHINER, V. J., Jr., and SMITH, M., *J. Am. Chem. Soc.* **80**, 4095–4098 (1958).

SH3a. SHOMAKER, V., in ALLEN, P. W., and SUTTON, L. E., *Acta Cryst.*, **3**, 46–72 (1950).

SH4. SHOSTAKOVSKIĬ, M. F., CHEKULAEVA, I. A., and KONDRAT'EVA, L. V., *Izvest. Akad. Nauk S.S.S.R., Otdel. Khim. Nauk* **1959**, 1690.

SH5.　SHREVE, R. N., and BURTSFIELD, D. R., *Ind. Eng. Chem.* **33**, 218–221 (1941).

SI1.　SIEBERT, H., *Z. anorg. u. allgem. Chem.* **273**, 161–169 (1953).

SI2.　SILVA, M., *Compt. rend.* **64**, 1299 (1867).

SI3.　SIMON, A., and GLAUNER, R., *Z. anorg. u. allgem. Chem.* **178**, 177–201 (1929).

SI4.　SIMON, A., and HUTER, J., *Z. Elektrochem.* **41**, 28–33 (1935).

SI5.　SIMON, A., and HUTER, J., *Z. Elektrochem.* **41**, 294 (1935).

SI6.　SIMONS, J. H., and LORENTZEN, K. E., *J. Am. Chem. Soc.* **74**, 4746–4750 (1952).

SK1.　SKITA, A., and KEIL, F., *Ber.* **61B**, 1452–1459 (1928).

SK2.　SKITA, A., and KEIL, F., *Ber.* **61B**, 1682–1692 (1928).

SK3.　SKITA, A., and KEIL, F., *Monatsh.* **53/54**, 753–763 (1929).

SK4.　SKITA, A., KEIL, F. (and, in part, HAVEMANN, H., and LAWROWSKY, K. P.), *Ber.* **63B**, 34–50 (1930).

SK5.　SKITA, A., KEIL, F., and HAVEMANN, H., *Ber.* **66B**, 1400–1411 (1933).

SK6.　SKRAUP, Z. H., and PHILIPPI, E., *Monatsh.* **32**, 364 (1911).

SK7.　SKRAUP, Z. H., and WIEGMANN, D., *Wien. Monatsh.* **10**, 732 (1889).

SK8.　SKRIPOV, V. P., *Termodinam. i Stroenie Rastvorov Trudy Soveshchaniya*, (Moskov. Gosudarst. Univ., Moscow) **1958**, 43–48 (1959).

SK8a.　SKRIPOV, V. P., and RUSINOV, N. Y., *Nauch. Doklady Vyssheĭ Shkoly, Khim. i Khim. Tekhnol.* **1959**, No. 2, 250–252.

SK8b.　SKRIPOV, V. P., and SEMENCHENKO, V. K., *Zhur. Fiz. Khim.* **29**, 174–184 (1955).

SL1.　SLOBODIN, YA. M., and KHOKHLACHEVA, N. M., *Zhur. Obshcheĭ Khim.* **23**, 164–167 (1953).

SM1.　SMALL, L., in H. Gilman, *Organic Chemistry*, John Wiley and Sons, Inc., New York, N.Y. (1944), 2nd ed., Vol. II, p. 1166.

SM2.　SMALL, L., in H. Gilman, *Organic Chemistry*, John Wiley and Sons, Inc., New York, N.Y. (1944), 2nd ed., Vol. II, p. 1172.

SM3.　SMEYKAL, K. (to I.G. Farbenindustrie A.-G.), German Patent 629,256 (Apr. 25, 1936).

SM4.　SMEYKAL, K. (to I.G. Farbenindustrie A.-G.), French Patent 779,913 (Apr. 16, 1935); German Patent 637,731 (Nov. 3, 1936); U.S. Patent 2,043,965 (June 9, 1936).

SM5.　SMITH, C. W. (to Shell Development Co.), U.S. Patent 2,565,529 (Aug. 28, 1951).

SM6.　SMITH, D. G., and YOUNG, E. G., *J. Biol. Chem.* **205**, 849–858 (1953).

SM7.　SMITH, H. W., *J. Phys. Chem.* **25**, 204–263, 605–615, 616–627, 721–734 (1921).

SM8.　SMITH, H. W., *J. Phys. Chem.* **25**, 160–169, 204–263, 605–627, 721–734 (1921); **26**, 256–271, 349–357 (1922).

SM9.　SMITH, P. A. S., and FRANK, S., *J. Am. Chem. Soc.* **74**, 509–513 (1952).

SM10.　SMITH, R. D., and CAVALLITO, J. C., *J. Am. Chem. Soc.* **75**, 3033 (1953).

SM11.　SMITH, G., and SWAN, G. A., *J. Chem. Soc.* **1962**, 886–904.

SM12.　SMOLENSKI, E., and SMOLENSKI, K., *Roczniki Chem.* **1**, 232–242 (1921).

SM13.　SMYTH, C. P., *J. Am. Chem. Soc.* **46**, 2151–2166 (1924).

SN1.　SNOW, O. W., and STONE, J. F. S., *J. Chem. Soc.* **123**, 1510 (1923).

SN2.   SNYDER, H. R., and BREWSTER, J. H., *J. Am. Chem. Soc.* **71**, 1061–1063 (1949).

SN3.   SNYDER, H. R., CARNAHAN, R. E., and LOVEJOY, E. R., *J. Am. Chem. Soc.* **67**, 1301–1304 (1954).

SO1.   SOMMELET, M., *Compt. rend.* **157**, 825–854 (1914).

SO2.   SOMMELET, M., and FERRAND, M., *Bull. soc. chim. France* **25**, 457 (1919).

SO3.   SOMMELET, M., and FERRAND, M., *Bull. soc. chim. France* **35**, 446 (1924).

SO3a. SOMERVILLE, I. C. (to Rohm and Haas Co.), U.S. Patents 1,836,047 (Dec. 15, 1931); 1,883,042 (Oct. 18, 1932); French Patent 696,328 (May 30, 1930).

SO4.   SOU, PHOU-TI, *Compt. rend.* **192**, 363–365 (1931).

SO5.   SOU, PHOU-TI, *Compt. rend.* **192**, 1462–1464 (1931).

SP1.   SPIALTER, L., and PAPPALARDO, J. A., private communication.

SP2.   SPIALTER, L., and PAPPALARDO, J. A., *J. Org. Chem.* **22**, 840–843 (1957).

SP3.   SPIALTER, L., and MOSHIER, R. W., *J. Am. Chem. Soc.* **79**, 5955–5957 (1957).

SP4.   SPIESECKE, H., and SCHNEIDER, W. G., *J. Chem. Phys.* **35**, 722–730 (1961).

ST1.   STANÉK, V., *Z. Zuckerind. Böhmen* **27**, 479–485 (1903).

ST2.   STANLEY, E. L., BAUM, H., and GOVE, J. L., *Anal. Chem.* **23**, 1779–1782 (1951).

ST3.   STAPLE, E., and WAGNER, E. C., *J. Org. Chem.* **14**, 559–578 (1949).

ST4.   STAUDINGER, H., and RÖSSLER, K., *Ber.* **69B**, 49–60 (1936).

ST5.   STAVELEY, L. A. K., and TUPMAN, W. I., *J. Chem. Soc.* **1950**, 3597–3606.

ST5a. STECHER, O., and WIBERG, E., *Ber.* **75B**, 2003–2012 (1942).

ST6.   STEIGER, O., *Physik. Z.* **32**, 425–434 (1931); *Helv. Phys. Acta* **3**, 161–162 (1930).

ST7.   STEINER, M., and KAMIENSKI, E. S. VON, *Naturwiss.* **40**, 483 (1953).

ST8.   STEINER, M., and KAMIENSKI, E. S. VON. *Naturwiss.* **42**, 345–346 (1955).

ST9.   STEINKOPF, W., and BESSARITSCH, R., *J. parkt. Chem.* **109**, 231–264 (1925).

ST10. STEVENS, P. G., and RICHMOND, J. H., *J. Am. Chem. Soc.* **63**, 3132–3136 (1941).

ST11. STEVENSON, G. W., and WILLIAMSON, D., *J. Am. Chem. Soc.* **80**, 5943–5947 (1958).

ST12. STEWART, A. T., Jr., and HAUSER, C. R., *J. Am. Chem. Soc.* **77**, 1098–1103 (1955).

ST13. STEWART, T. D., and ASTON, J. G., *J. Am. Chem. Soc.* **49**, 1718–1728 (1927).

ST14. STICHNOTH, O., WOLF, L., and PALM, A., German Patent 946,622 (Aug. 2, 1956).

ST14a. STONE, F. G. A., and GRAHAM, W. A. G., *Chem. & Ind. (London)* **1955**, 1181–1183.

ST14b. STIMSON, M. M., *J. phys. radium* **15**, 390–393 (1954).

ST15. STORONKIN, A. V., and MARKUZIN, N. P., *Vestnik Leningrad. Univ.* **13**, No. 4, *Ser. Fiz. i Khim.* No. 1, 100–116 (1958).

ST15a. STORONKIN, A. V., and MARKUZIN, N. P., *Zhur. Fiz. Khim.* **33**, 279–286; 581–588 (1959).

ST16. STORONKIN, A. V., and MARKUZIN, N. P., *Vestnik Leningrad. Univ.* **16**, No. 4, *Ser. Fiz. i Khim.* No. 1, 75–86 (1961).

ST17. STRECKER, W., and BALTES, M., *Ber.* **54**, 2693–2708 (1921).

ST18. STREULI, C. A., *Anal. Chem.* **28**, 130–132 (1956).

ST18a. STREULI, C. A., *Anal. Chem.* **31**, 1652–1654 (1959).

ST18b. STROHMEIER, W., GERLACH, K., and HOBE, D. V., *Chem. Ber.* **94**, 165–168 (1961).

ST19. STROMHOLM, D., *J. prakt. Chem.* **67**, 345–356 (1903).

ST20. STRÖMME, K. O., *Acta Chem. Scand.* **13**, 268–274 (1959).

SU1. SUGANUMA, T., JUBOTA, T., and OBAYASHI, Y., Japanese Patent 8861 (1956).

SU2. SUGDEN, S., and WILKINS, H., *J. Chem. Soc.* **1929**, 1291–1298.

SU2a. SUGDEN, T. M., WALSH, A. D., and PRICE, W. C., *Nature* **148**, 372–373 (1941).

SW1. SWAIN, C. G., MCKNIGHT, J. T., and KREITER, V. P., *J. Am. Chem. Soc.* **79**, 1088–1093 (1957).

SW1a. SWALLEN, L. C. (to Commercial Solvents Corp.), U.S. Patent 2,079,580 (May 4, 1937).

SW2. SWALLEN, L. C., and MARTIN, J. (to Commercial Solvents Corp.), U.S. Patent 2,092,431 (Sept. 7, 1937).

SW3. SWAN, G. A., TIMMONS, P. S., and WRIGHT, D., *J. Chem. Soc.* **1959**, 9–13.

SW4. SWANN, S., Jr., *Trans. Electrochem. Soc.* **84**, 165–172 (1943).

SW5. SWIETOSLAWSKI, W., and POPOW, M., *J. chim. phys.* **22**, 395–398 (1925).

SW6. SWIFT, E., Jr., *J. Am. Chem. Soc.* **64**, 115–116 (1942).

SW6a. SWIFT, E., JR., and CALKINS, C. R., *J. Am. Chem. Soc.* **65**, 2415–2417 (1943).

SW7. SWIFT, E., Jr., and HOCHANADEL, H. P., *J. Am. Chem. Soc.* **67**, 880–881 (1945).

SZ1. SZABO, K., GOROG, L., and HAMRÁN, J., *Novenytermeles* **5**, 185–192 (1956).

SZ2. SZARVASY, E., *Ber.* **30**, 305–309 (1897).

T

TA1. TADROS, W., SAKLA, A. B., and ISHAK, M. S., *J. Chem. Soc.* **1958**, 2631–2633.

TA1a. TAFT, R. W., Jr., in M.S. Newman, *Steric Effects in Organic Chemistry.* John Wiley and Sons, New York, N.Y. (1956), p. 619.

TA2. TAGLIAVINI, G., and BIANCANI, M., *Atti soc. nat. e mat. Modena* **32–33**, 102–108 (1954–1955).

TA3. TAIPALE, K. A., *Ber.* **56**, 954–962 (1923).

TA4. TAKEDA, K., *Arch. ges. Physiol.* **133**, 365–396 (1909).

TA5. TAMELE, M. W., and GROLL, H. P. A. (to Shell Development Co.), U.S. Patent 2,172,822 (Sept. 12, 1939).

TA6. TAMELE, M., OTT, C. J., MARPLE, K., and HEARNE, G., *Ind. Eng. Chem.* **33**, 115–120 (1941).

TA7. TAMRES, M., SEARLES, S., LEIGHLY, E. M., and MOHRMAN, D. W., *J. Am. Chem. Soc.* **76**, 3983–3985 (1954).

TA8. TANNENBAUM, E., COFFIN, E. M., and HARRISON, A. J., *J. Chem. Phys.* **21**, 311–318 (1953).

TA9. TARR, H. L. A., *Fisheries Research Board Can. Prog. Repts. Pacific Stas.*
      No. 52, 24–26 (1942).

TA9a. TARR, H. L. A., *Nature* **142,** 1078 (1938).

TA9b. TARR, H. L. A., *J. Fisheries Research Board Can.* **4,** 327–334 (1939).

TA10. TARR, H. L. A., *Fisheries Research Board Can. Progr. Repts. Pacific Stas.*
       No. 59, 15–18 (1944).

TA11. TARR, H. L. A., and NEY, P. W., *Fisheries Research Board Can. Progr.
       Repts. Pacific Stas.* **No. 78,** 11–13 (1949).

TA12. TAYLOR, A. W. C., DAVIES, P., and REYNOLDS, P. W. (to Imperial
       Chemical Industries Ltd.), U.S. Patent 2,636,902 (Apr. 28, 1953);
       British Patent 679,712 (Sept. 24, 1952).

TA13. TAYLOR, A. W. C., and Imperial Chemical Industries Ltd., British
       Patent 679,014 (Sept. 10, 1952).

TA14. TAYLOR, F. M., and DEWING, J. (to Imperial Chemical Industries Ltd.),
       British Patent 861,760 (Feb. 22, 1961).

TA14a. TAYLOR, H. M., and HAUSER, C. R., *J. Am. Chem. Soc.* **82,** 1960–1965
        (1960).

TA15. TAYLOR, T. W. J., and BAKER, W., *Sidgwick's Organic Chemistry of
       Nitrogen.* Oxford University Press, London, (1937), New Ed., p.
       331.

TE1. TERENT'EV, A. P., KOST, A. N., and GURVICH, S. M., *Zhur. Obshcheĭ
      Khim.* **23,** 615–617 (1953); *J. Gen. Chem. U.S.S.R.* **23,** 641–642
      (1953) (Eng. Transl.)

TE2. TERZYAN, A. G., *Izvest. Akad. Nauk Armyan. S.S.R., Ser. Fiz.-Mat.,
      Estestven. i Tekhi Nauk.* **6,** No. 4, 35–50 (1953).

TE3. TERZYAN, A. G., *Zhur. Obshcheĭ Khim.* **23,** 1346–1348 (1953).

TE4. TEUBER, W., *Industrie parfum* **8,** 273–274 (1953).

TH1. THIEL, M., ASINGER, F., and SCHMIEDEL, K., *Ann.* **611,** 121–123 (1958).

TH1a. THIERFELDER, H., and KLENK, E., *Die Chemie der Cerebroside und
       Phosphatide.* J. Springer, Berlin (1930).

TH1b. THOMPSON, C. M., and CUNDALL, J. T., *J. Chem. Soc.* **53,** 761–764 (1888).

TH2. THOMPSON, H. W., and FREWING, J. J., *Nature* **135,** 507–508 (1935).

TH3. THOMPSON, H. W., and LINNETT, J. W., *Trans. Faraday Soc.* **32,** 681–685
      (1936).

TH3a. THOMPSON, W. E., and KRAUS, C. A., *J. Am. Chem. Soc.* **69,** 1016–1020
       (1947).

TH4. THOMSEN, J., *Z. physik. Chem.* **52,** 343–348 (1905).

TH5. THOSAR, B. V., *J. Chem. Phys.* **6,** 654 (1938).

TI1. TIMMERMANS, J., *Z. physik. Chem.* **58,** 129–213 (1907).

TI2. TIMMERMANS, J., *Bull. soc. chim. Belges* **27,** 334–343 (1913).

TI3. TIMMERMANS, J., *Bull. soc. chim. Belges* **30,** 62–72 (1921).

TI4. TIMMERMANS, J., *Bull. soc. chim. Belges* **61,** 393–402 (1952).

TI4a. TIMMERMANS, J., *Physico-Chemical Constants of Pure Organic Compounds.*
       Elsevier Publishing Co. Inc., New York, N.Y. (1950).

TI5. TIMMERMANS, J., and HENNAULT-ROLAND, MME., *J. chim. phys.* **29,**
      529–568 (1932).

TI6. TIMMERMANS, J., and MATTAAR, T. F., *Bull. soc. chim. Belges* **30,** 213–219
      (1921).

TI6a.   TIMMERMANS, J., PIETTE, A. M., and PHILIPPE, R., *Bull. soc. chim. Belges* **64**, 5–23 (1955).

TI7.   TIMMERMANS, J., and POPPE, G., *Compt. rend.* **201**, 524–527 (1935).

TI8.   TINKLER, C. K., *J. Chem. Soc.* **105**, 995–1001 (1914).

TI9.   TITLEY, A. L., *J. Chem. Soc.* **1926**, 508–519.

TO1.   TOEPEL, T., and JAHN, J. (to Badische Anilin- und Soda-Fabrik A.-G.), German Patent 1,025,417 (Mar. 6, 1958).

TO2.   TOLBERT, B. M., ADAMS, P. T., BENNET, E. L., HUGHES, A. M., KIRK, M. R., LEMMON, R. M., NOLLER, R. M., OSTWALD, R., and CALVIN, M., *J. Am. Chem. Soc.* **75**, 1867–1868 (1953).

TR1.   TRAUBE, W., ZANDER, H., and GAFFRON, H., *Ber.* **57B**, 1045–1051 (1924).

TR2.   TRAYNELIS, V. J., GALLAGHER, SISTER A. I., and MARTELLO, R. F., *J. Org. Chem.* **26**, 4365–4368 (1961).

TR3.   TRÉMILLON, B., *Bull. Soc. chim. France* **1960**, 1940–1948.

TR4.   TRESZCZANOWICZ, E., JAWORSKA, I., and KAZMIEROWICZ, W., *Przemysl Chem.* **34**, 36–39 (1955).

TR5.   TREUMANN, J., *Chemiker-Ztg.* **33**, 49 (1909).

TR5a.   TRICHÉ, H., *Compt. rend.* **218**, 408–410 (1944).

TR6.   TROTMAN-DICKENSON, A. F., *J. Chem. Soc.* **1949**, 1293–1297.

TS1.   TSAKALOTOS, D. E., *Z. physik. Chem.* **68**, 32–38 (1909); *Compt. rend.* **148**, 1325 (1909).

TS2.   TSATSAS, G., and DAMIENS, R., *Ann. pharm. franç.* **7**, 444–455 (1949).

TS3.   TSCHESCHE, R., and SNATZKE, G., *Chem. Ber.* **90**, 579–585 (1957).

TS4.   TSUDA, K., and MATSUMOTO, T., *J. Pharm. Soc. Japan* **67**, 107–108 (1947).

TS5.   TSUDA, K., and MATSUMOTO, T., *J. Pharm. Soc. Japan* **67**, 109–110 (1947).

TS6.   TSUDA, K., and MATSUMOTO, T., *J. Pharm. Soc. Japan* **67**, 111–112 (1947).

TS7.   TSUDA, K., and MATSUMOTO, T., *J. Pharm. Soc. Japan* **67**, 113–114 (1947).

TS8.   TSUDA, K., and MATSUMOTO, T., *J. Pharm. Soc. Japan* **67**, 238 (1947).

TS9.   TSUDA, K., and MATSUMOTO, T. (to Shionogi Drug Manufacturing Co.), Japanese Patent 178,329 (Mar. 31, 1949).

TS10.   TSUDA, K., and NAKAMURA, T., *J. Pharm. Soc. Japan* **67**, 117 (1947).

TU1.   TURNER, W. E. S., and MERRY, E. W., *J. Chem. Soc.* **97**, 2069–2083 (1910).

TU2.   TURNER, W. D., and HOWALD, A. M., *J. Am. Chem. Soc.* **42**, 2663–2665 (1920).

TU3.   TUN TAO, and HSING-YUN YU, *Yao Hsueh Hsueh Pao* **8**, 206–216 (1960).

TY1.   TYERMAN, I. V. (to Imperial Chemical Industries Ltd.), U.S. Patent 2,547,064 (Apr. 3, 1951).

TY2.   TYERMAN, W., and Imperial Chemical Industries Ltd., British Patent 631,675 (Nov. 8, 1949).

TY3.   TYERMAN, W., and Imperial Chemical Industries Ltd., British Patents 631,672–3–4 (Nov. 8, 1949).

TY4.   TYERMAN, W. (to Imperial Chemical Industries Ltd.), U.S. Patent 2,570,291 (Oct. 9, 1951).

U

UC1. UCHIDA, H., and BANDO, K., *J. Chem. Soc. Japan, Ind. Chem. Sec.* **57**, 941–943 (1954).

UC2. UCHIDA, H., and BANDO, K., *Repts. Govt. Chem. Ind. Research Inst., Tokyo* **49**, 473–478 (1954).

UC3. UCHIDA, H., and ICHINOKOWA, H. (to Bureau of Industrial Technics), Japanese Patent 1623 (May 9, 1952).

UC4. UCHIDA, H., KURAISHI, M., ICHINOKAWA, H., and HOSOYA, T., *Repts. Govt. Chem. Ind. Research Inst., Tokyo* **49**, 468–472 (1954).

UC5. UCHIDA, H., KURAISHI, M., ICHINOKAWA, H., and HOSOYA, T., *Repts. Govt. Chem. Ind. Research Inst., Tokyo* **50**, 155–160 (1955).

UD1. UDDVENKO, V. V., VVEDENSKAYA, L. A., and DULOVA, V. I., *Zhur. Obshcheĭ Khim.* **23**, 2060–2063 (1953).

UE1. UENO, Y., NAWA, H., UEYANAGI, J., MORIMOTO, H., NAKAMORI, R., and MATSUOKA, T., *J. Pharm. Soc. Japan* **75**, 1258–1261 (1955).

UE2. UENO, Y., NAWA, H., UEYANAGI, J., MORIMOTO, H., NAKAMORI, R., and MATSUOKA, T., *J. Pharm. Soc. Japan* **75**, 836–840 (1955).

UF1. UFFER, A., and SCHLITTLER, E., *Helv. Chim. Acta* **31**, 1397–1400 (1948).

UL1. ULLMAN, F., *Enzyklopaedie der technischen Chemie.* Urban und Schwarzenberg, Berlin (1928), Vol. I, p. 349.

UN1. Union Carbide Chemicals Company, U.S.A., *Advance Technical Information Bulletin*, **F-40392**, Aug. 1958.

UN2. Union Carbide Chemicals Company, U.S.A., *Advance Technical Information Bulletin*, **F-40232**.

UR1. URRY, G., WARTIK, T., MOORE, R. E., and SCHLESINGER, H. I., *J. Am. Chem. Soc.* **76**, 5293–5298 (1954).

V

VA1. VAISEY, E. B., *Can. J. Biochem. and Physiol.* **34**, 1085–1090 (1956).

VA2. VALEUR, A., and LUCE, E., *Bull. soc. chim. France* **23** 174–200 (1918); *Compt. rend.* **166**, 392–394 (1918).

VA2a. VANAGS, G., and PILEGE, A., *Latvijas PSR Zinatnu Akad. Vestis* **1952**, No. 1 (54), 99–102.

VA3. VANDERBILT, B. M. (to Commercial Solvents Corp.), U.S. Patent 2,219,879 (Oct. 29, 1940).

VA4. VARTANYAN, S. A., and BADANYAN, SH. O., *Izvest. Akad. Nauk Armyan. S.S.R., Khim. Nauk* **11**, No. 5, 343–350 (1958).

VA5. VARTANYAN, S. A., MATSOYAN, S. G., and MUSAKHANYAN, G. A., *Izvest. Akad. Nauk Armyan. S.S.R., Ser. Fiz.-Mat., Estestven. i Tekh. Nauk* **9**, No. 10, 29–35 (1956).

VA6. VARTANYAN, S. A., and TERZYAN, A. G., *Izvest. Akad. Nauk Armyan. S.S.R., Khim. Nauk* **11**, 37–43 (1958).

VA7. VAUGHN, T. H., VOGT, R. R., and NIEUWLAND, J. A., *J. Am. Chem. Soc.* **56**, 2120–2122 (1934).

VE1. VEJDĚLEK, Z. J., and TRČKA, V., *Experientia* **15**, 215–215 (1959).

VE1a. VEČEŘA, M., and GASPARIČ, J., *Chem. Listy* **52**, 611–617 (1958).

VE1b. VEIBEL, S., and LINHOLT, S. C., *Acta Chem. Scand.* **8**, 1007–1016 (1954).

VE2. VELGHE, M., *Bull. soc. chim. Belg.* **33,** 467–478 (1924); *Bull. sci. acad. roy. Belg.* **11,** 301–308 (1925).

VE3. VENNER, H., *J. prakt. Chem.* **3,** 13–25 (1956).

VI1. VIGUIER, P. L., *Compt. rend.* **153,** 955–957 (1911); *Ann. chim.* **28,** 522–553 (1913).

VI2. VINCENT, C., *Compt. rend.* **103,** 208–211 (1886).

VI3. VINCENT, C., and CHAPPUIS, J., *Bull. soc. chim. France* **45,** 496–504 (1886).

VI4. VINCENT, C., and CHAPPUIS, J., *Compt. rend.* **103,** 379–384 (1886); *Jahresbericht über die Fortschritte der Chemie* **1886,** 202.

VI5. VINCENT, C., and CHAPPUIS, J., *Compt. rend.* **101,** 427 (1885).

VI6. VITOLS, V., and VANAGS, G., *Zhur. Obshchei̇ Khim.* **25,** 576–580 (1955).

VO1. VOGEL, A. I., *J. Chem. Soc.* **1948,** 1825–1853.

VO2. VOGEL, A. I., CRESSWELL, W. T., JEFFREY, G. H., and LEICESTER, J., *J. Chem. Soc.* **1952,** 514–549.

VY1. VYAS, A., and SRIVASTAVA, H. N., *J. Sci. Ind. Research (India)* **18B,** 195–197 (1959).

W

WA1. WACKER, A., (to Ges. für elektrochemische Industrie G.M.B.H.), French Patent 687,398 (Dec. 30, 1929).

WA2. WAGNER, L., *Z. Kryst. Mineral.* **43,** 148–201 (1907).

WA3. WALDEN, P., *Bull. acad. imp. sci. St. Petersburg* **1913,** 907–936.

WA3a. WALDEN, P., *Z. physik. Chem.* **70,** 569 (1910).

WA4. WALDEN, P., *Bull. acad. imp. sci. St. Petersburg* **8,** 405–422 (1914).

WA5. WALDEN, P., *Bull acad. imp. sci. St. Petersburg* **8,** 1161–1186 (1914).

WA6. WALDEN, P., *Bull. acad. imp. sci. St. Petersburg* **9,** 509–540 (1915).

WA7. WALDEN, P., *Bull. acad. imp. sci. St. Petersburg* **9,** 807, 789–820, 1021–1046 (1915).

WA8. WALDEN, P., *Kolloid-Z.* **27,** 97–101 (1920).

WA9. WALDEN, P., *Ann. Acad. Sci. Fennicae, Ser. A* **29,** No. 23, 57 (1927).

WA10. WALDEN, P., and BIRR, E. J., *Z. physik. Chem.* **163A,** 263–280 (1933).

WA11. WALDEN, P., and GLOY, H., *Z. Physik. Chem.* **144A,** 395–440 (1929).

WA12. WALDEN, P., ULICH, H., and BIRR, E. J., *Z. physik. Chem.* **130,** 495–515 (1927).

WA13. WALDSTEIN, S. S., and STEIGMANN, F., *Am. J. Digestive Diseases* **19,** 323–325 (1952).

WA14. WALKER, A. J., in J. N. Friend, *A Text-Book of Inorganic Chemistry.* Charles Griffin and Co., Ltd., London, (1924), Vol. II, p. 211.

WA14a. WALKER and JOHNSTON, *J. Chem. Soc.* **87,** 958 (1905).

WA15. WALLACH, O., *Ann.* **343,** 54–74 (1905).

WA15a. WALMANN, H. J., and ROTHHAAS, A. (to Badische Anilin- und Soda-Fabrik A.-G.), German Patent 896,649 (Nov. 12, 1953).

WA16. WARREN, F. L., and KLEMPERER, M. E. VON, *J. Chem. Soc.* **1958,** 4574–4575.

WA17. WARTH, A. H., *The Chemistry and Technology of Waxes.* Reinhold Publishing Co., New York, N.Y. (1956), 2nd ed., p. 367.

WA17a. WASHBURN, E. W., Ed.-in-Chief, *International Critical Tables*. McGraw-Hill Book Co., New York, N.Y. (1928), Vol. III, p. 243.

WA17c. WASHBURN, E. W., Ed.-in-Chief, *International Critical Tables*. McGraw-Hill Book Co., New York, N.Y. (1928), Vol. V, p. 148.

WA18. WATANABE, K., *J. Chem. Phys.* **26**, 542–547 (1957).

WA19. WATANABE, K., and MOTTL, J. R., *J. Chem. Phys.* **26**, 1773–1774 (1957).

WA20. WATERS, J. A., and WIESE, G. A., *J. Am. Pharm. Assoc.* **49**, 112–117 (1960).

WA20a. WATSON, J. S., *J. Chem. Soc.* **1956**, 3677–3679.

WA21. WATT, G. W., and OTTO, J. B., Jr., *J. Am. Chem. Soc.* **69**, 836–838 (1947).

WE1. WEBER, J. C., and WILSON, J. B., *J. Biol. Chem.* **35**, 385 (1918).

WE2. *Webster's Geographical Dictionary.* G. and C. Merriam Co., Springfield, Mass. (1949), pp. 39, 1051.

WE3. *Webster's New International Dictionary, Unabridged*, 2nd ed. G. & C. Merriam Co., Springfield, Mass. (1934).

WE4. WEDEKIND, E., *Ber.* **35**, 766–776 (1902).

WE5. WEDEKIND, E., *Ber.* **45**, 2941–2942 (1912).

WE6. WEDEKIND, E., and WEDEKIND, O., *Ber.* **41**, 456–463 (1908).

WE6a. WEGLER, R., and FRANK, W., *Ber.* **69B**, 2071–2077 (1936).

WE7. WEISS, J., *Ann.* **268**, 143–151 (1892).

WE8. WEITH, W., *Ber.* **8**, 458–462 (1875).

WE9. WEKUA, K., and BERGMANN, J., *Farbe u. Lack* **59**, 267–271, 311–316 (1953).

WE10. WELVART, Z., *Compt. rend.* **238**, 2536–2538 (1954).

WE11. WERNER, E. A., *J. Chem. Soc.* **89**, 1625–1639 (1906).

WE12. WERNER, E. A., *J. Chem. Soc.* **105**, 2762–2769 (1914).

WE13. WERNER, E. A., *J. Chem. Soc.* **113**, 899–902 (1918).

WE14. WERNER, E. A., *J. Chem. Soc.* **115**, 1010–1014 (1919).

WE15. WESTON, A. W., RUDDY, A. W., and SUTER, C. M., *J. Am. Chem. Soc.* **65**, 674–677 (1943).

WE15a. WESTON, R. E., Jr., *J. Am. Chem. Soc.* **76**, 2645–2648 (1954).

WE16. WESTPHAL, O., *Ber.* **74B**, 1365–1372 (1941).

WE17. WESTPHAL, O., and JERCHEL, D., *Ber.* **73B**, 1002–1011 (1940).

WE18. WEYGAND, F., and HELMUTH, D., *Chem. Ber.* **91**, 1691–1706 (1958).

WH0. WHEELER, O. H., and LEVY, E. M., *Can. J. Chem.* **37**, 1727–1732 (1959).

WH1. WHITAKER, A. C. (to Gulf Research & Development Co.), U.S. Patent 2,953,601 (Sept. 20, 1960).

WH2. WHITEHEAD, W. (to Imperial Chemicals Industries Ltd.), British Patent 649,980 (Feb. 7, 1951).

WH3. WHITEHEAD, W., and Imperial Chemical Industries Ltd., British Patent 649,980 (Feb. 7, 1951).

WH4. WHITMAN, G. M. (to E. I. du Pont de Nemours & Co.), U.S. Patent 2,501,556 (Mar. 21, 1950).

WI1. WIBAUT, J. P., HEIERMAN, F., and WAGTENDONK, H. M., *Rec. trav. chim.* **57**, 456–458 (1938).

WI1a. WIBERG, E., GRAF, H., SCHMIDT, M., USON-LACAL, R., *Z. Naturforsch.* **7b**, 578–579 (1952).

WI1b. WIBERG, E., and HORELD, G., *Z. Naturforsch.* **6b**, 338–339 (1951).

WI2. WIBERG, E., and JAHN, A., *Z. Naturforsch.* **11b**, 489–490 (1956).

500 REFERENCES

WI2a.   WIBERG, E., JOHANNSEN, T., and STECHER, O., *Z. anorgu. allgem. Chem.*
        251, 114–124 (1943).
WI3.   WIBERG, E., and SÜTTERLIN, W., *Z. Elektrochem.* **41,** 151–153 (1935).
WI4.   WIBERG, E., MODRITZER, K., and USON-LACAL, R., *Rev. acad. cienc.*
        exact. fis.-quim. y nat. Zaragoza **9,** No. 1, 91–116 (1954).
WI5.   WIERZCHOWSKI, J., KASIŃSKI, W., and DRABIKOWSKA, H., *Roczniki*
        Panstwowego Zakladu Hig. **1953,** 313–319.
WI6.   WIESNER, K., MACDONALD, D. N., and BANKIEWICZ, C., *J. Am. Chem.*
        Soc. **75,** 6348–6349 (1953).
WI7.   WILKINS, C. J., and GRANT, D. K., *J. Chem. Soc.* **1953,** 927–932.
WI8.   WILLE, F., DIRR, K., and KERBER, H., *Ann.* **591,** 177–191 (1955).
WI8a.   WILLIAMS, H., *Chem. & Ind. (London)* **1960,** 900–901.
WI9.   WILLIAMS, I., and NEAL, A. M. (to E. I. du Pont de Nemours & Co.),
        U.S. Patent 1,975,890 (Oct. 9, 1934).
WI10.   WILLIAMS, J. E., Ed., *Prentice-Hall World Atlas.* Prentice-Hall, New
        York, N.Y. (1958), p. 91.
WI11.   WILLIAMS, K. C., and ELLIS, S. R. M., *J. Appl. Chem. (London)* **11,**
        492–496 (1961).
WI12.   WILLIAMS, R., Jr., WILLNER, J. R., and SCHAEFFER, J. J., *Chem. Eng.*
        News **1955,** 3982–3985.
WI13.   WILLSTÄTTER, R., *Ber.* **33,** 365–379 (1900).
WI14.   WILLSTÄTTER, R., and HEUBNER, W., *Ber.* **40,** 3869–3876 (1907).
WI15.   WILLSTÄTTER, R., and KAHN, W., *Ber.* **35,** 2757–2761 (1902).
WI16.   WILLSTÄTTER, R., and SCHMADEL, W. VON, *Ber.* **38,** 1992–1999 (1905).
WI17.   WILLSTÄTTER, R., and WASER, E., *Ber.* **43,** 1176–1183 (1910).
WI18.   WILLSTÄTTER, R., and WIRTH, T., *Ber.* **46,** 535–538 (1913).
WI19.   WINKLES, G. H., *Ann.* **93,** 321–329 (1855).
WI20.   WINSTEIN, S., JACOBS, T. L., SEYMOUR, D., and LINDEN, G. B., *J. Org.*
        Chem. **11,** 215–222 (1946).
WI21.   WINTER, H., *Deut. Lebensm. Rundschau* **46,** 210–213 (1950).
WI22.   WINTERSTEIN, E., and GUYER, A., *Z. physiol. Chem.* **128,** 188 (1923).
WI23.   WISCHONKE, C. R., and KRAUS, C. A., *J. Am. Chem. Soc.* **69,** 2472–2481
        (1947).
WI24.   WISSMÜLLER, M., and GUTBIER, A., *J. prakt. Chem.* **90,** 491–508 (1914).
WI25.   WITTIG, G., and BURGER, T. F., *Ann.* **632,** 85–103 (1960).
WI26.   WITTIG, G., HEINTZELER, M., and WETTERLING, M.-H., *Ann.* **557,**
        201–205 (1947).
WI27.   WITTIG, G., KOENIG, G., and CLAUSS, K., *Ann.* **593,** 127–156 (1955).
WI28.   WITTIG, G., and POLSTER, R., *Ann.* **599,** 13–22 (1956).
WI29.   WITTIG, G., TENHAEFF, H., SCHOCH, W., and KOENIG, G., *Ann.* **572,** 1–22
        (1951).
WI30.   WITTIG, G., and WETTERLING, M.-H., *Ann.* **557,** 193–201 (1947).
WO1.   WÖHLISCH, E., *Biochem. Z.* **153,** 120–128 (1924).
WO2.   WOJCIK, B., and ADKINS, H., *J. Am. Chem. Soc.* **56,** 2419–2424 (1934).
WO3.   WOLF, V., *Ann.* **576,** 35–45 (1952).
WO4.   WOLF, V., and STILLE, G., *Arzneimittel-Forsch.* **7,** 85–91 (1957).
WO4a.   WOLFE, J. K., and TEMPLE, K. L., U.S. Patent 2,635,116 (Apr. 14, 1953).
WO5.   WOOD, A. J., and KEEPING, F. E., *J. Bact.* **47,** 309–310 (1944).

WO6. WOOD, A. J., SIGURDSSON, G. J., and DYER, W. J., *J. Fisheries Research Board Can.* **6**, 53–62 (1942).

WO7. WOTIZ, J. H., HOLLINGSWORTH, C. A., and SIMON, A. W., *J. Org. Chem.* **24**, 1202–1205 (1959).

WO8. WOTIZ, J. H., and MANCUSO, D. E., *J. Org. Chem.* **22**, 207–211 (1957).

WR1. WREDE, F., FANSELOW, H., and STRACK, E., *Z. physiol. Chem.* **163**, 219–228 (1927).

WR2. WRIGHT, W. B., Jr., *J. Org. Chem.* **24**, 1362–1363 (1959).

WU1. WURTZ, A., *Ann. chim. phys.* **30**, 493 (1850).

WU2. WURTZ, A., *Compt. rend.* **28**, 223 (1849); *Ann.* **71**, 326–342 (1849).

Y

YA1. *Yamamoto Scient. Pap. Inst. Phys. Chem. Res.* **3**, 221; *Chem. Zentr.* **1926**, I, 694.

YA2. YANO, K., IKEDA, T., SAWA, Y., and OSAWA, J., (to Shionogi Drug Manufacturing Co.), Japanese Patent 180,950 (Nov. 16, 1949).

YO1. YONEDA, H., *Bull. Chem. Soc. Japan* **31**, 708–714 (1958).

YO2. YONKMAN, F., PLUMMER, A. J., and REITZE, W. L., *Arch. intern. pharmacodynamie* **88**, 401–406 (1952).

YO3. YOSHIMURA, K., *Z. Untersuch. Nahr. u. Genussm.* **20**, 153–155 (1910); *Chem. Zentr.* **1910**, II, 892.

YO3a. YOUNG, G. J., and HEALEY, F. H., *J. Phys. Chem.* **58**, 881–884 (1954).

YO4. YOUNG, W. G., CLEMENT, R. A., and SHIH, C., *J. Am. Chem. Soc.* **77**, 3061 (1955).

YO5. YOUNG, W. G., WEBB, I. D., GOERING, H. L., *J. Am. Chem. Soc.* **73**, 1076–1083 (1951).

YO6. YOUNG, W. G., and WILK, I. J., *J. Am. Chem. Soc.* **79**, 4793–4795 (1957).

YU1. YU, C. T., and CRUESS, W. V., *Canner* **113**, No. 6, 12–14; No. 7, 14, 16, 18 (1951).

Z

ZA1. ZAIMIS, E. J., *Brit. J. Pharmacol.* **5**, 424 (1950).

ZA2. ZAKHARKIN, L. I., *Izvest. Akad. Nauk S.S.S.R., Otdel. Khim. Nauk* **1955**, 1009–1014.

ZA3. ZAKHARKIN, L. I., and KHORLINA, I. M., *Izvest. Akad. Nauk S.S.S.R., Otdel. Khim. Nauk* **1959**, 2146–2150; *Bull. Acad. Sci. (U.S.S.R.)* **1959**, 2046–2050 (Eng. Trans.).

ZA4. ZAKHARKIN, L. I., and SAVINA, L. V., *Izvest. Akad. Nauk S.S.S.R., Otdel. Khim. Nauk* **1960**, 1039–1043; *Bull. Acad. Sci. (U.S.S.R.)* **1960**, 970–974 (Eng. Trans.).

ZA5. ZANDER, A., *Ann.* **214**, 138–193 (1882).

ZE1. ZEEGERS-HUYSKENS, T., *Bull. Soc. Chim. Belges* **69**, 282–291 (1960).

ZH1. ZHIGACH, A. F., KAZAKOVA, E. B., and ANTONOV, I. S., *Zhur. Obshcheĭ Khim.* **27**, 1655–1663 (1957).

ZH2. ZHURAVLEV, E. F., *Zhur. Obshcheĭ Khim.* **31**, 363–367 (1961).

ZO1. ZORINA, E. L., and SEMENCHENKO, V. K., *Zhur. Fiz. Khim.* **33**, 523–533 (1959).

ZO2. ZORN, B., *Arch. Dermatol. u. Syphilis* **197**, 179–186 (1954).

INDEX

SUBJECT INDEX

FORMULA INDEX